Marine Petroleum Source Rocks

Geological Society Special Publications

Series Editor K . COE

GEOLOGICAL SOCIETY SPECIAL PUBLICATION NO. 26

Marine Petroleum Source Rocks

EDITED BY

J. BROOKS* & A. J. FLEET†

*Exploration Division, Britoil, Glasgow (current position:
Consultant, Langside Drive, Newlands, Glasgow),
and †Exploration and Production Division,
BP Research Centre, Sunbury-on-Thames

1987

Published for

The Geological Society by

Blackwell Scientific Publications

OXFORD LONDON EDINBURGH
BOSTON PALO ALTO MELBOURNE

Published by
Blackwell Scientific Publications
Osney Mead, Oxford OX2 0EL
8 John Street, London WC1N 2ES
23 Ainslie Place, Edinburgh EH3 6AJ
52 Beacon Street, Boston, Massachusetts 02108, USA
667 Lytton Avenue, Palo Alto, California 94301, USA
107 Barry Street, Carlton, Victoria 3053, Australia

First published 1987

Typeset by Clowes Computer Composition,
printed and bound in Great Britain by
William Clowes Limited, Beccles and London

DISTRIBUTORS

USA and Canada
  Blackwell Scientific Publications Inc.
  PO Box 50009, Palo Alto
  California 94303

Australia
  Blackwell Scientific Publications (Australia) Pty Ltd
  107 Barry Street, Carlton, Victoria 3053

British Library Cataloguing in Publication Data

Marine petroleum source rocks.—(Geological
  Society special publication ISSN 0305-8719; no. 26)
  1. Petroleum   2. Geochemistry
  I. Brooks, J.   II. Fleet, A. J.   III. Geological
  Society of London   IV. Series
  553.2'82   TN871

  ISBN 0 632 01137 8

Contents

Preface

Geochemical conferences have become a frequent feature of the earth sciences scene. There are good reasons for this—the wide range of chemistry involved across the spectrum of sediments, the fascinating problems of the origin and diastrophism of the organic element in the sediments and the light which the complex chemistry can throw on the thermal, temporal and pressure history of the rocks since their initial deposition. Added to this is the automated equipment for production of multiple analyses both in the lab and on the rig and the availability of computer programs to evaluate the results, and of course, the fundamental importance of the subject in the search for economic hydrocarbon accumulations. It is the last mentioned factor which has loosened purse strings and justified the very rapid build up of practitioners of the science.

However, this volume is the proceedings of an unusual event—a joint meeting of two Geological Society groups, one of which deals with marine studies and the other with petroleum geochemistry. This meeting is an indication of the extent to which these two very different fields have interests in common, and the scale of advance resulting from recent discoveries especially in the realm of deep ocean drilling.

The first two parts deal largely with the environment of source rocks in oceans and on continental margins, with an emphasis on concepts and methods in dealing with the organic-rich sediments generated during world-wide 'anoxic events'. The third part has a stronger stratigraphical bias, but still deals with the fruitful ground where oceanography and organic geochemistry are jointly concerned. The spatial relations between the contemporaneous anoxic muds on continental shelves and deep ocean circulation are a particularly interesting aspect of the joint studies.

As a geologist who has had a career in petroleum exploration I feel I should express concern about the regional validity of sampling based on industrial activity, a warning which is as relevant to offshore as to landward operations. Since hydrocarbons are lighter than formation water it is inevitable that they are sought in structural highs, whether in anticlinal crests, fault blocks or in stratigraphic traps. It is consequently rare for exploratory boreholes to plumb the depths of modern synclines, and well samples of a given formation are likely to be misleading as to the total basin-wide fill in terms of thermal history. Just as a reasonable reservoir rock on a high may be found to deteriorate for physico-chemical reasons down flank into a basin, so a source rock found to be immature in every (anticlinal) test well could have been effective a thousand metres or more lower in adjoining synclines. It is clearly important that 'whole basin studies' should be attempted wherever possible.

This historical factor is now increasingly kept in mind by geochemists but there is a corollary—that source sediments now too deep to generate oil in a temperature/pressure regime which is undoubtedly gas-prone, are likely in the normal course of basin subsidence during the geological past to have been at depths appropriate for oil generation. This is (hopefully) obvious to the geologist; the chemists will perhaps forgive my underlining this important and inescapable fact.

Linked with this may I plead for more precision in references to source-rock potential. It is rare to find clearly specified whether a given sediment has been or will in future be a good source for generation of hydrocarbons. A shale still rich in organic content may never have served as a source or one totally barren may have been stripped. The time element, the geological history, should be intrinsic in the definition, otherwise use of the terms may be quite misleading in relation to a given problem of petroleum generation, particularly when the data are used directly by the non-technical.

There are many questions in petroleum and oceanic geochemistry which are still unsolved; but this volume should considerably advance our knowledge even if we do not arrive at final conclusions to many of them.

Sir Peter Kent

[During the final stage of proof reading in July 1986, we learnt, with great sadness, of the death of Sir Peter Kent. In publishing this volume we wish to acknowledge and remember the great service made by Sir Peter to petroleum geology and exploration.]

Acknowledgements

On behalf of the Geological Society Petroleum and Marine Studies Specialists Groups, we thank the following oil companies for their generous financial support which ensured the scientific success of the meeting:

Arco Oil (UK)	Bow Valley Exploration
British Petroleum	Britoil
Burmah Oil	Charterhouse Petroleum
Core Labs (UK)	Elf-Aquitaine UK
ESSO exploration	Hamilton Bros.
ICI Petroleum	Lasmo North Sea
Marathon Petroleum UK	Mobil Oil (UK)
Phillips Petroleum	Shell UK Exploration
Sulpetro (UK)	Texaco UK

also financial help from the Petroleum Exploration Society of Great Britain.

The Geological Society contributed towards the travelling expenses of overseas speakers, which made it possible for the conference to be truly international.

The effectiveness of the four sessions of the meeting owed much to their chairmen: the late Sir Peter Kent, the late Professor Janet Watson (then-President of the Society), Dr Tony Laughton (IOS) and Dr John Martin (BP), whom we thank.

We also thank staff of the Geological Society for administration and organization before and during the meeting and to Mr and Mrs Ewens for making the essential, associated evening social functions at the Society so successful and enjoyable.

We are most grateful to the referees who undertook the onerous task of refereeing all the papers. The papers of this volume have benefited from the comments of various anonymous reviewers and also from:

Tony Barwise	Stewart Brown	Henry Buckley
Steve Cawley	Chris Clayton	Max Coleman
Chris Cornford	Peter Curran	Charles Curtis
Graham Dungworth	Brian Funnell	Jim Gardner
Jon Gray	Tony Hallam	Malcolm Hart
Stuart Hazeldine	David Hirst	John Hudson
Peter Kahn	Simon Kay	Mike Lines
Andrew Mackenzie	John McArthur	Nick McCave
Phil Park	Neil Piggott	Tom Quigley
Rob Raiswell	David Skevington	Colin Summerhayes
Jörn Thiede	John Thomson	Simon Wakefield
Doug Waples	Toine Wonders	Ron Woollam

Finally we thank the authors for their patience, which was long-suffering in many cases, but not all; Liz Healing of Blackwell Scientific Publications for her cheerful help and Hugh Jenkyns for his invaluable 'encouragement'.

We leave the readers to explore the various papers and trust they will gain some of the flavour of a very enjoyable few days at the conference.

Jim Brooks   Andy Fleet
Glasgow 1986   *Sunbury-on-Thames 1986*

Introduction

A. J. Fleet & J. Brooks

SUMMARY: Organic-rich marine sediments are the source of most of the world's oil. The need for an understanding of actual and potential marine source rocks is therefore of vital economic importance, but also poses many fascinating 'academic' questions. This introduction attempts to outline and link the papers on actual and potential marine petroleum source rocks which make up this volume. These papers were originally presented at a Geological Society meeting in London in May 1983. The volume is divided into three main parts. The first deals with concepts and methods of study, the second with depositional processes and environments, and the last with the stratigraphic record. Four topics merit discussion in many of the papers: the roles of primary productivity and stratification, or restricted circulation, in controlling organic matter preservation; the relationship between sedimentation rate and the organic content of potential source rocks; the palaeo-oceanographic characteristics of past oceans in contrast to those of the Plio-Pleistocene ones; and the need for a multidisciplinary approach to the study of organic-rich *and* associated sediments.

'*Marine Petroleum Source Rocks*' is a collection of papers which were first presented at a Geological Society special meeting held at the Royal Society, London in May 1983. The meeting was organized by the Marine Studies and Petroleum Geochemistry Groups of the Society.

Marine sediments which are rich in organic matter are the source rocks of most of the world's oil resources (Table 1; Figure 1) and a significant proportion of the world's gas. An understanding of marine petroleum source rocks is, therefore, critical in petroleum exploration. These source rocks and their precursor sediments also pose fascinating problems for the research geologist or oceanographer. The factors which control their deposition are related to the dynamics, chemistry, biology and sediments of the oceanic system and to the changes which have occurred within it through geological time. Marine petroleum source rocks, therefore, are of interest not only to petroleum geologists and geochemists but also to sedimentologists, stratigraphers and many oceanographers. The objective of the '*Marine Petroleum Source Rocks*' meeting was to bring together these various groups of workers from both the academic world and industry. Contributions from the latter group were mainly confined to discussion at the meeting. Nevertheless the collection of papers which resulted from the meeting fully debates the factors which control the deposition of organic-rich marine sediments, potential petroleum source rocks, and illustrates how environmental changes through geological time have influenced the accumulation of these sediments.

The volume is divided into three parts. The papers of the first, 'Concepts and Methods', discuss what constitutes a petroleum source rock and the techniques which can be used to characterize actual and potential source rocks and their depositional environments. The deposition and preservation of organic matter in the marine environment are considered in Part II, 'Depositional Processes and Environments'. Papers in this section discuss biological productivity in the oceans and follow the path of organic matter from its generation in the photic zone through the water column to its preservation or destruction in sediments. The factors which control preservation, and the marine environments in which preservation is likely to occur, are debated. Papers of the third part, 'The Stratigraphic Record', consider examples of source rocks and other organic-rich marine sediments from the geologic record. In particular they focus on Mesozoic sediments which are the source of most of the world's oil. Discussion centres on sediments recovered by the Deep Sea Drilling Project and equivalent epicontinental sequences which, over recent years, have provided much of the stimulus for understanding the deposition of organic-rich marine sediments.

Concepts and methods

For a sediment to constitute a potential petroleum source rock, it must contain a minimum amount of organic matter. The composition of this organic matter and the burial history of the source rock determine whether the source rock will yield and expel petroleum as oil, gas or a mixture of both products on maturation. Brooks *et al.* discuss the techniques by which source rocks are identified

From: BROOKS, J. & FLEET, A. J. (eds) 1987, *Marine Petroleum Source Rocks* Geological Society Special Publication No. 26 pp. 1–14.

TABLE 1. *Significant oil provinces of the world (i.e. those with* $> 10^9$ *bbls recoverable resources*) (Nehring 1980) and their source rocks (References as cited).*

Province	Location	Known recoverable oil resources* as of 31.12.78 (10^9 bbls)	Source rock (proven or reputed)	Reference
1. Arabian-Iranian	Arabian/Persian Gulf	523.0	Marine, Jurassic and Cretaceous	Stoneley, this volume
2. Maracaibo	Venezuela–Colombia	41.7	Marine, Cretaceous and ?Eocene	Bockmeulen et al. 1983
3. Volga–Ural	Soviet Union	40.0	Marine, Devonian	North 1980
4. West Siberian	Soviet Union	37.0	Marine, Jurassic	Demaison & Moore 1980
5. Reforma–Campeche	Mexico	36.4	Marine, Jurassic and Cretaceous	Krueger & North 1983
6. Permian	United States	30.6	Marine, Carboniferous and Permian	Galley 1958
7. Sirte	Libya	30.6	Marine, Cretaceous and Paleogene	Brady et al. 1980
8. Mississippi Delta	United States	21.5	Marine, Neogene	Frey & Grimes 1970
9. Niger Delta	Nigeria–Cameroon	20.5	Marine, Eocene	Weber & Daukoru 1975
10. Northern North Sea	UK–Norway–Denmark	20.0	Marine, Jurassic	Barnard & Cooper 1981
11. Texas Gulf Coast–Burgos	United States–Mexico	18.4	Marine, Tertiary	Dow 1978
12. Alberta	Canada	16.3	Marine, Devonian, Mississippian, Jurassic	Deroo et al. 1977
13. East Texas–Arkla	United States	15.2	Marine, Cretaceous	Krueger & North 1983
14. Eastern Venezuela	Venezuela–Trinidad	13.1	Marine, Cretaceous	North 1980
15. South Caspian	Soviet Union	12.0	Marine, Oligocene–Miocene	North 1980
16. North Caucasus–Mangyshlak	Soviet Union	11.8	Marine, Eocene–Oligocene	North 1971
17. San Joaquin	United States	11.6	Marine, Miocene	Demaison & Moore 1980
18. Triassic	Algeria–Tunisia	11.3	Marine, Silurian	Halbouty et al. 1970
19. Tampico–Misantla	Mexico	10.7	Marine Jurassic, Cretaceous, ?Paleogene	Coogan et al. 1972
20. North Slope	United States	9.9	Marine, Triassic, Jurassic, U. Cretaceous	Magoon & Claypool 1981
21. Amarillo–Anadarko–Ardmore	United States	9.8	Marine, Paleozoic	Gatewood 1970; Pippin 1970
22. Central Sumatra	Indonesia	9.0	Deltaic/Lacustrine Eocene–Miocene	Crostella 1981; Woodside 1984
23. Los Angeles	United States	8.6	Marine, Miocene	Mayuga 1970
24. Sungliao	China	8.5	Lacustrine, Cretaceous	Chin Chen 1980
25. Chautauqua	United States	6.5	Marine, Paleozoic	Woodward 1958
26. North China	China	6.0	Lacustrine, Oligocene	Zhou Guangjia 1981

TOTAL 980.0 (89% of World Total)

*Cumulative production plus proved and probable reserves.

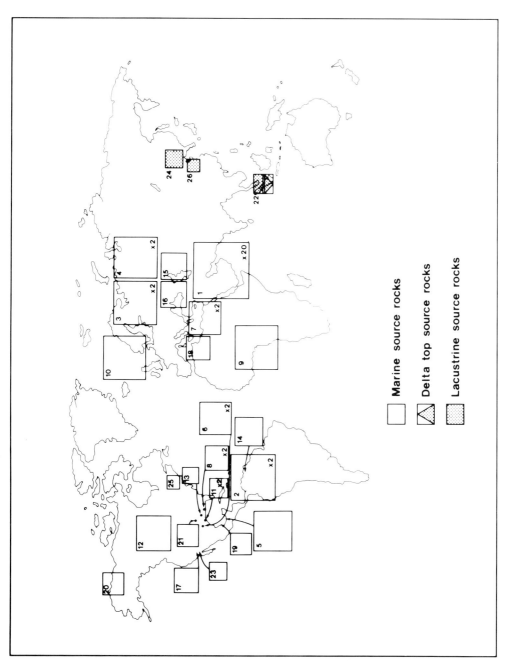

FIG. 1. The locations and probable source-rock types of the major oil provinces of the world (Table 1). The size of each square relates to the known recoverable oil resources of the province: some need to be multiplied by the factors shown. Numbers refer to the listing of the provinces in Table 1.

and characterized and those by which the maturity of source rocks is measured.

The palynofacies, or microscopic organic constituents, of a sediment can obviously provide important information on the petroleum potential of the sediment. Tyson discusses how palynofacies are described but stresses the need for palynofacies studies of individual sediments to be put in the context of the sedimentological, palaeontological and geochemical data for the sediment itself and associated sediments. By corollary, he advances the need for a multidisciplinary approach to source-rock evaluation and interpretation. This paper also provides a valuable introduction to the factors that determine the nature of marine source rocks. Tyson argues that source-rock characteristics are primarily controlled, at the time of deposition, by bottom-water oxygenation and proximity to rivers. Persistent oxygen-depleted or oxygen-deficient (dysaerobic—1.0 to 0.1 ml/l of dissolved oxygen; anaerobic—0.1 to 0.0 ml/l; anoxic—no dissolved oxygen, free hydrogen sulphide) conditions are necessary for the preservation of the abundant lipid-rich amorphous organic matter (AOM) from which oil is generated. Under aerobic conditions only refractory land-plant detritus or highly degraded, marine AOM are preserved: both these types of organic matter are gas-prone. Rich gas-prone marine source rocks are therefore deposited in the vicinity of rivers, where the supply of land plant detritus is high, even where conditions are dysaerobic to anoxic.

The terminology describing levels of oxygenation, which Tyson uses precisely, is not standard. Individual authors throughout the volume, and in the literature, adopt different definitions. For instance, Demaison & Moore (1980), in their classic paper on oil source-bed genesis, take 'anoxic' to be 'any water containing less than 0.5 millilitres of oxygen per litre of water (0.5 ml/l)' rather than truly oxygen-depleted conditions. Despite this variation in definition, the rationale that oil-prone organic matter is only preserved under oxygen-depleted or oxygen-deficient conditions is clear. It is that, at low levels of oxygenation, macrobenthic activity ceases or is at least inhibited. This, as Demaison & Moore and Tyson (this volume) stress, leads to the cessation or inhibition of bioturbation and, hence, the minimization of bacterial oxidation of organic matter. In particular, lipid-rich material, the precursor of the oil-prone components of kerogen, tends to undergo little degradation. The question of whether the oxygen level in depositional environments is the principal control on the formation of oil-prone source rocks or whether biological productivity is, or can be, the overriding factor is also discussed by other authors, notably Calvert, Pelet, Morris, and Bralower and Thierstein.

Fisher and Hudson introduce two other approaches, biofacies and isotopic analyses, which can contribute to the multidisciplinary evaluation of source rocks. The study of the biofacies of sediments can provide evidence of depositional conditions and be linked to sedimentary characteristics (e.g. bioturbation). In their paper Fisher & Hudson consider the nature of the molluscan fauna, but other taxa can provide equivalent information (see e.g. Hallam; Savrda *et al.* 1984). Similarly there are a variety of isotopic studies which can be undertaken. Fisher & Hudson discuss the sulphur isotope composition of pyrite in different facies but studies of other isotopes can provide vital data, notably those of carbon (e.g. Hallam; Arthur *et al.*; Shackleton).

Fisher's and Hudson's study highlights the role of sulphate reduction in the degradation of organic matter during deposition and early diagenesis. The isotopic nature of the pyrite formed provides evidence of whether the sulphate reduction process was limited by the availability of organic matter or sulphate. In the former case (probably due to low organic matter input), minor or negligible source potential is likely to be developed, despite favourable oxygen-deficient or oxygen-depleted conditions, because of the diagenetic destruction of the deposited organic matter through sulphate reduction. Fisher & Hudson point out that pyrite studies are applicable to shales of different ages and to material from wells which would not be amenable to biofacies or sedimentological studies.

The last two papers of Part I deal with the molecular characteristics of organic matter in source rocks. Very major advances have been made in this field of 'biomarkers' in the last decade or so, and are likely to be made in the near future, due to improvements and developments in analytical instrumentation and data handling facilities. Brassell *et al.* discuss how lipids, although only minor constituents of organic matter in sediments, can be used in attempts to characterize the contributions which different types of organic matter have made to potential source rocks. They show how certain classes of lipids can be linked to higher plants, unicellular algae or bacteria. These compounds can provide evidence of organic matter inputs not apparent from visual analysis, particularly those contributing to the often abundant amorphous organic material. Quantitative analyses can be used in determining the relative contributions of the different inputs to sediments. Comet & Eglinton further illustrate the role of lipid geochemistry and, in particular, discuss one approach which can be used in handling the large volumes of molecular data which modern gas chromatography–mass spectrometry can provide.

Finally, Brassell *et al.* stress that, although major advances in molecular organic geochemistry have been made, further major progress is needed. Firstly, there is a need to improve the characterization of organic matter at the molecular level. Secondly, the processes which modify these biochemical molecules in the water column and during deposition and diagenesis need to be elucidated further so that lipid extracts from potential source rocks can be correlated back more precisely to their parent organic matter. For further improvements in petroleum exploration methods, advances are also necessary to bridge the gaps in our understanding between immature organic-rich sediments, of the type described by Brassell *et al.* and Comet & Eglinton, actual source rocks and generated oils: this is further discussed by Brooks *et al.* As Brassell *et al.* point out, with organic diagenesis and maturation some molecular information is lost as defunctionalization occurs, leaving only the skeletal structure of the molecule and aliphatic and aromatic hydrocarbons as major components of the lipid extracts. Further work is needed to extend those links already established (e.g. Mackenzie 1984) between biomarkers in oils and source rocks and the characteristic molecules of precursor organic matter.

Depositional processes and environments

The papers in Part II of the volume mainly discuss the processes which lead to the preservation of organic matter in the marine environment. First Degens & Ittekkot consider the processes by which organic matter is deposited in the oceans. Initially, though, they briefly review the global carbon cycles.

The oceans contain just over one quarter of the world's organic carbon, but only about a third of one per cent of this oceanic organic carbon is found in the oceanic biomass (planktonic and bacterial), the bulk is present in dissolved compounds or particulate matter (Figure 2, Degens & Ittekkot). About a quarter of the annual input of organic carbon to surface waters occurs over the continental shelves (Figure 3, Degens & Ittekkot) which in area make up less than 5% of the oceans. Particulate matter from rivers constitutes little of this, as most is trapped in estuaries and deltas. The present-day continental shelves therefore constitute important potential sites for organic deposition. This is borne out by other data, for instance, those presented by Bralower & Thierstein in Part III. These data for Holocene sediments show that organic carbon preservation factors (percentage of organic carbon produced in surface waters which is preserved in underlying sediments) range from 1% to 25% at localities in less than 1 km water depth but are generally 0.5% or less in the deep sea.

Planktonic organisms are responsible for the transport to the seafloor, at rates of hundreds of metres per day, of much organic material and fine-grained mineral matter in faecal pellets or flocs held together by excreted mucus. Degens & Ittekkot describe the use of sediment traps in three areas to document these processes. They used the organic chemical contents of the trapped sediments to assess how the fluxes of different types of organic matter changed with time. They suggest that changes in planktonic communities either globally through geological time or locally in individual basins (e.g. the Black Sea) could have markedly affected depositional conditions and the sediments deposited. For instance, the influx of Mediterranean waters into the Black Sea 7500 years ago may have triggered stratification and eutrophication and the decline in the zooplankton population which can be inferred from the organic chemical contents of the contemporary sediments. The latter effect, in turn, would have inhibited the transport of clay-sized material to the seafloor and so contributed to the formation of organic-rich mineral-poor sapropels.

The organic content of marine sediments (degree of organic matter preservation) can be considered to be governed by three intimately, inter-related factors:
- primary productivity,
- rates of accumulation,
- bottom-water oxygenation.

Primary productivity determines how much organic matter is available for deposition (e.g. see Calvert and Tyson). As already discussed, in the present oceans this supply is highest over the continent shelves.

Rates of accumulation describe how much organic matter and how much sediment overall reaches the seafloor. Water depth, as the data of Bralower and Thierstein mentioned above illustrates, is important in determining how much of the organic carbon produced as a result of primary productivity reaches the seafloor. 'At a given production rate, the settling flux decreases by a factor of ten for every 10-fold increase in water depth; it is approximately 10% of the surface production at around 400 m and only 1% of the surface production at around 4000 m depth' (Calvert).

Preservation of organic matter reaching the seafloor can be considered to be partly a function of overall sedimentation rate. Fast burial of organic matter should remove labile organic compounds from the near surface sites of highest metabolic rates and therefore promote organic preservation (Calvert). Müller & Suess (1979) have indeed demonstrated that a relationship exists between the organic carbon contents of modern marine sediments and sedimentation rate: organic carbon content doubles with each 10-fold increase in sedimentation rate if other factors (primary productivity, sediment density, etc.) are constant. High sedimentation rates, though, as Tyson discusses, can lead to the dilution of organic matter. Also changes in the texture of accumulating sediments are likely to cause alterations in the ratio of organic:mineral matter being deposited. As Trask (1932) was one of the first to show, 'clays contain approximately twice as much organic matter as silt and silts about double that of fine sands'. Coarser grained sediments reflect deposition under more energetic hydrodynamic regimes which, by their very nature, favour organic degradation (Tyson). Finally in considering rates of accumulation with respect to source-rock deposition it is important to remember that it is the relative accumulation rates of different organic matter types which determine the petroleum potential of an organic-rich sediment (Tyson).

Bottom oxygenation, the third factor governing the organic content of marine sediments, has been identified by many authors (e.g. Demaison & Moore 1980; Degens & Ittekkot; Tyson) as the single major factor governing the accumulation of labile organic matter, and hence of potential oil-prone source rocks. This was briefly discussed in the preceding section. Bottom oxygenation is, of course, influenced by primary productivity. The greater the supply of organic matter from surface waters, the greater the demand for bottom-water oxygen as the organic matter is degraded. The supply of bottom-water oxygen comes from surface waters and, so, is controlled by the oxygen content of that surface water, the rate at which the water is supplied to the bottom, and any removal of oxygen through degradation which occurs *en route*. The supply decreases as truly persistent, static, stratified conditions are approached. Bottom oxygenation is therefore influenced by both primary productivity and water circulation. (Primary productivity itself being governed by nutrient supply which is inextricably bound up with water circulation.)

Primary productivity and 'anoxia' (*sensu* Demaison & Moore: oxygen deficiency as well as oxygen depletion) induced primarily by water stratification can, therefore, from the above discussion, be seen as 'end-member' controls on source-rock deposition, albeit inter-related controls. As stated above, the latter control, 'anoxia', has been judged to be the overriding control by Demaison & Moore (1980), among many others. They recognize three marine environments where 'anoxic' bottom conditions would lead to the deposition of potential source rocks:
- 'anoxic' silled basins,
- 'anoxic' layers caused by upwelling,
- open ocean 'anoxic' layers.

Calvert examines this proposition and finds that: '(a) modern anoxic basins do not contain exceptionally organic-rich sediments, (b) oxygen-minimum zones are not necessarily sites of preferential preservation of deposited carbon, (c) the highest fluxes and accumulations of organic matter in the modern ocean are found in areas of coastal upwelling'.

He argues that variations in the rate of primary productivity, and hence the flux of carbon to the seafloor, may provide the explanation for the occurrence of source rocks ('black shales') in the geological record. It may be felt that this reasoning helps to redress any imbalance that exists when primary productivity and stratification-induced 'anoxia' are considered as the end-member controls on source-rock deposition.

Morris returns to Calvert's theme. He presents studies from two deep-water areas, the Eastern Mediterranean and Guinea Basin, which show that productivity events can lead to the preservation of organic-rich intervals in otherwise oxic sediments without the development of widespread stagnant conditions.

Pelet presents a new, mathematical approach to the discussion of what controls the organic contents of marine sediments. As end members, he uses models which describe continental detrital input and purely pelagic sedimentation. He argues that a simple general relationship relating the organic carbon content of sediments and sedimentation rates cannot exist, and stresses that organic and mineral supply and biological alteration are not independent. Finally he deduces that macro or meio benthos operating under aerobic conditions are the agents which cause low organic preservation under oxic conditions. It is their absence under oxygen-deficient or -depleted conditions which allows organic preservation to occur. The influence of productivity, rates of accumulation and stratification/stagnation on organic deposition are discussed further in Part III (e.g. Zimmerman *et al.*; Summerhayes; Bralower & Thierstein).

Coastal upwelling

The link between high productivity and organic-rich sediment deposition is clear in one type of environment: that of persistent coastal upwelling. Upwelling brings to the surface nutrient-rich water which enhances biological productivity. This, in turn, *may*, but does not invariably, lead to organic-rich deposition. Suess *et al.* describe in detail the situation in one of the major present-day areas of upwelling, off the Peru–Chile coast. They show how interrelated local factors, notably current flow and bathymetry, which itself is related to tectonism, determine variations in sediment type within the upwelling area. In areas of relatively shallow water, sediments are continuously reworked by onshore and alongshore currents. Any organic matter deposited tends to be degraded, dominantly by sulphate reduction. A calcareous mud facies results. In deep areas along the upper continental slope, where current reworking is minimal, bulk sedimentation rates are high and abundant organic matter is preserved giving rise to an organic-rich mud. Diagenesis in this facies is dominated by microbial fermentation and methanogenesis (cf. Fisher & Hudson). Suess *et al.* interpret the sediment record of cores as showing that current regimes have changed with time and affected sediment distributions. Their study illustrates that source-rock distributions must be expected to be complex within palaeo-upwelling areas. Further detailed studies of the sediments and the related oceanography of upwelling areas are to be found in the proceedings of the recently-held NATO Advanced Research Institute on '*Coastal upwelling: its sediment record*' (Suess & Thiede 1983; Thiede & Suess 1983).

Palaeo-upwelling is considered by Parrish who, in her brief paper, builds on her previously published work (Parrish 1982; Parrish & Curtis 1982). In these papers she has presented predictions of wind-driven upwelling based on qualitative global atmospheric circulation models. Her analysis of palaeo-upwelling in this volume, which is based on revised palaeogeographies, indicates that, for the late Devonian to late Trias, most of the Cretaceous and the latter part of the Tertiary, two thirds of organic-rich rocks correspond to upwelling areas; two thirds of all Phanerozoic organic-rich sediments were deposited during these time intervals. However, only a few Jurassic and early Palaeozoic source rocks or black shales are explicable in terms of upwelling. Parrish points out that, judging by the present,

not all upwelling will lead to organic-rich sediment, that not all upwelling is wind-driven and therefore predictable from atmospheric models, and, finally, that not all organic-rich rocks are, of course, likely to have been deposited beneath areas of upwelling. She suggests that associated sediments might be used to indicate those organic-rich sediments which were probably associated with upwelling. Phosphorites are one such indicator, associated glauconitic sediments and cherts are probably others.

Other environments: ooids and the Gulf of California

The last two papers in Part II deal with very specific marine environments. Ferguson describes the micro-environments of carbonate ooids which contain organic matter from which light hydrocarbon gases have been generated microbially. He suggests that ooids might provide a model for evaluating the potential of carbonate source rocks. Simoneit & Kawka consider the environment of a young ocean basin, the Gulf of California. In particular, they discuss the nature of the petroleums of the basin which appear to have been generated by natural pyrolysis resulting from the intense magmatic activity in this relatively small, young basin.

The stratigraphic record

The distribution of source rocks and other organic-rich rocks in the stratigraphic records and their origins are the subjects of Part III of this volume. Source rocks are not evenly distributed spatially or temporally. The massive oil reserves of the Middle East (Table 1) point to the wealth of rich source rocks which must be present in that region. These source rocks and the source rocks of most oil reserves were mainly deposited during the Mesozoic (Table 1; Figure 2). This record for the Phanerozoic doubtlessly reflects the tectonic disruption of petroleum reservoirs as well as other factors such as maturity, but it must unequivocally indicate that conditions globally during the Mesozoic were particularly conducive to source-rock deposition.

The stratigraphic review, which the papers of Part III constitute, is by no means comprehensive but it does reflect the importance of Mesozoic organic-rich sediments and research and data in the public domain. More comprehensive reviews of the spatial and stratigraphic distributions of source rocks and other organic-rich rocks can be found in papers such as those by Duncan & Swanson (1965), North (1971, 1979, 1980) Tissot (1979), Bois *et al.* (1980) and Grunau (1983).

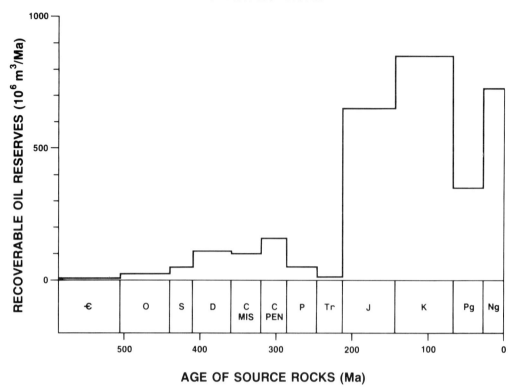

FIG. 2. Global in-place crude oil resources related to the stratigraphic age of the source rocks from which the oil is believed to have been generated (redrawn from Bois *et al.* 1980 after Tissot 1979 using the time scale of Harland *et al.* 1982). The areas of the blocks are proportional to the total resources.

The uneven distribution of organic-rich sediments in the stratigraphic record has been one of the major factors which has led to attention being focused on past global conditions (e.g. Irving *et al.* 1974), in particular the changing nature of the oceans. The probably atypical character of the present oceans, can be linked to deteriorating climate during Tertiary times (e.g. Shackleton; Haq 1981). Similarly the circulation and composition of past oceans must have reflected global climate which was generally warmer, and sometimes markedly warmer (during middle Triassic and late Jurassic to Eocene times), than the overall Plio-Pleistocene climate (e.g. Frakes 1979). Palaeogeography, especially continental configuration, must have also played its part in determining the nature of the oceans. High stands of sea level were a function of oceanic formation, being related to the existence of much young, and therefore relatively shallow, oceanic crust. The young ocean basins, themselves, were often geographically and bathymetrically restricted and so were at least at times, prone to poor circulation and organic-rich sediment preservation (e.g. Hallam; Zimmerman *et al.*).

Transgressions, by creating, often vast, epicontinental seas, provided sites for the deposition of many important source rocks, notably those of the Middle East. Epicontinental seas also probably provided the sources of much deep oceanic water. Today this dense, deep water is formed from cold surface waters at high latitudes and is therefore well oxygenated. At times in the past much of the deep water was probably supplied by dense, saline, warm and therefore poorly oxygenated, water from the epicontinental seas of mid and low latitudes (Brass *et al.* 1982). The link between young oceans, high sea levels, large epicontinental seas and poor bottom oxygenation is therefore made, at least in broad terms. A markedly warm global climate can, at times, be added to this link as an important factor which influenced oceanic conditions. It is therefore possibly not surprising that during the Cretaceous, at least, there were times when very widespread, perhaps worldwide, oceanographic phenomena, related to poor oceanic mixing, resulted in 'oceanic anoxic events' (OAE) (Schlanger & Jenkyns 1976). To these may possibly be added an OAE during early Toarcian times (Jenkyns 1980) and episodes of widespread 'black shale' deposition during the Ordovician, Silurian and Devonian (Berry & Wilde 1978). These episodes themselves may reflect rhythmic alternations in the oceans between 'polytaxic' times of maximum diversity, which coincide with eustatic sea-level rises, relatively high uniform oceanic temperatures and widespread oxygen-deficiency, and 'oligotaxic' episodes of lower diversity, during which regressions, low oceanic temperatures and marked lateral and vertical temperature gradients were the norm and oceanic oxygen deficiency was rare (Fischer & Arthur 1977).

The Palaeozoic

During the Lower Palaeozoic, organic-rich sediments accumulated in greater thicknesses and over wider areas than at any other time during the Phanerozoic. Thickpenny & Leggett conclude this from studying the distribution of early Palaeozoic organic-rich sediments in the three palaeocontinents of Gondwana, Baltica and Laurentia which now make up areas of Europe between Portugal and the Urals. Their survey builds on earlier work of Leggett (1980) which was restricted to the British Isles. They point out the difficulties associated with interpreting depositional settings and likely controls on deposition when dealing with Palaeozoic rather than Mesozoic or Cenozoic sediments. Nevertheless they recognize a variety of 'black shales' formed during three main episodes of deposition in various depositional environments. The Alum shales of Scandinavia, deposited during the Middle and Upper Cambrian, are organic-rich sediments of the shelf. While some Caradoc and Llandovery sediments are oceanic organic-rich deposits indicative of oxygen-deficient oceanic conditions. Thickpenny and Leggett call on an array of factors to account for these Palaeozoic deposits. These factors are similar to those invoked by other workers to explain Mesozoic and Cenozoic organic-rich sediments. In particular they identify high sea-level stands, warm climatic conditions and low hydrosphere oxygen contents as being favourable factors. Unlike Berry & Wilde (1978) they do not suggest that early Palaeozoic oceans were markedly different from younger oceans and undergoing progressive ventilation.

No contributions were available to cover the Devonian or Carboniferous. Numerous publications, though, are available elsewhere. In particular, they detail the organic-rich sediments of the epicontinental seas of the North American continent, such as the Devonian sediments of the Western Canadian (Alberta) basin (e.g. Deroo *et al.* 1977), the Devonian-Mississippian 'black shales' of the eastern USA (e.g. Ettensohm & Barron 1982) and the Pennsylvanian phosphatic black-shale facies of mid North America (e.g. Heckel 1977).

The only contribution dealing with late Palaeozoic sediments is concerned with another epicontinental sea—the Permian sea of Europe which covered the present southern North Sea and northern Germany and Poland. Only the summary of the contribution is available. In it, Gibbons attributes the formation of the organic-rich, oil-prone Marl Slate-Kupferschiefer to the accumulation of organic matter in the anoxic bottom waters of a stratified basin during early stages of evaporation. He suggests that the limited thickness, generally less than 2 m, of this organic-rich interval means that it is unlikely to have been the source of commercially significant amounts of oil.

The Mesozoic

The importance of Mesozoic marine petroleum, particularly oil-prone, source rocks has already been emphasized. Their importance, and the research interest which they and other organic-rich Mesozoic sediments have aroused, is underlined by the number of contributions on Mesozoic sequences. A succinct survey of the sediments in space and time is given by Hallam. He identifies the Upper Jurassic (Kimmeridgian–Volgian/Tithonian) and mid Cretaceous (Aptian–Turonian) as being particularly rich in organic-rich sediments. He also discusses the few Triassic examples, the widespread Liassic ones and the local organic-rich Callovian intervals. The marine depositional models of Demaison & Moore (1980) ('anoxic' silled basins; 'anoxic' layers caused by upwelling; open ocean 'anoxic' layers—see above) are applicable to various of these sediments. Hallam emphasizes, though, the link between transgression and the formation of many of the sediments. He suggests that transgression may have promoted organic productivity and/or, by producing deep epicontinental seas, enhanced bottom-water oxygen deficiency. He points out that a weakness of a purely eustatic explanation is that it fails to explain the cyclic nature of many organic-rich Mesozoic sediments. He suggests that regular climatic fluctuations may subtly control depositional conditions, possibly by influencing water stratification.

The immensely important Jurassic and Cretaceous source rocks of parts of the Middle East are reviewed by Stoneley. As he points out, very few published data are available, presumably reflecting the wealth of source rocks in the region and, so, the perceived need for minimal understanding of them. Source-rock deposition occurred in basins over a very extensive shelf which was approximately 2500 km wide and 5000 km long. The carbonate nature of the deposits presumably reflects the size of this shelf and only minor siliciclastic input. Anoxic bottom conditions, due to restricted circulation in the basins and high productivity, possibly due to upwelling, probably influenced source-rock deposition.

The Cretaceous of the Atlantic Ocean

Deep Sea Drilling Project (DSDP) drilling in the Atlantic Ocean has revealed a variety of organic-rich Mesozoic sediments both in the ocean basins and along the continental margins. Some equivalent sediments have been recognized cropping out onshore. In areas like Brazil and Gabon the presence of oilfields implies that these sediments, deposited as the Atlantic opened, have acted as source rocks. The natures and origins, though, of the organic-rich sediments of the Atlantic are varied. Four contributions, two dealing with the South Atlantic and two with the North Atlantic, present studies which deal with these sediments in detail.

The stratigraphic and geographic distributions of the organic-rich Cretaceous sediments of the South Atlantic are outlined and their origins discussed by Zimmerman *et al.* They consider a preservation model and a productivity model to explain the formation of these sediments. They conclude that the former is compatible with the history of the South Atlantic. The silled-basin nature and relative geographic isolation of the South Atlantic generally caused restricted circulation and generally 'dysoxic' conditions which at times became 'anoxic'. (The benign climatic conditions are assumed to have reinforced sluggish oceanic circulation. In contrast the modelling of Brass *et al.* 1982, suggests circulation may have been more vigorous.) The trapping of nutrients in bottom waters which were undergoing minimal circulation meant that productivity was probably low, as Bralower & Thierstein, in their paper, conclude was the case for the mid-Cretaceous in general. Zimmerman *et al.* can relate organic-rich sediments in epicontinental basins to transgressions, but suggest that regional rather than global factors, of the type which may be responsible for OAE, explain the organic-rich Cretaceous deposits of the South Atlantic.

Stow approaches the Cretaceous organic-rich sediments of the South Atlantic from another angle and also considers similar Jurassic and Neogene sediments. He describes in detail the lithologies of these sediments and the sequence in which they occur. He shows that they are very varied. They may contain marine or terrigenous organic matter and are interbedded with organic-poor sediments in cycles with irregular periods of 20,000 to 140,000 years. They were deposited in environments ranging from nearshore to deep ocean and result from a whole spectrum of depositional processes: sliding, debris flows, high and low concentration turbidity currents, hemipelagic and pelagic sediments, and winnowing by bottom currents. Stow, as others, cites bottom-water oxygenation, organic matter supply and sedimentation rate as controls on the accumulation of organic-rich sediments. He points out the dilutant effect of high sedimentation rates.

The somewhat contrasting sediments of the North Atlantic are considered by Summerhayes and de Graciansky *et al.* Summerhayes recognizes three episodes of organic-rich sedimentation (Valanginian–Barremian, Aptian–Cenomanian, Turonian–Santonian) which he believes were influenced by four controlling factors: rate of supply of marine vs. terrigenous organic matter, rate of burial of organic matter, bottom-water oxygenation and the oceanographic history of the North Atlantic. The supply of marine organic matter was broadly uniform except from Cenomanian times in the eastern North Atlantic when coastal upwelling led to enhanced productivity. Terrigenous input, however, to the western and northeastern North Atlantic reflected high run off from humid areas. The accumulation of organic matter increased with increasing burial rate. Intermittent anoxic or suboxic conditions aided preservation. Besides the increase in productivity in the eastern North Atlantic from Cenomanian times, Summerhayes argues for a productivity event at the time of the Cenomanian–Turonian boundary. He believes this occurred when highly saline, dense, deep water from the South Atlantic was first able to move into the North Atlantic. This dense water displaced nutrient-rich deep North Atlantic water towards the surface and so gave rise to a burst of productivity.

De Graciansky *et al.* review the Cretaceous of the North Atlantic in the light of a revised and rigorously applied stratigraphy. They present detailed examples of typical sequences of sediments, including ones reflecting redeposition and ones resulting from fluctuating bottom oxygenation. These include representative organic geochemical, micropalaeontological and clay mineral data. They use accumulation rates based on their revised dating to help define depositional units and, in doing so, recognize two disconformities or times of low sedimentation: Events E1 (Late Aptian) and E2 (mid-Cenomanian–early

Turonian), the latter being equivalent in time to the Cenomanian–Turonian OAE. These events coincide with the beginning and end of widespread 'black shale' deposition in the North Atlantic.

Mid-Cretaceous organic-rich sediments

The factors which controlled the worldwide deposition of organic-rich sediments during mid-Cretaceous times are the subjects of the next papers. Many of these factors are, of course, also discussed in the four preceding papers in the context of the Atlantic Ocean. Bralower & Thierstein address the problem of whether increased productivity was a controlling factor, while Arthur, Schlanger, Jenkyns and Scholle (Schlanger *et al.* and Arthur *et al.*) focus on the Cenomanian–Turonian 'oceanic anoxic event' (OAE) and its causes.

If primary production rates are plotted against organic carbon accumulation rates for particular locations, the organic-carbon preservation factor (percentage of organic carbon produced in surface waters which is preserved in underlying sediments—see above) can be estimated for each location. Bralower and Thierstein use this relationship in an attempt to estimate levels of Cretaceous productivity. They are able to calculate organic-carbon accumulation rates for individual Cretaceous sequences from biostratigraphic, chemical and physical properties data. They consider various approaches to estimating the magnitudes of the organic-carbon preservation factors, especially the relationship between transition-metal accumulation rates and depositional environment. Using sedimentological data and what they consider as conservative estimates of the organic-carbon preservation factor, they conclude that average primary productivities in the mid-Cretaceous oceans were never high in comparison with the Holocene, even in areas of probable upwelling.

Arthur, Schlanger, Jenkyns and Scholle first deal with the detailed evidence for the Cenomanian–Turonian OAE (Schlanger *et al.*). They stress that this OAE was a period of less than one million years, at or very close to the Cenomanian–Turonian boundary, during which there was widespread oxygen deficiency in the oceans. The use of the term 'events' is neither 'intended to imply that the entire, global oceanic water column was entirely anoxic at any one moment in time' nor 'imply that during the *whole* of Cenomanian–Turonian time the entire world ocean was undergoing a single, continuous OAE'. The evidence for the event is provided by the extensive development of organic-rich sediments which

contain predominantly marine organic matter and, being laminated, are interpreted as having been deposited under anoxic conditions. Corroborative evidence comes from coeval carbonates. They are enriched in the ^{13}C isotope relative to immediately younger and older limestones. This is taken to indicate removal of the ^{12}C isotope from the oceanic system as a result of the deposition of organic matter. The interpretation of the isotopic evidence, in terms of global rates of organic-carbon burial and, possibly, oxidation, is discussed in Arthur *et al.*

Schlanger *et al.* detail the distribution and age of the sediments on which their arguments are based. They conclude that, during the short period of the Cenomanian–Turonian OAE, the oxygen minimum zone intensified globally and expanded to within 100–200 m of the surface and to depths of 1.5–2.5 km. They argue that the synchronous deposition of organic sediments within a markedly brief period indicates a global control, not a coincidence of local events. The Cenomanian–Turonian OAE is therefore seen as a discrete global episode within the broad Jurassic–Cretaceous interval of frequent and widespread potential source-rock deposition.

Arthur *et al.* consider sea-level rise to be the ultimate driving force which led to the Cenomanian–Turonian OAE. Within individual basins the sea-level rise, and resulting high stand of sea level, would have resulted in different oceanographic feedback depending on local conditions. For instance, at lower latitudes, increases in the rate of production of warm, saline, deep water (see above), due to increases in the area of epicontinental seas, may have led to increased rates of upwelling and hence productivity. (This idea does not seem to be tested by Bralower's & Thierstein's estimates of average rates of production which necessarily, because of the limits of stratigraphic resolution, relate to the mid-Cretaceous in general and not to the very brief interval of the Cenomanian–Turonian OAE.) In contrast, at high latitudes, periods of high runoff may have led to the development of relatively fresh surface waters, hence stratification and consequently bottom-water oxygen deficiency.

In the summary of his presented contribution, Funnell briefly considers the idea of anoxic events. He suggests that, with the exception of the Cenomanian–Turonian OAE they 'seem to be more geographically than temporally constrained'. He lists examples of events (mass flows, turbidites, ash falls, meteoritic impact debris) which would lead to bottom-water oxygen deficiency, and hence, he argues, discrete potential source rocks in individual basins or specific regions.

The Cenozoic

In the final paper of Part III, Shackleton deals with the Cenozoic, the part of the stratigraphic column for which possibly the most continuous and best resolved record can be established, particularly in marine sequences. He discusses using the ^{13}C content of carbonates as a means of monitoring past changes in global rates of organic matter accumulation. This approach hinges on the time scale used for calculating accumulation rates; a point which emphasizes the problems which must be even more acute when interpreting data for Mesozoic and older sections. Carbon isotope shifts similar in scale to those of the Mesozoic (e.g. Schlanger *et al.* and Arthur *et al.*) occurred in the late Paleocene and middle Miocene. These do not relate to any known 'black shales' but must relate to some anomalous organic-carbon accumulation somewhere on the globe. These and other observations raise the question of 'whether changes in the global organic carbon reservoir are controlled mechanically, by the effect of global sea-level change on the accumulation and erosion of organic-rich sediment, or geochemically, through atmospheric and oceanic oxygen levels'.

Concluding remarks

It seems appropriate, in conclusion, to highlight four topics. Each merits discussion in many papers of the volume but all are equivocal to some extent and require further detailed investigation.

Primary productivity and stratification

Both primary biological productivity and water stratification, dynamic more usually than truly static, can lead to organic matter preservation by causing bottom-water oxygen deficiency. Both controls may fluctuate with time leading only to the episodic deposition of potential source rocks. Primary productivity is the main control when upwelling is involved, as probably was often the case when many source rocks were deposited (Parrish). It may even cause preservation, without wholesale bottom-water oxygen deficiency, through shear bulk deposition (e.g. Morris). Primary productivity alone, though, cannot always be the overriding control (Demaison & Moore 1980; Tyson). Restricted circulation seems the most plausible main control in some instances (e.g. Cretaceous South Atlantic: Zimmerman *et al.*). Complex interplay between primary productivity and stratification doubtlessly remains to be worked out in many cases.

Sedimentation rate

A relationship between organic carbon preservation and sedimentation rate apparently exists (e.g. Muller & Suess 1979; Summerhayes), though Pelet claims any observed co-variation is a coincidence rather than a direct relationship. The dilutant effect of high clastic inputs, suspected by a number of workers (e.g. Tyson; Stow) is logical but has not been defined. Does such a dilutant effect apply to fine-grained sediments which may have source potential or only to coarser sediments which are unlikely to have significant organic matter content? How do the accumulation rates of different types of organic matter, which will form kerogen with different petroleum potential, relate to bulk sediment accumulation rates, particularly in specific types of depositional environment? Given the limitations of stratigraphic resolution, can average rates calculated for Mesozoic sediments etc. help answer these questions?

The oceanography of past oceans

Much further work, particularly that based on sound and rigorous physics, needs to be applied to past oceans. Plausible models of surface currents and upwelling can be predicted from palaeogeographic reconstructions and climatic models of both the qualitative (Parrish 1982) and quantitative variety (Barron & Washington 1982). One aspect worth pursuing would be three-dimensional models of oceanic circulation to test the viability of two-dimensional ideas put forward to explain deep-water characteristics and, in particular, bottom-water oxygenation (e.g. those of Arthur *et al.*). An understanding of the oceanography of the extensive epicontinental seas produced by transgressions is obviously of prime importance; the first-order transgression: source-rock deposition relationship is apparent through the Phanerozoic record (e.g. Thickpenny & Leggett; Hallam; Arthur *et al.*). To understand this relationship, are new or special oceanographic insights needed, or can individual cases be explained if our understanding of present-day oceanography is judiciously applied, as Calvert and Funnell suspect? Also, as Shackleton asks, under what circumstances is the global carbon budget influenced by the physical impact of transgressions and when is it controlled by atmospheric and oceanic oxygen levels?

Multidisciplinary studies

This final topic is worthwhile including to underline the fact that sedimentological, geochemical, micropalaeontological and palynological studies, in all their various guises, all need to be integrated if organic-rich marine sediments are to be understood (e.g. Suess *et al.*; de Graciansky *et al.*). In particular associated sediments are as important as the organic-rich intervals themselves, as they provide evidence of how oceanic conditions must have fluctuated and what conditions were favourable for the deposition of potential source rocks.

ACKNOWLEDGEMENTS: We thank the managements British Petroleum and Britoil for permission to publish this introduction.

References

BARNARD, P. C. & COOPER, B. S. 1981. Oil and source rocks of the North Sea area. *In:* ILLING, V. C. & HOBSON, G. D. (eds) *Petroleum Geology of the Continental Shelf of Northwest Europe*, Institute of Petroleum, London, 169–175.

BARRON, E. J. & WASHINGTON, W. M. 1982. Atmospheric circulation during warm geologic periods: is the equator-to-pole surface temperature gradient the controlling factor? *Geology*, **10**, 633–636.

BERRY, W. B. N. & WILDE, P. 1978. Progressive ventilation of the oceans—an explanation for the distribution of the Lower Paleozoic black shales. *Am. J. Sci.*, **278**, 257–275.

BOCKMEULEN, H., BARKER, C. & DICKEY, P. A. 1983. Geology and chemistry of crude oils, Bolivar Coastal Fields, Venezuela. *Bull. Am. Assoc. Petrol. Geol.* **67**, 242–270.

BOIS, C., BOUCHE, P. & PELET, R. 1980. Histoire geologique et repartition des reserves d'hydrocarbures dans le monde. *Rev. Inst. Fr. Pet. Paris*, **35**, 273–298.

BRADY, T. J., CAMPBELL, N. D. J. & MAHER, C. E. 1980. Intisar 'D' Oilfeld, Libya. *Mem. Am. Assoc. Petrol. Geol.*, **30**, 543–564.

BRASS, G. W., SOUTHAM, J. R. & PETERSON, W. H. 1982. Warm saline bottom water in the ancient ocean. *Nature*, **296**, 620–623.

CHIN CHEN, 1980. Non-marine setting of petroleum in the Sungliao basin of northeastern China. *J. Petrol. Geol.*, **2**, 233–264.

COOGAN, A. H., BEBOUT, D. G. & MAGGIO, C. 1972. Depositional environments and geologic history of Golden Lane and Poza Rice trend, Mexico, an alternative view. *Bull. Am. Assoc. Petrol. Geol.*, **56**, 1419–1447.

CROSTELLA, A. 1981. Malacca Strait wrench fault controlled Lalang and Mengkapan oil fields. *Offshore East Asia Conference, Exploration III*, 1–12.

DEMAISON, G. J. & MOORE, G. T. 1980. Anoxic environments and oil source bed genesis. *Bull. Am. Assoc. Petrol. Geol.*, **64**, 1179–1209.

DEROO, G., POWELL, T. G., TISSOT, B. & McCROSSAN, R. G. 1977. The origin and migration of petroleum in the western Canadian sedimentary basin, Alberta—a geochemical and thermal maturity study. *Bull. Geol. Surv. Canada*, **262**.

DOW, W. G. 1978. Petroleum source beds on continental slopes and rises. *Bull. Am. Assoc. Petrol. Geol.*, **62**, 1584–1606.

DUNCAN, D. C. & SWANSON, V. E. 1965. Organic-rich shale of the United States and World land areas. *Circ. U.S. Geol. Surv.*, **523**, 30 pp.

ETTENSOHM, F. R. & BARRON, L. S. 1982. A tectonic-climatic approach to the deposition of the Devonian-

Mississippian black-shale sequence of North America. *1982 Eastern oil shale symposium*, Kentucky Dept. of Energy and Univ. of Kentucky, Lexington, 5–37.

FISCHER, A. G. & ARTHUR, M. A. 1977. Secular variations in the pelagic realm. *Spec. Publ. Soc. econ. Paleontol. Mineral.*, **25**, 19–50.

FRAKES, L. A. 1979. *Climates Throughout Geologic Time*. Elsevier, 310 pp.

FREY, M. G. & GRIMES, W. H. 1970. Bay Marchand-Timbalier Bay-Caillou Island salt complex, Louisiana. *Mem. Assoc. Petrol. Geol.*, **14**, 277–291.

GALLEY, J. E. 1958. Oil and geology in the Permian basin of Texas and New Mexico. *In:* WEEKS, L .G. (ed.), *Habitat of Oil*, Am. Assoc. Petrol. Geol., Tulsa, 395–446.

GATEWOOD, L. E. 1970. Oklahoma City field—anatomy of a giant. *Mem. Am. Assoc. Petrol. Geol.*, **14**, 223–254.

GRUNAU, H. R. 1983. Abundance of source rocks for oil and gas worldwide. *J. Petrol. Geol.*, **6**, 39–54.

HALBOUTY, M. T., MEYERHOFF, A. A., KING, R. E., DOTT, R. H. Sr., KLEMME, H. D. & SHABAD, T. 1970. World's giant oil and gas fields, geologic factors affecting their formation and basin classification. *Mem. Am. Assoc. Petrol. Geol.*, **14**, 502–555.

HAQ, B. U. 1981. Paleogene paleoceanography: Early Cenozoic oceans revisited. *Oceanol. Acta*, **SP**, 71–82.

HARLAND, W. B., COX, A. V., LLEWELLYN, P. G., PICKTON, C. A. G., SMITH, A. G. & WALTERS, R. 1982. *A Geologic Time Scale*. Cambridge University Press, Cambridge, 131 pp.

HECKEL, P. H. 1977. Origin of phosphatic black shale facies in Pennsylvanian cyclothems of mid-continent North America. *Bull. Am. Assoc. Petrol. Geol.*, **61**, 1045–1068.

IRVING, E., NORTH, F. K. & COUILLARD, R. 1974. Oil, climate and tectonics. *Can. J. Earth Sci.*, **11**, 1–17.

JENKYNS, H. C. 1980. Cretaceous anoxic events: from continents to oceans. *J. geol. Soc. London*, **137**, 177–188.

KRUEGER, W. C. & NORTH, F. K. 1983. Occurrences of oil and gas in association with the paleo-shelfbreak. *Spec. Publ. Soc. econ. Paleontol. Mineral.*, **33**, 409–427.

LEGGETT, J. K. 1980. British Lower Palaeozoic black shales and their palaeo-oceanographic significance. *J. geol. Soc. London*, **137**, 139–156.

MACKENZIE, A. S. 1984. Applications of biological markers in petroleum geochemistry. *In:* BROOK, J. & WELTE, D. (eds), *Advances in Petroleum Geochemistry*, Volume 1, Academic Press, 115–214.

MAGOON, L. B. & CLAYPOOL, G. E. 1981. Two oil types

on North Slope of Alaska—implications for exploration. *Bull. Am. Assoc. Petrol. Geol.*, **65**, 644–652.

MAYUGA, M. N. 1970. Geology and development of California's Giant—Wilmington oil field. *Mem. Am. Assoc. Petrol. Geol.*, **14**, 158–184.

MÜLLER, P. J. & SUESS, E. 1979. Productivity, sedimentation rate, and sedimentary organic matter in the oceans—I. Organic carbon preservation. *Deep-Sea Res.*, **26A**, 1347–1362.

NEHRING, R. 1980. The outlook for world oil resources. *Oil Gas Journ.*, **78** (43), 170–175.

NORTH, F. K. 1971. Characteristics of oil provinces: a study for students. *Bull. Can. Pet. Geol.*, **19**, 601–658.

—— 1979. Episodes of source-sediment deposition (1). *J. Petrol. Geol.*, **2**, 199–218.

—— 1980. Episodes of source-sediment deposition (2). The episodes in individual close up. *J. Petrol. Geol.*, **2**, 323–338.

PARRISH, J. T. 1982. Upwelling and petroleum source beds, with reference to the Paleozoic. *Bull. Am. Assoc. Petrol. Geol.*, **66**, 750–774.

—— & CURTIS, R. L. 1982. Atmospheric circulation, upwelling, and organic-rich rocks in the Mesozoic and Cenozoic eras. *Palaeogeogr., Palaeoclimatol., Palaeocol.*, **40**, 31–66.

PIPPIN, L. 1970. Panhandle-Hugston field, Texas-Oklahoma-Kansas—the first fifty years. *Mem. Am. Assoc. Petrol. Geol.*, **14**, 204–222.

SAVRDA, C. E., BOTTJER, D. J. & GORSLINE, D. S. 1984. Development of a comprehensive oxygen-deficient

marine biofacies model: evidence from Santa Barbara basins, California borderland. *Bull. Am. Assoc. Petrol. Geol.*, **68**, 1179–1192.

SCHLANGER, S. O. & JENKYNS, H. C. 1976. Cretaceous anoxic events: causes and consequences. *Geol. Mijnbouw*, **55**, 179–184.

SUESS, E. & THIEDE, J. 1983. *Coastal Upwelling: its Sediment Record, A.* NATO Conf. Ser. IV, **10A**. Plenum Press, New York.

THIEDE, J. & SUESS, E. 1983. *Coastal Upwelling: its Sediment Record, B.* NATO Conf. Serv. IV, **10B**. Plenum Press, New York.

TISSOT, B. 1979. Effects on prolific petroleum source rocks and major coal deposits caused by sea-level changes. *Nature*, **277**, 463–465.

TRASK, P. D. 1932. *Origin and Environment of Source Sediments of Petroleum.* American Petroleum Institute. 323 pp.

WEBER, K. J. & DAUKORU, E. 1975. Petroleum geology of the Niger delta. *Proc. 9th World Petroleum Congress*, **2**, 209–221.

WOODSIDE, P. R. 1984. A look at the petroleum geology of Indonesia. *Oil Gas Journ.*, **82** (8), 78–82.

WOODWARD, H. P. 1958. Emplacement of oil and gas in Appalachian basin. *In:* WEEKS, L. G. (ed.), *Habitat of Oil*, Am. Assoc. Petrol. Geol., Tulsa, 494–510.

ZHOU GUANGJIA 1981. Character of organic matter in source rocks of continental origin and its maturation and evolution. *In:* MASON, J. F. (ed.), *Petroleum Geology in China*, Pennwell Books, 26–47.

A. J. FLEET, Exploration and Production Division, BP Research Centre, Chertsey Road, Sunbury-on-Thames, Middlesex, TW16 7LN, UK.

J. BROOKS, Exploration Division, Britoil plc, 150 St. Vincent Street, Glasgow, G2 5LJ, UK. (current address: Consultant, Langside Drive, Newlands, Glasgow, G43 2EE, UK.)

Part I
Concepts and Methods

The role of hydrocarbon source rocks in petroleum exploration

J. Brooks, C. Cornford & R. Archer

SUMMARY: Petroleum is generated from organic-rich sediments (source rocks) containing organic matter originating from biological materials. During burial of sediments, the increase in temperature results in a series of geochemical reactions which leads from biopolymers to geopolymers, often collectively called kerogen, which are precursors of petroleum.

The amount, type and composition of petroleum generated is dependent upon the nature and geological history of the source rock. The most important parameters are the nature of the organic matter in the source rock and its maturity governed by its time/temperature history.

Petroleum exploration is now using modern understandings of hydrocarbon generation, migration and accumulation to help improve its success in predicting petroleum discoveries. The initial stages of an exploration programme can regionally evaluate the source rocks, together with the hydrocarbon potential of each source rock horizon and integrate this information with the geological development of the basin to enhance predictions of where and when hydrocarbon generation and accumulation have occurred.

Introduction

What constitutes a hydrocarbon source rock has intrigued petroleum geologists for many years, since the first discoveries of oil and gas. The same question is still discussed today, even amongst petroleum geochemists.

The very early views on source rocks were basic and often empirical and one of the earliest scientific summaries by Snider (1934) informed petroleum exploration that 'there seems to be a very nearly universal agreement that these organic materials are buried principally in argillaceous mud and to a less extent in calcareous muds and marls and in sand muds. Coarse sands and gravels and very pure calcareous deposits are generally without any notable content of organic material. Consequently, shales and bituminous limestones consolidated from muds and marls are generally regarded as source rocks for petroleum and natural gas'.

Although basically a correct definition, and of potential use to petroleum geologists in their exploration, the study of source rocks and integration of results into petroleum exploration philosophy was until relatively recently very much neglected. Until about the late 1960s most petroleum geologists evaluated an exploration prospect against a check list comprising 'trap', 'potential reservoir', 'caprock' and 'source', but this latter term 'source' was somewhat nebulous; generally it sufficed that there were shales in the vicinity of the potential reservoir, and if these shales were marine then so much the better. Generally explorers favoured prospects which lay between depths of about one and three kilometres, but were not sure why, since it was known that both shallower and deeper fields also existed. When all the 'geological conditions' were present, but no hydrocarbons were found, explorers generally explained their dry holes as lack of source rocks. Such conclusions were probably based solely on intuitive reasoning or even unprovable excuse, because studies, characterization, properties and data on source rocks were generally lacking.

Oil producing basins all contain at least one significantly mature hydrocarbon source rock. Such source rocks are usually stratigraphically widespread and were deposited in an oxygen-depleted (anoxic) environment. Although it has often been suggested that any dark shale is a source rock; geochemistry has clearly shown that the bulk of dark, fine-grained sediments in the sedimentary record, are not source rocks and were deposited under oxygen-rich water, as in most of today's world oceans and lakes (Demaison et al. 1983; Demaison 1984).

Characteristics and properties of source rocks are now much better understood and applied in exploration programmes (Figs 1 and 2), but what constitutes hydrocarbon source rocks is still debated. It is therefore necessary to define the criteria used in source-rock studies.

Current studies on source rocks all use proven geochemical concepts that oil and gas are formed via a series of complex approximately first-order geochemical processes from sedimentary organic matter (often termed kerogen).

Although hypotheses are periodically put forward for non-biological, earth mantle origins of petroleum (see Gold 1979), it is widely accepted that the origins are in sediments rich in biologically derived organic matter, from which there is

From: BROOKS, J. & FLEET, A. J. (eds) 1987, *Marine Petroleum Source Rocks*
Geological Society Special Publication No. 26 pp. 17–46.

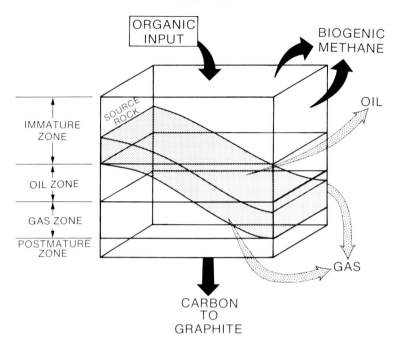

FIG. 1. Hydrocarbon source rocks: diagrammatic representation of source rock at different stages of maturation and hydrocarbon products.

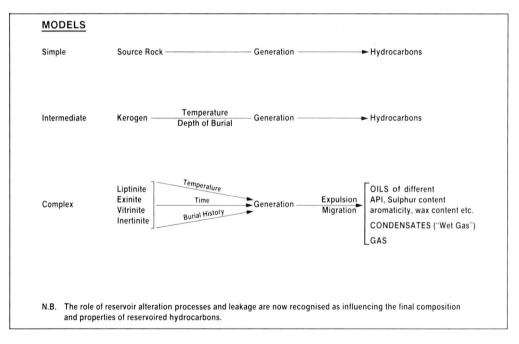

FIG. 2. Source rock evaluation: the development of the concept of source-rock models for hydrocarbon generation, expulsion and migration.

scientifically supported evidence. Therefore, a petroleum source rock may be defined as a fine-grained sediment which in its natural setting has generated, is generating, or will generate and release enough hydrocarbons to form a commercial accumulation of oil or gas.

Hunt (1979) considers definitions that do not include migration and accumulation are too general, because practically all fine-grained sediments form some hydrocarbons, but they cannot all be classed as source rocks. Even if this definition of a source rock is accepted for general use, the meaning and application to case studies can often be ambiguous and confusing. Dow (1978) comments that economic potential of an unexplored area depends in part on the source potential of the area, and whether or not potential source rocks are present. Potential is used to express something 'capable of coming into being or action; unrealised'. So the use of the term potential source rocks mean those rocks capable of generating and releasing oil and/or gas, but which have not yet reached that state. It is also proposed that the terms 'source rocks' and 'potential source rocks' should be more accurately defined and applied in petroleum geochemical studies. Our proposed definitions of source rock are based on Dow's proposals which have been slightly amended to:

Source rocks: a volume of rock that has generated or is generating and expelling hydrocarbons in sufficient quantities to form commercial oil and gas accumulations. The contained sedimentary organic matter must meet minimum criteria of organic richness, kerogen-type and organic maturity. (A special case is the *spent* source rock, one that has generated, possibly a long time ago, its hydrocarbons and now contains thermally altered organic matter).

Potential source rocks: a volume of rock that has the capacity to generate hydrocarbons in sufficient quantities to form commercial oil and gas accumulations, but has not yet reached the state of minimum hydrocarbon generation because of insufficient organic maturation.

These source-rock definitions are used in this chapter, but the reader is reminded that both definitions are based upon an interpretation of 'commercial accumulations' and such evaluations are usually economic and not solely geological.

Petroleum source rocks and oil shales

It is important to distinguish between petroleum source rocks and oil shales. There does not appear to be a precise geological or geochemical definition of an oil shale. Any shallowly buried rock

yielding oil in commercial quantities upon pyrolysis can be considered to be an oil shale (Chilligarian & Yen 1976).

Oil shales are diverse fine-grained rocks, which contain thermally degradable organic material that can be processed in hydrocarbon-based fuels. Extractable organic matter in such rocks usually constitutes about 20 per cent of the total organic matter, with the remainder existing as insoluble organic matter (kerogen) derived from plant (and animal) tissue by low temperature microbiological and geochemical alteration processes. Oil shales appear to have been deposited in shallow seas, lakes or marsh environments, which supported abundant algal biota. Oil shales have been defined as 'a compact, laminated rock of sedimentary origin, yielding over 33 per cent of ash and containing organic matter that yield oil when distilled, but not appreciably when extracted with ordinary solvents for petroleum' (Gavin 1924). In distinguishing between petroleum source rocks, oil shales and coals, it is necessary to define the origin, history and geochemical properties of the sedimentary organic matter and to determine by laboratory study the optical properties and thermally generated or potential products from the organic matter. Oil shales and coals must have a high content of organic matter to make them of economic use. Hydrocarbon generation processes are very different for a petroleum source rock compared with oil shales. Petroleum source rocks require sufficient geological burial history and a mature stage or organic maturation so that they can generate their maximum amount of liquid and gaseous hydrocarbons from the sedimentary organic matter. However, oil shales with potentially large pyrolytic yields of hydrocarbons usually originate in shallow, low temperature environments.

Tissot & Welte (1978) point out that the equivalent of an oil shale, sufficiently buried, constitutes a petroleum source rock. However, a petroleum source rock, shallowly buried does not necessarily constitute an oil shale, due to the requirement of organic riches.

The origin, composition and distribution of oil shales have been reviewed by Cane (1976), Robinson (1969), Duncan (1967), Chilligarian & Yen (1976) and Tissot & Welte (1984).

Marine and non marine (continental) source rocks

Source rocks are commonly divided into two subcategories, marine and non-marine. Marine source rocks are those that accumulate as sediments under marine conditions, but generally

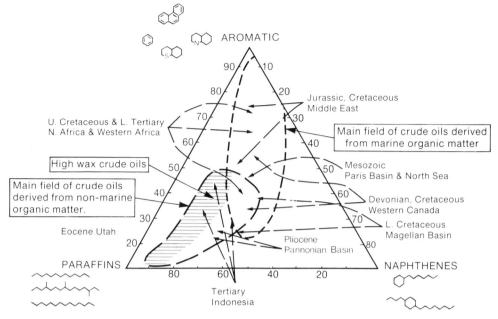

Crude oil composition, showing the principal field of
occurence of crude oils from marine and non-marine
origin (After Tissot and Welte 1978)

FIG. 3. Crude oil composition: showing the principal fields of occurrence of crude oils from marine and non-marine origin. (After Tissot & Welte 1978 and 84).

contain both marine and terrigenous organic matter. Non-marine source rocks are those accumulating in lakes and river basins and usually contain a mixture of fresh water algae and land plant tissue. The two types of source rocks are contrasted in Table 1. It should be remembered that intermediate zones such as brackish deltaic and hypersaline lacustrine environments do exist.

Crude oil and gas composition (Fig. 3) is dependent upon a number of geological and geochemical processes, such as:
- the composition and deposition environment of the organic matter which forms the hydrocarbon source rocks
- the thermal history of the source rock within the basin which results in generation, expulsion and migration of liquid and gaseous hydrocarbons

TABLE 1. *Hydrocarbon source rock potential of marine and non-marine sediments*

Marine	Kerogen-type	Non-marine
Liptinite-rich*	Kerogen-type	Vitrinite/exinite/inertinite rich
Phytoplankton and bacteria*	Source-organisms	High plants and non-marine algae
High H/C; low 'O' lipids, polysaccharides etc.	Chemical composition	Low H/C; high 'O' polysaccharides, lignin, sporopollenin, lipids etc.
Major precursors for world oil reserves. Gas at higher maturity	Hydrocarbons generated	Mainly gas, but some liquid H/C can be formed

* Note: Typical marine kerogen contains a mixture of autochthonous marine and allochthonous terrigenous kerogen

• alteration of the accumulated petroleum within the reservoir by such processes as water washing, biodegradation, diffusion and oxidation.

The accumulation and preservation of organic matter in sediments is not only a crucial process in the formation of the hydrocarbon source rock, but the origin of the marine or continental character has to be evaluated and related to the origin of the predominant organic material in sediments. The crude oils produced from non-marine source rocks are more paraffinic but more aromatic oils are formed from marine source rocks. The geochemical significance of the chemical differences between these oils of different sources is difficult to clarify (Tissot & Welte 1978).

Organic matter in sediments

Organic matter is usually a minor constituent in most sedimentary rocks. However, it is present in varying amounts, in all types of sediment. The amount of organic matter in both modern and ancient sediments varies from almost 100% in some peat and coal deposits, to little more than a few parts per million in some limestone and sandstone deposits. Organic matter can be visibly recognized when present in high concentrations as coal and peat deposits or as accumulations of natural gas, petroleum, tar sands and as oil shale deposits. Most significantly, it is found in greatest abundance as finely dispersed discrete, microscopic organic particles ('macerals') in clastic sediments.

Generally, the organic contents of sediments is between 0.1 and 5%; deep-sea sediments average about 0.2% organic carbon, geosynclinal sediments about 2%, and shelf sediments between 1 and 5%.

Carbon cycle

Carbon is present in sedimentary rocks in two forms: as reduced carbon in biologically produced organic matter over geological time, and as oxidized carbon mainly in the form of carbonate.

The major process for production of organic matter is photosynthesis and this is primarily responsible for the occurrence of reduced carbon in sediments (Fig. 4). Photosynthesis, which converts light energy into chemical energy, is a biochemical process which transfers hydrogen from water molecules to add carbon dioxide to produce simple organic materials and liberate free oxygen. These new organic molecules undergo further biochemical syntheses to produce larger molecules such as polysaccharides, e.g. cellulose and starch (see Brooks & Shaw 1973). Carbon is recycled through the biosphere by photosynthesis and oxidation. Like any set of chemical reactions, photosynthesis does not produce a net change in oxidation. Oxygen is produced, except in bacterial photosynthesis, together with a stoichiometric quantity of reduced carbon (photosynthesis, respiration or fermentation). Almost all the oxygen is eventually used to oxidize this reduced carbon and the only net gain in oxygen levels during geological time equals the amount of reduced carbon removed from the geochemical cycle and buried as sedimentary organic matter before it can be oxidized. Thus an important mechanism for the fixation of organic carbon in the earth's crust and the production of free oxygen into the atmosphere was the accumulation of sedimentary organic matter. These processes have been active since the first presence of photosynthetic organisms in the early Precambrian (Brooks 1981b).

Carbon is concentrated in sedimentary rocks in two main forms. About 18% of the total carbon is fixed in its 'reduced' form as organic carbon and the remaining 82% is present as carbonates (Schidlowskie *et al.* 1974). Much emphasis is put on the amount of organic carbon present in sedimentary rocks when determining their hydrocarbon source potential, but this can sometimes be misleading. Petroleum is formed by the thermal maturation of organic matter in sediments and involves an exchange of hydrogen atoms between a relatively hydrogen-poor source rock kerogen and relatively hydrogen-rich petroleum hydrocarbon products. Therefore it is important to evaluate source rocks not only by their organic carbon content but, also, whenever practicable by the amount of organic matter present, its type and therefore the amount of hydrogen available in such material to produce hydrocarbon products.

The biological productivity of aquatic environments, especially marine environments, is of great importance for the formation of potential petroleum source rocks (Fig. 5). However, the vast majority of dead organisms are rapidly chemically or microbiologically degraded (oxidized) to CO_2 in the biochemical cycle, and only an estimated 0.1% of organic carbon is typically deposited within sediments. Hunt (1979) has suggested that since the beginning of life, only about 1 part in 11,000 of this 0.1% carbon (i.e. about 1 part per million) has become commercial petroleum accumulations that have survived to the present time.

The total annual productivity in the oceans is about 5.5×10^{13} kg or 115 g per square metre.

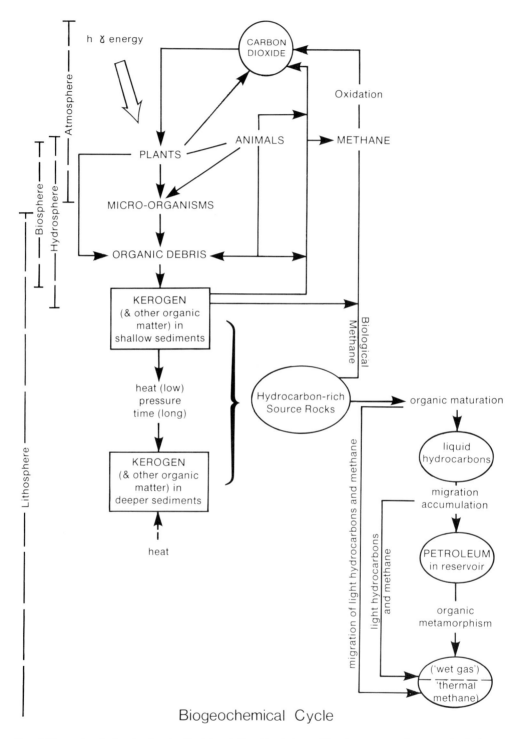

Biogeochemical Cycle

FIG. 4. Biogeochemical cycle; showing the interrelationships between biopolymers, geopolymers and petroleum in the atmosphere, biosphere, hydrosphere and lithosphere (Brooks 1981a).

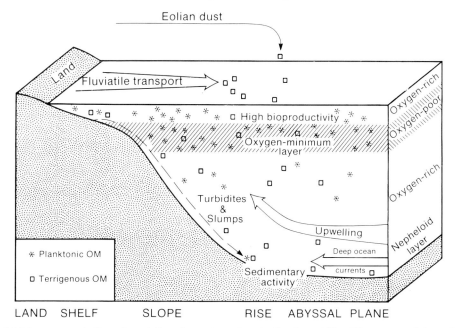

FIG. 5. Main processes in the sedimentation of organic matter at a Continental Rise. The oxygen-minimum layer is the area of maximum organic matter preservation. (After Cornford 1979).

Consideration of present oceanic productivity (Fig. 7) shows that vast regions of the seas are barren or almost devoid of organic matter, whilst other areas are relatively rich in material.

Areas of upwelling of deep ocean water correlate closely with regions of high marine organic productivity. Such areas overlay some of the richest source beds currently being deposited, which include parts of the Arctic and Antarctic Oceans, equatorial regions of the Pacific and some continental margins. The estimated total terrigenous production is probably twice the marine production, being about 10.9×10^{13} kg (dry weight) (Degens & Mopper 1976).

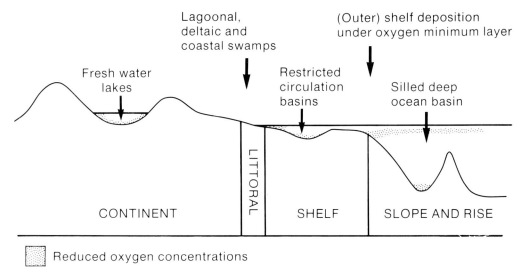

FIG. 6. Some major environments for the accumulation of organic-rich potential hydrocarbon source rock.

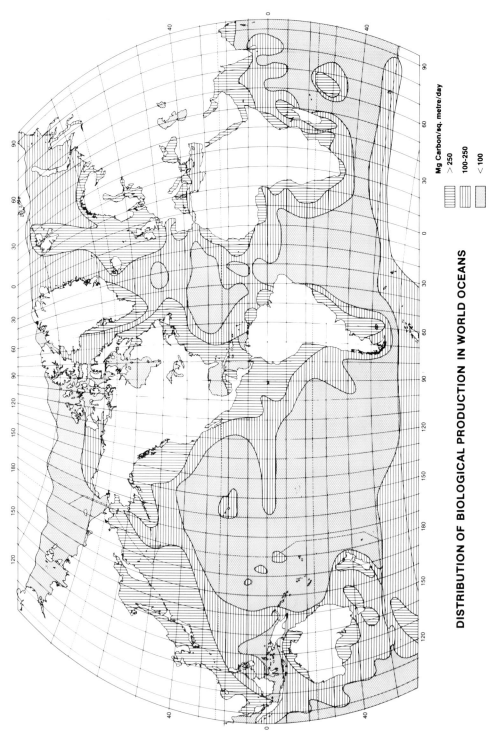

DISTRIBUTION OF BIOLOGICAL PRODUCTION IN WORLD OCEANS

Mg Carbon/sq. metre/day

> 250
100-250
< 100

Fig. 7. Distribution of biological production in world oceans (after various authors including Koblents-Mishke *et al.* 1970).

The most abundant chemical components of this organic productivity are of biological origin and comprise mainly lipids, carbohydrates, lignins, sporopollenins and proteins which vary greatly for different organisms.

The main contributors of organic matter to sediments are bacteria, phytoplankton, zooplankton and higher plants. Many factors affect the distribution of organic matter in sediments. Biological associations of groups of the organisms in different facies accumulations have great influence upon the type and composition of organic matter that is accumulated, deposited and preserved in sediments.

Production and accumulation of organic matter

Factors controlling and influencing the accumulation of organic matter in sediments may be classified into four main categories: biological, physical, chemical and geological. However, these divisions are interrelated and it is difficult to classify simple processes leading to accumulation of sedimentary organic matter. Some major environments for the accumulation of organic rich potential source rocks are summarized in Fig. 6.

Biological activity includes primary biological productivity within the earth's aqueous environs and landmasses, as well as the molecular and structural modifications brought about by highly active microbiological recycling. Physical factors principally influence the transport of organic matter prior to deposition, factors such as density (buoyancy), sedimentation rates and particle sorting. Chemical changes can occur during transport in the water column, during sedimentation and are usually very significant in the upper few metres of the sediment. These three factors—productivity, transport and preservation, control the type and amount of organic matter in sediments.

Production

The total annual primary production of organic matter has been calculated by various workers. In brief the land produces up to 6 times more organic carbon per year than the sea, while in the sea phytoplankton produces over 2000 times more carbon than zooplankton. Current estimates of the distribution of biological production in the world oceans is given in Fig. 7.

Huc (1980) has calculated that annual primary production of organic matter is about $1.5–1.7 \times 10^{10}$ tons of organic carbon in the oceans and $1.4–7.8 \times 10^{10}$ tons on the continents. It has also been estimated that current annual production of phytoplankton is about 55×10^{10} tons and 0.2×10^9 tons of phytobenthos in the oceans (Krey 1970). The standing crops of the ocean and the land are about 0.009 and 12.5 kg/metre respectively on a dry weight basis (Degens & Mopper 1976): therefore on a simplistic balance, marine phytoplankton photosynthesis is more efficient by a factor of almost 1500 relative to average land plants.

Production of organic matter is the first stage in the incorporation of organic matter into sediments to form potential source rocks. The principal sources of aquatic organic matter are the various groups of phytoplankton made up of blue-green algae (*Cyanophyceae*), dinoflagellates, diatoms and nannoplankton. These are mainly composed of single cell microscopic algae present in the uppermost photic layers of the aquatic medium.

Photosynthesis is the most fundamental biochemical process which produces the marine precursors of sedimentary organic matter. Solar energy enters the biological cycle through photosynthetic production of organic matter. The main limiting factor to phytoplanktonic productivity, in addition to light, is the availability of certain mineral nutrients (e.g. nitrates and phosphates), which are usually in short supply in certain zones where demand is high (particularly the euphotic zone of the water column).

Bacteria also 'produce' large amounts of organic matter in the marine environment. The exact amounts produced are still unclear, but aquatic environments containing dissolved and particulate organic matter provide extremely favourable conditions for the conversion of existing organic tissue to bacterial biomass. The effect of bacteria in the biological cycle is to decompose dead organic matter and make available degradation products which can be incorporated into the food-cycle of the systems. As such they do not increase the total organic matter, but merely transform, rather inefficiently, one type to another. Large quantities of bacteria are present as benthonic organisms in the water column, at the sediment/water interface, and also in the uppermost layer of sediments (Bordovskiy 1965).

The other main source of organic matter in aquatic environments is that transported from a terrigenous source via rivers, streams and winds. It is most common along continental margins generally decreasing to the deep open oceans. On continents, it is mainly climate which defines the bio-geographical regions of major biomass production (forests, grasslands, etc.). Land-plant biomass productivity is essentially controlled by temperature and the amount of rainfall, while growth of natural association (e.g. marshlands, peat bogs) also helps control organic matter production. At present, terrestrial plants and marine phytoplankton produce about equal quantities of organic matter. The current transgressive state in oceanic evolution (high world sea level stand) favours deposition of terrigenous debris in near-shore environments (Degens & Mopper 1976). In contrast, during regressive stages (low sea level stand) it is possible that a larger percentage of terrigenous organic matter may be carried over the continental shelves to be deposited into the open ocean. However, geochemical evidence (Degens & Mopper 1976) suggests that, regardless of whether oceanic evolution is in a transgressive or regressive stage, organic contributions from land are small relative to those from the marine biomass. Such a statement emphasizes the key role of preservation rather than production *per se* in controlling the amount and type of organic matter fully preserved in the sediments.

Taking a global view of these processes, sediments deposited along eastern coasts of continents generally contain higher percentages of terrigenous organic matter, mainly due to the lower biomass production of marine organic matter. Good oil-prone source rocks will contain relatively high concentrations of marine produced organic matter compared to terrestrially derived materials. Marine organic matter contains high proportions of hydrogen-rich lipid and lipid-like components which are necessary organic precursors of petroleum. Terrestrial plant materials contain dominantly hydrogen-deficient chemical components (e.g. lignin and cellulose) which have a greater capacity to produce large quantities of gas rather than oil. However, some terrestrially derived components (e.g. resins, pollen, spores and cuticles) are capable of producing large quantities of early condensate, naphthenic oils and condensate as well as gas at higher thermal maturation.

Since production of marine organic matter is controlled by light, temperature and the nutrients present in sea water, changes in the nutrient content can encourage production. Upwelling of deep ocean water can introduce large quantities of nutrients such as nitrate and phosphate into the euphotic zone, resulting in areas of high organic productivity (Dow 1978). Upwelling is most common along the west coasts of continents and such areas correlate closely with regions of high, marine organic productivity (Table 2).

Dow (1978) reports that such upwelling areas contain some of the richest known petroleum source beds. However, Demaison & Moore (1980)

TABLE 2. *Productivity of coastal waters as compared to the open ocean (Krey 1970)*

Area (km^2 × 10^6)		Average productivity (g cm^{-2} per year)	Total production in 10^9 t C per year
Open ocean	326	50	16.3
Coastal waters	36	100	3.6
Upwelling regions	0.4	300	0.1

question this traditional view that fields of high surface productivity in the ocean should be associated with high organic enrichment of underlying sediments; after many investigations they could not find a systematic correlation between primary biomass production and organic carbon content of bottom sediments in the oceans. Factors other than simply surface production of biomass must affect the production and preservation of marine organic matter, because some regions of high biomass production like the SW Shelf of Africa and the Peruvian Shelf were enriched; others of equally high productivity like the Grand Banks of Newfoundland, the NW Shelf of Africa or the NE Brazilian Shelf were not (Demaison & Moore 1980).

Demaison *et al.* (1983) reported on recent progress in understanding the palaeo-oceanographic aspects of petroleum source rock deposition and showed that it is now feasible, by mapping organic facies distribution, to determine the stratigraphy and distribution of source rocks in sedimentary basins.

The three main environments of deposition of organic matter have been defined in modern and geological sediments. A summary of these environments, based upon their degree of oxygenation is given in Fig. 8.

Various source bed depositional models have been proposed by Demaison *et al.* (1983). Fig. 9 illustrates hydrocarbon source rock deposition in open marine environments. In such environments the oxygen minimum layer contains an anoxic, or sub-oxic core which impinges upon a continental slope or shelf. Such environments for production and preservation of organic rich materials, when reinforced by coastal upwelling, generally result in the deposition of good hydrocarbon source rocks. Models for source rock deposition in lakes and silled basin (Figure 10) as proposed by Demaison *et al.* (1983) predict that anoxic/sub-oxic environments most favourable to good hydrocarbon source rocks occur when the water becomes stagnant because of permanent density

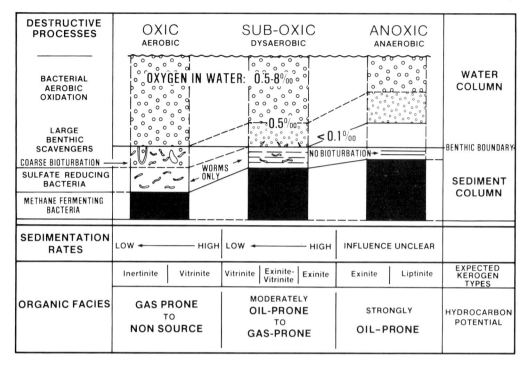

DESTRUCTIVE PROCESSES	OXIC AEROBIC		SUB-OXIC DYSAEROBIC			ANOXIC ANAEROBIC		
BACTERIAL AEROBIC OXIDATION	OXYGEN IN WATER: 0.5-8‰				→0.5‰	≤0.1‰		WATER COLUMN
LARGE BENTHIC SCAVENGERS								
COARSE BIOTURBATION →			WORMS ONLY			NO BIOTURBATION →		BENTHIC BOUNDARY
SULFATE REDUCING BACTERIA								SEDIMENT COLUMN
METHANE FERMENTING BACTERIA								
SEDIMENTATION RATES	LOW ← HIGH		LOW ← HIGH			INFLUENCE UNCLEAR		
ORGANIC FACIES	Inertinite	Vitrinite	Vitrinite	Exinite-Vitrinite	Exinite	Exinite	Liptinite	EXPECTED KEROGEN TYPES
	GAS PRONE TO NON SOURCE		MODERATELY OIL-PRONE TO GAS-PRONE			STRONGLY OIL-PRONE		HYDROCARBON POTENTIAL

FIG. 8. Benthic environment and petroleum source rock deposition. Organic facies mapping depends upon a clear understanding of the relationship between early depositional factors and kerogen types (after Demaison *et al.* 1983, with permission).

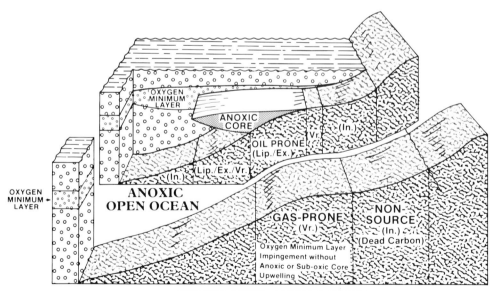

VENTILATED OPEN OCEAN

FIG. 9. Source bed deposition in open marine environment. Such environments occur where the oxygen-minimum layer contains an anoxic, or sub-oxic core which impinges upon a continental slope or shelf. These environments, when reinforced by coastal upwelling, can lead to profile source bed deposition (after Demaison *et al.* 1983; with permission). (Lip./Ex./Vr.)—Liptinite/Exinite/Vitrinite-rich, (In.)—Inertinite-rich, (Vr.)—Vitrinite-rich, (Lip./Ex.)—Liptinite/Exinite.

SILLED BASIN

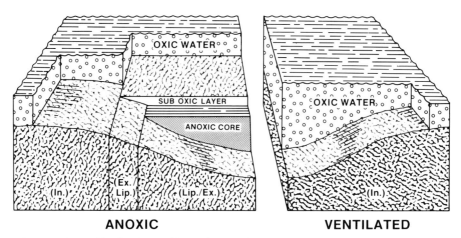

ANOXIC   **VENTILATED**

FIG. 10. Source bed deposition in lakes or silled basins. Anoxic or sub-oxic environments favourable to source bed deposition tend to occur when water becomes stagnant because of permanent density stratification. Well-ventilated silled-basins and lakes characterized by active mixing of the water masses tend to remain wholly oxic (after Demaison *et al.* 1983, with permission). (In.)—Inertinite-rich, (Lip./Ex.)—Liptinite/Exinite, (Ex./Lip.)—Exinite/Liptinite.

stratification. This work also predicts that well-ventilated basins or lakes (with active mixing processes) produce wholly oxic environments and little or no deposition of hydrocarbon source rocks.

Sedimentary organic matter and kerogen

Any consideration of the origin, mode of formation and definition of kerogen must be somewhat speculative. Kerogen from different parts of the earth and even from adjacent sedimentary basins varies, sometimes very widely, in composition. Nevertheless during recent years, there have been a number of studies (see Breger 1961; Brooks & Shaw 1968; Saxby 1978; Yen 1976; Tissot & Welte 1978; Durand 1980; Brooks 1981a) appertaining to kerogens which enable certain criteria to be applied.

The term kerogen will be used here to designate the organic matter in rocks which is insoluble in non-oxidizing mineral acids, aqueous alkaline and organic solvents. Such a geochemical definition includes the palynological components (pollen, spores and similar substances), and allows these to be classified independently from the amorphous and partially structured kerogen

components (Fig. 11). The term kerogen should have no inferred genetic significance either concerning its origin or even from the viewpoint of postulated hydrocarbon generation products (Durand 1980; Brooks 1981a). Although this definition summarizes the most frequent acceptance of the term kerogen in hydrocarbon source rocks, oil shales and other carbonaceous shales, it should be kept in mind that some authors (see Cane 1976) restrict the term kerogen to the insoluble organic matter present in oil shales.

The name kerogen was first applied by Crum Brown (see Stuert 1912) to describe the insoluble organic matter in the Lothian (Scotland) oil shales. Kerogen (Greek: *Keros* meaning 'wax or oil forming' and the root *-gen* meaning 'that which produces') was used to describe the shale organic components which, on heating and decomposition, gave rise to shale oil. Examination of the organic matter in oil shales using optical methods available in the 1890–1920s always showed the same general characteristics of the Lothian shales and the opinion was formed that kerogen was a relatively well defined (simple) substance. The Crum Brown definition remained unaltered for nearly half a century until improved optical and chemical analyses enabled much more detailed classifications or typing of kerogen to be made.

HYDROCARBON SOURCE ROCK

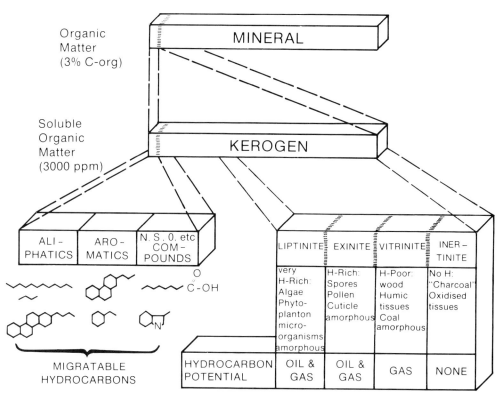

FIG. 11. Components of hydrocarbon source rocks. Kerogen can be sub-divided into main organic material components of liptinite, exinite, vitrinite and inertinite. Different materials have different potential for hydrocarbons.

The following definitions of kerogen have also been applied:
- total sedimentary organic matter (Manskaya & Drozdova 1968)
- the insoluble organic matter in any rock (Saxby 1976)
- the sedimentary organic matter insoluble in hot mineral acids
- the sedimentary organic matter insoluble in alkalis and in organic solvents
- the sedimentary organic matter which is insoluble in the usual organic solvents (Forsman & Hunt 1958; Durand 1980).

The majority of these definitions, include organic matter in humic coals of different ranks (humus, peat, lignite, bituminous coals and anthracites) boghead and cannel coals, asphaltoid substances (bitumens, asphaltenes, tars and tar sands) together with organic matter in recent sediments and soils. These definitions are considered too general, all encompassing and often

unworkable. A major weakness in these classifications is that in order to obtain a kerogen concentrate from rocks (see Durand & Nicaise 1980), the rocks require treatment with mineral acids and sometimes aqueous alkalis. So the accepted standard method of kerogen preparation (hydrochloric and hydrofluoric acid) immediately modifies many of the kerogen definitions.

It is also considered incorrect to use the term kerogen to describe the total organic matter in rocks. Such definitions include the organic components extractable with organic solvents. The extractables are a separate, and important, component and should not be grouped with kerogen but classed separately as bitumens or extractable organic matter (EOM).

Kerogen is the most abundant organic component on earth (often it is termed organic molecule, but such a definition is too precise, because kerogen structures vary in composition). It has been estimated (Hunt 1972; McIver 1967) that the total organic matter entrapped in the earth's sediments is about 1.2×10^{16} metric tons, with by far the majority present in the shales as insoluble matter, and kerogen occurrences are about 500 times greater than coal deposits and approximately 20,000 times the amount of known petroleum reserves. A suggested classification of sedimentary organic matter is given in Fig. 11 and a summary of the various terminologies are given in Table 3.

Calculations of the amounts of kerogenous organic carbon must be considered to be estimates only. Revision of these amounts is continually in progress and two main weaknesses are the average organic content determinations and sampling methods and techniques. It is a very fair assumption that sedimentary rock sampling programmes will be directed to the richer organic rocks and this will have resulted in published data which will have probably overestimated the average organic content of all sediments. The value 1.2×10^{16} metric tons must therefore be considered as representing only an order of magnitude for the amount of sedimentary organic matter.

Many and varied definitions of kerogen have been proposed in the literature. However it is probably better not to attempt to apply specific chemical definitions to this somewhat heterogeneous geopolymer and a simpler definition of 'disseminated sedimentary organic matter that is insoluble in non-oxidising mineral acids, aqueous alkali and organic solvents.'

Different types of kerogen can be recognized using geochemical analyses and such studies are important in basin studies and petroleum exploration.

Elemental composition of kerogen

Many elemental analyses of kerogens have been carried out (see Durand & Monin 1980) and show that a useful classification can be made based upon C, H, O with N and S composition. Such elemental analyses can also be used to define kerogens according to their ability to generate oil and gas (see Fig. 12).

Isolated kerogens often contain residual mineral matter, and its presence alters the elemental composition analysis, especially the O-content which is usually determined by difference. Procedures for kerogen isolation have been reviewed (Forsman 1963; Robinson 1969; Saxby 1976; Durand & Nicaise 1980). Different workers studying types of kerogen from different sediments use different methods of kerogen isolation. These differences are particularly marked with different scientific disciplines, for example the palynologist, coal petrographer, geochemist and even the marine oceanographer are asking somewhat different questions about 'their kerogen', which usually leads to variation in methods of isolation. There is no ideal method for isolating kerogen, and after various inter-laboratory studies, it does not appear that any agreed isolation procedure is possible or even desirable. However, it is becoming more and more essential that workers must accurately report their isolation methods. Such reports will give more accurate inter-laboratory correlations and could even lead to an improved understanding of the structure of kerogen.

Since kerogen is mainly composed of C, H and O it is these three elements that are usually chosen to define kerogen composition diagrammatically. In addition to simple, C, H, O triangular diagrams (McIver 1967; Brooks 1971), probably the most used is the relationship developed by Van Krevelen (1961). Van Krevelen-type diagrams (Figure 12) consist of an H/C vs. O/C (atomic ratios) rectangular diagram. Durand & Monin (1980) recommend that the Van Krevelen diagram is the most suitable for processing elemental analyses.

Detailed elemental analyses of a large number of kerogens show that kerogens group into four main distinct bands. Correlation of elemental composition with burial history of the various kerogens shows that increased thermal history causes kerogen composition (H/C vs. O/C) to move to lower values. Such changes in kerogen composition, carbon enrichment (increasing carbonization and aromaticity) loss of H_2O and CH_4 results in kerogen composition changing towards constant C, H, O values (see Fig. 12).

Kerogen—classification, components and composition

Organic petrographic and organic geochemical studies are used for characterizing the quality and quantity of organic components in sedimentary rocks. Organic petrography uses optical methods to identify and estimate the abundance of *individual* organic particles or macerals in the kerogen (Fig. 13) and is also used to examine their level of organic maturation (see Brooks 1981a). Organic geochemical studies, using physicochemical and chemical analyses aim to determine (usually quantitatively) the *gross* composition and degree of alteration of organic compounds in the sediments.

A major decision for the petroleum geochemist working on hydrocarbon source rock studies is to

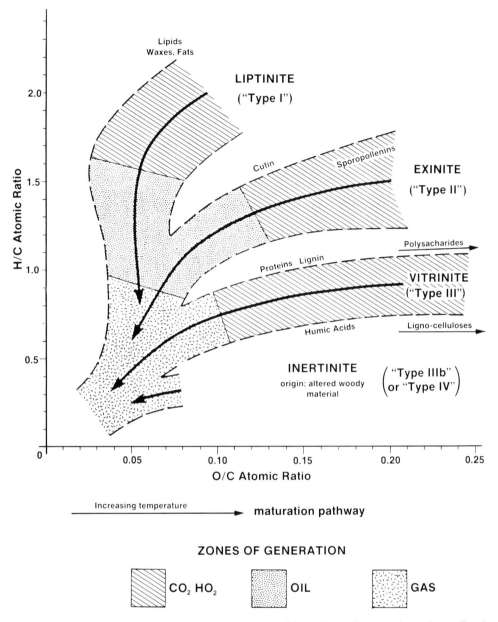

FIG. 12. Relationships between kerogen-types, elemental composition and organic maturation pathways (Brooks 1981a).

select the correct mix of analytical methods which provides sufficient geochemical data which is reliable, cost effective, readily interpreted and suitable for integration into the evaluation of exploration acreage.

Most oil companies use combined organic petrographic and organic geochemical analyses in their source rock evaluations. Both sets of analytical data have advantages and disadvan-

tages (see Brooks 1981a) and independent measurements provide supportive evidence for interpretation of source rock character and history (Jones & Edison 1978; Brooks 1981a; Powell *et al.* 1982). Organic petrography uses optical microscopy to study the structured and amorphous organic components in a sediment. Organic petrographers principally use the basis of experience obtained in coal petrography (see

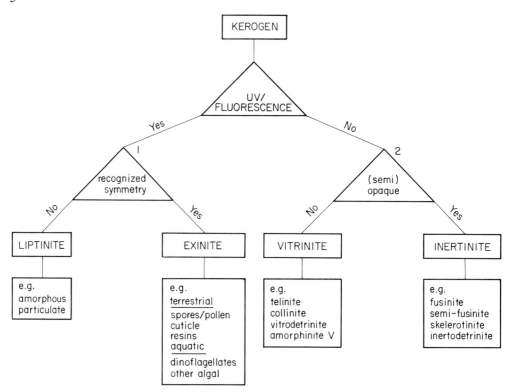

FIG. 13. A primary sub-division of immature and mature kerogen using microscopy (See Brooks 1981a).

TABLE 3. *Kerogen: main sub-groups with different classification and terminologies*

Origin	Terminologies					
Aquatic	Liptinite	Type I	Algal	Amorphous	Amorphous debris	Exinite
			Amorphous (Sapropel')			
	Exinite	Type II	Herbaceous			
Terrestrial	Vitrinite	Type III	Woody		Structured Plant Debris	Vitrinite
			Coaly	Humic		
	Inertinite	[Type IV or III b]	Intertinite			Inertinite

Stach *et al.* 1975), or in palynology (see Correia & Peniguel 1975; Brooks & Nicklas 1980) and the organic debris and microfossils are identified. Their main task is to define petrographically and classify maceral components (the term maceral was first used by Marie Stopes (1935) by analogy with mineral) using optical physical properties such as transmittance, colour, fluorescence and reflectance. Ideally a combination of transmitted and reflected light together with UV-excitation/fluorescence is used in optical studies of source rocks (see Fig. 13).

The rock can be prepared in different ways for different methods of study:

- transmitted light studies of organic particles isolated from rock by maceration with non-oxidizing mineral acids (e.g. hydrofluoric acid) and mounted as dispersed particles on a glass slide.
- reflected light examination of a polished surface of whole rock pieces or a polished concentrate of organic particles isolated from a rock.
- UV fluorescent investigation of dispersed organic particles or of organic matter present in a polished surface of a rock.

A number of reviews on organic petrographic and microscopic studies of organic macerals have been published (Correia 1971; Teichmuller 1974; Combaz 1980; Alpern 1980; Robert 1980; Masran & Pocock 1981; van Gijzel 1981).

Using a combination of transmitted, UV fluorescent and reflected light microscopy, kerogen can be usefully classified into various organic maceral classes (Fig. 13) and into four main groups: *liptinite*, *exinite*, *vitrinite* and *inertinite*. Use of more specialized and more expensive techniques such as electron microprobe (Oberlin *et al.* 1980; Muir & Giles pers. comm.) and scanning electron microscopy (Muir & Grant 1971) can in some cases locate individual maceral components in the kerogen, which can usefully be interpreted to give source rock information. High resolution electron microscopy has also been used to characterize kerogen (Oberlin *et al.* 1980). However, it is the optical methods which provide the most ready information and are therefore widely used in source rock studies.

One of the crucial aims of the application of geochemical techniques to petroleum exploration is accurately to define the kerogen-type and its regional maturities within the basin where hydrocarbon generation occurs. Classifications of organic matter in source rocks have been made by coal petrographers, palynologists and petroleum geochemists. Various techniques have been used and many parameters determined, but in recent studies combined organic petrography and organic geochemical methods (particularly pyro-

lysis) have proved the most widely used and applicable to source rock studies.

Using a combination of transmitted, reflected and UV-fluorescent light, organic matter in source rocks can be classified into various organic macerals and into four main groups (Figs 11 and 13).

Liptinite-type kerogen

This has a high hydrogen to carbon ratio, but low oxygen content, due to the presence of long-chain aliphatic moities and relatively few aromatic or oxygen-containing components in its structure. These kerogens are considered to be derived mainly from algal material after partial bacterial degradation and constitute the decomposition and condensation/polymerization products of the lipid components derived from bacteria and algae. Such liptinite-rich deposits are typically dark, finely laminated or structureless, with a dull appearance and canchoidal fracture. They form in relatively fine-grained organic-rich muds in quiet, oxygen-deficient shallow water environments such as lagoons, lakes and ponds (Demaison & Moore 1980) in which the organic matter is deposited under reducing conditions. Relatively pure liptinite-rich kerogens are variously called coorongite, torbanite, Tasmanite coal, boghead coal, alginite, sapropelic coal or kerosene shale. A modern freshwater lipid-secreting planktonic green algae, *Botryococcus braunii* (Maxwell *et al.* 1968) is the precursor of Australian coorongite (Cane 1976). The Carboniferous equivalent of *Botryococcus* formed the torbanites of the Scottish Oil Shales (Stuert 1912; Hunt 1979).

Tasmanite coals are fine-grained mudstones containing high concentrations (up to 85% organic content) of individual yellow organic spheroids, considered to be equivalent to the present-day planktonic algae *Pachysphaera* (Wall 1962). Tasmanites appear to have been formed in a low energy marine (or brackish) environment where algae form enormous blooms, often under unstable biochemical conditions.

The Eocene Green River Oil Shale of Colorado, Utah and Wyoming (Robinson 1976) has come to be considered the 'type material' for liptinite kerogen. This organic-rich sediment of the Green River Formation contains different amounts and types of organic macerals, where the organic content varies from less than 1% to as much as 40% by weight. Vast quantities of organic debris from organisms which grew in the uppermost portion of the chemically stratified lakes were deposited with mineral matter. However, variations occur due to both stream-carried and local precipitation of organic matter into the formations so that the often quoted type-material, shows many variations in composition and content and is not an homogeneous deposit.

Exinite-type kerogen

This contains a high hydrogen content (but lower than liptinite) with aliphatic chains, some naphthenic, aromatic rings and oxygen; and sometimes sulphur, containing functional groups in its structure. These exinite macerals are mainly derived from membranous plant debris such as spores, pollen, cuticle or, in general terms, the more resistant protective portions of plants. Membrane secretions such as resins and waxes are also classified within the grouping.

Vast amounts of pollen and spores are produced annually: wind pollinated (anemophilous) plants produce the bulk of the spores found in the atmosphere. It has been estimated that forest trees produce enough aerially dispersed pollen to give many billions of grains per acre. The spruce trees (*Picea*) alone in the central southern forest areas of Sweden are estimated to produce 75,000 tons of pollen each year. Similar, and often much larger, quantities of organic plant debris are produced by aquatic organisms. Estimates of such production are difficult but the quantities must be very large e.g. during blooms of dinoflagellates.

The exinite particles, leaf cuticle, pollen, resins, etc., can be concentrated during fluvial or deltaic transport, giving rise to resin rich coals, cuticle rich 'paper coals' or spore rich cannel coals. Each will accumulate in its own hydrodynamic regime.

Exinite-rich source rocks can also be associated with marine sediments where autochthonous organic matter derived from phytoplankton, bacterial microorganisms and sometimes zooplankton is deposited in anoxic environments. Exinite material does not often occur in pure concentrated form but usually occurs in mixed kerogens. It is similar in chemical composition and hydrocarbon potential to Tissot & Welte's Type II kerogen. The Type II kerogen, identified by elemental analysis or Rock Eval Pyrolysis, is however usually a mixture of exinitic, liptinitic and vitrinitic (see below) particles.

Exinite-rich source rocks that have good potential for oil, can generate early (Snowdon & Powell 1982) and/or thermal light oil and condensate at optimum maturities. Cuticle-rich sediments can generate waxy oils. At high maturity levels exinite-rich kerogen has good potential for wet gas.

Vitrinite-type kerogen

These have relatively low initial H:C ratios and high oxygen content. Their chemical structure consists mainly of aromatic structures, with short aliphatic chains connected by oxygen-containing functions. Heteroatomic ketones, carboxylic acid groups and ether bonds are present in the structure. Vitrinite-type kerogen corresponds closely with Type III kerogen defined by Tissot & Welte (1978). Vitrinite macerals are derived from structural, woody (lignified) components of terrigenous higher plants and often contain identifiable vegetal debris. This organic debris is incorporated either directly or via its alteration products in sedimentary humic acids (Tissot & Welte 1978). Microbiological degradation during deposition in basins is usually limited, due to *controlled* sedimentation and often rapid burial. Vitrinite concentrates often occur as coals or coally shales (carborgillites) in thick detrital sedimentation along continental margins.

Under the microscope, vitrinite-rich kerogen consists mainly of structured (often recognizable) higher plant debris and has a high concentration of vitrinite macerals. This type of kerogen has some potential for oil and condensate (Bailey 1981; Snowdon & Powell 1982) and high potential for gas at higher maturities. The proportion of vitrinite, liptinite and exinite (resinite) in terrestrially derived source rocks strongly controls both the level of organic maturation required for generation of hydrocarbons and also the ultimate product (oil, condensate or gas) generated and released from the source rock. Much discussion has recently taken place about the generation and occurrence of early mature oil and condensate (Snowdon & Powell 1982).

Inertinite-type kerogen

This is defined as the black opaque debris (high carbon, very low hydrogen) which has a definite angularity and is derived from lignified precursors highly altered mainly by oxidation and/or high levels of carbonization (Cope 1981). Inertinite, which is often termed 'dead-carbon' has no effective potential for oil or gas.

Source-rock analysis

There are now a number of important chemical, physical and microscopic techniques for characterization of potential source rocks (Fig. 14). The main criteria for characterizing a potential source rock are:
- quantity of organic matter
- type of organic matter

- maturity of organic matter
- amount of hydrocarbons generated
- expulsion of generated hydrocarbons from source (primary migration)

The *amount* of organic matter can be rapidly and accurately calculated by combustion analysis to determine the total organic carbon (TOC) of the sediment. The *type* and *maturation* of the sedimentary organic matter are usually determined in the same analysis. Microscopic and pyrolysis methods are used routinely to identify the type of organic matter and its level of maturity. It is

Analysis	Type of the analysis	Amount of organic matter	Type of organic matter	Maturation of organic matter	Correlation between source-rock on petroleum
Chemical (on rock)	Organic carbon	●			
Microscopy (on rock/kerogen)	Transmitted lights (Palynofacies, alteration)		●	●	
	Reflected light		○	●	
	Fluorescent light		●	◉	
Pyrolysis (on rock)	Rock-Eval, or Oil Show Analyzer	●	●	●	
Physicochemical (on kerogen)	Elemental analysis		●	●	
	Fluorescent Studies		◉	◉	
	Pyrolysis gc.		●	●	
	ESR		○	○	
	Carbon isotopes		◉		●
Chemical (on extract or crude oil)	Amount of HC			●	
	Light HC		◉	●	●
	n-Alkanes		◉	○	◉
	Isoprenoids		◉	○	◉
	Steroids, terpenes		◉	●	●
	Aromatics			◉	◉
	Porphyrins, metal			◉	◉
Physical (on extract oil or gas)	Carbon isotope		◉	◉	●

Applications ● Good   ◉ Fair   ○ Low or limitations of use

FIG. 14. Methods for source rock analysis and characterization: applications and efficiency in studies are indicated (after Tissot & Welte 1978).

often necessary in petroleum geochemical evaluations to correlate the generated hydrocarbons in the (assumed) source rock with reservoired petroleum and a number of increasingly sophisticated analytical methods have been developed (see Brooks & Welte 1984; Tissot & Welte 1984).

All the methods listed in Fig. 14 can be used to characterize petroleum source rocks. However, their degree of usefulness and efficiency varies from good to low (see Tissot & Welte 1984) and much care must be taken to choose the correct combination of analytical methods to evaluate the potential of hydrocarbon source rocks fully.

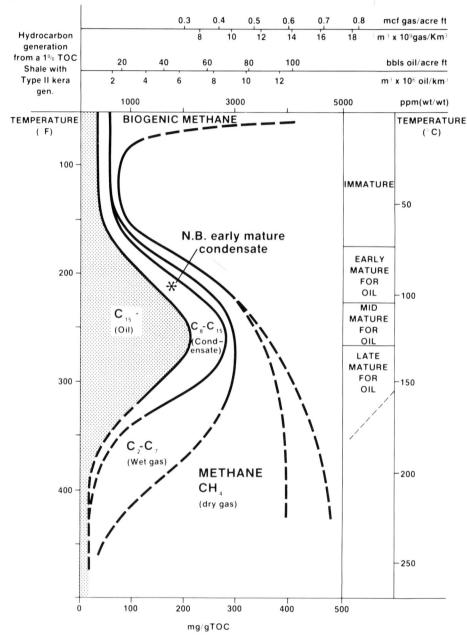

FIG. 15. Generation of hydrocarbons from source rocks. This diagram can be used to calculate the volume of hydrocarbons generated from a given source rock unit. The amount of hydrocarbons generated per 1% TOC is indicated on the horizontal axis in ppm (wt/wt). Conversion to bbls/acre ft, mcf/acre ft and metric equivalents are also given.

Generation and migration in source rocks

With burial and hence heating, a claystone containing adequate quantities of an appropriate kerogen type will generate hydrocarbons. Marine source rocks can contain both marine derived algal and bacterial and terrigenous (land plant) organic matter. In Figs 15 and 16 we have attempted to show quantitatively the amounts of hydrocarbons generated from 1% TOC of a Type II (liptinite/exinite-rich) kerogen resulting from a bacterially degraded algal debris + minor terrigenous input. This figure has been compiled from data from a number of published works and has been adjusted to a temperature scale appropriate to typical North Sea burial (time/temperature) history. The trends shown for temperatures greater than 320° F (160° C) are speculative, as are those for methane which is subject to

migration and hence difficult to quantify. The overall validity of the figures has been checked against mass balance data for a number of basinal volumetric calculations.

For the academic, the amount of hydrocarbons per 1% TOC is indicated on the horizontal axis in ppm (wt/wt): for the explorer this is converted to bbls/acre ft and mcf/acre ft (mcf = millions of cubic feet at standard temperature and pressure) over the appropriate compositional ranges. Metric equivalents are also given.

This diagram can be used to calculate the volume of hydrocarbons generated from a given source rock unit. It shows that C_8–C_{15} and $C_{15}+$ hydrocarbons (the major components of a typical North Sea 35° API gravity oil) are generated in large quantities from 175° F (80° C) to 265° F (130° C), while over this temperature range the light hydrocarbons (C_2–C_7 and methane) are present in relatively small quantities. Once heavy hydrocarbon generation has ceased, at about

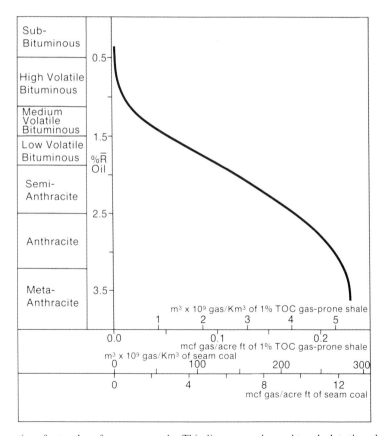

FIG. 16. Generation of natural gas from source rocks. This diagram can be used to calculate the volume of methane (natural gas) generated from source rocks. The volume of methane generated per 1% TOC of gas-prone source rock is given. MCF/acre ft and metric equivalent scales are given.

A) 250ft net of thick homogenous
claystones - restricted drainage.

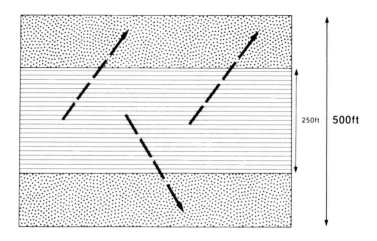

B) 250ft net of thin interbedded claystones-
highly effective drainage.

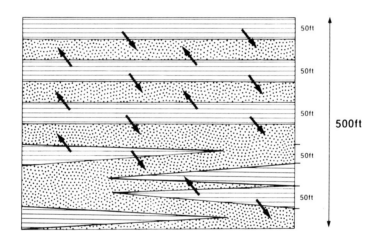

FIG. 17. Hydrocarbon migration from source rocks. Models for two sedimentological extremes: (A) Massive thick (250 ft net) homogeneous claystone, where source rock drainage may be a limiting factor for its efficiency as a source rock. (B) Thin (250 ft net) claystone inter-bedded in a sandstone or limestone sequence, where generated hydrocarbons can readily pass into the surrounding more permeable sediments for easier migration to a reservoir.

265° F (130° F) a presumed cracking reaction takes over boosting the yield of the C_2 to C_7 fraction, and methane at the expense of the heavy hydrocarbons.

In a typical marine source rock the liptinite/exinite (Type II) kerogen will be mixed with less oil-prone material. Once recognized and quanti-fied (e.g. by microscopy) this can be dealt with separately. For example, a 4% TOC rock comprising 50% liptinite/exinite and 50% exinite/vitrinite kerogen can be treated as containing 2% TOC of Type II kerogen, and related to Fig. 15, the remaining 2% TOC of Type III or vitrinite kerogen, being treated as a separate, dominantly gas generating, phase. Estimations of the quantitative generation of methane from vitrinite source rocks has been approached by laboratory simulations and stoichiometric calculations (Fig. 16). Direct measurement of indigenous methane in sediments is notoriously inaccurate due to migration in the subsurface, and loss during sampling.

Source-rock drainage and primary migration

Another recently emerging geological control of an effective hydrocarbon source rock is drainage. Drainage is the ability of the source rock unit to facilitate the expulsion and primary migration of hydrocarbons generated within it.

Movement of the generated hydrocarbons out of a source rock has been shown to occur by diffusion in the case of the low molecular weight hydrocarbons (Leythaeuser *et al.* 1982, and references therein). Heavier hydrocarbons such as constitute oil can redistribute themselves within a shale/sandstone sequence, but the mechanism by which they move is still not established. These 'micro scale' results show that hydrocarbons do move through shales, with light hydrocarbons moving more readily than heavy hydrocarbons, and both moving more rapidly parallel to the bedding than perpendicular to it. As illustrated by Leythaeser *et al.* (1982), the presence of fractures or interbedded sands should greatly facilitate the effective expulsion of hydrocarbons.

Using this model we can see two sedimentological extremes of source-rock associations:
• A massive thick homogeneous claystone where source rock drainage may be a limiting factor for its efficiency as a source rock (Fig. 17A).
• Thin claystone interbeds in a sandstone or limestone sequence where the generated hydrocarbons can rapidly pass into the surrounding more permeable sediments and start migration to a reservoir (Fig. 17B).
Both may occur in moving sedimentation but the former is more likely to occur in the basin centre, while the latter may comprise a more marginal facies.

A number of predictions can be made based on these models. In the case of the thin interbedded claystone, effective hydrocarbon expulsion should occur earlier allowing migration and accumulation of 'early mature' oil and lower TOC contents will be effective in generating commercial quantities of hydrocarbons. A higher proportion of the earlier, heavier hydrocarbons will

leave the source rock when generated, and hence decrease the amount of lighter hydrocarbons, condensate or gas available for generation from the source rock on further burial.

Any earlier, mature, light hydrocarbons (e.g. the early mature condensate of Snowdon & Powell 1982) would be susceptible to particularly efficient drainage. Oil expulsion efficiencies in excess of 50% can be envisaged in the interbedded claystone with little remaining from late mature oil or condensate generations. Poorer quality kerogens can hence be given a higher rating in this situation.

In contrast the thick homogeneous shale source rock will require a higher TOC content to generate a given amount of oil. The source rock will also need to have reached a higher level of maturity for effective expulsion to occur over a given

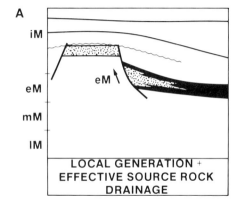

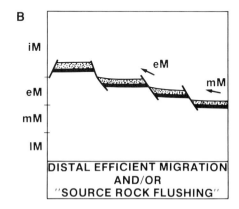

FIG. 18. Migration of early mature oils, such oils generally accumulate where the reservoir sands are closely associated or interbedded with early mature source beds. e.g. some Kimmeridge Clay source beds of the UKCS North Sea (See Cornford *et al.* 1983).

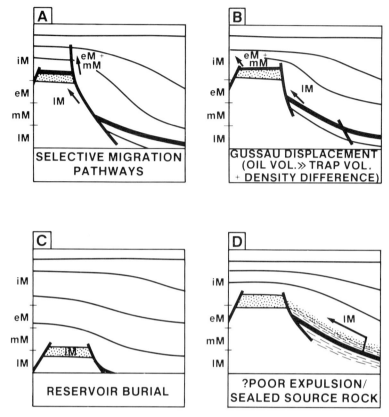

FIG. 19. Migration of late mature oils. This model predicts that a sealed source rock with poor expulsion properties will retain its hydrocarbons and will become deeper buried to late mature stage before it finally expels light oil, condensate or even gas.

period of time, making the generation of 'early mature' oils unlikely. A significant amount of heavy products will be retained within the source rock at the early and mid-mature stage, to be buried further and finally expelled as light as oil, condensate or even gas.

In the absence of further burial an early mid-mature source rock would be expected to retain high levels of migratable hydrocarbons, visible in the optical microscope as a fluorescent ground-mass, and to the geochemist as high carbon normalized hydrocarbon (CNH) yields or high pyrolysis S_1 peaks when analysed by Rock Eval pyrolysis methods (see Espitalie *et al.* 1979). These thick homogeneous shales may only show oil expulsion efficiencies of 5–25%. An optimum quality kerogen is required in this situation.

Elements of these two models are borne out by the distribution of oil types in the North Sea. Early mature oils as defined by Cornford *et al.* (1983) generally accumulate where the reservoir sands are closely associated or interbedded with early mature source rock shales of the Kimmer-

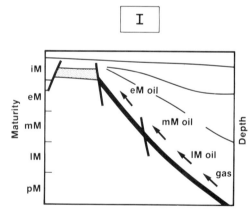

FIG. 20., FIG. 21 (next page). Generation of migration of full maturity spectrum of oils. These models represent typical examples of oil types in UKCS North Sea typical Northern North Sea Oil (36° API) are products of relatively inefficient expulsion of mid- and late-mature oil from the thick homogeneous organic-rich claystones of the Kimmeridge Clay Formation (see Cornford *et al.* 1983).

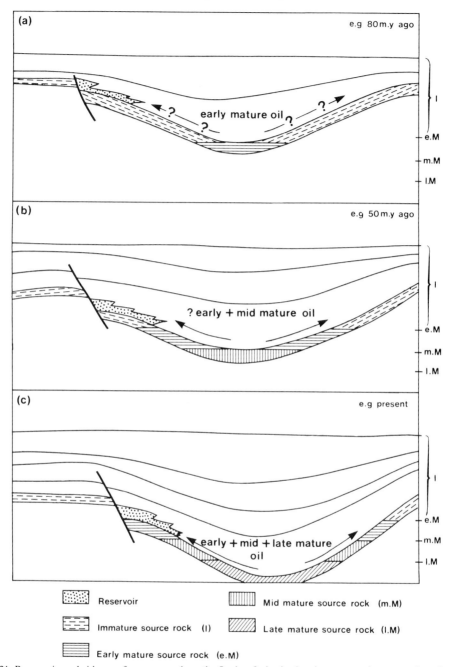

FIG. 21. Progressive subsidence of a source rock on the flanks of a basin showing progressive generation of hydrocarbons.

idge Clay Formation. Under these conditions the relatively small quantities of hydrocarbons generated in the early mature stage of burial (Fig. 18) are effectively drained from the source rock into the contiguous reservoirs.

This suggests that a third model combining the best points of the 'thick homogeneous' and 'thin interbedded' models. In the third model a thick organic-rich claystone is drained of its generated hydrocarbons by laterally extensive thin silt or sand laminae. These could originate where fan or turbidite sedimentation from an active fault scarp

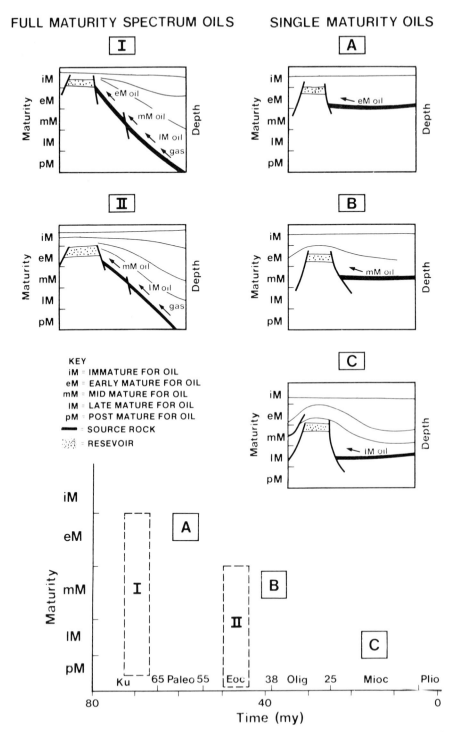

FIG. 22. Summary of the generation, migration and accumulation of Northern North Sea Oils from organic-rich source rocks. The geochemical stages are identified with timing of the generation from Late Cretaceous to present.

or shelf edge injects coarser clastics into the basin accumulating the fine grained source rock shales. Migration will be optimum if the sand/silt bodies are laterally continuous and run up-dip towards the shelf edge or fault scarp.

In contrast to this high efficiency drainage, the norm in the North Sea is a 'full maturity spectrum oil' (Cornford *et al.* 1983) which contains little early mature but mainly mid and late mature source rock products (Figs 19, 20 and 21). This is the typical 36° API gravity northern North Sea oil, and is the product of relatively inefficient

expulsion of mid and late mature oil from the thick homogeneous organic-rich claystones of the Kimmeridge Clay Formation. Typically this oil is reservoired in the underlying Middle and Lower Jurassic, Heather, Brent of Statfjord sands (Goff 1983; Cornford 1984) or in the overlying Lower Cretaceous sands, showing close analogies with Fig. 22 (see Cornford *et al.* 1983).

These source rock models can help to explain a number of contentious 'threshold' values. It may be significant that workers in exploration areas such as the Gulf Coast and the Far East

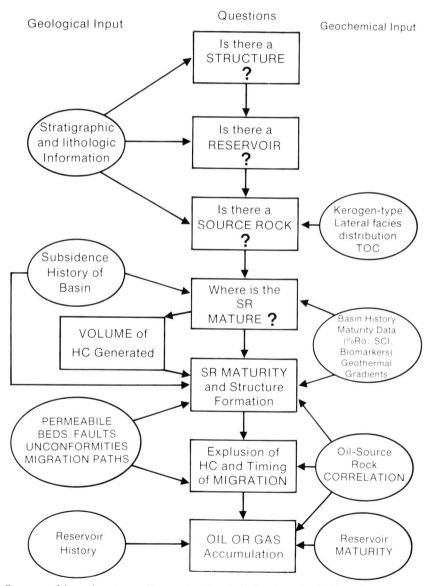

FIG. 23. Summary of the various stages of integration of geological and geochemical input into basin evaluation and petroleum accumulation in reservoirs.

where thick sequences of interbedded source rocks are the norm will quote lower TOC values as a minimum for effective generation and lower vitrinite reflectance values as signifying the onset of oil generation.

In contrast workers on thick homogeneous source rocks such as the Kimmeridge Clay Formation of the North Sea, the Miocene of offshore California, will quote higher TOC values as a prerequisite for a source rock and higher vitrinite reflectance values as indicating the onset of oil generation.

Integration of geological and geochemical studies in source-rock evaluation and petroleum exploration

Applications of petroleum geochemistry in exploration are drastically changing from a post-mortem science to a widely accepted predictive exploration tool (See Brooks & Welte 1984; Tissot & Welte 1984). Due mainly to progress in the development of new analytical techniques and interpretative concepts, and a new understanding of petroleum generation and migration, application of geochemistry has become more rapid and also capable of solving more specific petroleum exploration problems. These recent advances help to decrease the uncertainty in identifying hydrocarbon source rocks and in predicting a petroleum-filled structure. Based upon a combination of petroleum geochemistry and geology (Fig. 23) it is now possible to make quantitative prediction of hydrocarbon potential of basins and regions during the initial stages of petroleum exploration.

ACKNOWLEDGEMENTS: The authors wish to thank the management of Britoil plc for permission to publish this paper (although the work does not necessarily represent Britoil's methods and interpretations). We also thank Dr Gerard Demaison (Chevron Overseas Petroleum Inc., San Francisco) for permission to use Figures 8, 9 and 10.

References

ALPERN, B. 1980. Pétrographic du kérogène. *In:* DURAND, B. (ed.) *Kerogen—Insoluble Organic Matter from Sedimentary Rocks.* Edition Technip, Paris pp. 339–384.

BAILEY, N. J. L. 1981. Hydrocarbon potential of organic matter. *In:* BROOKS, J. (ed.) *Organic Maturation Studies in Fossil Fuel Exploration.* Academic Press, London and New York pp. 281–302.

BORDOVISKIY, O. K. 1965. Sources of organic matter in marine basins. *Marine Geology*, **3**, 5–31.

BREGER, I. 1961. Kerogen. *In: McGraw Hill Encyclopedia of Science and Technology.* McGraw Hill, New York.

BROOKS, J. 1971. Some chemical and geochemical studies on sporopollenin. *In:* BROOKS, J. *et al.* (eds) *Sporopollenin.* Academic Press, London and New York pp. 351–407.

—— 1981a. Organic Maturation of Sedimentary Organic Matter and Petroleum Exploration: A Review. *In:* BROOKS, J. (ed.) *Organic Maturation Studies and Fossil Fuel Exploration.* Academic Press, London and New York pp. 1–37.

—— 1981b. Organic matter in meteorites and Precambrian rocks: clues about the origin and development of living systems. *Phil Trans R. Soc Lond A*, **303**, 596–609.

—— & NIKLAS, K. J. 1980. The chemistry of fossils: biochemical stratigraphy of fossil plants. *In:* DILCHER, D. L. & TAYLOR, T. N. (eds) *Biostratigraphy of Fossil Plants.* Dowden Hutchison & Ross, Pennsylvania pp. 227–250.

—— & SHAW, G. 1968. Identity of sporopellenin with older kerogen and new evidence for the possible biological source of chemicals in sedimentary rock. *Nature*, **220**, 678–679.

—— & —— 1973. *Origin and Development of Living Systems.* Academic Press, London and New York.

—— & WELTE, D. H. 1984. *Advances in Petroleum Geochemistry Volume 1.* Academic Press, London and New York.

CANE, R. F. 1976. Origin and formation of oil shale. *In:* CHILLIGARIAN, G. V. & YEN, T. F. (eds) *Oil Shale.* Elsevier, Amsterdam pp. 27–60.

COMBAZ, A. 1980. Les kérogènes vus au microscope. *In:* DURAND, B. (ed.) *Kerogen-Insoluble Organic Matter From Sedimentary Rocks.* Edition Technip, Paris pp. 55–112.

COPE, M. J. 1981. Products of natural burning as a component of the dispersed organic matter of sedimentary rocks. *In:* BROOKS, J. (ed.) *Organic Maturation Studies in Fossil Fuel Exploration.* Academic Press, London and New York pp. 89–109.

CORNFORD, C. 1979. Organic deposition at a continental rise. organic geochemical interpretation and synthesis at DSDP site 397, Eastern North Atlantic. *In:* VON RAD, A. & RYAN, W. B. F. (eds) *Report DSP Volume XLVII Part 1.* US Gov. Printing Office, Washington pp. 503–510.

—— 1984. Source rocks and hydrocarbons of the North Sea. *In:* GLENNIE, K. W. (ed.) *Introduction to the Petroleum Geology of the North Sea.* Blackwell Scientific, Oxford. pp. 171–204.

—— MORROW, J., TURRINGTON, A., MILES, J. A. & BROOKS, J. 1983. Some geological controls on oil composition in the North Sea. *In:* BROOKS, J. (ed.) *Petroleum Geochemistry and Exploration of Europe.* Geological Society Special Publication No 12 pp. 175–194, Blackwell Scientific, Oxford.

CORREIA, M. 1971. Diagenesis of sporopollenin and other comparable organic substances: application to hydrocarbon research. *In:* BROOKS, J. *et al.* (eds) *Sporopollenin.* Academic Press, London & New York. pp. 569–620.

—— & PENIGUEL, G. 1975. Étude microscopique de la matière. Ses applications à l'exploration pétroléire. *Bull Centre Rech, Pau.,* **9**, 99–127.

DEGENS, E. T. & MOPPER, K. 1976. Factors controlling the distribution and early diagenesis of organic material in marine sediments. *In:* RILEY, I. R. & CHESTER, R. (eds) *Chemical Oceanography.* Academic Press, London and New York.

DEMAISON, G. J. 1984. The generative basin concept. *In: Petroleum Geochemistry and Basin Evaluation.* AAPG Memoir **35**, Tulsa, USA. pp. 1–14.

——, HOLK, A. J. J., JONES, R. W. & MOORE, G. T. 1983. Predictive source bed stratigraphy; a guide to regional petroleum occurrence. *In: 11th World Petroleum Congress—London 1983.* Panel Discussion PDI Paper 2.

—— & MOORE, G. T. 1980. Anoxic environments and oil source bed genesis. *AAPG Bulletin,* **64**(8), 1179–1209.

DOW, W. G. 1978. Petroleum source-beds on continental slopes and rises. *AAPG Bull.,* **62**, 1584–1606.

DUNCAN, D. C. 1967. Geologic setting of oil shale deposits and world prospects. *Proc. 7th World Petr. Cong.,* **3**, 659–667.

DURAND, B. 1980. *Kerogen-Insoluble Organic Matter from Sedimentary Rocks.* Editions Technip, Paris.

—— & MONIN, J. C. 1980. Elemental analysis of kerogens. *In:* DURAND, B. (ed.) *Kerogen—Insoluble Organic Matter from Sedimentary Rocks.* Edition Technip, Paris. pp. 113–142.

—— & NICAISE, G. 1980. Procedures for kerogen isolation. *In:* DURAND, B. (ed.) *Kerogen—Insoluble Organic Matter from Sedimentary Rocks.* Edition Technip, Paris. pp. 35–53.

ESPITALIE, J., LAPORTE, J. L. *et al.* 1977. Méthode rapide de caractérisation des roches mères de leur potentiel petrolier et de leur degré d'evolution. *Rev. Inst. Fr Petr.,* **32**, 23–42.

FORSMAN, J. P. 1963. Geochemistry of kerogen. *In:* BREGER, I. A. (ed.) *Organic Geochemistry.* Pergamon Press, New York. pp. 48–182.

—— & HUNT, J. 1958. Insoluble organic matter (kerogen) in sedimentary rocks of marine origin. *In:* WEEKS, G. (ed.) *Habitat of Oil.* AAPG, Tulsa. pp. 747–778.

GAVIN, J. M. 1984. *Oil Shale.* Government Printing Office, Washington D.C., USA.

GOFF, J. C. 1983. Hydrocarbon generation and migration from Jurassic source rocks in the East Shetland Basin and Viking Graben of the northern North Sea. *J. Geol. Soc.,* **140**, 445–474.

GOLD, T. 1979. Terrestrial sources of carbon and earthquake outgassing. *J. Pet. Geol.,* **1**(3), 3–19.

HUC, A. Y. 1980. Origins and formation of organic matter in recent sediments and in relation to kerogen. *In:* DURAND, B. (ed.) *Kerogen—Insoluble Organic Matter from Sedimentary Rocks.* Editions Technip, Paris. pp. 445–474.

HUNT, J. 1972. Distribution of carbon in crust of earth. *AAPG Bull,* **56**, 2273–2277.

—— 1979. *Petroleum Geochemistry and Geology.* W. H. Freeman, San Francisco.

JONES, R. W. & EDISON, T. A. 1979. Microscopic observation of kerogen related to geochemical parameters with emphasis on thermal maturation. *In:* OLTZ, D. F. (ed.) *Symp. on Geochemistry Low Temperature metamorphism of Kerogen and Clay minerals.* pp. 1–24.

KREY, J. 1970. Die Urproduktion des Meeres. *In:* DIEFRICH, G. (ed.) *Erforschung des Meeres.* Umschau, Frankfurt. pp. 189–195.

KOBLENZ-MISHKE, O. I. V., VOLKONSKY, V. V. & KABANOVA, J. G. 1970. Planktonic primary production of the world oceans. *In:* WOOSTER, W. S. (ed.) *Symposium on Scientific Exploration of the South Pacific.* Natl. Acad. Sci., Washington. pp. 183–193.

LEYTHAUSER, D., HAGEMAN, H. W., HOLLERBACK, A. & SCHAFER, R. G. 1980. Hydrocarbon generation in source beds as a function of type and maturation of their organic matter: a mass balance approach. *In: Proceedings of 10th World Petroleum Congress Bukarest 1979 Volume 2.* Heyden, London. pp. 31–41.

MACKENZIE, A. S. 1984. Applications of biological markers in petroleum geochemistry. *In:* BROOKS, J. & WELTE, D. H. (eds) *Advances in Petroleum Geochemistry Vol 1.* Academic Press, London & New York. pp. 115–215.

MASRAN, TH. C. & POCOCK, S. A. J. 1981. The classification of plant-derived particulate organic matter in sedimentary rocks. *In:* BROOKS, J. (ed.) *Organic Maturation Studies and Fossil Fuel Exploration.* Academic Press, London & New York. pp. 145–175.

MAXWELL, J. R., DOUGLAS, A. G., EGLINTON, G. & MCCORMICK, A. 1968. The botryococcenes-hydrocarbons of novel structure from algae *Botryococcus braunii* Kutzing. *Phytochemistry,* **7**, 2157–2171.

MCIVER, R. D. 1967. Composition of kerogen—clue to its role in the origin of petroleum. *Proc 7th World Petr. Congr.,* **2**, 25–36.

MANSKAYA, S. M. & DROZDOVA, T. V. 1968. *Geochemistry of Organic Substances.* Pergamon Press, Oxford.

MUIR, M. D. & GRANT, P. R. 1971. Application of scanning electron microscope techniques and optical microscopy to the study of sporopollenin. *In:* BROOKS *et al.* (eds) *Sporopollenin.* Academic Press, London & New York. pp. 422–349.

OBERLIN, A., BOULMIER, J. L. & VILLEY, M. 1980. Electron microscopy study of kerogen microtexture selected criteria for determining the evolution path and evolution stage of kerogen. *In:* DURAND, B. (ed.) *Kerogen-Insoluble Organic Matter from Sedimentary Rocks.* Edition Technip, Paris. pp. 191–241.

POWELL, T. G., CREANEY, S. & SNOWDON, L. R. 1982.

Limitation of use of organic petrographic techniques for identification of petroleum source rocks. *AAPG Bull.*, **66**, 430–435.

ROBERT, P. 1980. The optical evolution of kerogen and geothermal histories applied to oil and gas exploration. *In:* DURAND, B. (ed.) *Kerogen-Insoluble Organic Matter from Sedimentary Rocks.* Edition Technip, Paris. pp. 385–414.

ROBINSON, W. E. 1969. Isolation procedures of kerogen and associated soluble organic materials. *In:* EGLINTON, G. & MURPHY, M. T. J. (eds) *Organic Geochemistry.* pp. 181–195.

—— 1976. Organic and characterisation of Green River oil shale. *In:* YEN, T. F. & CHILLINGARIAN, G. V. (eds) *Oil Shale.* Elsevier, Amsterdam. pp. 61–79.

SAXBY, J. D. 1976. Chemical separation and characterisation of kerogen from oil shale. *In:* YEN, T. F. & CHILLIGARIAN, G. V. (eds) *Oil Shale.* Elsevier, Amsterdam. pp. 103–128.

SCHIDLOWSKI, M., EICHMANN, R. & JUNGE, C. E. 1974. Evolution des iridischen Saverstoff-Budgets und Entwicklung der Erdatmosphare. *Umschau,* **22**, 703–707.

SNIDER, L. C. 1934. Current ideas on source beds for petroleum. *In:* RATHER, W. E. W. & LAHEE, S. H. (eds) *Problems of Petroleum Geology.* AAPG Memoir 1, AAPG Tulsa. pp. 51–66.

SNOWDON, L. R. & POWELL, T. G. 1982. Immature oil and condensate—modifications of hydrocarbon

generation model for terrestrial organic matter. *AAPG Bull.,* **66** (6), 775–778.

STACH, E. 1975. *Stach's Textbook of Coal Petrography. In:* STACH, E. (ed.). Gebruder, Berlin.

STOPES, M. 1935. *Fuel,* **14**, 4–32.

STUERT, D. R. 1912. Lothian oil shales of the Lothians—part III. *In: The Chemistry of Oil Shales* (2nd Edition) Memoirs of the Geol. Survey, Scotland.

TEICHMULLER, M. 1974. Uber neue Macerale der Liptinit-Gruppe und die Entstehung von Micrinit. *Fortschr. Geol. Rheinld, Wastfal.,* **24**, 37–64.

TISSOT, B. & WELTE, D. H. (1978 & 1984). *Petroleum Formation and Occurrence.* Springer-Verlag, Berlin.

WALL, D. 1962. Evidence from recent plankton regarding the biological affinities of *Tasmanites* (Newton 1875) and *Leiosphaeridia* (Eisenack 1958). *Geol Mag.,* **99**, 353–362.

VAN GIJZEL, P. 1981. Applications of geomicrophotometry of kerogen, solid hydrocarbons and crude oil to petroleum exploration. *In:* BROOKS, J. (ed.) *Organic Maturation Studies and Fossil Exploration.* Academic Press, London and New York. pp. 351–377.

VAN KREVELEN, D. 1961. *Coal.* Elsevier, Amsterdam.

YEN, T. F. 1976. Structural aspects of organic components in oil shales. *In:* YEN, T. F. & CHILLIGARIAN, G. V. (eds) *Oil Shale.* Elsevier, Amsterdam. pp. 129–148.

—— & CHILLIGARIAN, G. V. 1976. *Oil Shale.* Elsevier, Amsterdam.

J. BROOKS†, C. CORNFORD* and R. ARCHER, Exploration Division, Britoil plc, 150 St Vincent Street, Glasgow, G2 5LJ, UK.

Present address: IGI Ltd, Hallsannery, Bideford, Devon EX39 5HE, UK.

†*Present address:* Consultant, Langside Drive, Newlands, Glasgow, G43 2EE, UK.

The genesis and palynofacies characteristics of marine petroleum source rocks

R. V. Tyson

S U M M A R Y: This paper attempts to demonstrate that the multi-disciplinary philosophy behind palynofacies investigations is of great value to the meaningful interpretation of the origins and palaeoenvironment of marine petroleum source rocks (MPSRs).

The key control on the formation of MPSRs is identified as bottom water oxygenation (correlated with the location of the Eh interface and the intensity of macrobenthic activity). Particular emphasis is placed on the necessity for greater accuracy in the terminology used to describe levels of oxygenation. Aerobic environments are characterized by organically lean sediments (0–3.0% TOC) with Type III kerogen assemblages composed of relatively refractory land plant debris or highly degraded, marine-derived, amorphous organic matter (AOM). Their organic richness is largely dependent on sediment accumulation rate and proximity to sources of terrestrial organic matter supply. They produce mainly gas at maturation. Dysaerobic to anoxic environments are characterized by MPSR facies with high TOC values and Type II kerogen assemblages dominated by relatively lipid-rich AOM. These represent the classic 'black shale' source rocks and are the main source of petroleum in marine basins.

Except where they are redeposited, dinocysts are characteristically absent or rare in marine 'black shales'. They are mainly produced in unstable, seasonally mixed water masses and may consequently be regarded as indices of hydrographic stability. Prasinophycean phycomas, which differ from dinocysts in their function, are often the dominant, or most conspicuous, marine palynomorphs of pelagic sediments and stably stratified 'black shale' basins.

The term *palynofacies* was first introduced by Combaz (1964) to describe the total assemblage of microscopic organic constituents present in a rock that remain after maceration (in HCl and HF), concentration and mounting using normal palynological preparation procedures. It is not precisely synonymous with the total kerogen content, generally defined as that part of the organic matter which is insoluble in ordinary organic solvents (for a discussion of the evolution of the usage of the term kerogen see Durand 1980). The palynofacies of sedimentary rocks is generally studied by a combination of techniques including transmitted light microscopy, reflected light microscopy, fluorescence microscopy, and organic geochemistry (especially Rock Eval pyrolysis). Optical palynofacies investigations of the overall kerogen assemblage (frequently called the 'organic facies') are generally made on unoxidized organic residues (but see also Habib 1979 and Batten 1981). More detailed studies of the palynomorph component utilize oxidized preparations (see Barss & Williams 1973).

If they are to be effective and yield their full potential, palynofacies investigations must be conducted in the context of the overall facies organization of the sediment sequences analysed. Ideally, therefore, they involve the integrated expertise of palynologists, sedimentologists, organic geochemists, marine biologists and palaeo-oceanographers. Such hybridization provides an invaluable perspective from which to interpret and evaluate the data bearing upon the major questions of marine petroleum source rock (MPSR) deposition. This paper attempts to review and identify the main controls on the palynofacies of MPSRs and relate them to the overall facies context of organic-rich mudrock (ORM) deposition. A more general discussion of palynofacies can be found in Tyson (1985).

Controls on the total organic content of sediments

Consideration of the factors which control the overall organic content of marine sediments is crucial to palynofacies since the proportions of different kinds of organic matter in the kerogen assemblage are generally expressed as *percentage* particle abundances and therefore require calibration by weight percent organic carbon values. The total organic carbon (TOC) content of marine sediments is controlled by the interplay of six main parameters:

1 Sediment texture (especially grain size)
2 Water depth
3 Primary productivity

From: BROOKS, J. & FLEET, A. J. (eds) 1987, *Marine Petroleum Source Rocks*
Geological Society Special Publication No. 26 pp. 47–67.

4 Rate of allochthonous (terrestrial *and marine*)
   organic matter supply
5 Rate of sediment accumulation
6 Bottom water oxygenation

Sediment texture

Organic matter is preferentially concentrated in
fine grained sediments because most organic
particles are hydrodynamically equivalent to clay
and silt grade clastics (Trask 1939; Cross *et al.*
1966; Stanley 1969; Wall *et al.* 1977). In addition,
coarser grained sediments tend to be organic-
poor because they usually occur in more highly
oxidizing regimes where organic matter is degraded with greater efficiency. The better porosity
and permeability of well sorted coarse sediments
will also assist in the oxidation of whatever
organic matter is deposited. Most organic particles are non-Stokesian in their hydrodynamic
behaviour (Brush & Brush 1972; Davis & Brubaker 1973). Their sedimentation is, however,
probably strongly influenced by the formation of
organic aggregates and flocs (Riley 1970; Wiebe
& Pomeroy 1972) and incorporation within
zooplankton faecal pellets (Honjo & Roman
1978; Turner & Ferrante 1979).

Water depth

Bathymetry is an important control on the TOC
content of marine sediments since the proportion
of organic matter surviving sedimentation decreases with increasing residence time in the
water column. Suess (1980) has presented a
synthesis of data which indicate that significant
decreases in carbon flux occur in water depths
greater than 100 m. However, it is also apparent
from the relative residence times of organic
matter in the water column and at the sediment/
water interface, that most organic matter is
destroyed at the bottom (Müller & Suess 1979).
The accelerated sinking of organic matter by the
formation of aggregates and flocs and incorporation within faecal pellets must be of critical
importance in this respect. Hargrave (1973) has
indicated that it is the depth of the mixed layer
(i.e. the wind mixed upper portion of the water
column) rather than the *total* water depth which
is the most important control on the extent of
remineralization within the watermass. His data
also show that for a given mixed layer depth the
proportion of organic matter which is remineralized at the bottom increases as productivity
decreases. This presumably reflects the higher
degree of pelagic recycling, the shorter food
chains, and the greater incorporation of carbon
within the herbivorous nekton biomass which

characterize eutrophic ecosystems (see Landry
1977; Walsh 1981).

While considering depth related factors it is
also worth remembering that the *in situ* metabolic
activity of the deep-sea bacteria in cold ocean
bottom waters is much lower than that of shelf
bacteria (Jannasch *et al.* 1971; Degens & Mopper
1976). However, in the geologic past, ocean
bottom waters may sometimes have been considerably warmer than at present (Brass *et al.* 1982),
which indicates the possibility of significant
variations in the 'efficiency' of the bacteria
through geologic time. Any favourable effects on
the preservation of organic matter from reduced
bacterial metabolism in the ocean psychrosphere
may, however, be generally compensated by the
longer residence time of particles at the sediment-
water interface which is to be expected in pelagic
sediments.

Primary productivity

In my opinion this is a much overstressed control
on the TOC content of marine sediments. Along
with other reviewers of this topic (e.g Demaison
& Moore 1980) I have not observed any consistent
general correlation between organic carbon values and the productivity of the overlying waters.
Moreover, it is apparent that even in areas of
high productivity (such as offshore Brazil and
north west Africa) markedly organic-rich sediments will not accumulate unless other, preservational, factors are fulfilled (Demaison & Moore
1980; Summerhayes 1983). Even in environments
characterized by higher organic matter preservation, like the modern Black Sea, there is no
correspondence between sediment TOC and
productivity (Shimkus & Trimonis 1974). This
general lack of correlation has a basic ecological
explanation: in most circumstances the level of
primary productivity is strongly influenced by
the efficiency of nutrient recycling *within* the
ecosystem. The sequestering of organic carbon
along with other nutrient elements must inevitably lower primary productivity unless there is a
major external source of allochthonous nutrients.
Even shelf productivity is often based on efficient
'local' recycling, which may sometimes be a much
greater nutrient source than, for example, river
water (Rowe *et al.* 1975; Nixon 1981; Flint &
Kamykowski 1984).

The main marine environments in which the
negative feedback between carbon sequestering
and productivity do not apply are the zones of
coastal Ekman divergence ('upwelling'). They
are the corner-stones of the argument of those
workers who propose the pre-eminence of productivity as the key to understanding source-rock

deposition. However, they are also very atypical marine ecosystems (presently covering 0.1% of the oceans; Ryther 1969). Their productivity is driven by the highly localized recycling of a nutrient pool which may have accumulated in the bottom water by remineralization of organic matter over larger areas and for longer periods of time. It is this allochthonous source of excess nutrients, that 'leaks' from below the pycnocline during upwelling, which permits *simultaneous* high productivity and large scale burial of organic matter. If this were not the case, we would have the paradoxical 'chicken and egg' situation of which came first—the nutrients or the productivity? Large scale burial of organic matter in ORMs still only occurs if the bathymetric profile and continental margin circulation regime allow the nutrient regeneration processes to cause intensification of the sub-pycnocline oxygen minimum to dysaerobic or anaerobic values (see reviews by Diester-Hass 1978; Demaison & Moore 1980; Barber & Smith 1981; Summerhayes 1983). Krissek and Scheidegger (1983) have also recently shown that the organic carbon signal of upwelling is lost in the presence of aerobic conditions and bottom currents.

From the above reasoning it is clear that most ORMs (other than those which are clear analogues of the intensified oxygen minimum-upwelling facies) were probably deposited under conditions of low or unexceptional primary productivity (De Boer 1983; Tyson 1985). Recent investigations lend considerable support to this view (Bralower & Thierstein this volume; Glenn & Arthur 1985). As noted earlier, one of the ecological consequences of the different functioning of low productivity ecosystems may be that more of the primarily produced organic carbon reaches the bottom (see Hargrave 1973). Such ecological differences may partly explain why deoxygenation is usually observed to occur from the bottom upward (e.g. Deuser 1974; Waples 1983) when, theoretically, it might appear that it should expand from the oxygen minimum downward (Southam *et al.* 1982).

Rate of allochthonous organic matter supply

The most readily identifiable allochthonous component of the TOC content of marine sediments is terrestrial organic matter. Very few organisms possess the necessary enzymes to hydrolyse the structural polysaccharides and other polymers (e.g. lignin) which compose macrophyte tissues and hence they are relatively refractory and can survive long enough to be potentially widely distributed (Fenchel & Jørgensen 1977; Godshalk & Wetzel 1977). What labile component they have is generally rapidly degraded during transport prior to final deposition, and the remainder decomposes very slowly. This decomposition is usually incapable of creating sufficient oxygen demand to result in significant oxygen deficiency in the bottom water (Waples 1983; Tyson 1985), although this is sometimes suggested (Jenkyns 1980; Cornford *et al.* 1981). Ligno-cellulosic debris is, however, somewhat better preserved under anoxic conditions by the exclusion of lignolytic fungi (Huc 1980). The absolute abundance of terrestrial plant debris is mainly a function of the climatic controls on the parent vegetation and the proximity to fluvial inputs, which, together with sedimentation rate, appear to determine the background levels of TOC values in oxygenated environments (e.g. Summerhayes 1981). Cuticular plant debris is much less refractory and is a potential oil source, but it exhibits a very restricted primary distribution (see later). The conditions normally associated with MPSR formation normally result in low contents of terrestrial organic matter except in the immediate proximity of fluvial sources (Tyson 1984, 1985). Mass movements of organic-rich sediments deposited on upwelling-influenced continental margins could be a significant source of organic matter in deeper continental slope sediments (q.v. Arthur *et al.* 1984). This may account for the higher than expected TOC values which are sometimes observed in aerobic facies *below* the oxygen minimum zone (e.g. Summerhayes 1983).

Rate of sediment accumulation

Sediment accumulation rates have a significant effect on the TOC content of marine sediments (Heath *et al.* 1977; Müller & Suess 1979; Bralower & Thierstein this volume). Calculations by Müller and Suess (1979) indicate that where all other factors remain constant, the organic content of a sediment deposited in oxygenated conditions apparently doubles with every ten-fold increase in the rate of sediment accumulation (see also Pelet, this volume). Müller and Suess interpreted this relationship in general terms of the residence time of organic matter in the region of the sediment/water interface. Heath *et al.* (1977) have laid particular emphasis on the effect of sedimentation rate on the efficiency with which the benthos utilize the available sedimented organic matter.

Some workers attribute the correlation between sedimentation rate and sediment TOC values in terms of a hypothetical decrease in the extent of bacterial degradation at higher rates of sediment accumulation (Curtis 1978; Coleman *et al.* 1979).

This is believed to be a consequence of reducing the transit time of non-refractory organic matter through the near-surface interval of peak bacterial metabolic activity, and the bacterially active part of the sediment column in general. However, it is apparent that increased sedimentation rates result in increased rates of bacterial sulphate reduction (Goldhaber & Kaplan 1975; Berner 1978), rapid depletion of pore water sulphate, and consequently the early onset of methanogenesis (e.g. Kelts & McKenzie 1982; Gautier 1982; Suess, this volume). Bacterial methanogenesis may continue to depths of several hundred metres in the sediment (Claypool & Kaplan 1974). Therefore, no great decrease in the efficiency of *anaerobic* bacterial diagenesis can be inferred, except at very high sedimentation rates, where lowered TOC values are likely to result from increased rates of organic matter dilution by terrigenous or biogenic mineralic material (e.g. Ibach 1982).

It is self evident that *if* factors other than sedimentation rate *do* lead to a greater preservation of organic matter (and this assumption has been challenged by Calvert, this volume), increases in sedimentation rate should result in higher dilution factors and lower TOC values (e.g. Jones 1983). This conclusion can only be affected by changes in the ratio of supply of organic and mineralic material. The dilution effect of sedimentation rate has been well demonstrated by Brumsack (1980, Table 9), whose calculations exclude any potential preservational effects related to sediment accumulation rates. It is important that increased rates of sedimentation should not automatically be considered the key to MPSR formation.

Most Mesozoic and Cenozoic ORMs occur as comparatively organic-rich interbeds within otherwise organically lean host sequences. Thick, uniform ORM sequences are the exception. They occur only in unusual, tectonically influenced palaeogeographic settings—usually restricted, rapidly subsiding, 'deep' water depocentres—with sufficient stability and inertia to resist the 'oxidizing', unfavourable, phases of climatic cycles (Tyson 1985). Because ORMs mainly occur as subordinate interbeds it is generally impossible to determine the sedimentation rate of such beds with any great degree of accuracy. It would be foolhardy when studying the host sequence to include TOC values from the ORM interbeds, and ridiculous to use averaged sedimentation rates for the whole host sequence to make genetic assumptions about the formation of the contained ORMs. Where appropriate biostratigraphic data is available, it frequently suggests a correlation between MPSR facies and

low rates of sediment accumulation (e.g. de Graciansky *et al.* 1984) which would be in agreement with the intuitive view of most 'black shale' geologists. Recent ORM interbeds have been dated more precisely by isotopic methods (e.g. eastern Mediterranean 'sapropel' S5, Mangini & Dominik 1979). The latter has been shown to have been deposited at significantly slower rates than the background sediments. As such layers not only show an excess TOC according to the Müller and Suess model, but also a reversal of the expected trend when compared with the host sequences, increased palaeoproductivity has been invoked to explain 'sapropel' deposition (Calvert 1983; and this volume). This is not in itself an unreasonable hypothesis, but the observations could also be explained by higher TOC preservation factors resulting from oxygen deficient bottom waters—if this mechanism can be substantiated.

Bottom water oxygenation

Bottom water oxicity has several effects on the TOC content of sediments of which the most important is the inhibition or exclusion of macrobenthic activity (see later). This conclusion is derived from several lines of evidence:

(i) The sediment/water interface appears to be the main site of organic matter degradation (Müller & Suess 1979), although this probably varies with water depth, the trophic status of the ecosystem and the contribution of faecal pellet transfer to the total carbon flux.

(ii) In anoxic sediment columns, *preburial* factors are probably the greatest source of variability as the magnitude of TOC losses due to early diagenesis is rather small (Bralower & Thierstein this volume), especially in relation to the efficiency with which organic matter is recycled in the environment (Pelet 1983).

(iii) There is no *apparent* large difference in the quantitative efficiency with which aerobic and anaerobic bacteria degrade organic matter (Foree & McCarty 1970; Orr & Gaines 1974; Doemel & Brock 1977).

(iv) Higher TOC values tend to be exhibited by sediments deposited under conditions of oxygen deficiency which are sufficient to exclude or seriously inhibit macrobenthic activity (Demaison & Moore 1980; Pelet 1983; Waples 1983; Bralower & Thierstein this volume).

(v) The macrobenthos is observed to play a major part in the rate of benthic nutrient regeneration (Flint & Kamykowski 1984).

This evidence strongly implicates the macrobenthos as playing a fundamental role in the process of organic matter destruction. However, it would be incorrect to believe that it is solely the consumption of the organic matter *by the macrobenthos* which leads to generally lower TOC values in oxygenated environments (Degens & Mopper 1976; Pelet this volume). The macrobenthos is generally believed to be responsible for only about 20% or less of the benthic respiration observed at the sediment/water interface (Gray 1981).

I believe that the principle effect of the macrobenthos is probably due to the associated bioturbation. This prolongs the residence time of organic matter in the chemically 'open' pore water–bottom water system between the sediment/water interface and the redox potential discontinuity (RPD). The RPD is taken to indicate the base of quantitatively significant bioturbation, where mixing is largely succeeded in importance by diffusive processes. It is probable that bioturbation actively stimulates bacterial metabolism by maintaining a constant supply of organic substrates and oxidants (Yingst & Rhoads 1980). A significant expansion of the surface area of the RPD will also result, and this is the best site in the sediment for the supply of electron donors and acceptors (Nedwell 1982), whose gradient is occupied by the most efficient 'syntrophic' bacterial floras. The net effect is probably that the benthos catalyse a much more efficient remineralization and recycling of organic matter and consequently result in lowered TOC values.

Both sediment accumulation rates and the effects of low oxygen levels on the macrobenthos act in a similar way to reduce the extent of preburial organic matter degradation which occurs between the sediment water interface and the RPD. Given the normally occurring range of sediment accumulation rates encountered in the marine environment, and the rates and depths to which sediments can be bioturbated, it is apparent that the level of oxygenation is probably a far more efficient way of achieving this aim than is increasing the sedimentation rate. The preceding discussion has an interesting implication. If we:

(a) exclude such complications as allochthonous organic matter inputs,

(b) consider the role of sedimentation rate to be a control on the pre-burial residence times of organic matter via the agency of macrobenthic bioturbation,

(c) accept that there is little or no correlation between the *depth-integrated* efficiency of *anaerobic* bacteria and the rate of sedimentation (as discussed earlier)

then, once oxygen levels are so low as to exclude effective bioturbation, it is difficult to see why the relationship described by Müller and Suess (1979) should any longer hold true. Under such circumstances one would anticipate that sediment accumulation rates would become merely a dilution factor (see earlier).

Although there has been considerable controversy over the *extent* of bacterial degradation under 'anoxic' conditions, there has been a general acceptance that there are significant *qualitative* differences between 'oxic' and 'anoxic' degradation of organic matter (Foree & McCarty 1970; Zsolnay 1971; Cranwell 1976; Kendrick 1979; Demaison & Moore 1980; Pelet 1983; Reimers & Suess 1983; Simoneit 1983). Many of these differences are correlated with the trends reported above for TOC values and relate to the extent of degradation of the organic matter by aerobic bacteria.

There is, by definition, an empirical correlation between increased contents of marine lipids and MPSRs. Since the latter are evidently frequently formed in anaerobic or anoxic waters, it is of significant interest that the sulphate reducing bacteria which characterize such milieu (Jørgensen 1983) are reported to exhibit low lipid utilization (Foree & McCarty 1970). This clearly suggests that if lipids survive long enough to pass through the RPD or chemocline, then most will probably survive early diagenesis. This is particularly likely for the relatively refractory, lipid-rich, structural material of algal cell walls (exinites and alginites). Although it has recently been shown that the sulphate reducers can metabolize a much wider range of substrates than was previously thought prior to 1980 (see Trüper 1980; Billen & Verbeustel 1980; Nedwell 1982; Laanbroeck & Veldkamp 1982; Jørgensen 1983), it is evident that they are *still* restricted to relatively simple compounds which must first be produced by aerobic and anaerobic fermentative bacteria.

Although Foree and McCarty (1970) are quite often cited with regard to the low lipid utilization of sulphate reducers, I have never seen any discussion of their complementary observation, that methanogenic bacteria can *apparently* metabolize lipids. In the presence of sulphate the methanogenic bacteria are inhibited by the sulphate reducers which can out-compete them for substrates (Laanbroeck & Veldkamp 1982). Methanogenesis is therefore only quantitatively significant once sulphate has been exhausted. From the source rock point of view it would be pointless if lipids survived the sulphate reducing zone only to be subsequently consumed by methanogenic bacteria at greater depths.

If Foree and McCarty's conclusions are correct,

why do lipids survive *anaerobic* diagenesis? One way to achieve this would be to extend the sulphate reducing zone down to the base of the 'bacterial window' or to such a depth where the metabolic activity of the succeeding methanogens would be negligible. In non-bioturbated organic-rich sediments, where sulphate supply is limited by the diffusional gradient, sulphate would normally be expected to become the limiting factor before all the suitable substrates were exhausted. This is more likely to reduce the thickness of the sulphate reducing zone than to expand it. Sulphate reduction normally only occurs to great sediment depths when the bacteria are being forced to utilize relatively 'refractory', non-preferred organic substrates. This is usually because the more suitable compounds have been destroyed by extensive aerobic degradation prior to burial (Berner 1978; Jørgensen 1982). The latter is clearly not likely in ORMs deposited under oxygen deficient or oxygen-free conditions. How else could the sulphate reducers become substrate limited?

The most logical explanation at present, is that the answer may lie with the poorly understood fermentative bacteria upon which the sulphate reducers and, indeed, the methanogenic bacteria, depend for prior substrate 'processing'. Their activity may be inhibited by high sulphide concentrations (Laanbroeck & Veldkamp 1982) and competition with more efficient respiratory metabolisms (Billen & Verbeustel 1980). Consequently, it is possible that where organic matter diagenesis occurs completely or predominantly under anoxic conditions, the efficiency of degradation may be sufficiently impaired to allow the survival of lipids. In euxinic basins the maintenance of inhibitory pore water sulphide concentrations will be encouraged by the lack of uncombined iron in the sediments and the reduction or absence of a diffusive concentration gradient of sulphide between the sediment and bottom water. The food-chain like organization of bacterial diagenesis, although very much a simplification (Laanbroeck & Veldkamp 1982), tends to suggest that once one level is inhibited (by whatever mechanism), there should be some degree of 'knock-on' effect to magnify the overall scale of the consequences. If this is true, then fermentative bacteria are certainly the best 'target' for producing an overall decline in bacterial efficiency. To place this into perspective, however, the quantitative effect (on TOC values) *seems* to be small although the qualitative effect (as seen in H/C ratios) is possibly highly significant. The further elucidation of these problems lies in the hands of the geomicrobiologists.

The trends outlined above again suggest that high sedimentation rates (which lead to early methanogenesis) are not particularly favourable for MPSR formation. One further aspect of bacterial dynamics will be mentioned. In euxinic basins (where the RPD occurs within the water column as an $O_2:H_2S$ interface) as much as half or more of the total sulphate reduction may occur in the watermass (Indrebø *et al.* 1979; Sorokin 1983). It is in fact this extra-sediment sulphate reduction which produces some of the most hopeful geochemical indices of bottom water anoxia (Brumsack 1980; Leventhal 1983). The consequences of this condition for microbial diagenesis of the underlying sediment are far from clear, but some disruption in the flow of bacterial substrates may be implied.

Discussion

To my mind the most telling and pertinent fact about the genesis of MPSRs is the empirical observation that high TOCs and high contents of marine organic matter are predominantly correlated with *dark-coloured, fine grained mudrocks having the sedimentological, palaeoecological and geochemical characteristics associated with deposition under oxygen-deficient or oxygen-free bottom waters.* The latter is probably the most succinct and meaningful definition of the black shale concept that it is possible to give. Unfortunately the compelling nature of the correlation referred to above has resulted in a confusing, and frequently inappropriate, interchange and virtual synonymy of usage of such terms as 'black shale', 'carbonaceous shale', 'bituminous shale', 'oil shale', 'sapropel', etc. This has obscured and detracted from the underlying observation. The above definition of the black shale concept (which is a genetic one and does not place undue emphasis on the precise colour or lithology), incorporates all the known classic source rocks such as the Posidonienschiefer, Kimmeridge Clay, La Luna Formation, etc. This is not to say that this 'facies' represents the only type of MPSR, but its contribution to total petroleum output probably dwarfs that of 'oxic facies' (which, however, probably include important source rocks for natural gas with which this work is not primarily concerned). Nor should it be taken to mean that all sediments deposited under oxygen-deficient or oxygen-free conditions will necessarily make good petroleum source-rocks, if at all. The level of oxygenation in the marine environment is not the only factor but it is the most important single one.

Given the empirical facts referred to above, I believe that any controversy which exists must be confined to whether oxygen deficiency is the prime factor or something else which usually correlates with it. If the latter were true, and this factor might, to some extent, show a distribution in time and space which was partially independent of the occurrence of bottom water deoxygenation, it would critically affect the exploration strategy for MPSRs. Because the petroleum industry has, in fact, located most of the classic MPSRs within its reach that occur in those areas favourable to hydrocarbon generation, it is being forced to reappraise the 'source-rock situation'. It is being progressively driven to include an ever-increasing variety of sediments in its source-rock 'catchment' and to improve its modelling and prediction to provide the motivation for exploration in new areas which are not especially favourable for source rocks according to conventional wisdom. This has led directly to a much greater interest in the roles of sediment accumulation rate and productivity in the genesis of MPSRs than was hitherto the case. Productivity, of course, has the advantage of being, at least partly, geographically predictable (e.g. Parrish this volume), and great interest has been stimulated by the increasing elucidation of the modern upwelling ecosystems.

The petroleum industry generally uses a TOC content of about 0.5% to demarcate the lower limit of source-rock potential (Tissot & Welte 1978). This is in fact rather optimistic and depends on the type of organic matter present. However, given the context discussed above, it indicates that sediment accumulation rates are of significance for low grade MPSRs deposited in oxic conditions, and the general *background level* of hydrocarbon potential. The same is true of productivity effects in oxic facies. The best petroleum source rocks, however, are, and will remain, black shales as defined above. Not all oxygen-deficient or oxygen-free basins will produce ORMs with high TOC values because of variations in clastic dilution, productivity and other factors. It will, therefore, always be possible to find an apparently equivalent oxygenated environment which has sediments with similar or even higher TOCs than its 'anoxic' counterpart. It is very rare, however, for such comparisons to be strictly appropriate and to take into account all differences in such factors as oxygen concentrations, water depths, sediment textures, primary productivities, hydrographic regimes, ratio of supply of different types of organic matter, rates of sediment accumulation, processes of sedimentation, clastic and biogenic mineralic dilution effects, and the spatial and temporal variability and interplay of these parameters.

Perhaps the most significant difference between 'anoxic' and oxygenated sediments is the preservation of *differing types* of organic matter. An ORM which contains only inert carbon (inertinite) is no use to anyone, man or beast. In an 'anoxic' environment where primary productivity is weak or moderate, and where there is not a particularly favourable sedimentation rate (dilution factor), the TOC content may be 'low' although the rate of organic matter preservation is high (as in the modern Black Sea). However, because the sediment contains the right kind of organic matter, the TOC can fall to the lower limit of 0.5% and the rock can still be a good potential MPSR. This cannot be said of most oxic facies.

Levels of oxygenation: terminology and significance

From the preceding discussion it is evident that the level of oxygenation in the marine environment is the most crucial factor controlling the amount and character of the organic matter preserved in ORMs. Given the importance of this parameter it is essential for terminological precision, but this is generally sadly lacking at present. Based on data from the Black Sea, Gulf of California and the Californian borderland, Rhoads and Morse (1971) have used changes in the diversity and calcification of macrobenthic organisms to define the terms *aerobic, dysaerobic,* and *anaerobic,* which correspond to dissolved oxygen concentrations of 1.0 ml/l, 1.0–0.3 ml/l and 0.1–0.0 ml/l respectively. The interval of 0.1–0.3 ml/l was regarded as the transition from azoic (metazoan free) conditions to those containing the mainly soft bodied infaunal organisms of the 'dysaerobic biofacies'. Subsequent usage (e.g. Byers 1977, 1979) has frequently extended the definition of *dysaerobic* to cover all oxygen concentrations between aerobic and anaerobic values and has placed greater emphasis on the sedimentary fabric.

The ecological literature on macrobenthic responses to low oxygen levels indicate that the macrobenthos is generally unaffected at oxygen concentrations greater than 2.0–1.5 ml/l (e.g. Rosenberg 1977, 1980; Andersin *et al.* 1978). Below these levels, however, species diversity and benthic activity drop rapidly until the macrobenthos is eventually eliminated at about 0.15–0.1 ml/l (Rhoads & Morse 1971; Soutar *et al.* 1981). In the present context the most important consideration is the level of oxygenation at which bioturbation becomes absent or insignificant. According to Calvert (1964) this

R. V. Tyson

level is at 0.5 ml/l, but more recent work has shown that echinoids and galatheid crabs cause extensive bioturbation down to dissolved oxygen values of 0.3 and 0.25 ml/l respectively (Thompson *et al.* 1983; Soutar *et al.* 1981). Douglas (1981) has shown that the most significant change occurs at 0.2 ml/l where effective bioturbation ceases as the fauna changes to an assemblage of sedentary, mainly soft bodied, epifaunal, deposit feeders. Sedimentary laminations of pelagic/hemipelagic origin are consequently only preserved under bottom waters containing 0.2 ml/l or less of dissolved oxygen. This suggests that the dysaerobic:anaerobic boundary in ancient sediments should possibly be equated with 0.2 ml/l (in the middle of Rhoads and Morses' transitional interval) rather than 0.1 ml/l as indicated by Byers (1977, 1979).

Several authors have proposed palaeoecological and palaeoenvironmental classifications of sequences containing ORMs which are based on the relative position of the RPD and sediment/water interface at the time of deposition (Kauffman 1978; Morris 1979; Dean & Gardner 1982). Such classifications are necessarily based upon the *mean* position of the RPD which varies in time and space depending upon a number of factors, not least bottom temperature (see Fenchel & Riedl 1970; Ankar & Jansson 1973). These schemes can be related to the dissolved oxygen gradients discussed above, where aerobic conditions generally correspond with a deep RPD (up to tens of centimetres), dysaerobic with a shallow RPD (a few centimetres at most), anaerobic with

an RPD just below the sediment/water interface (0–2 millimetres), and anoxic with the RPD actually in the water column.

In this paper I have restricted the use of *anoxic* to describe waters totally devoid of oxygen which also contain free H_2S. The widely used adjective *oxic* is equated with the aerobic-dysaerobic range of oxygen values, and *suboxic* (see Breck 1974; Froelich *et al.* 1979) is equated with anaerobic oxygen concentrations of 0–0.1 ml/l. *Note that the latter term has been precisely defined and is not synonymous with dysaerobic as has been indicated by Demaison* et al. (1984). The term *hypoxic*, which has a strong historical precedent in the ecological and biological literature, is considered to correspond primarily to dysaerobic conditions, as is *kenoxic*, recently introduced by Cepek and Kemper (1981). The relationship of these terms are summarized in Table 1 and the scheme used here is presented in Figure 1.

Hulsemann and Emery (1961) and Leclaire and Kelts (1982) have found that there is apparently no significant difference in the TOC content of laminated and homogeneous sediments in the oxygen deficient basins of the Californian borderland and Gulf of California. Simoneit (1983) has, however, found that although they may be small, there are predictable quantitative differences in TOC values between laminated and bioturbated sediments which correlate with significant qualitative differences in the composition of the organic matter preserved. This tends to suggest that the fauna, and consequently the sedimentary fabric, is probably

TABLE 1. *The equivalence of the most widely used terms employed to describe levels of oxygenation in the marine environment.*

Dissolved oxygen ml/l	Rhoads & Morse (1971)	Berner (1981)	Breck (1974)	Other terms in use	This paper
8.0					
	Aerobic				Aerobic
1.0		Oxic	Oxic		
1.0	Dysaerobic			Hypoxic	
	----0.3 ml/l----			Kenoxic	Dysaerobic
0.1	'transition'			Dysoxic	
0.1		Non-sulphidic anoxic			
	Anaerobic	(post oxic)	Suboxic		Anaerobic
0.0					
H_2S		Sulphidic anoxic	Anoxic	Euxinic	Anoxic

It is suggested that the schemes of Berner (1981) and Breck (1974) should be restricted to within-sediment diagenetic conditions and that they should not be used loosely to describe 'anoxic' or 'suboxic' sediments. The boundary of laminated sediments corresponds to 0.2 ml/l (Douglas 1981).

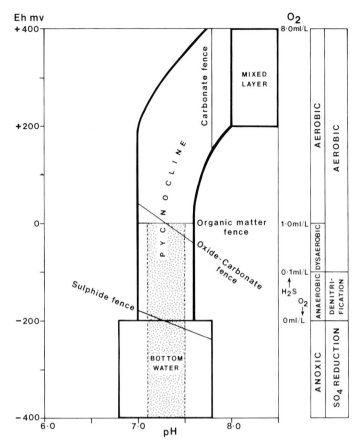

FIG. 1. Eh, pH and dissolved oxygen characteristics of the main *watermass* layers in anoxic basins. Basic framework is the Krumbein & Garrels (1952) Eh–pH fence diagram; approximate fields of the watermass layers derived from multiple sources including Richards (1965) and Grasshoff (1975); Eh calibration of bacterial processes from Fenchel & Jørgensen (1977). The upper limit of anaerobic conditions (which are strictly speaking oxygen-free by literal definition) is taken at 0.1 ml/l because anaerobic denitrification is observed to occur at very low oxygen tensions (e.g. Sugahara *et al.* 1974; Sorokin 1978), and because this provides better correlation with the scheme of Rhoads & Morse (1971). The stippled area is the phosphorite stability field (slightly modified from Krumbein & Garrels (1952)). The main site of phosphorite formation may be the dysaerobic–anaerobic boundary (q.v. Veeh *et al.* 1973; Tyson 1985).

somewhat *more* sensitive to changes in bottom water oxygenation than are geochemical parameters. Although there may be a critical oxygen value which controls the sedimentary fabric, the geochemical effect is clearly a more progressive one related to the *gradient* of decreasing bioturbational 'efficiency'. This is supported by the fact that 'dysaerobic sediments', although they are not usually laminated, frequently exhibit 'platey grain alignment' (Govean & Garrison 1981) and are often significantly enriched in marine organic matter. Bioturbated sediments will probably only develop their maximum differentiation from interbedded laminites if they are deposited under sustained aerobic conditions. The gradational

effect of oxygen values on geochemical parameters probably explains why there is no infallible geochemical index of 'anoxia' apart from those features related to extra-sediment sulphate reduction (see earlier).

The actual thickness of dysaerobic and anaerobic conditions in a stratified anoxic watermass is very small when compared to the total water depth (e.g. Byers 1977). Such conditions are, therefore, only widespread in oxygen minima and during initial or cyclic deoxygenation events. In most sediments the 'dysaerobic facies' probably represents a temporal and physical mixture of aerobic, dysaerobic, anaerobic, and anoxic conditions, and all the ORM facies are probably determined by the relative residence times of the environment in each of these four modes. Temporal stability of the environment is, therefore, at least as important as any other factor, and MPSR formation probably demands that depositional conditions remain predominantly dysaerobic to anoxic for long periods. Short term deoxygenation is not sufficient to produce MPSR-type ORMs if the mean conditions remain aerobic (e.g. Falkowski *et al.* 1980). The useful genetic terms of *gyttja* and *sapropel* refer to organic-rich sediments deposited under oxygen containing (aerobic–anaerobic) and oxygen-free (anaerobic–anoxic) conditions respectively (e.g. Krejci-Graf 1964). Unfortunately there is a long history of confusion over the definition of the term sapropel, which has mistakenly come to be associated more with the kind of organic matter in the sediment than the depositional conditions (Hansen 1959). Ironically, in its kerogen sense, 'sapropelic' is usually used to describe algal-derived organic matter (which frequently predominates under the anoxic conditions of sapropel deposition), whereas some early definitions of sapropel (from lacustrine settings) place stress on the *coincidental* macrophyte-dominated organic content (q.v. Calvert 1983). More recently this genetically significant and useful term has been rendered meaningless by the arbitrary definition given to it during the Deep Sea Drilling Project (Kidd *et al.* 1978).

I hope that the general geological community will become increasingly aware of the need, relevance and value of terminological accuracy in describing levels of oxygenation. Far too many papers casually equate 'anoxic' with 'oxygen deficiency' or define their own limits. Since the most significant effect of lowered oxygenation is arguably the effect that it has on the macrobenthos, it seems only logical that the terminology used should have ecologic significance. This is why the scheme of Rhoads and Morse (1971) has been adopted here. This is especially valuable because it provides palaeoecological criteria for making independent assessments of the levels of oxygenation during the deposition of ancient sediments. I have added the term 'anoxic' (as used here) to differentiate anaerobic environments with free H_2S, because there now appear to be promising geochemical criteria for making this distinction in ancient sediments (e.g. S/C ratios, isotopic fractionation of sulphur, molybdenum concentrations). Although the difference may seem small and not that common in marine environments, there are *significant* contrasts in conditions free of oxygen, and those free of oxygen but *also* containing H_2S—not least because of the toxicity of the latter (see also

Revsbech *et al.* 1980; Berner 1981). It is extremely unfortunate, and not a little confusing, that the phrase 'anoxic sediment' is invariably used to describe sediments deposited under aerobic (or dysaerobic) conditions which are reducing at depth, since this is characteristic of nearly all but the most-oxidized, pelagic sediments. This in itself demonstrates the need for such genetic terms as gyttja and sapropel.

Although not emphasized in this paper it should be stressed that because of their effects on bacterial activity and pore water chemistry, gradients of oxygenation and bioturbational intensity are also major controls on the extent of carbonate dissolution (Sholkovitz 1973; Aller 1982), diagenetic mineralogy (Berner 1981; Curtis 1978) and phosphorite genesis.

Kerogen trends

The main types of particulate organic matter found in sediments and the most commonly used equivalent kerogen classifications are summarized in Table 2. Of the three major types of organic matter (palynomorphs, phytoclasts and AOM), the phytoclasts and AOM generally comprise the bulk of the kerogen in marine sediments. As phytoclasts are predominantly refractory, and AOM consists (at least initially) of mainly labile marine organic matter, the overall kerogen assemblage is principally a function of the redox status of the depositional environment and the proximity to fluvial inputs. In the following account, palynomorphs, which are generally a minor component of the total kerogen in marine sediments, are treated separately.

Preservational biases result in aerobic facies having low TOCs (maximum values generally less than 2–3%; Demaison & Moore 1980; Waples 1983) and phytoclast dominated kerogens. The latter change predictably in an offshore (proximal–distal) direction. With increasing distance from fluvial sources, prolonged reworking, exposure and oxidation, the phytoclasts tend to become smaller, more equigranular, darker in colour and highly oxidized, eventually becoming what is termed 'residual organic matter' (Tissot *et al.* 1980; see also Cornford *et al.* 1981; Habib 1982). In areas totally removed from fluvial influences the aerobic facies may also exhibit kerogen assemblages characterized by highly degraded AOM (of marine origin) which produces somewhat misleading Type III kerogen compositions (*sensu* Tissot & Welte 1978) when the sediments are analysed by Rock Eval

TABLE 2. *Classification of particulate organic matter found in marine sediments and the approximate equivalence of the most commonly used kerogen terms.*

| Particulate Organic Matter (P.O.M.) | | | | | Kerogen | | | | Kerogen type | |
Category	Source	Constituents	Coal maceral group	Coal maceral	A	B	C	D	General	E
Structured — Palynomorphs	Plankton	Chlorococcale algae, Blue-green algae and Prasinophycean phycomas	Exinite or liptinite	Alginite	Vegetal (M.O.V.)	Algal	Phyrogen	Aqueous	Sapropelic (oil prone)	I
		Dinocysts and acritarchs								
Palynomorphs	Sporomorphs	Spores and pollen		Sporinite		Herbaceous		Spores and pollen	Sapropelic (oil prone)	II
Phytoclasts	Higher plant debris (macrophyte tissues)	Cuticle		Cutinite				Terrestrial		
		Ligno-cellulosic material	Vitrinite or huminite	Telinite	Tracheal (M.O.T.)	Woody	Hylogen		Humic (gas prone)	III
		Carbonized material	Inertinite	Fusinite	Lignitic (M.O.L.)	Coaly	Melanogen	Charcoal		III / IV
Unstructured — Amorphous Organic Matter (A.O.M.)	Polygenetic and heterogeneous	Organic aggregates and flocs formed from dissolved organic matter, products of biochemical degradation of P.O.M., and faecal pellets	Variable, but often with components of the following macerals:	Collinite / Liptodetrinite / Bituminite	Colloidal (M.O.C.)	Amorphous	Amorphogen	Amorphous	Humic III — Sapropelic II/I (variable)	III / II/I

Column A after Correia (1971) and McLachlan & Pieterse (1978); B after Staplin (1969) and Hunt (1979); C after Bujak *et al.* (1977); D after Masran & Pocock (1981); and E after Tissot & Welte (1978). Coal maceral terminology (much abbreviated) after Stach *et al.* (1975).

R. V. Tyson

pyrolysis. Such degraded AOM is highly susceptible to destruction during palynological preparation procedures, and partial oxidation (as employed by Habib 1979) must consequently distort any resulting interpretations. The state of degradation of AOM can be assessed by the eye of the experienced palynofacies investigator, but a more reliable, although still subjective method, utilizes ultra violet fluorescence (Powell *et al.* 1982), which is often sufficient to separate Type II and Type III AOM (Tyson 1985).

The high preservation of marine organic matter under dysaerobic to anoxic conditions results in kerogen assemblages overwhelmingly dominated by AOM (70–90%), in all areas except those immediately adjacent to fluvial inputs and/or loci of redeposition (Tyson 1985). In most cases the allochthonous phytoclast fraction is drowned by the much larger reservoir of marine carbon which is available to be preserved in the sediments under these conditions. It also appears that the oceanographic and hydrographic changes associated with bottom water oxygen depletion also frequently lead to a diminished supply of allochthonous materials to the basin (Tyson 1984, 1985). Nearly all marine black shales (i.e. dysaerobic, anaerobic and anoxic facies) consequently exhibit Type II, AOM-dominated kerogen compositions and high TOC values (3–57%).

Type I kerogen compositions are very rare in marine sediments since their formation additionally requires the supply of very lipid-rich organic matter which is not produced by the normal marine plankton (q.v. Pelet 1983). The main sources of such organic matter include the cyanobacteria ('blue green algae') which are comparatively unimportant in the marine environment except in very nutrient-rich waters (e.g. eutrophicated parts of the Baltic Sea, Jansson 1980; northern Indian Ocean, Jayaraman 1972) and the algal mats of intertidal areas (Bauld 1981). The planktonic cyanobacteria appear to be best adapted to stably stratified watermasses where the boundary between the mixed layer and nutrient-rich, oxygen-deficient bottom waters occurs within the euphotic zone (Fogg 1982; Padan & Cohen 1982). Such a condition is rare or transient in the marine realm but is quite common in lakes, which probably explains why most Type I kerogens are lacustrine. The ecological 'preference' of the planktonic cyanobacteria, as noted above, is very reminiscent of that of the photosynthetic sulphur oxidizing bacteria which also proliferate near the RPD (Jørgensen 1982; see earlier). The latter, with their non-photosynthetic equivalents, may be significant contributors of similar lipid-rich organic matter in dysaerobic to anoxic environments (Williams &

Reimers 1983). Under ultra violet fluorescence, recognizable detrital alginitic and bituminitic material of probable cyanobacterial origin is sometimes found to be abundant within the AOM of marine ORMs, and is occasionally sufficient to elevate the kerogen to an intermediate Type II–Type I composition (e.g. see Cook *et al.* 1981).

From the preceding discussion, it can be seen that kerogen trends generally reveal little about the palaeoenvironments of marine source rocks except very general and relative estimates of proximity to fluvial sources, the degree of redeposition, and bottom water oxygenation. The only non-palynomorph kerogen component which appears to show a limited and diagnostic distribution in marine sediments is cuticular plant debris, which tends to be concentrated in pro-delta sediments opposite the mouths of large distributaries (Müller 1959; Cross *et al.* 1966). Because of the favourable geochemical composition of this material it may confer some marginal petroleum source potential on sediments which are generally only gas-prone. More refined palaeoenvironmental information can be derived from the detailed examination of the palynomorph component of the kerogen.

Palynomorphs as palaeoenvironmental indices

Sporomorphs

The abundance of *terrestrial* palynomorphs (here collectively referred to as sporomorphs) in marine sediments, is controlled by the climate of the source area, texture of the sediment and the proximity of fluvial inputs (Müller 1959; Cross *et al.* 1966; Darrell & Hart 1970; Heusser & Balsam 1977). As aeolian transport is quantitatively insignificant (Stanley 1969), high absolute concentrations of sporomorphs are generally confined to estuarine, pro-deltaic and submarine fan sediments. Although the composition of sporomorph assemblages in marine sediments partly reflect the nature of the parent vegetation (Heusser & Balsam 1977), they are strongly affected by hydrodynamic sorting processes which fractionate the original sporomorph populations according to size, density and morphotype. The lower degree of sorting in delta top environments results in strong biases of the sporomorph population in favour of the local vegetation, but in the marine environment sorting has an averaging effect which results in generally higher diversities (Müller 1959; Darrell & Hart 1970).

The most common onshore–offshore trend (or more strictly proximal–distal trend with respect to fluvial source) is the progressive elimination of the larger, denser and more strongly ornamented pteridophyte spores. This coincides with a gradual increase in the ratio of bisaccate pollen to simple unornamented spores (Hughes & Moody-Stuart 1967; Batten 1974; Habib 1979, 1982; Tyson 1985). Frequently, however, the most abundant sporomorphs are simple spherical pollen which consequently show little fractionation but increase proportionately as other morphotypes decline. This is illustrated by the widespread distribution of *Classopollis* in oceanic sediments of the Mesozoic central Atlantic (Habib 1979; Tyson 1984). As most MPSRs are clearly basinal ('distal') sediments, sporomorphs are of relatively little use for palaeoenvironmental purposes, except in determining proximal–distal trends and variations in the degree of redeposition through host sequences.

Plankton

The principal marine palynomorphs are the acritarchs (uncertain affinities), the dinoflagellate cysts (dinocysts), and the phycomas of the prasinophycean algae (for general background information see Tappan 1980). The dinocysts are of particular value because of their widespread occurrence in the Mesozoic–Cenozoic record, their biostratigraphic utility, and the growing appreciation of the ecology of modern dinoflagellates which promises major advances in the palaeoenvironmental applications of palynofacies studies (see also Davies *et al.* 1982).

The relatively small proportion of dinoflagellates that produce fossilizable cysts are mainly meroplanktonic forms which are adapted to the unstable hydrographic regimes of shelf seas (Wall *et al.* 1977; Margalef *et al.* 1979). The motile stage of the dinoflagellate life cycle is adapted to stably stratified water columns (Landry 1977). During seasonal breakdown of hydrographic stability, or during conditions of overcrowding, the dinoflagellates produce 'hypnozygotes' (benthic resting cysts) which 'over-winter' on the sea floor, then release their contents in the following spring (see Dale 1983). It is evident that since the motile stage lives in stratified waters and that encystment and excystment both occur in response to seasonal cues in unstable hydrographic regimes, the benthic cysts should only be produced in abundance in the seasonally stratifying and destratifying parts of the shelf watermass. Wall *et al.* (1977) and Tyler *et al.* (1982) have in fact shown that there is generally a good correlation between the dinoflagellate community and the cyst thanatocoenosis, and that the major boundaries in cyst assemblages coincide with hydrodynamic frontal systems in the overlying waters (see also Reid 1982). As might also be anticipated from their ecological function, dinocysts are most abundant and diverse in temperate shelf seas (Harland 1983; Wall *et al.* 1977).

In Quaternary sediments of the central and northern Atlantic and its marginal seas, only one genus of dinoflagellate, *Impagidinium* (Harland 1983; equivalent to *Leptodinium* of Wall *et al.* 1977), has an ocean-centred distribution. Most oceanic dinoflagellates do not produce cysts (or fossilizable cysts) and must have a very different life cycle from the meroplanktonic forms. Presumably the *Impagidinium* cysts must be 'designed' to remain in suspension within the mixed layer (i.e. the seasonal part of the ocean water-mass) until excystment has occurred. Other dinocysts do have a partly oceanic distribution but this is probably due to oceanward redeposition across the presently narrow continental shelves. The latter results in maximum dinocyst concentrations in continental slope and rise sediments (Wall *et al.* 1977). The predominantly meroplanktonic rather than pelagic habit of cyst-forming dinoflagellates appears to extend back into the Mesozoic since dinocysts are rarely abundant in pelagic sediments except where there are sedimentological or other palynological indications of redeposition (Tyson 1984, 1985). It should be noted that there is a major difference in the significance of dinocyst abundance depending upon whether the host sediments are neritic or pelagic. Dinocyst densities may be in part related to productivity (Davey 1971; Davey & Rogers 1975), but hydrodynamic factors are probably of greater general importance, particularly since many dinoflagellates do not produce cysts, or cysts which are likely to be preserved. The well known offshore increase in the ratio of gonyaulacean:peridinoid dinocysts (e.g. Harland 1983; Wall *et al.* 1977) could well partly result from preservational bias (see Dale 1976). The nearshore maxima of peridinoid dinocysts probably reflects a combination of their more euryhaline character and also their enrichment in all areas of upwelling (Wall *et al.* 1977; Davey 1971; Bujak 1984).

Differential sorting of dinocyst morphotypes is frequently reported from ancient sediments (e.g. Scull *et al.* 1966; Scott & Kidson 1977; Aurisano 1980; Tyson 1985). Ancient dinocyst assemblages tend to have become sorted along a gradient of hydrodynamic equivalence resulting in proximal assemblages characterized by robust, simple *proximate* cysts, and distal assemblages dominated by more elaborate and delicate *chorate* cysts with long and complex processes. However, intermediate morphotypes are common and there is a complete continuum of assemblage types. This morphotype fractionation is probably purely hydrodynamic in origin and there is little evidence to suppose that the chorate morphotype represents a functional adaptation for reduced settling rates in 'offshore', 'deep' or 'oceanic' watermasses. It is unlikely that the possession of long processes has a beneficial effect on settling rates other than to encourage the entrainment of the cyst in microconvection currents, thereby delaying the final sedimentation and promoting greater dispersal (see Smayda 1970).

Along with many other workers I have observed that dinocysts are very rare in black shales (as defined here), even when the AOM has been removed by oxidation; (Correia 1971; McLachlan & Pieterse 1978; Habib 1982; Wille 1982; Tyson 1984a, 1984b). This rarity of plankton has sometimes been used to support the erroneous notion that the marine palynomorphs were swamped by a large influx of sporomorphs and/or that the AOM is principally of terrestrial origin (e.g. Ioannides *et al.* 1976; Davey 1978). My observations suggest that dinocysts are only significant in black shales where there is evidence of redeposition, or in neritic black shales, where there is evidence of brief periods of improved oxygenation (watermass overturn) associated with slight bioturbation and/or benthic recolonization. Comparison of the general kerogen and detailed palynomorph trends indicates that this distribution results mainly from a decreased supply of dinocysts during black shale (MPSR) deposition rather than an increase in terrestrial influence.

Although dinocysts may be rare in MPSR facies, prasinophycean algae (e.g. *Tasmanites, Leiosphaeridia, Crassophaera, Cymatiosphaera, Pterospermella*) are frequently conspicuous (e.g. McLachlan & Pieterse 1978; Hochuli & Kelts 1979, Wise *et al.* 1982; Wille 1982; Rawson & Riley 1982; Tyson 1984, 1985). This observation is usually due to the conspicuous nature of the palynomorphs themselves and the rarity of other plankton, rather than their absolute abundance. Unlike most of the dinocysts produced by dinoflagellates, the phycoma of prasinophycean algae does not represent a resting stage in the life cycle and is certainly not benthic (Boalch & Parke 1971; Tappan 1980). The prasinophyceae exhibit a pelagic distribution since the phycoma is only sedimented after the release of the contents or by being ingested by zooplankton and included in faecal pellets.

As dinocysts are predominantly produced by the meroplanktonic dinoflagellates of unstable hydrographic regimes, the establishment of permanent watermass stratification will result in the offshore dinoflagellate population being predominantly non cyst-forming. Consequently during episodes of stable stratification and MPSR formation, the only dinocysts which are present will be the small amount redeposited from the less hydrographically-stable basin margins. This is indicated by the ratio of the dinocysts to prasinophycean algae and the morphotype sorting of the dinocyst assemblages. It is possible that the watermass conditions associated with MPSR deposition may have positively favoured 'blooms' of prasinophyceae, but there is no apparent reason why this should be so from our current knowledge of this group. As the oceans have always been stratified, the use of dinocysts as indicators of palaeostability in the watermass is really only of value in neritic sediments; in oceanic sediments they indicate redeposition only.

The remaining group of marine palynomorphs, the acritarchs, are generally unimportant or of unknown significance in Mesozoic–Cenozoic MPSR facies. The relative distributions of acritarchs and dinoflagellate cysts suggests that they may have been more euryhaline. It is possible that some of the acanthomorph acritarchs may have been the small, sphaeromorph, spined cysts of peridinoid dinoflagellates (Dale 1976). Further comments on acritarchs may be found elsewhere (e.g. Tappan 1980); they do not warrant more extensive treatment here.

Discussion and conclusions

The source-rock characteristics of clay grade sediments are primarily controlled by bottom water oxygenation and proximity to fluvial sources. Aerobic environments are characterized by sediments with low TOC values and refractory phytoclast or degraded AOM dominated, Type III kerogen (especially at lower accumulation rates). Deposits of dysaerobic to anoxic environments (black shales as defined here) are characterized by high TOC values and AOM-dominated, Type II kerogen (except in areas immediately adjacent to fluvial inputs). They represent the most favourable MPSR facies. The palynomorph assemblages of neritic sediments primarily reflect the stability of the watermass (which determines the ecology of the dinoflagellate populations and the degree of hydrodynamic sorting), the proximity of fluvial inputs, and the nature of the climate and coastal vegetation. The palynomorph characteristics of oceanic sediments (or of any stably stratified basin) are controlled almost exclusively by the pattern and mechanism of redeposition, including such factors as the tapping of proximal shelf sediment source areas via submarine valleys (by-passing).

There are three principal genetic facies of marine black shales (MPSRs): the euxinic facies (silled or barred basin model), the upwelling-intensified oxygen minimum facies, and the epeiric facies. The first two have been reviewed extensively elsewhere (e.g. Demaison & Moore 1980) and are not discussed further; however, it should be noted that the euxinic facies is mainly anoxic (as used here) and the upwelling-intensified oxygen minimum facies predominantly dysaerobic to anaerobic. Epeiric black shale facies are particularly interesting and deserve further mention. Review of the relevant literature suggests that these extensive deposits were deposited under dysaerobic to anaerobic conditions with probably only localized or transient anoxia. Their formation appears to have resulted from a combination of factors including: (a) transgressive maxima, (b) warm, equable global climates (which promoted regional watermass stratification and oxygen depletion), and (c) large scale palaeogeographic features which restricted the free exchange and mixing of epeiric and oceanic watermasses (Tyson 1985). The latter features are not sills in the conventional sense of the barred basin model, but are related, for example, to the ratio of the epeiric sea area to the length of the oceanic seaboard.

The characteristic internal uniformity, continuity and synchroneity of epeiric black shales implies a regional nutrient supply mechanism rather than localized directional sources such as upwelling or runoff (Tyson 1985). Such a regional mechanism would be entirely in keeping with the belief that shelf productivity is based on essentially autochthonous nutrient recycling. The most likely mechanism is the relatively slight, seasonal, lowering of a regional pycnocline and the consequent turbulent entrainment of nutrients from the top of the bottom waters. Such mixing events appear to have encouraged coccolith blooms (Tyson 1985), while stable conditions favoured dinoflagellates (but not dinocysts!) and cyanobacteria. A number of authors (e.g. Jenkyns 1980) have suggested that the transgressive maxima resulted in an increase in shelf productivity which in turn promoted oxygen deficiency. Apart from the fact that such models overstress productivity, it is apparent that although an overall increase in the total area of shelf seas might increase the *global* marine productivity, there is no reason why an increase in productivity per unit area, and increased organic loading, should result. This is particularly true if watermass stratification was widespread and the productivity of the epeiric seas consequently generally diminished.

The conditions which would have been *optimal* for the intensified oxygen minimum facies (namely strong circulation during periods of higher latitudinal temperature gradient, which would boost nutrient recycling and productivity), are exactly those which would be *unfavourable* for the epeiric black shales (Tyson 1985). The latter require generally diminished mixing during equable, stable climates. This discrepancy is probably reflected in the poor correlation between areas of predicted upwelling and MPSR distribution for the Jurassic noted by Parrish (this volume). I would also like to stress that epeiric seas were probably often hydrographically and palaeogeographically decoupled from the marginal shelf seas and oceans (Tyson 1985). Because of this, and their differing functioning, true epeiric black shales probably do *not* represent the expansion of the upwelling intensified oxygen minimum facies into the epeiric seas during transgressive maxima (which has been frequently suggested or inferred by many authors). Even when their stratigraphic distribution coincides, the epeiric black shales may represent a largely independent shallow-water response to common global climatic factors.

References

ALLER, R. C. 1982. Carbonate dissolution in nearshore terrigenous muds: the role of physical and biological reworking. *J. Geol. Chicago*, **90**, 79–95.

ANDERSIN, A-B., LASSIG, J., PARKKONEN, L. & SANDLER, H. 1978. The decline of macrofauna in the deeper parts of the Baltic proper. *Kieler Meeresforsch. Sonderh.* **4**, 23–52.

ANKAR, S. & JANSSON, B. O. 1973. Effects of an unusual temperature increase on a Baltic soft-bottom community. *Mar. Biol.* **18**, 9–18.

ARTHUR, M. A., DEAN, W. E. & STOW, D. A. V. 1984.

Models for the deposition of Mesozoic-Cenozoic fine-grained organic-carbon-rich sediment in the deep sea. *In:* STOW, D. A. V. & PIPER, D. J. W. (eds) *Fine-grained sediments, Spec. Publ. geol. Soc. London*, **15**, 527–60.

AURISANO, R. W. 1980. *Upper Cretaceous Subsurface Dinoflagellate Stratigraphy and Paleoecology of the Atlantic Coastal Plain of New Jersey.* Ph.D. thesis, Rutgers University, Brunswick, New Jersey, (University microfilms No. 8022541). 204pp.

BARBER, R. T. & SMITH, R. L. 1981. Coastal upwelling

ecosystems. *In:* LONGHURST, A. R. (ed) *Analysis of Marine Ecosystems.* Academic Press, London, 31–68.

BARSS, M. S. & WILLIAMS, G. L. 1973. Palynology and nannofossil processing techniques. *Pap. geol. Surv. Can.* 73–26, 25pp.

BATTEN, D. J. 1974. Wealden palaeoecology from the distribution of plant fossils. *Proc. geol. Assoc. London*, **85**, 433–58.

—— 1981. Palynofacies, organic maturation and source potential for petroleum. *In:* BROOKS, J. (ed), *Organic Maturation Studies and Fossil Fuel Exploration.* Academic Press, London. 201–24.

BAULD, J. 1981. Geobiological role of cyanobacterial mats in sedimentary environments: production and preservation of organic matter. *B.M.R. J. Aust. Geol. Geophys.* **6**, 307–18.

BERNER, R. A. 1978. Sulfate reduction and the rate of deposition of marine sediments. *Earth plan. Sci. Lett.* **37**, 492–8.

—— 1981. A new geochemical classification of sedimentary environments. *J. Sediment. Petrol.* **51**, 359–65.

BILLEN, G. & VERBEUSTEL, S. 1980. Distribution of microbial metabolisms in natural environments displaying gradients of oxidation-reduction conditions. *In:* DAUMAS, R. (ed) *Biogeochimie de la Matiere Organique a l'Interface Eau-Sediment Marin, Colloq. Int. C.N.R.S.* **293**, 291–300.

BOALCH, G. T. & PARKE, M. 1971. The prasinophycean genera (Chlorophyta) possibly related to fossil genera, in particular the genus *Tasmanites. In:* FARINACCI, A. (ed) *Proceedings of the Second Planktonic Conference, Rome 1970*, **1**, Edizioni Tecnoscienza, Roma. 99–105.

BRASS, G. W., SOUTHAM, J. R. & PETERSON, W. H. 1982. Warm saline bottom water in the ancient ocean. *Nature, London*, **296**, 620–3.

BRECK, W. G. 1974. Redox levels in the sea. *In:* GOLDBERG, E. D. (ed) *Marine Chemistry, The Sea*, **5**, Wiley Interscience, New York. 153–79.

BRUMSACK, H.-J. 1980. Geochemistry of Cretaceous black shales from the Atlantic Ocean (D.S.D.P. Legs 11, 14, 36 and 41). *Chem. Geol.* **31**, 1–25.

BRUSH, G. S. & BRUSH, L. M. Jr. 1972. Transport of pollen in a sediment laden channel: a laboratory study. *Am. J. Sci.* **272**, 359–81.

BUJAK, J. P. 1984. Cenozoic dinoflagellate cysts and acritarchs from the Bering Sea and northern North Pacific, D.S.D.P. Leg 19. *Micropaleontology*, **30**, 180–212.

BUJAK, J. P., BARSS, M. S. & WILLIAMS, G. L. 1977. Offshore eastern Canada—Part I: offshore east Canada's organic type and hydrocarbon potential. *Oil and Gas J.* **75**, 198–201.

BYERS, C. W. 1977. Biofacies patterns in euxinic basins: a general model. *In:* COOK, H. E. & ENOS, P. (eds) *Deep Water Carbonate Environments. Spec. Publ. Soc. econ. paleontol. Mineral.* **25**, 5–17.

BYERS, C. W. 1979. Biogenic structures of black shale paleo-environments. *Postilla*, 174, 43pp.

CALVERT, S. E. 1964. Factors affecting the distribution of laminated diatomaceous sediments in Gulf of California. *In:* VAN ANDEL, T. J. & SHOR, G. G.

(eds) *Marine Geology of Gulf of California. Mem. Am. Assoc. Petrol. Geol.* **3**, 311–30.

—— 1983. Geochemistry of Pleistocene sapropels and associated sediments from the Eastern Mediterranean. *Oceanol. Acta*, **6**, 255–67.

CEPEK, P. & KEMPER, E. 1981. Der Blättertonstein des nordwestdeutschen Barreme und die Bedeutung des Nanoplanktons für die fein laminierten, anoxisch entstandenen Gesteine. *Geol. Jahrb. Hanover*, **58A**, 3–13.

CLAYPOOL, G. E. & KAPLAN, I. R. 1974. The origin and distribution of methane in marine sediments. *In:* KAPLAN, I. R. (ed) *Natural Gases in Marine Sediments.* NATO Conf. Ser. IV, 3. Plenum Press, New York. 99–139.

COLEMAN, M. L., CURTIS, C. D. & IRWIN, H. 1979. Burial rate a key to source and reservoir potential. *World Oil*, **188**, 83–92.

COMBAZ, A. 1964. Les palynofaciès. *Rev. Micropaleontol. Paris*, **7**, 205–18.

COOK, A. C., HUTTON, A. C. & SHERWOOD, N. R. 1981. Classification of oil shales. *Bull. Cent. Rech. Explor. Prod. Elf Aquitaine*, **5**, 353–81.

CORNFORD, C., RULLKOTTER, J. & WELTE, D. H. 1981. A synthesis of organic petrographic and geochemical results from D.S.D.P. sites in the eastern central North Atlantic. *In:* DOUGLAS, A. G. & MAXWELL, J. R. (eds) *Advances in Organic Geochemistry, 1979. Phys. Chem. Earth*, **12**, Pergamon Press, London, 445–54.

CORREIA, M. 1971. Diagenesis of sporopollenin and other comparable organic substances: application to hydrocarbon research. *In:* BROOKS, J., GRANT, P., MUIR, M. D., SHAW, G. & GIJZEL, P. Van, (eds) *Sporopollenin.* Academic Press, London. 569–620.

CRANWELL, P. A. 1976. Decomposition of aquatic biota and sediment formation: lipid components of two blue-green algal species and of detritus resulting from microbial attack. *Freshwat. Biol.* **6**, 481–8.

CROSS, A. T., THOMPSON, G. G. & ZAITZEFF, J. B. 1966. Source and distribution of palynomorphs in bottom sediments, southern part of the Gulf of California. *Mar. Geol.* **4**, 467–524.

CURTIS, C. D. 1978. Possible links between sandstone diagenesis and depth-related geochemical reactions occurring in enclosing mudstones. *J. geol. Soc. London*, **135**, 107–17.

DALE, B. 1976. Cyst formation, sedimentation and preservation: factors affecting dinoflagellate assemblages in recent sediments from Trondheimsfjord, Norway. *Rev. Palaeobot. Palynol.* **22**, 39–60.

—— 1983. Dinoflagellate resting cysts: 'benthic plankton'. *In:* FRYXELL, G. A. (ed) *Survival strategies of the Algae*, Cambridge Univ. Press. 69–136.

DARRELL, J. H. II & HART, G. F. 1970. Environmental determinations using absolute miospore frequency, Mississippi River delta. *Bull. geol. Soc. Am.* **81**, 2513–518.

DAVEY, R. J. 1971. Palynology and palaeoenvironmental studies, with special reference to the continental shelf sediments of South Africa. *In:* FARINACCI, A. (ed) *Proceedings of the Second Planktonic Conference, Rome 1970*, **1**, Edizioni Teconoscienza, Roma, 331–47.

—— 1978. Marine Cretaceous palynology of Site 361, D.S.D.P. Leg 40, off southwestern Africa. *In:* BOLLI, H. M., RYAN, W.B.F. *et al. Initial Rep. Deep Sea drill. Proj.*, **60**, U.S. Government Printing Office, Washington, D.C. 883–913.

—— & ROGERS, J. 1975. Palynomorph distribution in recent offshore sediments along two traverses off S.W. Africa. *Mar. Geol.* **18**, 213–25.

DAVIES, E. H., BUJAK, J. P. & WILLIAMS, G. L. 1982. The application of dinoflagellates to paleoenvironmental problems. *In:* MAMET, B. & COPELAND, M. J. (eds) *Proceedings 3rd N. American Paleontological Convention, Montreal*, **1**, 125–31.

DAVIS, B. & BRUBAKER, B. 1973. Differential sedimentation of pollen grains in lakes. *Limnol. Oceanogr.* **18**, 635–46.

DEAN, W. E. & GARDNER, J. V. 1982. Origin and geochemistry of redox cycles of Jurassic to Eocene age, Cape Verde Basin (DSDP Site 367), continental margin of northwest Africa. *In:* SCHLANGER, S. O. & CITA, M. B. (eds) *Nature and Origin of Cretaceous Carbon-Rich Facies*. Academic Press, London. 55–78.

DE BOER, P. L. 1983. Aspects of Middle Cretaceous pelagic sedimentation in Southern Europe: production and storage of organic matter, stable isotopes, and astronomical influences. *Geologica Ultraiectina*, **31**, Univ. Utrecht, 112pp.

DEGENS, E. T. & MOPPER, K. 1976. Factors controlling the distribution and early diagenesis of organic material in marine sediments. *In:* RILEY, J. P. & CHESTER, R. (eds) *Chemical Oceanography*, **6**, 2nd Ed., Academic Press, London. 56–113.

DEMAISON, G. J. & MOORE, G. T. 1980. Anoxic environments and oil source bed genesis. *Bull. Am. Assoc. Petrol. Geol.* **64**, 1179–1209.

——, HOLCK, A. J. J., JONES, R. W. & MOORE, G. T. 1984. Predictive source bed and stratigraphy; a guide to regional petroleum occurrence: North Sea basin and eastern North American continental margin. *Proceedings 11th World Petroleum Congress, London 1983*, **2**, 17–29.

DEUSER, W. G. 1974. Evolution of anoxic conditions in Black Sea during Holocene. *In:* DEGENS, E. T. & ROSS, D. A. (eds) *The Black Sea—Geology, Chemistry and Biology. Mem. Am. Assoc. Petrol. Geol.* **20**, 133–6.

DIESTER-HAASS, L. 1978. Sediments as indicators of upwelling. *In:* BOJE, R. & TOMCZAK, M. (eds) *Upwelling Ecosystems*. Springer Verlag, Berlin. 261–81.

DOEMEL, W. N. & BROCK, T. D. 1977. Structure, growth and decomposition of laminated algal-bacterial mats in alkaline hot springs. *Appl. environ. Microbiol.*, **34**, 433–52.

DOUGLAS, R. G. 1981. Paleoecology of continental margin basins: a modern case history from the Borderland of Southern California. *In:* DOUGLAS, R. G., COLBURN, I. P. & GORSLINE, D. S. (eds) *Depositional Systems of Active Continental Margin Basins: Short Course Notes*. Pacific Sect. S.E.P.M., Los Angeles. 121–56.

DURAND, B. 1980. Sedimentary organic matter and kerogen. Definition and quantitative importance of kerogen. *In:* DURAND, B. (ed) *Kerogen: Insoluble Organic Matter from Sedimentary Rocks*. Editions Technip, Paris. 13–24.

FALKOWSKI, P. G., HOPKINS, T. S. & WALSH, J. J. 1980. An analysis of factors affecting oxygen depletion in the New York Bight. *J. Mar. Res.* **38**, 479–506.

FENCHEL, T. M. & JØRGENSEN, B. B. 1977. Detritus food chains of aquatic ecosystems: the role of bacteria. *In:* ALEXANDER, M. (ed) *Advances in Microbial Ecology*, **1**, Plenum Press, New York, 1–58.

—— & RIEDL, R. J. 1970. The sulphate system: a new biotic community underneath the oxidised layer of marine sand bottoms. *Mar. Biol.* **7**, 255–68.

FLINT, R. W. & KAMYKOWSKI, D. 1984. Benthic nutrient regeneration in South Texas coastal waters. *Estuarine Coastal Shelf Sci.* **18**, 221–30.

FOGG, G. E. 1982. Marine plankton. *In:* CARR, N. G. & WHITTON, B. A. (eds) *The Biology of Cyanobacteria, Bot. Monogr.* **19**, 491–513.

FOREE, E. G. & MCCARTY, P. L. 1970. Anaerobic decomposition of algae. *Environ. Sci. Technol.* **4**, 842–49.

FROELICH, P. N., KLINKHAMMER, G. P., BENDER, M. L., LUEDTKE, N. A., HEATH, G. R., CULLEN, D., DAUPHIN, P., HAMMOND, D., HARTMAN, B. & MAYNARD, V. 1979. Early oxidation of organic matter in pelagic sediments of the eastern equatorial Atlantic: suboxic diagenesis. *Geochim. Cosmochim. Acta*, **43**, 1075–90.

GAUTIER, D. L. 1982. Siderite concretions: indicators of early diagenesis in the Gammon Shale (Cretaceous). *J. Sediment. Petrol.* **52**, 859–71.

GLENN, C. R. & ARTHUR, M. A. 1985. Sedimentary and geochemical indicators of productivity and oxygen contents in modern and ancient basins: the Holocene Black Sea as the 'type' anoxic basin. *Chem. Geol.* **48**, 325–354.

GODSHALK, G. L. & WETZEL, R. G. 1978. Decomposition of aquatic angiosperms. III. *Zostera marina* L, and a conceptual model of decomposition. *Aquatic Bot.* **5**, 329–54.

GOLDHABER, M. B. & KAPLAN, I. R. 1975. Controls and consequences of sulphate reduction rates in marine sediments. *Soil Sci.* **119**, 42–55.

GOVEAN, F. M. & GARRISON, R. E. 1981. Significance of laminated and massive diatomites in the upper part of the Monterey Formation, California. *In:* GARRISON, R. E. & DOUGLAS, R. G. (eds) *The Monterey Formation and Related Siliceous Rocks of California*. Pacific Sect. S.E.P.M., Los Angeles. 181–89.

DE GRACIANSKY, P. C., DEROO, G., HERBIN, J. P., MONTADERT, L., MULLER, C., SCHAAF, A. & SIGAL, J. 1984. Ocean-wide stagnation episode in the late Cretaceous. *Nature, London*, **308**, 346–9.

GRASSHOFF, K. 1975. The hydrochemistry of landlocked basins and fjords. *In:* RILEY, J. P. & SKIRROW, G. (eds) *Chemical Oceanography*, **2**, 2nd Ed., Academic Press, London. 456–598.

GRAY, J. S. 1981. *The Ecology of Marine Sediments: an Introduction to the Structure and Function of Benthic Communities*. Cambridge University Press, 185pp.

HABIB, D. 1979. Sedimentology of palynomorphs and

palynodebris in Cretaceous carbonaceous facies south of Vigo Seamount. *In:* SIBUET, J.-C., RYAN, W. B. F. *et al., Initial Rep. Deep Sea drill. Proj., 47,* (2), U.S Government Printing Office, Washington, D.C. 451–67.

—— 1982. Sedimentary supply origin of Cretaceous black shales. *In:* SCHLANGER, S. O. & CITA, M. B. (eds) *Nature and Origin of Cretaceous Carbon-Rich Facies,* Academic Press, London. 113–27.

HANSEN, K. 1959. Sediments from Danish lakes. *J. Sediment. Petrol.* **29,** 38–46.

HARGRAVE, B. T. 1973. Coupling carbon flow through some pelagic and benthic communities. *J. Fish Res. Board Can.* **30,** 1317–26.

HARLAND, R. 1983. Distribution maps of recent dinoflagellate cysts in bottom sediments from the North Atlantic and adjacent seas. *Palaeontology,* **26,** 321–87.

HEATH, G. R., MOORE, T. C. & DAUPHIN, J. P. 1977. Organic carbon in deep-sea sediments. *In:* ANDERSON, N. R. & MALAHOFF, A. (eds) *The Fate of Fossil Fuel CO_2 in the Oceans,* Plenum Press, New York. 605–25.

HEUSSER, L. & BALSAM, W. L. 1977. Pollen distribution in the north east Pacific Ocean. *Quat. Res.* **7,** 45–62.

HOCHULI, P. & KELTS, K. 1979. Palynology of Middle Cretaceous black clay facies from Deep Sea Drilling Project Sites 417 and 418 of the western North Atlantic. *In:* DONNELLY, T., FRANCHETEAU, J., BRYAN, W., ROBINSON, P., FLOWER, M., SALISBURY, M. *et al., Initial Rep. Deep Sea Drill. Proj. 51–53 Part 2,* U.S. Govt. Printing Office, Washington, D.C. 897–935.

HONJO, S. & ROMAN, M. R. 1978. Marine copepod fecal pellets: production, preservation and sedimentation. *J. Mar. Res.* **36,** 45–57.

HUC, A. Y. 1980. Origin and formation of organic matter in recent sediments and its relation to kerogen. *In:* DURAND, B. (ed) *Kerogen: Insoluble Organic Matter from Sedimentary Rocks.* Editions Technip, Paris. 445–74.

HUGHES, N. F. & MOODY-STUART, J. C. 1967. Palynological facies and correlation in the English Wealden. *Rev. Palaeobot. Palynol.* **1,** 259–68.

HULSEMANN, T. & EMERY, K. O. 1961. Stratification in recent sediments of Santa Barbara Basin as controlled by organisms and water characteristics. *J. Geol. Chicago,* **69,** 279–90.

HUNT, J. M. 1979. *Petroleum Geochemistry and Geology.* W. H. Freeman & Co., San Francisco. 617 pp.

IBACH, L. E. J. 1982. Relationship between sedimentation rate and total organic carbon content in ancient marine sediments. *Bull. Am. Assoc. Petrol. Geol.* **66,** 170–88.

INDREBØ, G., PENGERUD, B. & DUNDAS, I. 1979. Microbial activities in a permanently stratified estuary. 1. Primary production and sulphate reduction. *Mar. Biol.* **51,** 295–304.

IOANNIDES, N. S., STAVRINOS, G. N. & DOWNIE, C. 1976. Kimmeridgian microplankton from Clavell's Hard, Dorset, England. *Micropalaeontology,* **22,** 443–78.

JANNASCH, H. W., EIMHJELLEN, K. & WIRSEN, K. O.

1971. Microbial degradation of organic matter in the deep sea. *Science,* **171,** 672–5.

JANSSON, B.-O. 1980. Natural systems of the Baltic Sea. *Ambio,* **9,** 128–36.

JAYARAMAN, R. 1972. On the occurrence of blooms of blue-green algae and the associate oceanographic conditions in the Northern Indian Ocean. *In:* DESIKACHARY, T. V. (ed) *Taxonomy and Biology of Blue-green Algae.* Centre for advanced study in Botany, Univ. Madras. 428–32.

JENKYNS, H. C. 1980. Cretaceous anoxic events: from continents to oceans. *J. geol. Soc. London,* **137,** 171–88.

JONES, R. W. 1983. Organic matter characteristics near the shelf-slope boundary. *In:* STANELY, D. J. & MOORE, G. T. (eds) *The Shelf-Break: Critical Interface on Continental Margins. Spec. Publ. Soc. econ. Palaeontol. Mineral.* **33,** 391–405.

JØRGENSEN, B. B. 1982. Mineralisation of organic matter in the sea bed—the role of sulphate reduction. *Nature, London,* **296,** 643–5.

—— 1983. The microbial sulphur cycle. *In:* KRUMBEIN, W. E. (ed) *Microbial Geochemistry,* Blackwell Scientific Publications, Oxford. 91–124.

KAUFFMAN, E. G. 1978. Benthic environments and paleoecology of the Posidonienschiefer (Toarcian). *Neues Jahrb. Geol. Palaeontol. Abhandlungen,* **157,** 18–36.

KELTS, K. & MCKENZIE, J. A. 1982. Diagenetic dolomite formation in Quaternary anoxic diatomaceous muds of Deep Sea Drilling Project Leg 64, Gulf of California. *In:* CURRAY, J. R., MOORE, D. G. *et al., Initial Rep. Deep Sea drill. Proj.* **64** Part 2. U.S. Govt. Print. Off., Washington, D.C. 553–69.

KENDRICK, J. W. 1979. Geochemical studies of black clays from Leg 43, D.S.D.P. *In:* TUCHOLKE, B. E., VOGT, P. R., *et al., Initial Rep. Deep Sea drill. Proj.* **43.** U.S. Govt. Print. Off., Washington, D.C. 633–42.

KIDD, R. B., CITA, M. B. & RYAN, W. B. F. 1978. Stratigraphy of eastern Mediterranean sapropel sequences recovered during D.S.D.P. Leg 42A and their palaeoenvironmental significance. *In:* HSU, K. J., MONTADERT, L. *et al. Initial Rep. Deep Sea drill. Proj.* **42** Part 1. U.S. Government Printing Office, Washington, D.C. 421–43.

KREJCI-GRAF, K. 1964. Geochemical diagnosis of facies. *Proc. Yorkshire geol. Soc.* **34,** 469–521.

KRISSEK, K. A. & SCHEIDEGGER, K. F. 1983. Environmental controls on sediment texture and composition in low oxygen zones off Peru and Oregon. *In:* THIEDE, J. & SUESS, E. (eds) *Coastal upwelling: its sediment record, B, Sedimentary Records of Ancient Coastal Upwelling.* NATO Conf. Ser. IV, **10b.** Plenum Press, New York, 163–80.

KRUMBEIN, W. C. & GARRELS, R. M. 1952. Origin and classification of chemical sediments in terms of pH and oxidation-reduction potentials. *J. Geol. Chicago,* **60,** 1–33.

LAANBROECK, H. J. & VELDKAMP, H. 1982. Microbial interactions in sediment communities. *Phil. Trans. R. Soc. London,* **298B,** 533–50.

LANDRY, M. R. 1977. A review of important concepts

in the trophic organisation of pelagic ecosystems. *Helgolander wiss. Meeresunters*, **30**, 8–17.

LECLAIRE, J. P. & KELTS, K. R. 1982. Calcium carbonate and organic carbon stratigraphy of Late Quaternary laminated and homogeneous diatom oozes from the Guaymas Slope, HPC Site 480, Gulf of California. *In:* CURRAY, J. R., MOORE, D. G. *et al. Initial Rep. Deep Sea drill. Proj., 64*, part 2. U.S. Government Printing Office, Washington, DC. 1263–75.

LEVANTHAL, J. S. 1983. An interpretation of carbon and sulfur relationships in Black Sea sediments as indicators of environments of deposition. *Geochim. Cosmochim. Acta*, **47**, 133–7.

MANGINI, A. & DOMINIK, J. 1979. Late Quaternary sapropel on the Mediterranean Ridge: U-budget and evidence of low sedimentation rates. *Sediment. Geol.* **23**, 113–25.

MARGALEF, R., ESTRADA, M. & BLASCO, D. 1979. Functional morphology of organisms involved in red tides, as adapted to decaying turbulence. *In:* TAYLOR, D. L. & SELIGER, H. H. (eds) *Toxic Dinoflagellate Blooms*, Elsevier, Amsterdam. 89–94.

MASRAN, T. C. & POCOCK, S. A. J. 1981. The classification of plant-derived particulate organic matter in sedimentary rocks. *In:* BROOKS, J. (ed) *Organic Maturation Studies and Fossil Fuel Exploration*. Academic Press, London. 145–76.

MCLACHLAN, I. R. & PIETERSE, E. 1978. Preliminary palynological results: Site 361, Leg 40, Deep Sea Drilling Project. *In:* BOLLI, H. M., RYAN, W. B. F. *et al. Initial Rep. Deep Sea drill. Proj.*, **40**, U.S. Government Printing Office, Washington, DC. 857–81.

MORRIS, K. A. 1979. A classification of Jurassic marine shale sequences: an example from the Toarcian (Lower Jurassic) of Great Britain. *Palaeogeogr. Palaeoclimatol. Palaeoecol.* **26**, 117–26.

MÜLLER, J. 1959. Palynology of recent Orinoco Delta and shelf sediments: reports of the Orinoco Shelf Expedition 5. *Micropalaeontology*, **5**, 1–32.

MÜLLER, P. J. & SUESS, E. 1979. Productivity, sedimentation rate and sedimentary organic matter in the oceans—1. Organic carbon preservation. *Deep Sea Res.* **26A**, 1347–62.

NEDWELL, D. B. 1982. The cycling of sulphur in marine and freshwater sediments. *In:* NEDWELL, D. B. & BROWN, C. M. (eds) *Sediment Microbiology*, Academic Press. 73–106.

NIXON, S. W. 1981. Remineralisation and nutrient cycling in coastal marine ecosystems. *In:* NEILSON, B. J. & CRONIN, L. E. (eds) *Estuaries and Nutrients*. Humana Press, Clifton, New Jersey. 111–38.

ORR, W. L. & GAINES, A. G. Jr. 1974. Observations on rate of sulphate reduction and organic matter oxidation in the bottom waters of an estuarine basin: the upper basin of the Pettaquamscutt River (Rhode Island). *In:* TISSOT, B. & BIENNER, F. (eds) *Advances in Organic Geochemistry 1973*, Editions Technip, Paris. 791–812.

PADAN, E. & COHEN, Y. 1982. Anoxygenic photosynthesis. *In:* CARR, N. G. & WHITTON, B. A. (eds) *The Biology of Cyanobacteria, Bot. Monogr.*, **19**, 215–35.

PELET, R. 1983. Preservation and alteration of present-day sedimentary organic matter. *In:* BJØROY, M. *et al.* (eds) *Advances in Organic Geochemistry 1981*, Wiley, Chichester. 241–50.

POWELL, T. G., CREANEY, S. & SNOWDON, L. R. 1982. Limitations of use of organic petrographic techniques for identification of petroleum source rocks. *Bull. Am. Assoc. Petrol. Geol.* **66**, 430–5.

RAWSON, P. F. & RILEY, L. A. 1982. Latest Jurassic–Early Cretaceous events and the 'Late Cimmerian unconformity' in North Sea Area. *Bull. Am. Assoc. Petrol. Geol.* **66**, 2628–48.

REID, P. C. 1982. The present is the key to the past. *In:* MAMET, B. & COPELAND, M. J. (eds) *Proceedings 3rd N. American Palaeontological Convention, Montreal*, **2**, 411–6.

REIMERS, C. E. & SUESS, E. 1983. Late Quaternary fluctuations in the cycling of organic matter off central Peru: a proto-kerogen record. *In:* SUESS, E. & THIEDE J. (eds) *Response of the Sedimentary Regime to Present Coastal Upwelling. Coastal Upwelling: its Sediment Record*, A. NATO Conf. Ser. IV, 10A. Plenum Press, New York. 497–526.

REVSBECH, N. P., JØRGENSEN, B. B. & BLACKBURN, T. H. 1980. Oxygen in the sea bottom measured with a microelectrode. *Science*, **207**, 1335–6.

RHOADS, D. C. & MORSE, J. W. 1971. Evolutionary and ecologic significance of oxygen deficient marine basins. *Lethaia*, **4**, 413–28.

RICHARDS, F. A. 1965. Anoxic basins and fjords. *In:* RILEY, J. P. & SKIRROW, G. (eds) *Chemical Oceanography*, 1, Academic Press, London. 611–45.

RILEY, G. A. 1970. Particulate organic matter in seawater. *Advances in Marine Biology*, **8**, 1–118.

ROSENBERG, R. 1977. Benthic macrofaunal dynamics, production and dispersion in an oxygen-deficient estuary of West Sweden. *J. Exp. Mar. Biol. Ecol.* **26**, 107–33.

ROSENBERG, R. 1980. Effect of oxygen deficiency on benthic macrofauna in fjords. *In:* FREELAND, H. J., FARMER, D. M. & LEVINGS, C. D. (eds) *Fjord Oceanography*, NATO Conf. Ser. IV, 9, Plenum Press, New York. 499–514.

ROWE, G. T., CLIFFORD, C. H. & SMITH, K. L. Jr. 1975. Benthic nutrient regeneration and its coupling to primary productivity in coastal waters. *Nature, London*, **255**, 215–17.

RYTHER, J. H. 1969. Photosynthesis and fish production in the sea. *Science*, **166**, 72–76.

SCOTT, R. W. & KIDSON, E. J. 1977. Lower Cretaceous depositional systems West Texas. *In:* BEBOUT, D. G. & LOUCKS, R. G. (eds) *Cretaceous Carbonates of Texas and Mexico: Applications to Subsurface Exploration. Rept. Invest. Bur. econ. Geol.* Univ. Texas, Austin, **89**, 169–81.

SCULL, B. J., FELIX, C. J., MCCALEB, S. B. & SHAW, W. G. 1966. The inter-discipline approach to paleoenvironmental interpretations. *Trans. Gulf Coast Assoc. geol. Soc.* **16**, 81–117.

SHIMKUS, R. M. & TRIMONIS, E. S. 1974. Modern sedimentation in Black Sea. *In:* DEGENS, E. T. & ROSS, D. A. (eds) *The Black Sea Geology, Chemistry and Biology. Mem. Am. Assoc. Petrol. Geol.* **20**, 249–78.

SHOLKOVITZ, E. 1973. Interstitial water chemistry of Santa Barbara Basin sediments. *Geochim. Cosmochim. Acta*, **37**, 2043–73.

SIMONEIT, B. R. T. 1983. Organic geochemistry of laminated sediments from the Gulf of California. *In:* SUESS, E. & THIEDE, J. (eds) *Responses of the Sedimentary Regime to Present Coastal Upwelling. Coastal Upwelling: its Sediment Record*, A. NATO Conf. Ser. IV, 10a. Plenum Press, New York. 527–43.

SMAYDA, T. J. 1970. The suspension and sinking of phytoplankton in the sea. *Oceanogr. Mar. Biol. Annu. Rev.* **8**, 353–414.

SOROKIN, Y. I. 1978. Decomposition of organic matter and nutrient regeneration. *In:* KINNE, O. (ed) *Dynamics. Marine Ecology*, 4, Wiley, New York. 501–616.

—— 1983. The Black Sea. *In:* KETCHUM, B. H. (ed) *Estuaries and Enclosed Seas: Ecosystems of the World*, 26, Elsevier, Amsterdam. 253–92.

SOUTAR, A., JOHNSON, S. R. & BAUMGARTNER, T. R. 1981. In search of modern depositional analogues to the Monterey Formation. *In:* GARRISON, R. E. & DOUGLAS, R. G. (eds) *The Monterey Formation and Related Siliceous Rocks of California*. Pacific Sect. S.E.P.M. Los Angeles. 123–47.

SOUTHAM, J. R., PETERSON, W. H. & BRASS, G. W. 1982. Dynamics of anoxia. *Palaeogeogr. Palaeoclimatol. Palaeoecol.* **40**, 183–98.

STACH, E., MACKOWSKY, M. T., TEICHMULLER, K., TAYLOR, G. H., CHANDRA, D. & TEICHMULLER, R. 1975. *Stach's Textbook of Coal Petrology*, 2nd Edn., Gebruder Borntraeger, Berlin. 428pp.

STANLEY, E. A. 1969. Marine palynology. *Oceanogr. Mar. Biol. Annu. Rev.* **7**, 227–92.

STAPLIN, F. L. 1969. Sedimentary organic matter, organic metamorphism and oil and gas occurrence. *Bull. Can. Petrol. Geol.* **17**, 47–66.

SUESS, E. 1980. Particulate organic carbon flux in the oceans—surface productivity and oxygen utilisation. *Nature, London*, **288**, 260–3.

SUGAHARA, I., SUGIYAMA, M. & KAWAI, A. 1974. Distribution and activity of nitrogen-cycle bacteria in water sediment systems with different concentrations of oxygen. *In:* COLWELL, R. R. & MORITA, R. Y. (eds) *Effect of the Ocean Environment on Microbial Activities*. Univ. Park Press, Baltimore. 327–40.

SUMMERHAYES, C. P. 1981. Organic facies of Middle Cretaceous black shales in deep North Atlantic. *Bull. Am. Assoc. Petrol. Geol.* **65**, 2364–80.

—— 1983. Sedimentation of organic matter in upwelling regimes. *In:* THIEDE, J. & SUESS, E. (eds) *Sedimentary Records of Ancient Coastal Upwelling. Coastal Upwelling: its Sediment Record*, B, NATO Conf. Ser. IV, **10b**, Plenum Press, New York, 29–72.

TAPPAN, H. 1980. *The Paleobiology of Plant Protists*. W. H. Freeman & Co., San Francisco. 1028pp.

THOMPSON, J. B., MULLINS, H. T. & NEUTON, C. R. 1983. Macroinvertebrates from the modern, open-ocean oxygen minimum zone offshore central California: an alternative biofacies model for dysaerobic communities. *Abstr. 1st Int. Congr.*

Palaeoecol. Univ. Claude Bernard, Lyon, July 1983, 143.

TISSOT, B., DEMAISON, G., MASSON, P., DELTEIL, J. R. & COMBAZ, A. 1980. Paleoenvironment and petroleum potential of Middle Cretaceous black shales in Atlantic basins. *Bull. Am. Assoc. Petrol. Geol.* **64**, 2051–63.

—— & WELTE, D. H. 1978. *Petroleum Formation and Occurrence*. Springer Verlag, Berlin. 538pp.

TRASK, P. D. 1939. Organic content of recent marine sediments. *In:* TRASK, P. D. (ed) *Recent Marine Sediments*. Am. Assoc. Petrol. Geol. Tulsa, Oklahoma, 428–53.

TRÜPER, H. G. 1980. Distribution and activity of phototrophic bacteria at the marine water-sediment interface. *In:* DAUMAS, R. (ed) *Biogeochimie de la Matiere Organique a l'Interface Eau-Sediment Marin. Colloq. Int. C.N.R.S.* **293**, 275–83.

TURNER, J. T. & FERRANTE, J. G. 1979. Zooplankton fecal pellets in aquatic ecosystems. *Bioscience*, **29**, 670–6.

TYLER, M. A., COATS, D. W. & ANDERSON, D. M. 1982. Encystment in a dynamic environment: deposition of dinoflagellate cysts by a frontal convergence. *Mar. Ecol. Prog. Ser.* **7**, 126–78.

TYSON, R. V. 1984. Palynofacies investigation of Callovian (Middle Jurassic) sediments from D.S.D.P. Site 534, Blake–Bahama Basin, western central Atlantic. *Mar. Petrol. Geol.* **1**, 3–13.

—— 1985. *Palynofacies, palaeoenvironments and sedimentology of some Late Jurassic sediments from the British Isles and northern North Sea*. Ph.D. Thesis, Open University, Milton Keynes.

VEEH, H. H., BURNETT, W. C. & SOUTAR, A. 1973. Contemporary phosphorites on the continental margin of Peru. *Science*, **181**, 844–5.

WALL, D., DALE, B., LOHMANN, G. P. & SMITH, W. K. 1977. The environmental and climatic distribution of dinoflagellate cysts in modern marine sediments from regions in the North and South Atlantic oceans and adjacent seas. *Mar. Micropalaeontol.* **2**, 121–200.

WALSH, J. J. 1981. A carbon budget for overfishing off Peru. *Nature, London*, **290**, 300–4.

WAPLES, D. W. 1983. Reappraisal of anoxia and organic richness with emphasis on Cretaceous of North Atlantic. *Bull. Am. Assoc. Petrol. Geol.* **67**, 963–78.

WIEBE, W. J. & POMEROY, L. R. 1972. Micro-organisms and their association with aggregates and detritus in the sea: a microscopic study. *In:* MELCHIORRI-SANTOLINI, U. & HEPTON, J. W. (eds) *Detritus and its Role in Aquatic Ecosystems. Mem. 1st Ital. Idrobiol. Suppl.* **29**, 325–52.

WILLIAMS, L. A. & REIMERS, C. 1983. Role of bacterial mats in oxygen-deficient marine basins and coastal upwelling regimes: preliminary report. *Geology*, **11**, 267–69.

WILLE, W. 1982. Evolution and ecology of upper Liassic dinoflagellates from S.W. Germany. *Neues Jahrb. Geol. Palaeontol. Abhandlungen*, **164**, 74–82.

WISE, S. W., CIESIELSKI, P. F., MACKENZIE, D. T., WIND, F. H., BUSEN, K. E., GOMBROS, A. M., HAQ, B. U., LOHMANN, G. P., TJALSMA, R. C., HARRIS,

W. K., HEDLUND, R. W., BEJU, D. N., JONES, D. L., PLAFKER, G. & SLITER, W. V. 1982. Palaeontologic and palaeoenvironmental synthesis for the southwest Atlantic ocean basin based on Jurassic to Holocene faunas and floras from the Falkland Plateau. *In:* CRADDOCK, C. (ed) *Antarctic Geoscience,* Univ. Wisconsin Press, Madison, Wisconsin. 155–63.

YINGST, J. Y. & RHOADS, D. C. 1980. The role of bioturbation in the enhancement of bacterial growth rates in marine sediments. *In:* TENORE, K. R. & COULL, B. C. (eds) *Marine Benthic Dynamics.* Univ. S. Carolina Press. 407–21.

ZSOLNAY, A. 1971. Diagenesis as a function of redox conditions in nature: a comparative study of certain organic and inorganic compounds in an oxic and anoxic Baltic basin. *Kieler Meeresforsch.* **27,** 135–65.

R. V. TYSON, School of Environmental Sciences, University of East Anglia, Norwich, NR4 7TJ. Present address: Department of Geological Sciences, University College London, Gower Street, London, WC1E 6BT.

NOTE ADDED IN PROOF

During the period in which this publication has been in press a number of papers have appeared which have a significant bearing on the matters discussed within this contribution. None of this new material substantially alters the author's views but it does provide additional supportive and qualifying information which would have been incorporated within this review had it been possible to do so. Some of the most significant papers (in the present author's view) are given below.

ALLER, R. C. & MACKIN, J. E. 1984. Preservation rates of reactive organic matter in marine sediments. *Earth plan. Sci. Lett.* **70,** 260–66.

BENNER, R., MACCUBBIN, A. E. & HODSON, R. E. 1984. Anaerobic degradation of the lignin and polysaccharide components of ligno-cellulose and synthetic lignin by sediment microflora. *Appl. environ. Microbiol.* **47,** 998–1004.

DOYLE, L.J. & GARRELS, R. M. 1985. What does percent organic carbon in sediments measure? *Geo-Mar. Lett.* **5,** 51–3.

EKDALE, A. A. 1985. Trace fossils and mid-Cretaceous anoxic events in the Atlantic Ocean. *In:* CURRAN, H. A. (ed) *Biogenic Structures, Their Use In Interpreting Depositional Environments. Spec. Publ. Soc. econ. Paleontol. Mineral.* **35,** 333–42.

EMERSON, S., FISCHER, K., REIMERS, C. & HEGGIE, D. 1985. Organic carbon dynamics and preservation in deep-sea sediments. *Deep Sea Res.* **32,** 1–21.

GAUTIER, D. L. 1986. Cretaceous shales from the western interior of North America: Sulfur/carbon ratios and sulfur-isotope composition. *Geology,* **14,** 225–28.

HARVEY, H. R., FALLON, R. D. & PATTON, J. S. 1986. The effect of organic matter and oxygen on the degradation of bacterial membrane lipids in marine sediments. *Geochim. Cosmochim. Acta.* **50,** 795–804.

PRATT, L. M. 1984. Influence of paleoenvironmental factors on preservation of organic matter in the mid-Cretaceous Greenhorn Formation, Pueblo, Colorado. *Bull. Am. Assoc. Petrol. Geol.* **68,** 1146–59.

PRATT, L. M., CLAYPOOL, G. E. & KING, J. D. 1986. Geochemical imprint of depositional conditions on organic matter in laminated-bioturbated interbeds from fine-grained marine sequences. *Mar. Geol.* **70,** 67–84.

RAISWELL, R. & BERNER, R. A. 1985. Pyrite formation in euxinic and semi-euxinic sediments. *Am. J. Sci.* **285,** 710–24.

SAVRDA, C. E., & BOTTJER, D. J. 1986. Trace-fossil model for reconstruction of paleo-oxygenation in bottom waters. *Geology,* **14,** 3–6.

SAVRDA, C. E., BOTTJER, D. J. & GORSLINE, D. S. 1984. Development of a comprehensive oxygen-deficient marine biofacies model: evidence from Santa Monica, San Pedro, and Santa Barbara Basins, California continental borderland. *Bull. Am. Assoc. Petrol. Geol.* **68,** 1179–92.

THOMPSON, J. B., MULLINS, H. T., NEWTON, C. R. & VERCOUTERE, T. L. 1985. Alternative biofacies model for dysaerobic communities. *Lethaia,* **18,** 167–79.

WIDDEL, F. 1986. Sulphate-reducing bacteria and their ecological niches. *In:* BARNES, E. M. & MEAD, G. C. (eds) *Anaerobic Bacteria In Habitats Other Than Man.* Blackwell Scientific Publications, Oxford, 157–84.

Pyrite formation in Jurassic shales of contrasting biofacies

I. St. J. Fisher & J. D. Hudson

SUMMARY: The quantity and composition of organic matter passing into the hydrocarbon window is dependent on the extent of organic degradation occurring during early diagenesis. An important early diagenetic reaction in which organic matter is consumed is sulphate reduction. Relationships exist between pyrite sulphur (a product of sulphate reduction), organic carbon, and degree of pyritization of available iron, which can be used to help characterize the source-rock potential. In Jurassic, marine, organic-rich shales, these parameters are related to the environment of deposition, as indicated by biofacies analysis, and to variations in bottom water oxygenation and supplies of organic carbon, sulphate and iron. The best preservation of organic matter, for reaction in subsequent diagenetic zones, does not necessarily occur in the most anoxic sediments, but in those in which the organic matter buried in the sediment is more than sufficient to satisfy the supply of sulphate by diffusion. In the shales studied this is indicated by the most positive ($> -28\%$) $\delta^{34}S$ values for fine grained pyrite.

All marine organic-rich shales contain pyrite. Pyrite results from the anaerobic bacterial reduction of seawater sulphate to sulphide, which reacts with iron. This process follows the exhaustion of dissolved oxygen by aerobic decay which, together with sulphate reduction, is the principal mechanism by which sedimentary organic carbon is destroyed. The quantity, petrography and sulphur isotopic composition of pyrite formed depends mainly on the oxygenation of the depositional environment, the supply of metabolizable organic carbon, and the availability of iron. These factors also affect the shale's biofacies and early diagenetic history and thus help determine whether enough reactive organic matter survives into later burial to produce a potential source rock.

Five Jurassic shale units have been studied. Their stratigraphical (Fig. 1), sedimentological and palaeoecological attributes are reasonably well-known. This study concentrates on fine-grained dispersed pyrite in order to show that chemical aspects of pyrite formation differ in a predictable way among shales of different biofacies. Elsewhere (Hudson 1982; Fisher 1983) we describe the petrography and chemistry of pyrite associated with fossils as a replacement mineral or as a void filling, and of pyrite concretions. This also contributes to the characterization of shales as diagenetic systems, and yields information concerning the later burial history.

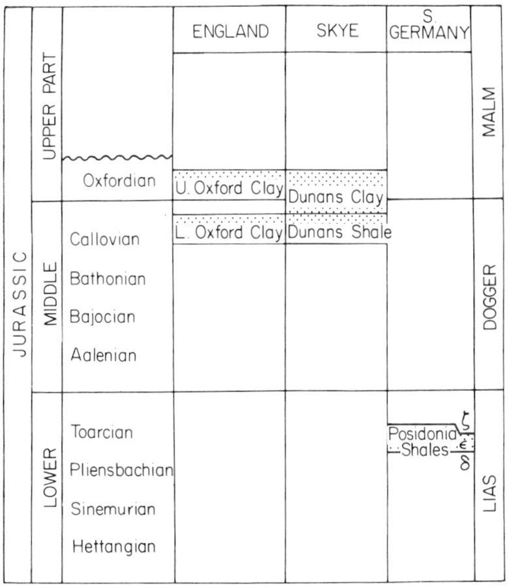

Biofacies classification of shales

Morris (1979, 1980) studied several Jurassic shales and generalized from earlier work (e.g.

FIG. 1. Stratigraphic distribution of formations studied.

Duff 1975) to erect a three-fold classification of shales based on types of bivalve mollusc present. These are the dominant macrofossils in Jurassic (and many other) shales and can be referred to different groups in terms of mode of life (infaunal, epifaunal) and feeding (deposit feeders, suspension feeders). Morris showed that his classification corresponded with other factors such as degree of preservation of lamination versus bioturbation. We have characterized our shales on a Morris triangular plot (Fig. 2).

From: BROOKS, J. & FLEET, A. J. (eds) 1987, *Marine Petroleum Source Rocks* Geological Society Special Publication No. 26 pp. 69–78.

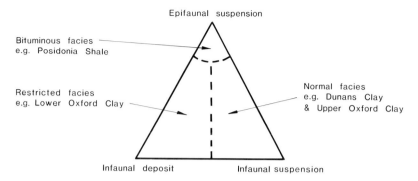

FIG. 2. Shales classified by bivalve ecology. Adapted from Morris (1980).

(1) Normal Facies (Dunans Clay and Upper Oxford Clay)

These contain a mixed fauna of infaunal and epifaunal types, with both shallow and deep burrowers, but with deposit feeders representing <20% of the fauna. They contain abundant *Chondrites* and horizontal burrows. Bioturbation has destroyed primary lamination. In this facies the benthic waters were well oxygenated and the action of burrowing organisms allowed oxic conditions to persist for several tens of centimetres in the sediment.

(2) Restricted Facies (Lower Oxford Clay)

The fauna is dominated by infaunal deposit feeders, with few infaunal suspension feeders, but epifaunal suspension feeders are often numerous and may have lived attached to floating wood or to weed (Duff 1975). Trace fossils are not abundant, with only occasional *Chondrites* and horizontal pyrite-filled burrows. The presence of benthic organisms indicates oxygenated bottom waters, although many forms were tolerant of low oxygen conditions (Duff 1975). The mobile infaunal deposit feeders totally reworked the sediment producing a somewhat soupy sediment surface (Aller 1977; Rhoads 1963; Rhoads and Young 1970). Below this layer the sediment rapidly became anoxic.

(3) Bituminous Facies (Posidonia Shales and Dunans Shales)

The fauna comprises almost entirely epifaunal suspension feeders with infaunal species rare or absent. There is debate as to the habitat of the epifaunal bivalves: benthic or pseudo-planktonic? (Kauffman 1978; Seilacher 1982). Trace fossils are absent except at occasional horizons, and sedimentary lamination is well preserved. The lack of benthic organisms suggests that the

bottom water was anoxic. The extent of anoxic water could be anything from a few centimetres to several hundred metres, and is a much debated quantity (see Morris 1980; Kauffman 1978; Seilacher 1982; for the Lias).

Controls of pyrite formation and sulphate reduction

The formation of pyrite in marine sediments is due to the action of sulphate-reducing bacteria on seawater sulphate to form sulphide, which reacts with iron to form pyrite, either directly or via a monosulphide precursor (Goldhaber & Kaplan 1974). The reactions may be summarized as follows:

$$SO_4^{2-} + 2CH_2O \rightarrow 2HCO_3^- + H_2S \quad (1)$$
$$3H_2S + 2FeO.OH \rightarrow 2FeS + S^0 + 4H_2O \quad (2)$$
$$FeS + S^0 \rightarrow FeS_2 \quad (3)$$

The first equation represents bacterial sulphate reduction, with organic matter represented by carbohydrate, the second the reaction of bacterially-produced sulphide with oxidized iron compounds (represented by goethite) to form an iron monosulphide (mackinawite), and the third the conversion of mackinawite to pyrite. This last reaction may proceed via an intermediate greigite (Fe_3S_4) phase, in which case the characteristic framboidal texture results (Sweeney & Kaplan 1973). The formation of greigite from mackinawite is an oxidation reaction with every fourth sulphur oxidized to S^0, suggesting that the formation of framboids requires conditions which are not totally reducing. Hudson (1982) noted that the more oxic Upper Oxford Clay contained larger framboids than the anoxic Posidonia Shales.

There are four prerequisites for the formation of pyrite:

(1) Anoxic conditions in which the sulphate-reducing bacteria may function, as they are obligate anaerobes. It is not necessary for the overlying water column to be anoxic, as sulphate reduction may occur in anoxic sediments beneath a layer of oxic sediment. Pyrite formation is also seen to occur in generally oxidizing sediments, within reducing microenvironments, e.g. disused burrows or faecal pellets, or enclosed voids such as foram tests or ammonite chambers (Kaplan *et al.* 1963, Aller 1980; Hudson 1982).

(2) Sulphate supply. The chief source of sulphate in marine sediments is seawater. If reduction occurs within the water column then sulphate-reducing bacteria are in contact with an essentially infinite reservoir. Similarly in oxic sediments, bioturbation and mixing serve to keep the concentrations in that sediment layer close to that of seawater. Beneath such a mixed zone, sulphate is supplied to the sediment by diffusion, the gradient being mainly controlled by the rate of sulphate reduction (Berner 1980).

(3) Organic matter is necessary as the material on which sulphate-reducing bacteria feed. Various laboratory experiments indicate that the rate of sulphate reduction is dependent both on the quantity and quality of organic matter; high rates of reduction are associated with large concentrations of organic matter (Harrison & Thode 1958; Ramm & Bella 1974). A general covariance between pyrite sulphur content and organic matter has been noted by several authors (Berner 1970; Sweeney 1972; Goldhaber & Kaplan 1974). Initially, large concentrations of organic matter give rise to larger quantities of pyrite sulphur. If the metabolized organic matter forms a constant proportion of the total initial organic matter entering the sulphate reduction zone, then a linear correlation between pyrite sulphur and organic carbon should result. Sweeney (1972) produced a compilation for recent sediments and found a C/S ratio of about three. In the Black Sea, C/S ratios consistently less than three and regression lines with positive intercepts on the S axis have been demonstrated (Leventhal 1983; Berner & Raiswell 1983). This is because sulphate reduction in the anoxic water column produces sulphide that is deposited unaccompanied by its complementary organic matter. On the other hand, aerobic degradation and benthic scavenging of organic matter, prior to entry into the sulphate reduction zone, reduces the total and the metabolizable proportion of organic matter. Therefore the more aerobic the conditions the less metabolizable organic matter enters the sulphate reduction zone (Zolnay 1971; Demaison & Moore 1980).

(4) Iron is necessary for the conversion of H_2S

into iron sulphide. Iron is supplied to the sediment in detrital minerals and as iron oxide coatings on grains, and is mainly in the ferric form. H_2S may react *in situ* with ferric iron and simultaneously reduce it and precipitate iron sulphide (Berner 1969).

In most sediments only a small proportion of the H_2S produced by sulphate reduction is fixed as iron sulphides: 4.5% according to Berner's (1982) global balance, 10% in the Danish sediments studied by Jørgensen (1978). In other cases, however, trapping of H_2S is more efficient and the increasing pyrite content of the sediments with depth mirrors the decreasing sulphate concentration of the pore waters (Berner 1980). This was most likely the case for the more pyrite-rich sediments described here for, if the pyrite represents only 10% of the bacterially-reduced H_2S produced in them, then they must have been deposited with unreasonably high original organic contents of up to 70%. In conditions where H_2S fixation is small, H_2S can either diffuse out of the sediment or accumulate in the pore water (Jørgensen 1979). In the bioturbated surface layers of Normal facies muds loss to the water column is inevitable, and also iron sulphides may be oxidized, so losing still more reduced sulphur from the sediment (Aller 1977).

If sufficient organic carbon and sulphate are present to maintain high H_2S concentrations then the amount of pyrite formed will be limited by the iron present. Berner (1970) used the parameter degree of pyritization (DOP), defined as:

$$DOP = \frac{\%Fe \text{ as pyrite}}{\%Fe \text{ as pyrite} + \%Fe \text{ HCl}}$$

%Fe HCl is the amount of iron liberated on treatment with hot concentrated HCl, and is a measure of the Fe still available which would be reactive to H_2S. If pyrite formation is limited by Fe then DOP will approach 1.

Controls of $\delta^{34}S$ variation

Three factors may affect the $\delta^{34}S$ value of fine-grained pyrite formed in shales:
(1) The natural fractionation between sulphate and the sulphide produced from it.
(2) The $\delta^{34}S$ value of the sulphate. As the $\delta^{34}S$ value of seawater has varied with time (Holser & Kaplan 1966) it is often useful, when comparing data from different geological periods, to refer to S-isotopic data in terms of its difference from contemporary seawater: $\Delta^{34}S$. Jurassic seawater had a composition of

$+16\pm1.5\%_0$ (Claypool *et al.* 1980). If the environment of sulphate reduction becomes closed or partially closed to the access of sulphate $\delta^{34}S$ will change, becoming enriched in ^{34}S due to the prior removal of light sulphide.

(3) The proportions of the total sulphide formed at each stage of burial, either within a closed or open system.

Fractionation factors for bacterial sulphate reduction have been experimentally investigated by several authors (a review is given by Chambers & Trudinger 1979). Experiments show fractionations between $+3$ and $-46\%_0$ and indicate that the greatest fractionations are obtained at the slowest specific rates of reduction. It has been suggested that at extremely slow rates of reduction fractionations may approach equilibrium values, $-74\%_0$ at $25°C$ (Tudge & Thode 1950; Trudinger & Chambers 1973). Chambers and Trudinger (1979) show that fractionations in recent sediments range between -34 and $-59\%_0$, with a mean of $-50\%_0$, and for reduction occurring in anoxic water columns, $-43\%_0$. These values are more negative than those found by experiment. This may be due to slower specific rates of reduction in sediments or to the addition of isotopically light sulphate by the reoxidation of sulphide.

If sulphate reduction takes place in an open system in contact with the seawater reservoir, i.e. in an anoxic water column or the bioturbated and mixed sediment surface, the sulphate reservoir is essentially infinite and the removal of light sulphide does not significantly alter the isotopic composition. On further burial sulphate is supplied by diffusion and the removal of light sulphide enriches the sulphate in ^{34}S. Goldhaber and Kaplan (1980) have demonstrated that the ^{32}S gradient is enhanced by its preferential removal and that on total reduction the resulting sulphide has a displacement from seawater $\Delta^{34}S$ of $-25\%_0$ and not $0\%_0$ as would otherwise be expected.

There are therefore two zones in which sulphate is reduced:

(1) An open system zone in an anoxic water column or bioturbated sediment with sulphide forming at $\Delta^{34}S$ of about $-50\%_0$.

(2) A partially closed system where sulphate is supplied by diffusion and sulphide ranges up to $\Delta^{34}S = -25\%_0$.

Goldhaber and Kaplan (1980), using a similar system, modelled the isotopic composition of pyrite in a sediment core from the Gulf of California. The majority of sulphate reduction takes place in the surface layers of the sediment, biasing the result towards the open system value.

The addition of sulphide in the diffusion zone is partly dependent on the concentration of organic matter. If organic matter is exhausted prior to sulphate the most positive $\delta^{34}S$ values will not be reached. It can be demonstrated from the equations of Berner (1980) that, when the metabolizable organic matter is more than sufficient to satisfy the sulphate in the diffusion zone, the quantity of sulphide formed is dependent solely on the diffusivity of the sediment and the concentration of sulphate in the overlying water. Therefore, for sediments with similar diffusive properties the quantity of sulphide formed in the zone of diffusion is more or less constant and of the order of 0.5% S if trapped as pyrite.

As discussed above, it is often the case that, due to limited reactivity of iron-bearing phases or to their total exhaustion, H_2S is not trapped within the sediment but is free to diffuse upwards. As the H_2S formed within the sediment is isotopically heavier than that formed in the surface layer, such diffusion will increase the $\delta^{34}S$ of H_2S in the near-surface pore waters (Jorgensen 1979). This will lead to the precipitation of heavier pyrite than might be expected in the surface layers. The generation of isotopically heavy H_2O in this way depends on sufficient metabolizable organic matter being buried to reduce all the sulphate diffusing into the sediment.

Results

The results of pyrite sulphur, $\delta^{34}S$, organic carbon and degree of pyritization (DOP) are summarized in the histograms in Fig. 3. Details of sampling and analyses for each unit are given in Fisher (1983).

(1) Normal Facies (Dunans Clay and Upper Oxford Clay)

Low organic carbon contents and DOPs suggest that pyrite formation and sulphate reduction were limited by organic carbon. The light $\delta^{34}S$ values suggest that the majority of sulphide was produced in the surface bioturbated layer and that the organic carbon content was insufficient to continue sulphate reduction to any extent in the zone of diffusion.

(2) Restricted Facies (Lower Oxford Clay)

The DOPs suggest that iron was not limiting in pyrite formation. The greater organic carbon input and the effects of lower bottom water oxygenation on bioturbation allowed greater quantities of organic matter into the zone of

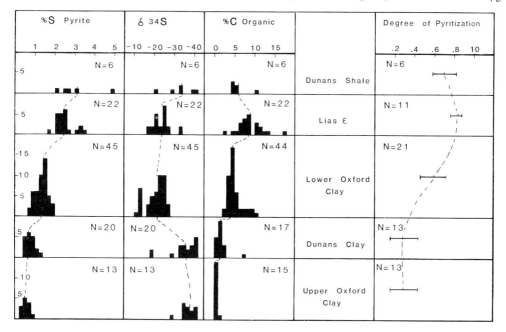

FIG. 3. Variation in % pyrite sulphur, $\delta^{34}S$, % organic carbon, and degree of pyritization (Fisher 1983). Dashed lines join the means of the units. Shale units are arranged with those of highest mean pyrite content at the top.

diffusion and so prolonged sulphate reduction, as indicated by the more positive ^{34}S values.

(3) Bituminous Facies

Posidonia Shales: the high DOPs (>0.8) indicate that pyrite formation was limited by iron. The heavy isotopic composition (mean $\delta^{34}S = -24\%$) shows a significant contribution of closed system reduction.

Dunans Shale: the greater range of DOPs is probably the result of weathering, producing iron oxides which give spuriously large %Fe HCl and low DOPs. The pyrite sulphur concentrations indicate that large amounts of iron were available at times during deposition, as the most pyrite-rich samples have a %Fe pyrite greater than the total %Fe pyrite+%Fe HCl in any of the Posidonia Shale samples. The $\delta^{34}S$ values (mean -34%) are consistent with dominantly open system reduction, and suggest that sulphate reduction was limited by the supply of metabolizable organic matter.

Relationship between pyrite sulphur and organic carbon

Fig. 4 shows a plot of pyrite sulphur versus organic carbon for the various shales. The mean C/S ratio of 3.2 is close to that found in Recent sediments. Taken separately, only the data for the Normal facies show a significant positive correlation. This is probably due to it being the only facies in which organic carbon limits pyrite formation.

In the Restricted facies the most organic-rich samples do not show correspondingly high pyrite sulphur contents. As suggested above, large quantities of organic matter passed into the zone of diffusion where, even if sufficient reactive iron is present, the maximum amount of pyrite formed is limited by the diffusion of sulphate into the sediment. Hence, since more organic matter was present than was required to reduce the inward-diffusing sulphate, the excess was preserved through the sulphate reduction zone, and the large range of organic carbon contents is not accompanied by a correspondingly large variation in pyrite sulphur.

The Bituminous Facies can be divided into two:

(1) The Posidonia Shales show moderate to high C/S ratios. As pyrite formation was limited by iron, the pyrite sulphur content represents a smaller fraction of the total sulphate reduced, raising the C/S ratio. The heavier ^{34}S values (see below) suggest that sulphate reduction was limited by diffusion, allowing excess organic matter to survive, further raising the C/S ratio.

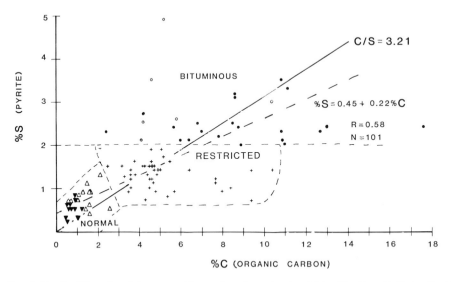

FIG. 4. Graph of % pyrite sulphur versus % organic carbon, showing fields of the three biofacies. Best fit and mean C/S ratio lines plotted.

(2) The Dunans Shale shows the lower C/S ratios associated with deposition beneath an anoxic water column. This is probably due to two factors: (a) sulphate reduction was limited by organic carbon, as indicated by the lighter $\delta^{34}S$ values; (b) more iron was available to precipitate the majority of H_2S formed.

It is not obvious why the mean C/S ratio of all samples is so close to that of Sweeney (1972). The regression line on the S versus C plot is controlled mainly by the Normal and Restricted Shales. For the Restricted Shales, although sulphate is ultimately limiting, the majority of sulphate is reduced in the first ten or so centimetres of the sediment (Goldhaber & Kaplan 1974) in an essentially open system. Therefore, it is only the samples with the extreme organic carbon contents which show noticeable deviations from the Sweeney line.

Relationship of pyrite sulphur and $\delta^{34}S$

Fig. 5 shows the fields occupied by samples from the three biofacies on a pyrite sulphur—$\delta^{34}S$ plot. Samples from the Normal Facies have low %S and strongly negative $\delta^{34}S$, because of limitation of sulphate reduction by organic carbon supply

within the zone of bioturbation. The very light values ($\Delta^{34}S$ down to -58%) found for some samples are probably due to the recycling of light sulphide in the mixed oxic/anoxic conditions. Such lowering of the sulphate isotopic composition has been postulated from studies of structural sulphate in francolite (Benmore et al. 1983) showing depletion in ^{34}S of up to 10%.

In the Restricted Facies, prolonged sulphate reduction led to the formation of heavier sulphide. The less extensive zone of bioturbation in this facies makes the pyrite formed in the zone of diffusion a significant proportion of the total, up to 35% in some samples.

In Fig. 5, the Bituminous Facies has been divided into Type 1 and Type 2. In both cases the anoxic overlying water allowed the formation of greater quantities of pyrite. For Type 1 (Dunans Shale) the lighter $\delta^{34}S$ values (mean 10% lighter than the Posidonia Shales) resulted from sulphate reduction being limited by organic carbon. The lower organic carbon input and probably more extensive exposure to anoxic conditions led to the exhaustion of the organic matter before all sulphate was reduced in the zone of diffusion and heavier $\delta^{34}S$ values did not develop.

In Type 2 (Posidonia Shales), the greater

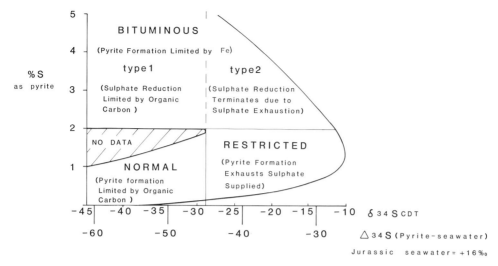

FIG. 5. Distribution of biofacies on plot of % pyrite sulphur versus δ^{34}S, generalized from our data. Λ^{34}S values indicated for comparison with shales of other geological periods.

quantity of organic matter and more limited exposure to anaerobic degradation in the water column and at the sediment surface allowed large quantities of organic matter to enter the zone of diffusion, and reduction of sulphate diffusing into the sediment went to completion. The heavier H_2S may have diffused up towards the sediment surface where some was precipitated as pyrite, raising its δ^{34}S value.

In the Bituminous Facies, a substantial proportion of the pyrite sulphur was produced by reduction in the anoxic water column, which is an open system for sulphate supply. The corresponding open system reduction zone in the Restricted Facies is the narrow zone of bioturbation, through which relatively more organic matter survives into the zone of diffusion. Hence, on average the Posidonia Shales have lighter δ^{34}S values than the Lower Oxford Clay.

Discussion

Biofacies discrimination

Fig. 6 summarizes some of the environmental variations, the production of pyrite, and the theoretical Λ^{34}S values produced in the three biofacies.

In the Normal Facies the formation of pyrite is limited by the oxic nature of the sediments. Pyrite is formed mainly in the zone of bioturbation and mixing, and only in the more organic-rich sediments continues slightly into the zone of diffusion. The resulting pyrite contents are low and the ^{34}S values approach their most negative.

In the Restricted Facies the lower degree of oxygenation allows a greater proportion of metabolizable organic matter to enter the sediment. The zone of bioturbation is less extensive as deep burrowers are not present. Sulphate reduction continues to greater depths in the zone of diffusion and Λ^{34}S values are less negative. The extent of the zone of diffusion is dependent on the rate of sulphate reduction, which is tied to the input of organic matter and the rate of sedimentation (Berner 1980).

In Bituminous Shale Facies the O_2/H_2S boundary crosses the sediment water interface, preventing the development of a benthic fauna. This facies can include sediments deposited beneath anything from a few centimetres to several hundred metres of anoxic water. Sulphate reduction occurs within the anoxic water column with open system Λ^{34}S values and within the sediment where sulphate is supplied by diffusion. The formation of pyrite is limited by the availability of iron. Free H_2S produced in the sediment may diffuse upwards into the overlying sediment and water column. Sulphate reduction is limited by either sulphate or organic carbon, and is controlled by the input of organic matter and its degradation within the anoxic water and at the sediment surface. Where organic input is lower and the anoxic water column more extensive organic matter can become exhausted by anaerobic degradation prior to entry into the zone of diffusion and, hence, heavier sulphide is not

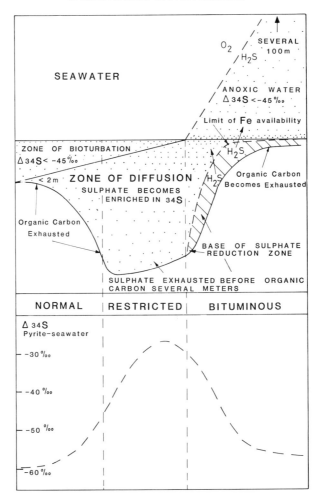

FIG. 6. Environmental variations between three biofacies. Plot indicates controlling factors for pyrite formation in each biofacies.

produced: this occurs in Type 1 Bituminous Shales. Where organic input is greater and degradation less the organic matter survives into the sediment and the zone of diffusion and reduction is limited by sulphate, resulting in more ^{34}S enriched sulphide: this occurs in Type 2 Bituminous Shales.

The results thus reinforce the broad-scale discrimination of shale facies-types proposed by Morris (1979, 1980). Short term perturbations, like the oxic events within the generally anoxic Posidonia Shales postulated by Seilacher (1982), are not resolved by our present approach, but such fluctuations no doubt contribute to the considerable scatter observed in our data from all the facies types.

Burial of organic matter

In order for substantial quantities of reactive organic matter to be buried within the sediment, the quantity entering the zone of diffusion must be more than sufficient to satisfy the reduction demand of the diffusing sulphate. This generally occurs in Restricted and Type 2 Bituminous Shale facies. In Normal and Type 1 Bituminous Shale facies organic matter is limited, in the first case by oxic degradation and in the second by extensive anaerobic degradation. These correspond to two of the unfavourable cases for organic matter survival discussed by Curtis (1977). On the other hand, Restricted and Type 2 Bituminous Shale facies are favoured as source rocks. They are characterized particularly by having relatively heavy $\delta^{34}S$ values: $> -28\%$ in our Jurassic examples. Of the cases we studied, the stratigraphic equivalents of the Posidonia Shales are the source rocks for oil in the Jurassic of the Paris Basin (Tissot *et al.* 1971). The Lower Oxford Clay would no doubt be an excellent source rock except that it is immature. Its organic content (and other favourable properties) support a major brick industry (Callomon 1968).

We have shown that shales of differing biofacies, as recognized in Morris' (1979, 1980) bivalve feeding-type plots, have correspondingly different early diagenetic histories, resulting in radically different organic preservation and pyrite formation. Studies like those reported here have some advantage over other ways of characterizing shales. Unlike most biofacies schemes, they are not limited by the stratigraphic range of particular fossils. In that they rely on the fine-grained component, they do not depend on collecting macrofossils or finding concretions: they are easily carried out on core material. The relationships described should be fairly independent of maturity. They can be easily combined with palynofacies kerogen-typing analyses (Tyson, this volume) or with maturity determinations. The relationships proposed should be tested with shales of different ages and geological settings.

ACKNOWLEDGEMENTS: The work for this paper was undertaken during the tenure by Fisher of a NERC, CASE studentship with the British Geological Survey. We thank Dr M. L. Coleman who co-supervised the project and the staff of the stable isotope facility at Grays Inn Road. This paper is published with the permission of the Director, British Geological Survey (NERC). We thank Wolfgang Küspert of Tübingen University who supplied samples and data for the Posidonia Shales, London Brick Company plc. and the late John Horrell for permission to collect from their pits, Dr Keith Duff and Dave Martill who assisted in the sample collecting, and Sue Button who drew the diagrams. Drs R. W. Raiswell, C. D. Curtis and A. J. Fleet provided criticism of an earlier version but are, of course, not responsible for our interpretations.

References

ALLER, R. C. 1977. *The influence of macro benthos on chemical diagenesis of marine sediments.* Ph.D. Thesis, Univ. Yale (unpubl.).

—— 1980. Diagenetic processes near the sediment water interface of Long Island Sound. I. Decomposition and nutrient element geochemistry (SNP). *In*: B. SALTZMAN (ed), *Estuarine physics and chemistry: studies in Long Island Sound.* Advances in geophysics **22**, 238–350.

BENMORE, R. A., COLEMAN, M. L. & McARTHUR, J. M. 1983. The origin of sedimentary francolite from its sulphur and carbon isotope composition. *Nature*, **302**, 516–518.

BERNER, R. A. 1969. Migration of iron and sulfur within anaerobic environments during early diagenesis. *Am. J. Sci.* **267**, 19–24.

—— 1970. Sedimentary pyrite formation. *Am. J. Sci.* **268**, 1–23.

—— 1980. *Early diagenesis.* Princeton University Press, 241 pp.

—— 1982. Burial of organic carbon and pyrite sulfur in the modern ocean: its geochemical and environmental significance. *Amer. J. Sci.*, **282**, 451–473.

—— & RAISWELL, R. 1983. Burial of organic carbon and sulfur in sediments over Phanerozoic time: a new theory. *Geochim. Cosmochim. Acta,* **47**, 855–862.

CALLOMON, J. H. 1968. The Kellaways Beds and Oxford Clay. *In*: SYLVESTER-BRADLEY, P. C. & FORD, T. D. (eds.), *The geology of the East Midlands.* Leicester University Press. 264–290.

CHAMBERS, L. A. & TRUDINGER, P. A. 1979. Microbiological fractionation of stable sulfur isotopes. *Geomicrobiology Jour.* **1**, 249–292.

CLAYPOOL, G. E., HOLSER, W. T., KAPLAN, I. R., SAKAI, H. & ZAK, I. 1980. The age curves for sulfur and oxygen isotopes in marine sulphate and their mutual interpretation. *Chem. Geol.* **28**, 199–260.

CURTIS, C. D. 1977. Sedimentary geochemistry: environments and processes dominated by involvement of an aqueous phase. *Philos. Trans. R. Soc.* **A286**, 353–371.

DEMAISON, G. J. & MOORE, G. T. 1980. Anoxic environments and oil source bed genesis. *Bull. Amer. Assoc. Petr. Geol.* **64**, 1179–1209.

DUFF, K. L. 1975. Palaeoecology of a bituminous shale—the Lower Oxford Clay of Central England. *Palaeontology*, **18**, 443–482.

FISHER, I. ST. J. 1983. *Studies on the formation of pyrite in Jurassic shales.* Ph.D. Thesis, Univ. Leicester (unpubl.).

GOLDHABER, M. B. & KAPLAN, I. R. 1974. The marine sulphur cycle. *In*: GOLDBERG, E. D. (ed.), *The Sea, Volume 5.* John Wiley & Son. 569–655.

—— & —— 1980. Mechanism of sulfur incorporation and isotope fractionation during early diagenesis in sediments of the Gulf of California. *Marine Chem.* **9**, 95–143.

HARRISON, A. G. & THODE, H. G. 1958. Mechanism of bacterial reduction of sulphate from isotope fractionation studies. *Trans. Faraday Soc.* **54**, 84–92.

HOLSER, W. T. & KAPLAN, I. R. 1966. Isotope geochemistry of sedimentary sulfates. *Chem. Geol.* **1**, 93–135.

HUDSON, J. D. 1982. Pyrite in ammonite-bearing shales from the Jurassic of England and Germany. *Sedimentology*, **29**, 639–667.

JØRGENSEN, B. B. 1978. A comparison of methods for

the quantification of bacterial sulphate reduction in coastal marine sediments. III. Estimation from chemical and bacteriological field data. *Geomicrobiology Jour.* **1**, 49–64.

—— 1979. A theoretical model of the stable sulphur isotope distributions in marine sediments. *Geochim. Cosmochim. Acta*, **43**, 363–374.

KAPLAN, I. R., EMERY, K. D. & RITTENBERG, S. C. 1963. The distribution and isotopic abundance of sulphur in Recent marine sediments off South California. *Geochim. Cosmochim. Acta*, **27**, 297–331.

KAUFFMAN, E. G. 1978. Benthic environments and the palaeoecology of the Posidonienschiefer (Toarcian). *N. Jb. Geol. Palaont. Abh.* **157**, 18–36.

LEVENTHAL, J. S. 1983. An interpretation of the carbon and sulphur relationships in the Black Sea sediments as indicators of the environment of deposition. *Geochim. Cosmochim. Acta*, **47**, 133–137.

MORRIS, K. A. 1979. A classification of Jurassic marine sequences and an example from the Toarcian (Lower Jurassic) of Great Britain. *Palaeogeogr. Palaeoclim. Palaeoecol.* **26**, 117–126.

—— 1980. Comparison of major sequences of organic-rich mud deposition in the British Jurassic. *J. Geol. Soc. Lond.* **137**, 157–170.

RAMM, A. E. & BELLA, D. A. 1974. Sulphide production in anaerobic microcosms. *Limnology & Oceanography*, **19**, 110–118.

RHOADS, D. C. 1963. Rates of reworking by *Yoldia*

limatula in Buzzards Bay, Massachussetts and Long Island Sound. *J. Sed. Pet.* **23**, 723–727.

—— & YOUNG. 1970. The influence of deposit-feeding organisms on sediment stability and community trophic structure. *J. Mar. Res.* **28**, 150–178.

SEILACHER, A. 1982. Ammonite shells as habitats in the Posidonia Shales of Holzmaden—floats or benthic islands? *N. Jb. Geol. Palaont. Mh.* **2**, 98–114.

SWEENEY, R. E. 1972. *Pyritization during diagenesis of marine sediments.* Ph.D. Thesis, Univ. California (unpubl.).

—— & KAPLAN, I. R. 1973. Pyrite framboid formation: laboratory synthesis and marine sediments. *Econ. Geol.* **68**, 618–634.

TISSOT, B., CALIFET-DEBYSER, Y., DEROO, G. & OUDIN, J. L. 1971. Origin and evolution of hydrocarbons in Early Toarcian shales. *Bull. Am. Assoc. Petrol. Geol.* **55**, pp. 2177–2193.

TRUDINGER, P. A. & CHAMBERS, L. A. 1973. Reversibility of bacterial sulphate reduction and its relevance to isotope fractionation. *Geochim. Cosmochim. Acta*, **37**, 1775–1778.

TUDGE, A. P. & THODE, H. G. 1950. Thermodynamic properties of isotopic compounds of sulphur. *Can. J. Res.* **B28**, 567–578.

ZOLNAY, V. A. 1971. Diagenesis as a function of redox conditions in nature. A comparative survey of certain organic and inorganic compounds in an oxic and anoxic Baltic basin. *Kieler Meeresforschungen*, **27**, 135–165.

I. ST. J. FISHER and J. D. HUDSON, Department of Geology, University of Leicester, Leicester LE1 7RH.

NOTE ADDED IN PROOF

Further discussion of the Normal facies can be found in Fisher (1986). A more detailed discussion of the environment of deposition is presented. The problem of the large apparent fractionations between sulphate and pyrite sulphur ($\triangle^{34}$S reaching $-58\%_{oo}$) is discussed,

in particular the role of re-oxidation of sulphide in the surface sediments in producing light δ^{34}S valves.

Reference:

FISHER, I. St.J. 1986. Pyrite formation in bioturbated clays from the Jurassic of Britain. *Geochim. cosmochim. Acta*, **50**, 517–523.

Palaeoenvironmental assessment of marine organic-rich sediments using molecular organic geochemistry

S. C. Brassell, G. Eglinton & V. J. Howell

SUMMARY: The solvent extracts of contemporary aquatic sediments contain a complex assemblage of compounds derived from living organisms. Among such biological debris many lipid components occur which possess structural and stereochemical characteristics that attest their origin from terrigenous higher plants, unicellular algae such as diatoms and dinoflagellates, or bacteria, including methanogens. Such compounds are markers of the organisms contributing to a given environment, and can provide information not available from micropalaeontological studies, namely evidence of bacterial activity, contributions from calcareous algae to sediments deposited below the calcite compensation depth and possibly sediment inputs from coccolithophorids in their non-coccolith bearing growth stage. In certain circumstances, especially in sedimentary sequences not subjected to elevated temperatures, many source-specific compounds can survive unaltered and thus are found in Mesozoic marine sediments deposited over 165 million years ago. In such immature ancient sediments, unaltered lipids occur together with their early stage diagenetic products, many of which retain molecular features that reflect their biological origins and are therefore also of value as source indicators. As diagenesis proceeds to catagenesis and kerogen breakdown increases, part of the molecular information is gradually lost as defunctionalization occurs and aliphatic and aromatic hydrocarbons come to dominate the sedimentary lipid distributions. Hence, attempts to identify the detailed sources of sedimentary organic matter from geolipid distributions become more difficult and rely more heavily on the occurrence of particular biologically-specific skeletons (e.g. head-to-head isoprenoids). The recognition of the diagenetic products of biolipids does, however, provide the basis for understanding lipid diagenetic pathways and offers the possibility of extending the scope of molecular assessment of sediment inputs to older and more thermally mature sediments. Despite these limitations imposed by the processes of sediment diagenesis and catagenesis, molecular organic geochemistry provides a unique record of past and present environments, with the potential of evaluating both biological inputs and subsequent sedimentary processes.

A number of molecular organic geochemical features, principally derived from empirical observations, can be applied to the interpretation and evaluation of marine palaeoenvironments. In particular, two aspects of sedimentary depositional environments have been assessed, (i) their nature, in terms of terrestrial vs. marine inputs of organic matter and (ii) their oxicity/anoxicity.

(i) Several biological marker compounds occasionally found in source rocks and oils have been used to distinguish between terrestrial and marine depositional environments. For example, two biological markers whose occurrence is used to assign a terrestrial/lacustrine nature for oils and source rocks are botryococcane (Moldowan & Seifert 1980) and gammacerane (Hills *et al.* 1966). In addition, a triangular diagram describing the proportion of steranes has been suggested as an indicator of palaeoenvironments (Huang & Meinschein 1979), based on the dominance of C_{29} steroids in organic matter of terrigenous origin. Although of value in empirical geochemical correlations, this approach has several limitations in environmental assessment (Mackenzie *et al.* 1982; Brassell & Eglinton 1983a). For example,

C_{29} steroids are dominant in many pre-Devonian source rocks and oils and also in modern Antarctic sediments (Matsumoto *et al.* 1982), where they cannot be derived from terrigenous sources. Also, in certain environments, such as Solar Lake, it appears that C_{27} sterols undergo preferential diagenetic alteration, leaving an anomalous predominance of C_{29} compounds (Boon *et al.* 1983).

(ii) Pristane/phytane (Pr/Ph) ratios have been used to assess the oxicity/anoxicity of sedimentary depositional environments (Didyk *et al.* 1978). The basis of this application of Pr/Ph ratios lies in the presumption that diagenesis of phytol tends to favour the formation of phytane as a major product under anoxic conditions, but pristane under oxic depositional conditions (Didyk *et al.* 1978 and references therein). In recent years the importance of archaebacteria as sources of sedimentary acyclic isoprenoids has been recognized (Holzer *et al.* 1979; Brassell *et al.* 1981). Indeed, it now seems probable that the dominance of phytane over pristane in many sediments actually reflects a major input of archaebacterial lipids with the C_{20} phytane skeleton in anoxic environments and pristane

From: BROOKS, J. & FLEET, A. J. (eds) 1987, *Marine Petroleum Source Rocks* Geological Society Special Publication No. 26 pp. 79–98.

derived from tocopherols (Goossens *et al.* 1984). Hence, the Pr/Ph ratio may not be as dependent on differences in the pathway of phytol diagenesis between oxic and anoxic depositional conditions as had been previously supposed.

These examples illustrate some of the problems that arise when attempting to use organic geochemical data for environmental assessment. Anomalies and ambiguities arise from the incompleteness of the knowledge relating to the origin and fate of biological marker compounds. Some general features of sediment deposition, however, such as terrigenous vs. marine inputs of organic matter can be recognized. Given the complexity of both sedimentary lipid inputs and early-stage diagenetic processes it seems appropriate, therefore, to characterize the features of modern sediments and sedimentation processes prior to tackling the assessment of mature source rocks. Thus, attempts to understand and interpret the palaeoenvironmental conditions of sediment deposition from organic geochemical criteria first require the characterization of Recent environments, and the post-depositional changes affecting organic matter, namely diagenesis and catagenesis.

The approach to palaeoenvironmental assessment using molecular organic geochemistry is examined in this paper in three ways.

(1) Biological marker compounds indicative of sediment inputs are illustrated.

(2) The value and potential of such compounds in the evaluation of present-day environments is demonstrated for sediments from the Middle America Trench.

(3) The task of extending such geochemical assessment of environments to ancient sediments is considered via investigations of the geological survival of biological marker compounds derived intact from organisms and the processes and pathways of their diagenetic and catagenetic alteration.

Biological marker compounds

Biological marker compounds are components of sediments or petroleums with chemical structures that can be related to those of biological materials (e.g. Brassell & Eglinton 1983b). They form only a portion of the soluble extract of sediments, which, in turn, constitutes perhaps 5% of the total organic matter, with the remainder being the insoluble component of organic matter, the kerogen. Ideally, both portions of the organic matter are evaluated. Among the major features of biological marker compounds are the wide range of their structural types and functionalities, as illustrated in Fig. 1. Combinations of these

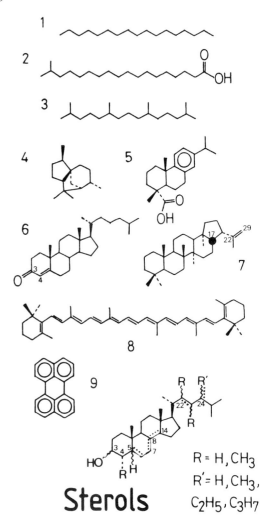

FIG. 1. Chemical structures of examples of biological marker compounds including acyclic (1. straight-chain: heptadecane; 2. branched chain: *iso*-nonadecanoic acid; 3. isoprenoid: pristane), cyclic (4. sesquiterpenoid: cedrane; 5. diterpenoid: dehydroabietic acid; 6. steroid: cholest-4-en-3-one; 7. triterpenoid: 17β(H), 21β(H)-hop-22(29)-ene; 8. tetraterpenoid: β-carotene) and other miscellaneous components (e.g. 9. aromatic hydrocarbons: perylene). The sterol structure shows the positions of possible alkylation (C-4, C-22, C-23 and C-24) and of unsaturation (C-5, C-7, C-8(14), C-22 and C-24).

two features, taking stereochemical configurations into account, yield a total of several thousand biological marker compounds. For example, the variability in the sterol structure (Fig. 1) in terms of alkylation (at C-4, C-23, C-24), unsaturation (at C-5, C-7, C-8(14), C-22, C-24) and stereochemistry (at C-3, C-5, C-24) has meant that for this single compound type, about 100 different components have now been identified in sediments (Mackenzie *et al.* 1982 and subsequent unpublished results). The vast range of known biological marker compounds therefore provides a fundamental basis for the evaluation of present-day and past sedimentary environments.

Molecular assessment of environments

The use of biological marker compounds in the assessment of natural environments has a wide range of applications in biology, ecology, chemistry and geology (Table 1). In the present context it is relevant to make special mention of two of these, namely the assessment of the productivity and biomass of present-day ecosystems and the development of biological markers as stratigraphic tools. The former provides a link between the molecular signatures of planktonic organisms, their survival through environmental processes, such as those occurring in the food web, and their preservation in underlying sediments. The latter reflects the major aim that forms the theme of this paper, that is the elucidation of environmental features (Table 1) using molecular organic geochemical criteria. The basis of these studies lies in our belief that variations in the biology of

TABLE 1. *Suggested applications of molecular assessments*

---

1 **In biology & ecosystems**
  a Estimates of productivity & biomass
  b Fluxes of ecosystems
  c Measure of the extent & specialization of biosphere
2 **In chemical studies**
  a Diagenetic reactions (v. slow)
    —their mechanisms & rate constants
  b Organic/inorganic interactions
    (e.g. metal chelation in humics)
3 **In geology**
  a Use of 'molecular' stratigraphy
    —characterization of geological events (e.g. black shale formation)
    —palaeoceanography (e.g. environments of deposition)
    —palaeogeography (e.g. proximity to land)
    —palaeoclimatology (e.g. ice ages)
    —sediment 'fingerprinting'; for correlation purposes
  b Diagenetic profiling
    —burial history of sediments
    —geological modelling of sedimentary basins
  c Evolution
    —biological & biochemical
  d Origin of life
    —Archean studies

---

an environmental system in response to climatic and other changes will be reflected in the lipid biochemistry of the organisms of the system and will, in turn, be preserved in the molecular composition or 'fingerprint' of the underlying sediments.

Applications of molecular organic geochemistry

The two major applications of molecular organic geochemistry to petroleum source rocks are in the assessment of their thermal history and the sources of their organic matter. Of particular value in maturity studies is the sensitivity of the sequences of stereochemical changes that occur in biological marker compounds, such as pristane, steranes, hopanes and aromatic steroid hydrocarbons (Mackenzie 1984 and references therein). The features of biological marker compounds that are indicative of the sources of organic matter fall into three categories:

(1) The presence of key components with structures uniquely attributable to specific classes of organisms.
(2) The distributions of homologous and pseudohomologous series that are similarly characteristic of particular biota, and
(3) The ratios of particular marker compounds from different origins that reflect the relative contributions from their respective sources.

Clearly, on an individual basis 1 and 2 are largely qualitative assessments of inputs of organic matter, whereas the ratios of 3 require semi-quantitative or quantitative information. The biological marker compounds that are source-specific fall into two categories, (a) those that are indicative of inputs from a general class of organism, such as higher plants (e.g. Brassell *et al.* 1980) or bacteria and (b) those that derive from a more limited group of organisms, such as methanogenic bacteria (Brassell *et al.* 1981) or dinoflagellates (Boon *et al.* 1979; Brassell & Eglinton 1983a, b).

A major objective in the application of biological marker compounds is an extension of the understanding of recent sediments to ancient sediments. During sediment consolidation the compounds derived directly from organisms (biolipids) are converted into geolipids with increasing geological time and increasing thermal stress (diagenesis/catagenesis). The recognition of such changes, namely lipid precursor/product relationships, can provide a basis for assessing the original lipid inputs to the sediment and, hence, its depositional environment.

It is not intended here to detail the experimental procedures used in the analysis of sediment lipids, but rather to illustrate the methodologies required

TABLE 2. *Procedures and their scope in molecular assessments**

1 **Extraction & separation procedures**
   • Appropriate for soluble & insoluble organic matter
2 **Analytical techniques for complex mixtures**
   • Major molecular size ranges (from C_{15} to C_{40+})
   • Molecular functionalities (e.g. ketones, carboxylic acids, alcohols)
   • Range of structural types (e.g. various terpenoids & steroids)
   • Homologies & pseudohomologies (e.g. series of *n*-alkanes & steranes)
   • Stereochemical isomerism (e.g. differentiation of 20S- & 20R-diasterenes)
   • Quantitation (of individual components)
3 **Data handling**
   • Automated data acquisition & processing
   • Derivation of molecular ratios
   • Derivation of molecular distributions
   • Statistical evaluation of parameters
4 **Data bases**
   • Generation & manipulation
   • Joint: geological, chemical, biochemical, biological.

* These procedures are largely sequential 1–4.

for molecular assessments (Table 2). First, there is a need to search for molecular information from both the soluble and insoluble organic matter (kerogen). The former is the minor portion but is more amenable to analysis. Chemical degradation processes are necessary for tackling the molecular structure of the insoluble organic matter, and have already revealed the prominence of archaebacterial lipids bound into some kerogens (Chappe *et al.* 1980). Second, the individual lipid fractions obtained by separation of total sediment extracts are highly complex mixtures within which a multiplicity of compound types can be recognized and characterized from specific features of their structures. Third, the molecular abundance data requires evaluation by comparative and statistical treatments. Finally, such data concerning sedimentary lipid occurrences require a link to geological and other information through data bases. This broader framework of data correlation and inter-relation is necessary in order that the full potential of the molecular assessment of sedimentary environments can be realized.

Biological marker compounds as indicators of sediment inputs

A large number of biological marker compounds possess specific features of structure or stereochemistry that attest their origin from either algal, terrestrial higher plant or bacterial origins. A comprehensive listing of such proposed marker compounds is published elsewhere (Brassell & Eglinton 1983b), but selected examples of direct biological inputs to sediments are given below.

Algal markers

From the many known (cf. Brassell & Eglinton 1983b), four compounds have been selected as examples of those believed to be indicative of direct inputs from algae to sediments. They are shown in Fig. 2 and described in Table 3. For the sterols (compounds 2 and 3) it can be seen that relatively minor differences in their structure (e.g. addition of methyl groups at C-4 and C-23 and reduction of Δ^5 double bond) can distinguish their biological origins. Diatoxanthin is a tetra-terpenoid carotenoid, one of this group of compounds which are particularly diagnostic markers of contributions from organisms to sediments, notable in lacustrine environments (Züllig 1982; Brassell *et al.* 1983). Unfortunately their use as marker compounds is limited by the fact that they are labile molecules which rarely survive even low temperature diagenesis.

Terrestrial higher plant markers

Examples of lipids thought to signify direct inputs from terrestrial higher plants are given in Table 4 and Fig. 3. In general such marker compounds tend to be less specific indicators than those for algae and bacteria, mainly because the diversity of their lipid structures appears to be less species dependent. These non-specific marker compounds include many triterpenoid structures, often with alcohol, ketone, acid or methyl ether functionalities (e.g. compounds 5 and 8), which are characteristic of sediment inputs of terrigenous organic matter. In various petroleums, notably from Nigeria, pentacyclic triterpanes formed from precursors originating from land plant sources can occur as prominent constituents (e.g. Brassell *et al.* 1983). Other terpenoids, that is diterpenoid compounds (e.g. compound 6), are particularly prominent components of resinous plants, especially conifers (Simoneit 1977), and are thought to reflect sediment inputs from these more specific terrigenous sources. A number of A-ring degraded triterpenoids have been recognized in sediments (Corbet *et al.* 1980; Brassell & Eglinton 1983b), although few of their structures have been fully elucidated. Such compounds have been described as photochemical or photomimetic sedimentary degradation products of triterpenoids (Corbet *et al.* 1980), but there is also evidence to suggest that such compounds can be

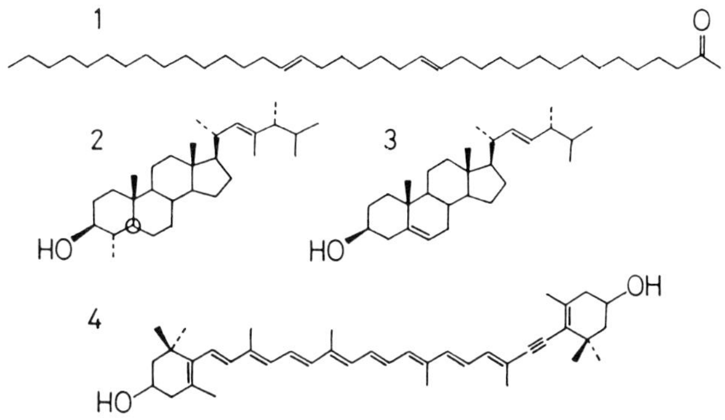

FIG. 2. Chemical structures of examples of biological marker compounds which are indicators of algal inputs as described in Table 3.

TABLE 3. *Biological marker compounds—I Examples of indicators of direct inputs from algae to sediments*

No (Fig. 2)	Compound	Inferred origin	Reference
(1)	C_{37} alkadienone	coccolithophorids	Volkman *et al.* 1980a
(2)	dinosterol	dinoflagellates	Boon *et al.* 1979
(3)	24-methylcholesta-5,22-dienol	algae (especially diatoms, coccolithophorids)	Mackenzie *et al.* 1982
(4)	diatoxanthin	diatoms	Brassell *et al.* 1980

TABLE 4. *Biological marker compounds—II Examples of indicators of direct inputs from terrestrial higher plants to sediments*

No. (Fig. 3)	Compound	Inferred origin	Reference
(5)	*β*-amyrin	higher plants	Dastillung *et al.* 1980
(6)	ferruginol	conifers	Baset *et al.* 1980
(7)	friedelanone	higher plants	Dastillung *et al.* 1980
(8)	de-A-lupane	higher plants	Corbet *et al.* 1980

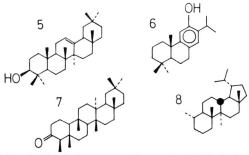

FIG. 3. Chemical structures of examples of biological marker compounds which are indicators of terrestrial higher plant inputs as described in Table 4.

formed by photochemical reactions within plant waxes (Baas 1982). Hence, it seems probable that sedimentary A-ring degraded triterpenoids represent components contributed as direct inputs of terrigenous leaf waxes, perhaps further modified by bacterial and geochemical processes during sediment diagenesis.

Bacterial markers

A selection of four marker compounds indicative of bacterial contributions to sedimentary organic matter is given in Table 5 and Fig. 4. *iso*-pentadecanoic acid (compound 9) has often been used to denote bacterial contributions of organic matter to sediments, but it is a non-specific indicator that occurs in most bacterial types, including aerobes, anaerobes and sulphate-reducers. In contrast, 2,6,10,15,19-pentamethyleicosane (compound 10) has only been recognized in methanogenic bacteria and appears therefore to be diagnostic of sediment inputs from these archaebacteria (Brassell *et al.* 1981). Bacteriohopanetetrol (compound 11) has only been identified in prokaryotic organisms (Ourisson *et al.* 1979) and is therefore thought to derive from bacterial organic matter in environments where blue-green algae are rare or absent. Its major geochemical significance lies, however, in the presumption that it is the major biosynthetic precursor of the

TABLE 5. *Biological marker compounds—III Examples of indicators of direct inputs from bacteria to sediments*

No. (Fig. 4)	Compound	Inferred origin	Reference
(9)	iso-pentadecanoic acid	bacteria	Cranwell 1973
(10)	2,6,10,15,19-penta- methyleicosane	methanogens	Brassell et al. 1981
(11)	bacteriohopanetetrol	prokaryotes	Ourisson et al. 1979
(12)	fern-9(11)-ene	anaerobic bacteria	Brassell et al. 1981

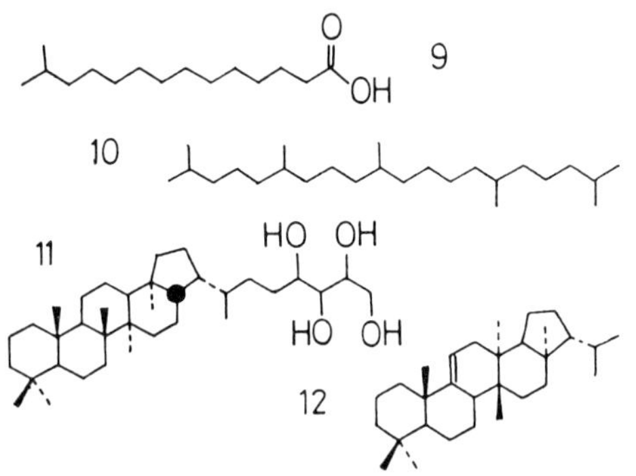

FIG. 4. Chemical structures of examples of biological marker compounds which are indicators of bacterial inputs as described in Table 5.

extended ($>C_{31}$) hopanoids (Ourisson *et al.* 1979). The presence of fernenes, such as fern-9(11)-ene (12), in sediments was provisionally attributed to lipid inputs from ferns (Brassell *et al.* 1980) until the recognition of these compounds in an anaerobic photosynthetic bacterium (Howard 1980) suggested that they originated from bacteria (Brassell *et al.* 1981). This latter explanation of their origin seems more consistent with the sedimentary occurrence of fernenes (Brassell *et al.* 1981) in that they are observed in sediments which, from other evidence, contain little terrigenous organic matter. The fernenes also illustrate a further aspect of the assessment of sediment inputs using biological marker compounds; namely that all assignments of lipid origins constitute working hypotheses based on their known distribution in organisms. Such hypotheses are clearly subject to revision as additional information on biological lipid compositions emerges.

Examples

Many examples of the use of biological marker compounds to assess sediment inputs exist in the literature. Several are cited above in the discussion of particular compounds, but two are selected for special mention here. First, the long chain alkenones (e.g. compound 1, Fig. 2) recognized

in the coccolithophorid *Emiliania huxleyi* (Volkman *et al.* 1980a) are thought to be markers for inputs from these organisms to sediments (Brassell *et al.* 1980). They occur in many Cenozoic marine sediments, including diatomaceous oozes from the Japan Trench deposited below the calcite compensation depth (Volkman *et al.* 1980a; Brassell *et al.* 1980). Hence, molecular signatures of calcareous algae can survive even when no skeletal debris is present.

Second, the mixed assemblage of sterols in marine sediments can be derived from a combination of phytoplankton, such as diatoms, dinoflagellates and calcareous and unicellular algae, terrestrial plants and higher organisms such as coelenterates, sponges and zooplankton (Mackenzie *et al.* 1982 and references therein). The contributions of this diverse range of organisms can be evaluated from the structures of sterol side chains (Mackenzie *et al.* 1982; Brassell & Eglinton 1983b), although such source assignments may be ambiguous. In many cases, however, a number of different organisms contributing to a given sediment can be recognized from the sterol profile (Brassell & Eglinton 1983a & b).

Quaternary sediments: Middle America Trench, DSDP Leg 67

As an example of the application of biological marker compounds to the recognition of the sources of organic matter in a modern environment we shall discuss selected lipids of four shallow sediments from the transect of the Middle America Trench off Guatemala made during Deep Sea Drilling Project Leg 67 (Aubouin, Von Huene, *et al.* 1982). Lithological and petrographic details of the samples are given in Table 6 and the locations of the drilling sites are shown in Fig. 5.

Lipid distributions

In the four sediments the concentrations of general algal marker compounds such as phytol (the side chain of chlorophyll a: d, Fig. 6) and

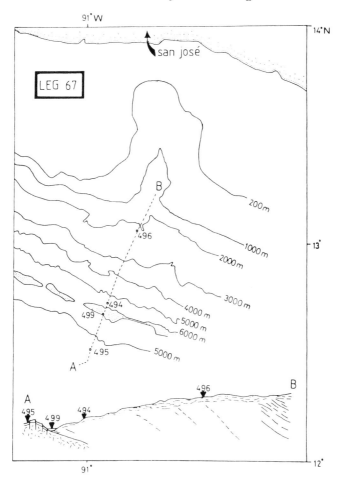

FIG. 5. Location of DSDP sites in the Middle America Trench drilled during Leg 67 and an interpreted seismic cross section of the Trench (vertical scale exaggerated).

hop-22(29)-ene (diploptene) plus hop-21-ene (a, Fig. 6) and specific biological markers for dinoflagellates (dinosterol; b, Fig. 6) and diatoms (24-methylcholesta-5,22-dien-3β-ol; c, Fig. 6) are all greatest in Section 496-2-4. These observations suggest that algal productivity is greatest on the landward side of the trench, a feature not apparent from the distribution of organic matter types or morphological remains of diatoms, dinoflagellates or coccolithophorids (Table 6). Furthermore, the only sample in which dinoflagellate cysts were recognized was Section 499-2-6 which contains markedly less dinosterol (b, Fig. 6) than Section 496-2-4. Hence, for these trench sediments, as elsewhere (Comet *et al.* 1981; Smith *et al.* 1982), the occurrence of dinoflagellate cysts and the abundance of dinosterol show little correlation. This observation is consistent with the fact that dinoflagellates have a non-cyst

growth stage that comprises their major biomass (Brasier 1980). The organic carbon contents of the four sediments are, however, highest for Section 496-2-4 (Table 6) suggesting that they may reflect this inferred higher productivity.

The concentration of the long chain alkenones (e.g. e, Fig. 6) that are markers for coccolitho-phorids is greatest in Section 494-2-7, which contains no coccoliths (Table 6). This apparent ambiguity can be explained in terms of sediment inputs from *E.huxleyi* at its non-coccolith bearing growth stage when it still produces the long chain alkenones (Volkman *et al.* 1980b) or an input from a non-coccolith bearing prymnesiophyte (Marlowe *et al.* 1984) may provide, at least in part, independent records of sediments. The relative concentrations of the non-specific marker compound hexadecanoic acid (n-C_{16} carboxylic acid; f, Fig. 6) suggest greater lipid inputs on the

TABLE 6. Quaternary sediments from the Middle America Trench, DSDP Leg 67

Code (Figs 6 & 7)	Section	Depth (M)	Lithology	Organic Carbon (%)[a]	Organic Matter Types (%)[b-d]				Diatoms[c,e]	Coccoliths[c,e]	Dinoflagellate Cysts[c,d,e]
					ST	PS	AM	SM			
A	494-2-7	18	Diatomaceous mud	1.8	10	5	75	10	+	−	−
B	495-3-5	23	Diatomaceous hemipelagic mud	2.0	10	−	90	−	+	+	−
C	496-2-4	12	Diatomaceous mud	2.4	5	−	95	−	+	+	
D	499-2-6	9	Biogenic mud	1.8[f]	5	−	90	5	−	−	+

[a] Values for adjacent sections (Summerhayes & Gilbert 1982)
[b] ST structured terrestrial; PS pollen and spores; AM amorphous marine; SM structured marine
[c] Estimates from microscopic examination of sediments
[d] Data provided by British Petroleum plc.
[e] + abundant, − rare or absent
[f] In this turbiditic section such values may not be representative.

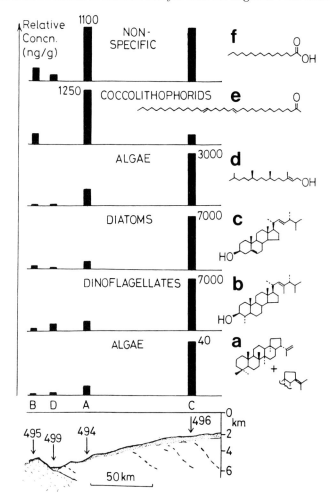

FIG. 6. Plots of the relative concentrations (ng/g) of six biological marker compounds in four sediments from the Middle America Trench (Table 6). a, $17\beta(H),21\beta(H)$-hop-22(29)-ene + $17\beta(H)$-hop-21-ene; b, dinosterol ($4\alpha,23,24$-trimethyl-$5\alpha(H)$-cholest-22-en-3β-ol); c, 24-methylcholesta-5,22-dien-3β-ol; d, phytol (3,7,11,15-tetramethylhexadec-2(E)-enol); e, heptaconta-15,22-dien-2-one; f, hexadecanoic acid.

landward side of the trench. Any further significance in these observations is difficult to evaluate, however, because of the multitude of possible sources for this particular compound.

The relative concentrations of three proposed markers for higher plant inputs to sediments are shown for the Middle America Trench samples in Fig. 7. Of these the greater concentrations of *n*-nonacosane (*n*-C_{29} alkane, f, Fig. 7) and de-A-lupane (e, Fig. 7) in the samples from the landward side of the trench can be readily explained in terms of the presumed greater lipid inputs from terrigenous sources in these hemipelagic sediments. In contrast, the relative concentration of the higher plant triterpenoid taraxerol

(a, Fig. 7) is highest in Section 499-2-6, which might be a reflection of the origin of these turbiditic sediments. The discrepancy between the abundance pattern for taraxerol and that for the other terrigenous higher plant marker compounds may reflect their origins from different component parts of terrestrial organic matter, perhaps linked to their association with different sediment size fractions (cf. Thompson & Eglinton 1978). The turbiditic nature of the sediments at Site 499 is certainly consistent with some degree of sorting. Alternatively, it is possible that the assignment of taraxerol as a terrigenous higher plant marker may require revision.

The two bacterial marker compounds (*iso*-C_{15}

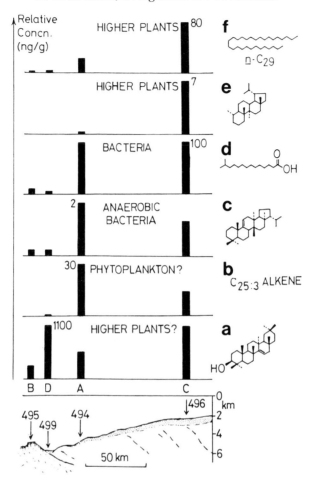

FIG. 7. Plots of the relative concentrations of six biological marker compounds in four sediments from the Middle America Trench (Table 6). a, taraxer-14-en-3β-ol; b, unknown $C_{25:3}$ alkene; c, fern-9(11)-ene; d, *iso*-pentadecanoic acid (13-methyltetradecanoic acid); e, de-A-lupane; f, nonacosane.

carboxylic acid, d and fern-9(11)-ene: c, Fig. 7) are both relatively more abundant in Section 494-2-7, compared with Section 496-2-4, than the algal and terrestrial higher plant lipids, with the exception of the coccolithophorid long chain alkenones. Perhaps bacterial activity is proportionally greater at Site 494, or the rain of organic debris settling through the water column is more degraded. Certainly the hierarchy of organisms in upwelling systems changes in moving away from the area of peak nutrient supply to surrounding waters (Jones *et al.* 1983). This feature should be reflected in the lipids of the underlying sediments and may appear in the bacterial lipid signatures. Another compound that shows a maximum concentration in Section 494-2-7 is a $C_{25:3}$ alkene (b, Fig. 7) of unknown structure. It has been suggested (Barrick *et al.*, 1980) that this

hydrocarbon is derived from a phytoplanktonic source, although this has yet to be confirmed. From its relative abundance in these Middle America Trench sediments an origin from either algae or bacteria seems reasonable.

Sterol ratios as environmental indicators

From the analysis of their relative concentrations in three Leg 67 sediments (Sections 496-22-1, 497-34-1 and 500-4-1) it has been proposed (Curiale & Harrison, 1982) that the β-sitosterol/stigmasterol (24-ethylcholest-5-en-3β-ol/24-ethylcholesta-5,22-dien-3β-ol) ratio may reflect inputs of terrestrial *vs.* marine organic matter. The values obtained in the above study were 2.56, 1.81 and 1.43 for sediments from Sites 496, 497 and 500, respectively, showing a decrease in the ratio with increasing distance from land. Calculation of this ratio for the four samples examined in the paper is hampered by the coelution of 24-ethylcholest-5-en-3β-ol (β-sitosterol) and 24-ethylcholesta-5,22-dien-3β-ol (stigmasterol) with 23,24-di-methyl-5α-cholestan-3β-ol and 23,24-dimethyl-5α-cholest-22-en-3β-ol, respectively (cf. Brassell & Eglinton 1983b). Indeed, inspection of the weak mass spectra given by Curiale & Harrison (1982) suggests that they are mixed, which is not unexpected since GC-MS separation of the above 23,24-dimethyl and 24-ethyl sterol components is difficult to achieve. Allowing for sterol coelutions the approximate ratios for β-sitosterol/stigmasterol in Sections 496-2-4, 494-2-7, 499-2-6 and 495-3-5 are 5, 3, 3 and 6, respectively. These values do not support the proposal (Curiale & Harrison 1982) that this ratio is a measure of terrigenous vs. marine organic matter as they show no relationship to their proximity to land or variations in sediment origins (i.e. pelagic vs. hemi-pelagic). Furthermore, in shallow sediments from the Namibian Shelf, where inputs of terrigenous organic matter are minimal, the values for 2 cm intervals of the top 10 cm of sediment range between 1.8 and 6.3 (Smith *et al.* 1982). In another study of sedimentary sterols in this area it has been suggested (Lee *et al.* 1980) that 24-ethylcho-lest-5-en-3β-ol reflects inputs from diatoms, and is therefore of marine algal origin. The distinction of 24-ethyl sterols from terrigenous higher plants and algal sources seems clearly to require an evaluation of their C-24 stereochemistry (cf. Mackenzie *et al.* 1982), as they are dominantly 24β-ethyl (β-sitosterol) and 24α-ethyl compo-nents, respectively. These considerations suggest that particular care is needed in the use of these sterols, or ratios derived from their abundances, in the assignment of sediment inputs.

Diagenetic effects further complicate the use of sterol ratios as markers for the sources of organic matter as preferential diagenetic degra-dation of particular sterols such as those with Δ^{22} unsaturation, cannot be excluded. In addition, two of the samples (Sections 496-22-1 and 497-34-1) examined by Curiale & Harrison (1982) were from depths (199 m and 311 m, respectively) at which a marked degree of diagenetic lipid alteration, such as sterol dehydration, would have occurred. In this respect the amounts of sterols in a sample are a poor indication of the extent of diagenesis because significant sterol concentra-tions can persist in organic-rich ancient sediments where their diagenetic product sterenes and steranes are dominant (Comet *et al.* 1981). Overall, the use of sterol or other lipid ratios for quantitative environment assessment without an evaluation of details such as their stereochemistry and the proportions of their diagenetic products seems premature.

Summary

In the molecular organic geochemical data for Quaternary sediments from the Middle America Trench there is evidence for several specific sources of organic matter, including diatoms, dinoflagellates, coccolithophorids, methanogenic bacteria and terrestrial higher plants. The differ-ences in the distributions of biological marker compounds between the four samples may reflect variations in the relative proportion of these biological sources. These variations stem from the relative importance of inputs to the sediments from different parts of the trench from (i) terrigenous organic matter, (ii) various marine algae, linked to water column productivity and (iii) bacteria. The abundance of alkadienones attributed to sediment inputs from coccolitho-phorids in Section 494-2-7, in which fossil coccoliths are rare, suggests that these marker compounds were derived from coccolithophorids at their non-coccolith bearing growth stage. This result suggests that micro-palaeontological and molecular organic geochemical data may reflect different aspects of the biological debris contrib-uted to sedimentary environments. An appraisal of sterol data for other Middle America Trench sediments (Curiale & Harrison 1982) suggests that great care must be taken in the quantitative assignment of relative inputs of terrigenous and marine organic matter, based on the β-sitosterol/stigmasterol ratio.

Molecular assessment of palaeoenvironments

The major problems in the use of biological marker compounds for palaeoenvironmental as-sessment are the recognition of the extent of their survival during diagenesis and the elucidation of the diagenetic relationships that link the lipid distributions of immature and mature sediments. This problem can be approached in a number of ways. First, the survival of biolipid signatures can be studied from the downhole profiles of lipid concentrations in stratigraphic successions of uniform lithology. Second, the diagenetic changes that affect specific biological marker compounds can be evaluated through a combination of studies of sediments of different thermal histories and downhole sediment sequences. The identification of the diagenetic products of biolipid precursors would permit the use of the former in the assessment of the inputs of organic matter to ancient sediments. Third, a comparison of the lipid compositions of ancient sediments recognized from various geological criteria to have been laid down in particular types of environment would help establish the links between specific lipid characteristics and the conditions of sediment deposition.

Survival of biolipids in ancient sediments

The ages of oldest sediments in which the selected marine algal (Table 3), terrigenous (Table 4) and bacterial (Table 5) marker compounds have been found are given in Table 7. Undoubtedly the best survival of sedimentary biolipid signatures is observed in areas of low geothermal gradient, and in this respect DSDP sediments from continental margins provide many suitable samples for study.

Some biolipids, such as most carotenoids (e.g. diatoxanthin: Table 7, compound 4), are highly labile and readily degrade in sediments. Other marker compounds, notably alkanes (Table 7, compound 10) and aromatic components (e.g. Table 7, compound 6), are more stable and can be preserved in buried sediments. Inevitably the sedimentary survival of biolipids is a function of their resistance to microbiological, chemical and thermal degradation, which will be linked to the conditions of their deposition. It seems likely that certain microbial reactions that degrade specific lipids during early diagenesis may be restricted to individual, narrow depth zones of the sediment,

such as the zone of sulphate reduction. Hence, it is possible that in organic-rich sediments certain abundant biolipids may not be completely degraded during their passage through such a microbially active zone during sedimentation. A portion of them could therefore survive unaltered until the advent of thermal degradation processes. This interpretation would explain the existence of sedimentary molecular anachronisms where original biolipids co-occur with a wide variety of their immediate and later-stage diagenetic products. The present age limit (165 Ma) for the occurrence of several of these original biolipids in sediments results from the fact that they are the oldest immature sediments in which complex functional lipids such as polycyclic alcohols, ketones and acids have been examined. Given this paucity of data it may be expected that the age ranges given in Table 7 will be extended by subsequent analyses.

An additional factor, other than their diagenetic stability, also influences the recognition of biolipids in ancient sediments; namely the possibility of evolutionary changes in the lipid compositions of organisms. For example, terrigenous higher plant marker compounds would not be expected to occur in pre-Devonian sediments. The recognition of biolipids in ancient sediments clearly offers scope for the evaluation of palaeobiochemistry. For example, the long chain alkenones attributed to coccolithophorid inputs to Recent sediments also occur in Eocene sediments from the Middle America Trench and the Falkland (Malvinas) Plateau (Marlowe *et al.* 1984) and have recently been identified in

TABLE 7. *Survival of biolipids in sediments*

No. (Figs 2–4)	Compound	Oldest* sediment	References
Marine algal inputs			
(1)	C_{37} alkadienone	105 Ma	Farrimond *et al.* in press
(2)	Dinosterol	165 Ma	This paper
(3)	24-methylcholesta-5,22-dienol	115 Ma	This paper
(4)	Diatoxanthin	1 Ma	Brassell *et al.* 1980
Terrestrial inputs			
(5)	β-amyrin	6 Ma	Brassell & Eglinton 1983a
(6)	Ferruginol	165 Ma	This paper
(7)	Friedelanone	6 Ma	Brassell & Eglinton 1983a
(8)	De-A-lupane	50 Ma	Corbet *et al.* 1980
Bacterial inputs			
(9)	*Iso*-pentadecanoic acid	120 Ma	This paper
(10)	2,6,10,15,19-Pentamethyleicosane	125 Ma	Brassell *et al.* 1981
(11)	Bacteriohopanetetraol	10 years	Boon *et al.* 1983
(12)	Fern-9(11)-ene	165 Ma	This paper

* Of those examined to date

Cretaceous black shales from the Blake-Bahama Basin (Farrimond *et al.* in press). The biosynthetic systems for the generation of these compounds has therefore existed for at least 45 Ma. It seems possible that the diversification of organisms during certain geological periods widely recognized in palaeontological data may be accompanied by a similar increase in the range of lipids produced by biosynthetic processes. There is also convincing evidence, however, that some biolipids, notably archaebacterial glycerol tetraethers were developed during the Precambrian and have been continuously biosynthesized since that time (P. Albrecht personal communication). Clearly, further studies of the lipid compositions of ancient sediments may provide evidence for the relative rates of biolipid evolution in comparison with the evolution of the morphological features of organisms.

Biolipid to geolipid conversion

During sediment burial the lipids inherited from organisms are transformed by a variety of processes that involve defunctionalization, stereochemical isomerization and structural re-arrangement. Initially, in early diagenesis, these processes are dominated by microbial reworking, but, as temperatures increase with increasing depth of sediment burial, physicochemical reactions become the major agents effecting changes in lipids. The microbial processes of early diagenesis result in a gradual loss of functional groups through reactions such as dehydration, dehydrogenation, hydrogenation and decarboxylation. Stereochemical features, however, remain largely unaltered during these conversions of biolipids into geolipids. A convenient arbitrary division between early and late diagenesis corresponds to the stage when natural product organic compounds have essentially lost their functional groups and are present as alkanes and partially or fully aromatized hydrocarbons or have been bound into kerogen (Mackenzie *et al.* 1982). Certain molecular features attributed to specific classes of organisms, such as head-to-head isoprenoid linkages in archaebacteria, can survive diagenesis and subsequent catagenic breakdown and thus occur in mature sediments and oils (Chappe *et al.* 1982).

For some compound classes, notably steroids (Mackenzie *et al.* 1982), the detailed pathways of diagenetic and catagenetic transformations of biolipids and geolipids are becoming reasonably well understood. Many questions relating to the microbial processes that modify biolipids in the upper part of the sedimentary column have, at present, not been satisfactorily answered and

warrant further study. For example, the microbes responsible for particular reactions, such as sterol dehydration, and the conditions under which these transformations occur have not been recognized. Similarly, little is known of the selectivity and specificity of many diagenetic processes and the factors that influence their rates. These aspects of lipid diagenesis have a significant bearing on the survival of molecular information and its significance as an indicator of environmental conditions of deposition.

Ancient sediments: Malvinas Plateau, DSDP Leg 71

As an example of the application of biological marker compounds to the recognition of the sources of organic matter in ancient sediments we shall discuss the lipids of four Mesozoic black shales from the Malvinas Plateau drilled at Site 511 during DSDP Leg 71. The location and stratigraphy of the site are given in Fig. 8 and Fig. 9 respectively. The lithological, petrographic and isotopic details for the samples (Table 8) point to deposition of these sediments with variable amounts of terrigenous and marine organic matter. Their spore colouration indicates their immaturity (Batten 1981).

Lipid occurrence and distributions

In the Malvinas Plateau black shales, there are many biological marker compounds that reflect specific inputs of organic matter to the sediments (Table 9). Some of these compounds are biolipids inherited directly from organisms; others are geolipids formed from biolipids during diagenesis. Among the intact biolipids are markers for dinoflagellates, methanogenic bacteria and higher plants; all of these marker compounds also occur in younger sediments. The two major geolipids cited in Table 9 are the extended hopanones and simonellite. The former group of compounds are presumed to be diagenetic products of bacteriohopanetetraol (Ourisson *et al.* 1979) and therefore representative of bacterial inputs. Simonellite is an aromatic diterpenoid thought to be formed from resin acids characteristic of higher plants, notably conifers.

In addition to the occurrence of specific marker compounds, two features of the lipid distributions, namely the prominence of odd *n*-alkanes and even *n*-alkanoic acids in the C_{24}–C_{29} region, also attest higher plant inputs to the sediments (Table 9).

The marker lipids in these black shales suggest that their organic matter originates from mixed sources, which agrees with the petrographic

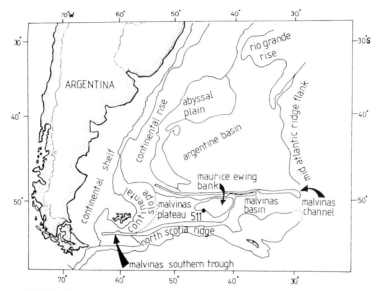

FIG. 8. Location of DSDP site 511 to the west of the Maurice Ewing bank on the Malvinas Plateau (redrawn from Ludwig, Krasheninikov *et al.* 1983).

details for the samples (Table 8). The quantitative lipid compositions of the samples are not examined in detail here (cf. Howell 1984), but show considerable variability. Similarly, there are many differences in the distributions of *n*-alkanes, *n*-alkanols, steranes, sterenes, triterpanes, sterols and sterones between the samples. Such qualitative and quantitative differences are due, in part, to minor changes in the degree of diagenetic alteration of the black shales with increasing depth of burial, but environmental factors also appear to have left their signature on the observed lipid distributions. Significantly the petrographic, lithological and isotopic data for the black shales are rather variable and show no definite trends (Table 8); features that the different trends seen in the lipid results.

The presence of several functionalized biolipids in these Leg 71 black shales indicates their immaturity, which is consistent with their low spore colouration (Table 8). These results serve to illustrate futher the remarkable survival of biolipids in ancient sediments from an area of low geothermal gradient.

Lipid ratios

The relative amounts of C_{27}, C_{28} and C_{29} steroids have been proposed (Huang & Meinschein 1979) as a similar indicator of sediment inputs although the proportion of C_{28} components has little influence. There are several limitations in this

approach (Brassell & Eglinton 1983a), but the proportion of C_{27} to C_{29} steroids is readily determined and provides a useful indication of similarities and differences between individual samples. The ratios of various C_{27}/C_{29} steroids (Fig. 10) in the four black shales show no consistent trends or systematic differences. As the specific steroid components whose ratios are illustrated include both precursor biolipids and their product geolipids, the extent of sample diagenesis is clearly significant. Any diagenetic influence on the steroid ratios would be expected to be systematically related to sediment depth. It is possible that the decrease in the C_{27}/C_{29} ratio with depth for ster-4-enes and the postulated ster-8-enes may reflect the preferential reaction of C_{27} components in the process of diagenetic steroidal rearrangement (cf. Boon *et al.* 1983). Overall, the downhole variability in the C_{27}/C_{29} steroid ratios, however, does not appear to be related to diagenetic processes.

The marked differences in the value of this ratio (i.e. 0.4 to 1.8) suggest that the various types of steroids and their C_{27} and C_{29} components may have different origins. For example, in marine sediments cholest-4-en-3-one (C_{27}) is generally markedly more abundant than its C_{29} counterpart (Brassell & Eglinton 1983a), so that diagenetic products derived from such precursors might be expected to be similarly dominant in the C_{27} component. The higher C_{27}/C_{29} ratio for $5\beta(H)$-stanones, compared to other steroidal

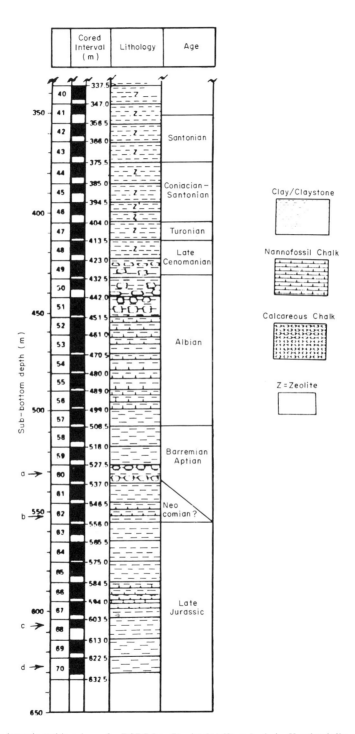

FIG. 9. Simplified stratigraphic column for DSDP Leg 71, site 511 (from Ludwig, Krasheninikov *et al.* 1983) showing the position of the four black shale samples examined (Table 8).

TABLE 8. *Mesozoic sediments from the Malvinas Plateau, DSDP Leg 71, Site 511*[a]

Section[b]	Depth[b] (m)	Age[b]	Lithology	Organic Carbon (%)[c]	Spore Colour	Organic Matter Types[d, e]						Kerogen $\delta^{13}C$ (%)[c]
						P	T	A	V/I	M	C	
60–5	535	Barremian–Aptian	Claystone	5.7	2/3	+ +	+ +	+ + +	+	+ +	+	−29.3
62–5	554	Barremian–Aptian/ Neocomian	Nannofossil Claystone	1.5	2/3	+	+	+ + +	+	+	+	−27.6
68–2	606	Oxfordian/Callovian	Claystone	3.5	3	+	+ + +	+ + +	+ +	+ +	−	−27.7
70–3	627	Oxfordian/Callovian	Mudstone	4.8	3	+ +	+	+ + +	+ +	+ +	−	−27.0

[a] For location see Fig. 8
[b] See Fig. 9
[c] Data supplied by British Petroleum plc.
[d] P phytoplankton; T tasmanitids; A amorphous algal matter; V/I vitrinite & inertinite; M microspores; C cuticles.
[e] + scarce, + + common, + + + abundant.

compounds, may therefore be linked to their formation, in part, from Δ^4-stenones (Brassell & Eglinton 1983a) during early diagenesis, in addition to their generation from $5\beta(H)$-stanols. In general, the steroid ratios of geolipid products appear to be related to those of their precursor biolipids, which can be derived from mixed sources.

The proportion of lipid contributions from particular origins or the extent of specific microbial diagenetic processes may, in turn, be influenced by environmental factors. For example, cholest-4-en-3-one may be derived directly from organisms or formed by microbial degradation of cholest-5-en-3β-ol (Brassell & Eglinton 1983a and references therein), both in sediments and in marine water columns (Gagosian *et al*. 1982). It also appears to be a precursor, *inter alia* of $5\beta(H)$-stanols and $5\beta(H)$-stanones. Like other lipids its content in a given sediment will be determined

by the net balance of generative and degradative processes, which may be dependent on the environment of deposition. The variations in the C_{27}/C_{29} steroid ratios seen in Fig. 10 may therefore reflect changes in environmental features such as the organisms contributing lipids to the sediments and the depositional conditions. Such intricate lipid patterns reflected in relatively simple relationships, such as C_{27}/C_{29} steroid ratios (Fig. 10), illustrates the magnitude of the task, but they also demonstrate the potential sensitivity of lipid distributions as palaeoenvironmental indicators.

Summary

The lipids identified in Mesozoic black shales from the Malvinas Plateau include marker compounds of sediment inputs from dinoflagellates, methanogenic bacteria and terrigenous higher

TABLE 9. *Biological marker compounds reflecting inputs to Cretaceous sediments from DSDP Leg 71, Malvinas Plateau*

Compound	Inferred source	Reference
Dinosterol	Dinoflagellates	Boon *et al*. 1979
Dinosterone	Dinoflagellates	Brassell & Eglinton 1983a
C_{31}–C_{34} Hopanones	Bacteria	Ourisson *et al*. 1979
Squalane	Methanogenic bacteria	Brassell *et al*. 1981
Fernenes	Anaerobic bacteria	Brassell *et al*. 1981
Iso-pentadecanol	Bacteria	Brassell *et al*. 1980
Iso-pentadecanoic acid	Bacteria	Cranwell 1973
Ferruginol	Higher plants	Baset *et al*. 1980
Simonellite	Higher plants	Simoneit 1977

Feature	Inferred origin	
High carbon preference index (CPI) in C_{24}–C_{29} range		
n-Alkanes	Higher plants	Simoneit 1978; Brassell *et al*. 1980
n-Alkanoic acids	Higher plants	Simoneit 1978; Brassell *et al*. 1980

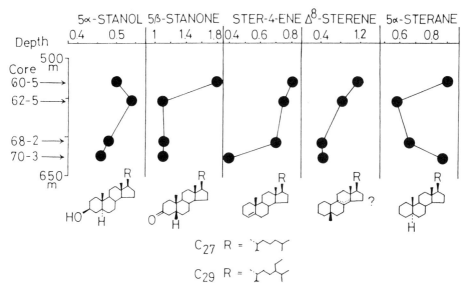

FIG. 10. Downhole plots of C_{27}/C_{29} (cholesteroid/24-ethylcholesteroid) steroid ratios for five selected compounds in the four black shales from site 511 (Table 8).

plants. The recognition of such compounds suggests a mixed source for the organic matter of these black shales, in agreement with their petrographic and lithological data (Table 8). The lipid distributions also confirm the immaturity of these black shales.

The differences in the distributions of biological marker compounds between the four black shale samples may reflect a combination of (i) slight differences in sample maturity, (ii) variations in the nature and source of the sedimentary organic matter, and (iii) minor changes in their conditions of deposition. It is significant that such prominent differences exist between the lipid distributions of such generically similar samples; an observation which illustrates the potential of this approach to palaeoenvironment assessment.

Conclusions

The results from molecular organic geochemical studies of Recent and ancient sediments indicates that such information provides evidence of the sources of sediment inputs, in terms of both general and specific biological inputs. There are clear indications that palaeontological and other morphological data and organic geochemical results need not agree, as shown by three specific examples. First, in sediments deposited below the carbonate compensation depth where calcareous skeletal debris has been dissolved, specific biological marker compounds attest inputs from

coccolithophorids (Brassell *et al.* 1980). Second, the same lipids might reflect sediment contributions from coccolithophorids in their non-coccolith bearing growth stage, which are not evident from palaeontological studies. Third, sterols indicative of dinoflagellate inputs occur in many Recent and ancient sediments that contain no dinoflagellate cysts. Such discrepancies between molecular and micropalaeontological characteristics of sediments may stem from the fact that the former are extracted, in part, from amorphous materials within the sediment matrix, or from organic matter absorbed on clay minerals. In addition, the biolipids and the microfossils may differ in their resistance to degradative processes, notably bacterial attack, and to breakdown during transportation. Sedimentation processes can also achieve the selective deposition of a limited range of grain sizes of particulate matter, perhaps concentrating pollen, spores or dinoflagellate cysts with respect to those 'soft' parts of organisms rich in lipids. Some biological processes can serve, however, to concentrate the morphological debris and the lipids of specific organisms together. In particular, zooplankton faecal pellets are sealed capsules of both the calcareous skeletal debris and the lipids of phytoplankton which can reach underlying sediments intact, after rapid passage through the water column (Volkman *et al.* 1980a).

The evaluation of sedimentary sequences of near-uniform lithology reveals differences in lipid compositions between samples of similar maturity which cannot be explained in terms of slight variations in their degree of diagenetic alteration. Such observations suggest that the molecular signatures of ancient sediments preserve features attributable to the sources of organic matter and the conditions of sediment deposition. At present, these features are partly understood, but further studies evaluating the high resolution molecular stratigraphy of such sediment sequences will undoubtedly clarify the significance of lipid signatures as environmental indicators.

In areas of low geothermal gradient and shallow burial biolipids can be remarkably well preserved. Hence, many functionalized lipids inherited unaltered from organisms have been recognized in immature early Cretaceous sediments and even in Late Jurassic black shales (*ca.* 165 Ma; Table 7). In immature sediment sequences, however, lipids are subject to systematic structural modification by diagenetic processes, causing a gradual loss in the detail of various aspects of environmental information. The elucidation of lipid precursor/product relationships offers the possibility of inferring the original biolipid patterns that gave rise to the geolipid distributions observed. Hence, a partial reconstruction of the sediment's original molecular profile could be realized.

For the future there are several aspects of molecular organic geochemical research that can be considered as major objectives for further study. These priority areas for future investigations (Table 10) all relate to the improved molecular characterization of (i) the sources of sedimentary organic matter, (ii) the processes of

TABLE 10. *Current major objectives*

A Improved survey of lipids in:
1 Marine organisms
2 Relevant microbial cultures (especially benthic microbiota)
3 Bottom sediments beneath specific water columns (oxic/anoxic)
4 Ancient sediments of known depositional environment (e.g. upwelling systems)
5 Insoluble organic matter (kerogen).

B Improved understanding of:
1 Diagenetic & catagenetic processes
2 Reasons for certain ubiquitous patterns of geolipids (e.g. hopanes)
3 Lipid incorporation into kerogen.

lipid modification in the water column and sediment and (iii) the diagenetic fate of lipids. In particular, there is a need for this molecular approach to be applied more extensively in the study of insoluble sedimentary organic matter.

ACKNOWLEDGEMENTS: We thank the Natural Environment Research Council for financial support (GR3/2951 and GR3/3758) and colleagues at Bristol, especially those connected with the DSDP project, for helpful discussions, practical assistance and access to unpublished results. We are grateful to the British Petroleum Co. Ltd, especially Drs P. J. Park and G. Dungworth and Mr G. Cooles, for the visual kerogen data, organic carbon and isotopic analyses of samples from DSDP Legs 67 and 71. We are also grateful to Mrs A. P. Gowar for help with C-GC-MS analyses. The DSDP samples were supplied with the aid of the National Science Foundation.

References

AUBOUIN, J., VON HUENE, R., *et al.* 1982. Site Reports. *In*: AUBOUIN, J., VON HUENE, R. *et al.*, *Initial Rep. Deep Sea drill. Proj.*, **67**, U.S. Government Printing Office, Washington, D.C. 5–374.

BAAS, W. J. 1982. Investigations on leaf waxes III. Pentacyclic triterpenes, seco-triterpenes and non-volatile aliphatics of four *Hoya* species and *Ficus benjamina* in relation to leaf age. *Acta Bot. Neerl.* **31**, 449–476.

BARRICK, R. C., HEDGES, J. I. & PETERSON, M. L. 1980. Hydrocarbon geochemistry of the Puget Sound region-I. Sedimentary acyclic hydrocarbons. *Geochim. Cosmochim. Acta* **44**, 1349–1362.

BASET, Z. H., PANCIROV, R. J. & ASHE, T. R. 1980. Organic compounds in coal: Structures and origins. *In*: DOUGLAS, A. G. & MAXWELL, J. R. (eds) *Advances in Organic Geochemistry 1979*, Pergamon Press, Oxford. 619–630.

BATTEN, D. J. 1981 Palynofacies, organic maturation and source potential for petroleum. *In*: BROOKS, J. (eds), *Organic Maturation Studies and Fossil Fuel Exploration*, Academic Press, London. 201–223.

BOON, J. J., RIJPSTRA, W. I. C., DE LANGE, F., DE LEEUW, J. W., YOSHIOKA, M. & SHIMIZU, Y. 1979. The Black Sea sterol—a molecular fossil for dinoflagellate blooms. *Nature* **277**, 125–127.

——, HINES, H., BURLINGAME, A. L., KLOK, J., RIJPSTRA, W. I., DE LEEUW, J. W., EDMUNDS, K. E. & EGLINTON, G. 1983 Organic geochemical studies of Solar Lake laminated cyanobacterial mats. *In*: BJORØY, M. *et al.* (eds), *Advances in Organic Geochemistry 1981*, Wiley, Chichester. 207–227.

BRASIER, M. D. 1980. *Microfossils.* George Allen & Unwin, London. 193 pp.

BRASSELL, S. C. & EGLINTON, G. 1983a. Steroids and triterpenoids in deep sea sediments as environmental and diagenetic indicators. *In*: BJORØY, M. *et al.* (eds), *Advances in Organic Geochemistry 1981*, Wiley, Chichester. 684–697.

—— & EGLINTON, G. 1983b. The potential of organic geochemical compounds as sedimentary indicators of upwelling. *In*: SUESS, E. & THIEDE, J. (eds) *Coastal Upwelling: Its Sediment Record, A.* NATO Conf. Ser. IV, **10A.** Plenum Press, New York. 545–571.

——, COMET, P. A., EGLINTON, G., ISAACSON, P. J., MCEVOY, J., MAXWELL, J. R., THOMPSON, I. D., TIBBETTS, P. J. C. & VOLKMAN, J. K. 1980. The origin and fate of lipids in the Japan Trench. *In*: DOUGLAS, A. G. & MAXWELL, J. R. (eds), *Advances in Organic Geochemistry 1979*, Pergamon Press, Oxford. 375–391.

——, WARDROPER, A. M. K., THOMSON, I. D., MAXWELL, J. R. & EGLINTON, G. 1981. Specific acyclic isoprenoids as biological markers of methanogenic bacteria in marine sediments. *Nature* **290**, 693–696.

——, EGLINTON, G. & MAXWELL, J. R. 1983. The geochemistry of plant terpenoids. *Biochem. Soc. Trans.* **11**, 575–586.

CHAPPE, B., MICHAELIS, W. & ALBRECHT, P. 1980. Molecular fossils of archaebacteria as selective degradation products of kerogen. *In*: DOUGLAS, A. G. & MAXWELL, J. R. (eds) *Advances in Organic Geochemistry 1979*, Pergamon Press, Oxford. 265–274.

—— ALBRECHT, P. & MICHAELIS, W. 1982. Polar lipids of Archaebacteria in sediments and petroleums. *Science*, **217**, 65–66.

COMET, P. A., MCEVOY, J., BRASSELL, S. C., EGLINTON, G., MAXWELL, J. R. & THOMSON, I. D. 1981. Lipids of an Upper Albian limestone, Section 465A–38–3. *In*: THIEDE, J., VALLIER, T. *et al.*, *Initial Rep. Deep Sea drill. Proj. 62*, U.S. Government Printing Office, Washington, D.C. 923–937.

CORBET, B., ALBRECHT, P. & OURISSON, G. 1980. Photochemical or photomimetic fossil triterpenoids in sediments and petroleum. *J. Amer. Chem. Soc.* **102**, 1171–1173.

CRANWELL, P. A. 1973. Branched-chain and cyclopropanoid acids in a recent sediment. *Chem. Geol.* **11**, 307–313.

CURIALE, J. A. & HARRISON, W. E. 1982. Beta-sitosterol and stigmasterol in slope sediments. *In*: AUBOUIN, J., VON HUENE, R. *et al.*, *Initial Rep. Deep Sea drill. Proj. 67*, U.S. Government Printing Office, Washington, D.C. 587–590.

DASTILLUNG, M., ALBRECHT, P. & OURISSON, G. 1980. Aliphatic and polycyclic ketones in sediments. C_{27}–C_{35} Ketones and aldehydes of the hopane series. *J. Chem. Res.* (S) 166–167, (M) 2325–2352.

DIDYK, B. M., SIMONEIT, B. R. T., BRASSELL, S. C. & EGLINTON, G. 1978. Organic geochemical indicators of palaeoenvironmental conditions of sedimentation. *Nature* **272**, 216–222.

FARRIMOND, P., EGLINTON, G. & BRASSELL, S. C. *in press*. Alkenones in cretaceous black shales, Blake-Bahama Basin. *In*: LEYTHAUSER, D. & RULLKÖTTER, J. (eds), *Advances in Organic Geochemistry 1985*, Pergamon Press, Oxford.

GAGOSIAN, R. B., SMITH, S. O. & NIGRELLI, G. E. 1982. Vertical transport of steroid alcohols and ketones measured in a sediment trap experiment in the equatorial Atlantic Ocean. *Geochim. Cosmochim. Acta*, **46**, 1163–1172.

GOOSSENS, H., DE LEEUW, J. W., SCHENCK, P. A. & BRASSELL, S. C. 1984. Tocopherols as likely precursors of pristane in ancient sediments and crude oils. *Nature*, **312**, 440–442.

HILLS, I. R., WHITEHEAD, E. V., ANDERS, D. E., CUMMINS, J. J. & ROBINSON, W. E. 1966. An optically active triterpane, gammacerane, in Green River, Colorado, oil shale bitumen. *J. Chem. Soc. Chem. Commun.* **20**, 752–754.

HOLZER, G., ORO, J. & TORNABENE, T. G. 1979–8. Gas chromatographic/mass spectrometric analysis of neutral lipids from methanogenic and thermoacidophilic bacteria. *J. Chromatogr.* **186**, 795–809.

HOWARD, D. L. 1980. Polycyclic triterpenes of the anaerobic photosynthetic bacterium *Rhodomicrobium vanielli*. Ph.D. Thesis, University of California, Los Angeles (unpubl.).

HOWELL, V. J. 1984. *Organic geochemistry of sediments from Legs 67, 71 and 72 of the Deep Sea Drilling Project*. MSc. Thesis, University of Bristol (unpubl.).

HUANG, W.-Y. & MEINSCHEIN, W. G. 1979. Sterols as ecological indicators. *Geochim. Cosmochim. Acta*, **43**, 739–745.

JONES, B. H., BRINK, K. H., DUGDALE, R. C., STUART, D. W., VAN LEER, J. C., BLASCO, D. & KELLEY, J. C. 1983. Observations of a persistent upwelling center off Point Conception, California. *In*: SUESS, E. & THIEDE, J. (eds) *Coastal Upwelling: Its Sediment Record, Part A*. NATO Conf. Ser. IV, **10A**. Plenum Press, New York. 37–60.

LEE, C., GAGOSIAN, R. B. & FARRINGTON, J. W. 1980. Geochemistry of sterols in sediments from the Black Sea and the Southwest African Shelf and slope. *Org. Geochem.* **2**, 103–113.

LUDWIG, W. J., KRASHENINIKOV, V. A., *et al.* 1983. Site 511 *In*: LUDWIG, W. J. KRASHENINIKOV, V. A. *et al.*, *Initial Rep. Deep Sea drill. Proj. 71* U.S. Government Printing Office, Washington, D.C. 21–109.

MACKENZIE, A. S. 1984. Applications of biological markers in petroleum geochemistry. *In*: BROOKS, J. & WELTE, D. H. (eds), *Advances in Petroleum Geochemistry Vol 1*, Academic Press, London. 115–214.

——, BRASSELL, S. C., EGLINTON, G. & MAXWELL, J. R. 1982. Chemical fossils: the geological fate of steroids. *Science*, **217**, 491–504.

MARLOWE, I. T., GREEN, J. C., BRASSELL, S. C. & EGLINTON, G. 1984. Long chain unsaturated ketones and esters in living organisms and marine sediments. *Org. Geochem.* **6**, 135–141.

MATSUMOTO, G., TORII, T. & HANYA, T. 1982. High abundance of algal 24-ethyl-cholesterol in Antarctic lake sediment. *Nature* **299**, 52–54.

MOLDOWAN, J. M. & SEIFERT, W. K. 1980. First discovery of botryococcane in petroleum. *J. Chem. Soc. Chem. Commun.* 912–914.

OURISSON, G., ALBRECHT, P. & ROHMER, M. 1979. The hopanoids. Palaeochemistry and biochemistry of a group of natural products. *Pure Appl. Chem.* **51**, 709–729.

SIMONEIT, B. R. T. 1977. Diterpenoid compounds and other lipids in deep sea sediments and their geochemical significance. *Geochim. Cosmochim. Acta* 41, 463–476.

—— 1978. The organic chemistry of marine sediments. *In*: RILEY, J. P. & CHESTER, R. (eds), *Chemical Oceanography, 2nd Edition, Vol. 7*, Academic Press, London. 233–311.

SMITH, D. J., EGLINTON, G., MORRIS, R. J. & PONTANEU, E. L. 1982. Aspects of the steroid geochemistry of a recent diatomaceous sediment from the Namibian Shelf. *Oceanologica Acta*, **5**, 365–378.

SUMMERHAYES, C. P. & GILBERT, D. 1982. Distribution, origin, and hydrocarbon potential of organic matter in sediments from the Pacific margin of Guatemala. *In:* AUBOUIN, J., VON HUENE, R. *et al. Initial Rep. Deep Sea drill. Proj. 67.* U.S. Government Printing Office, Washington, D.C. 595–599.

THOMPSON, S. & EGLINTON, G. 1978. The fractionation of a recent sediment for organic geochemical analysis. *Geochem. Cosmochim. Acta*, **42**, 199–207.

VOLKMAN, J. K., EGLINTON, G., CORNER, E. D. S. & SARGENT, J. 1980a. Novel unsaturated straight-chain C_{37}–C_{39} methyl and ethyl ketones in marine sediments and a coccolithophore *Emiliania huxleyi. In:* DOUGLAS, A. G. & MAXWELL, J. R. (eds), *Advances in Organic Geochemistry 1979* Pergamon Press, Oxford, 219–227.

—— EGLINTON, G., CORNER, E. D. S. & FORSBERG, T. E. V. 1980b. Longchain alkenes and alkenones in the marine coccolithophorid. *Emiliania huxleyi. Phytochem.* **19**, 2619–2622.

ZÜLLIG, H. 1982. Untersuchungen über die Stratigraphie von Carotinoiden im geschichteten Sediment von 10 Schweizer Seen sur Erkundung früherer Phytoplankton-Entfaltungen. *Schweiz Z. Hydrol.* **44**, 1–98.

S. C. BRASSELL & G. EGLINTON, Organic Geochemistry Unit, University of Bristol, School of Chemistry, Cantock's Close, Bristol BS8 1TS.

V. J. HOWELL, Masspec Analytical, Bath Road, Wallbridge, Stroud, Gloucestershire GL5 3JA.

The use of lipids as facies indicators

P. A. Comet & G. Eglinton

SUMMARY: An approach to palaeoenvironmental interpretation of sediments using lipid data, is developed. This approach initially attempts to summarize the major lipid components of plants, bacteria and invertebrate animals and to relate these data to sedimentary lipid distributions. Most of the major lipid groups found in sediments are used in this study. The very large amount of lipid data generated, necessitated the development of a simple system for data processing. The method of data analysis used involved the construction of a simple taxonomic hierarchy based on 'Ruzicka's Rules' i.e. the biosynthetic origins of the major lipid types. By bringing in the concept of taxonomic hierarchy based on the biosynthetic pathways, a palaeontological approach towards lipid geochemistry is being evolved.

Secondly, DSDP lipid data (derived from the O.G.U., Bristol University) are collated and grouped using matrices of lipid data and histograms of the lipid groups, i.e. all compounds of a common structure are 'summed'. These data are compared with the geological data and the results briefly discussed for each sediment.

In conclusion, the diagenetically stable lipid patterns of three representative environments, i.e. marine planktonic, bacterially-dominated marine, and a lacustrine facies, are presented and discussed. From these data the rules by which environments are described are extended; the parameters so derived have good potential for source correlation.

This paper attempts to evaluate biological markers in environmental interpretation and source evaluation, using a representative suite of Deep Sea Drilling Project sediments, as well as sediments from other localities (Table 1; Fig. 1). The analytical data which are reported here were produced using thin layer chromatography (TLC), gas chromatography (GC) and gas chromatography–mass spectrometry (GC–MS). Major objectives were:

 (i) To identify, group and classify the various lipid-based structures found in sediments.
 (ii) To compare the chemical data with the geological data (particularly micropalaeontology).
 (iii) To understand the chemical data and to rationalize its palaeoenvironmental variations.
 (iv) To use the chemical data to correlate and compare environments.

Choosing a method of data analysis

A vast amount of lipid data was produced which necessitated the construction of a system for logically dealing with several hundred identifications and quantifications.

The conventional way of coping with organic geochemical data is to group them by functionality (Table 2; Fig. 2). This method suffers from the problem of diagenetic alteration of functionalized compounds to hydrocarbons. This implies that it might be expected that two different sediment samples from the same rock layer would contain very different hydrocarbon and other lipid distributions if their thermal histories were different. Classification by carbon skeleton would minimize the problems of diagenetic interconversion.

Comparison with conventional methods of dealing with organic material in sediments, in the case of kerogens or coal macerals (Table 3) revealed only a small number of rather non-specific variables for manipulation, thus being an inappropriate method for describing lipid data. Pollen and spores, which often occur as several hundred different varieties within a sediment, are analogous in their diversity to the lipid diversity of recent sediments. A series of pollen taxonomic groups are conventionally used for reducing down the volumes of these types of data. Pollen and spores are classified by shape alone (in ancient sediments) rather than by their parent plant. Pollen diagrams (histograms of pollen genera) are a rapid and conventional method of comparing sedimentary environments.

Molecular classification of biolipids

The great diversity of lipids in sediments makes necessary the need for a classification that:
(1) Allows insertion of newly discovered lipids.
(2) Reduces the great mass of information into fewer, but environmentally more meaningful groups.
(3) Is chemically acceptable.
(4) Reflects the biosynthetic hierarchy.

From: BROOKS, J. & FLEET, A. J. (eds) 1987, *Marine Petroleum Source Rocks* Geological Society Special Publication No. 26 pp. 99–117.

TABLE 1. *Localities investigated*[a]

Sample Locality	DSDP Leg	Number of samples investigated	Age	Environment of deposition	Ref.[c]
E. Mediterranean	42A[b]	3	Plio–Pleistocene	Bathyal, marine, sapropelic	1, 2
Blake–Bahama Plateau	44	2	Miocene	Abyssal, marine, clay facies	10
Bay of Biscay	48	3	Albian	Marine, black shale facies	3
Moroccan Basin	50	3	Hauterivian Valanginian	Marine, turbidite facies	4
Japan Trench W. Pacific	56/57	10	Pleistocene– Miocene	High productivity, marine bathyal, diatomaceous ooze	5
Nauru Basin N.W. Pacific	61	3	Campanian	Marine, organic poor carbonate facies	—
Hess Rise N.W. Pacific	62[b]	1	Albian	Marine, carbonaceous, 'black shale facies'	6
California Continental Borderland	63	2	Pleistocene– Miocene	Marine, high productivity bathyal, diatomaceous ooze	7
Gulf of California	64	1	Pleistocene	Marine, high productivity bathyal, diatomaceous ooze	8
Middle America Trench	66	2	Pleistocene	Marine bathyal mud	9
Black Sea	Not DSDP	1	Recent	Anoxic, sapropelic abyssal clay	—
Walvis Bay	Not DSDP	1	Recent	Marine, neritic, anoxic diatomaceous	10, 11
Rostherne Mere	Not DSDP	1	Recent	Fresh water, lacustrine peat, mud	—
Messel Shale	Not DSDP	1	Eocene	Gyttja (organic-rich sediment deposited under anoxic conditions)	2, 12
Corner Inlet	Not DSDP	1	Recent	Intertidal flat	—

[a] See Fig. 1. [b] Data given in this paper.

[c]
1. Kidd and Worstell 1978.
2. Kidd *et al.* 1978.
3. Barnes *et al.* 1979.
4. Brassell *et al.* 1980a.
5. Brassell *et al.* 1980b.
6. Comet *et al.* 1981.
7. McEvoy *et al.* 1981.
8. Thomson *et al.* 1982.
9. Brassell *et al.* 1981.
10. Wardroper 1979.
11. Wardroper *et al.* 1978.
12. Kimble 1972.

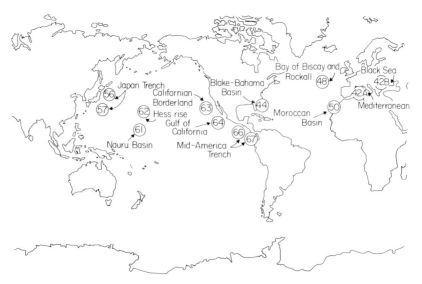

FIG. 1. DSDP/IPOD Legs examined. (62 and 42A discussed in this paper.)

TABLE 2. *Organic components found in sediments classified by their chemistry (modified after Eglinton 1973)*

Alkanes[a]	Alcohols[a]	Quinones[d]	Carbohydrates[e]
I–XIII	XVIII	XXII	XXVI
Alkenes[a]	Ketones[a]	Porphyrins[d]	Amino-acids[e]
XIV	XIX	XXIII	XXVII
Aromatics	Fatty acids[a]	Chlorins[d]	Biopolymers[e]
XV	XX	XXIV	
Keto-ols & Diols[b]	Hydroxy acids[b]	Carotenoids[c, d]	Kerogen[e]
XVI+XVII	XXI	XXV	

I–XXV—the structures of examples of these types of compounds are shown in Figure 2.

[a] Normal, branched; acyclic and cyclic isoprenoids.
[b] Multifunctional compounds.
[c] Carotenoids usually disappear in older sediments.
[d] Pigments.
[e] Carbohydrates, amino-acids and other biopolymers may react together to give insoluble kerogen etc. (these are not discussed).

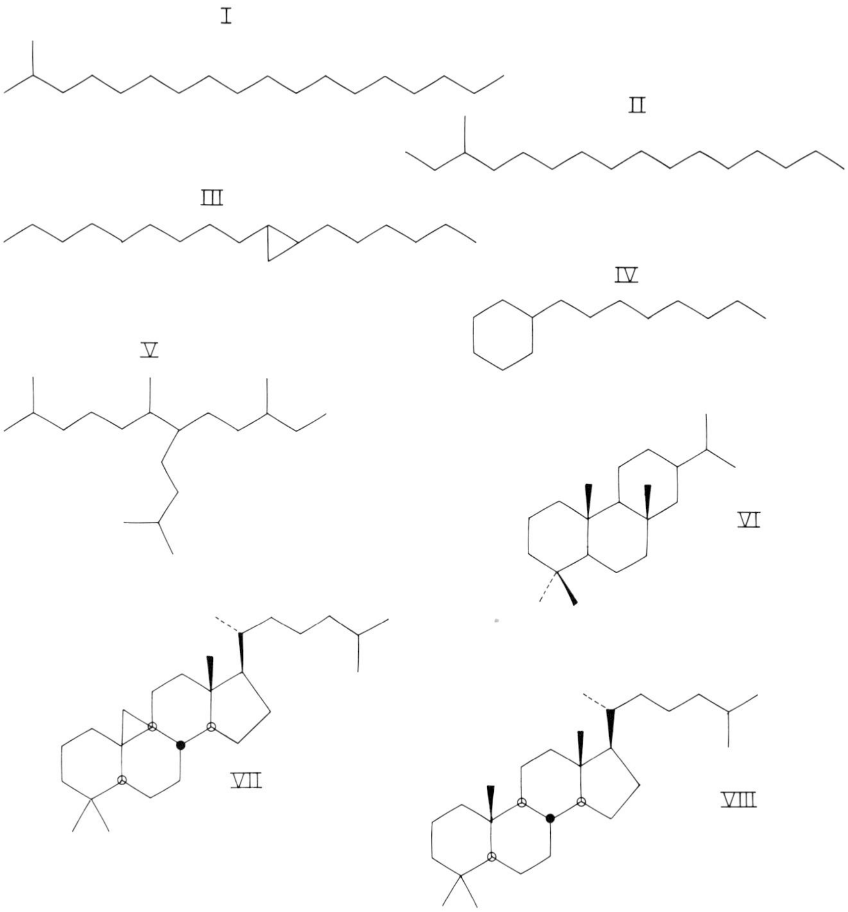

FIG. 2. Structures of organic components found in sediments (see Table 2).

FIG. 2. (*continued*)

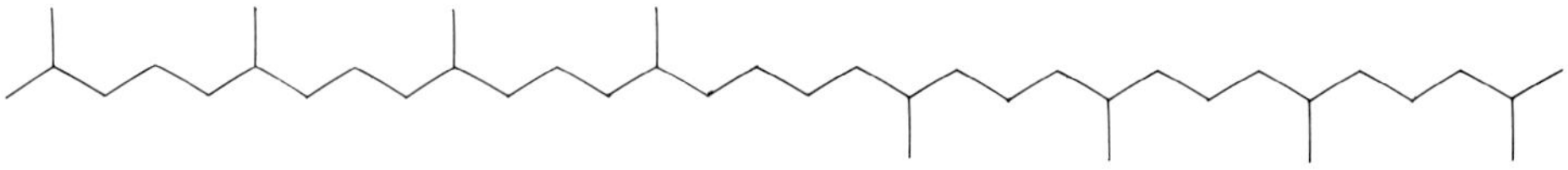

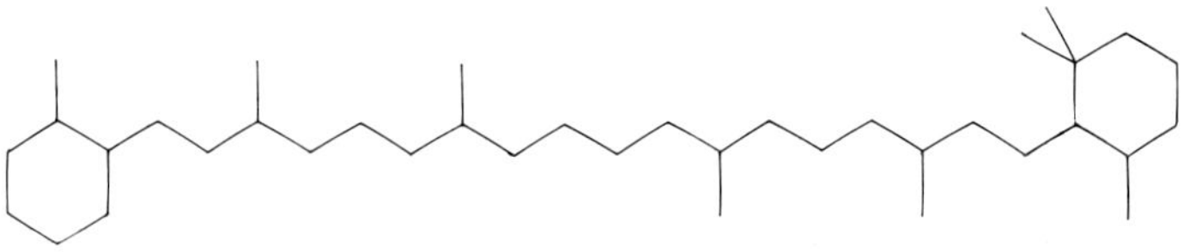

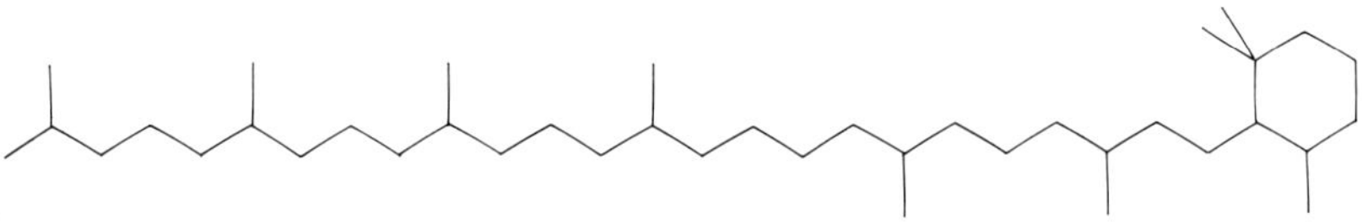

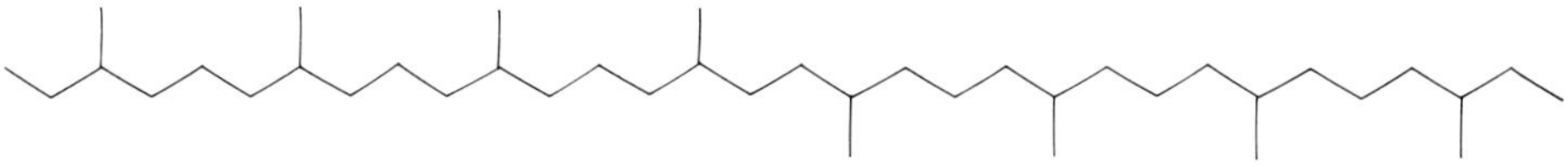

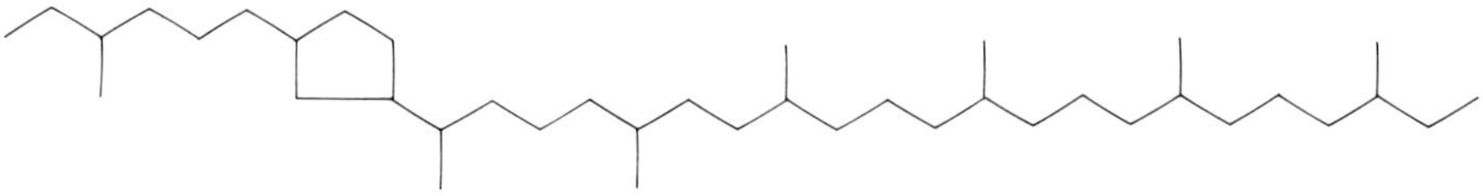

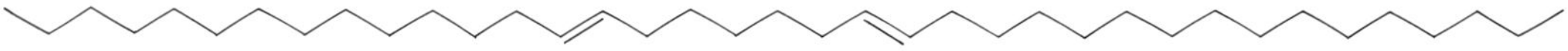

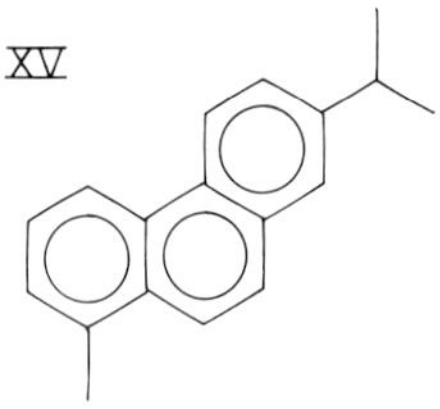

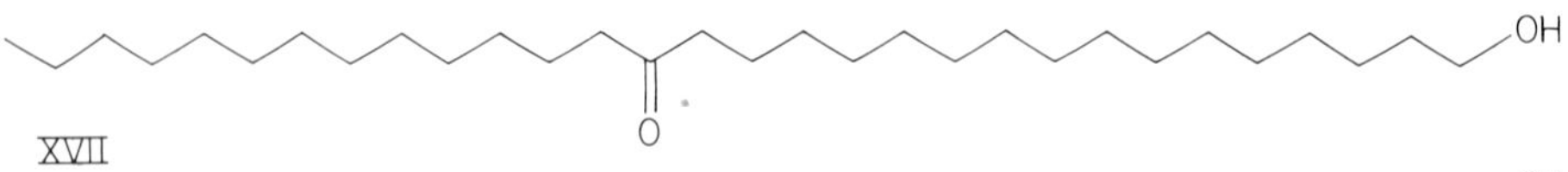

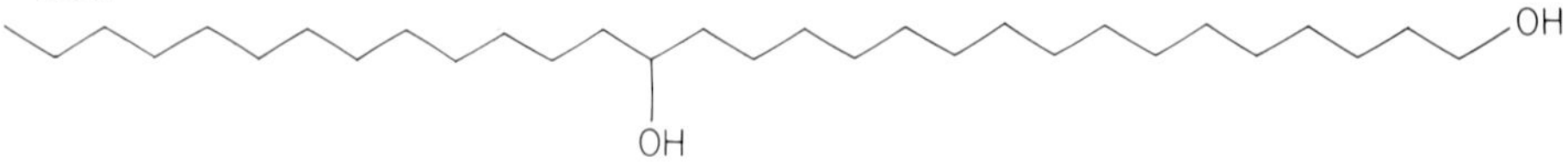

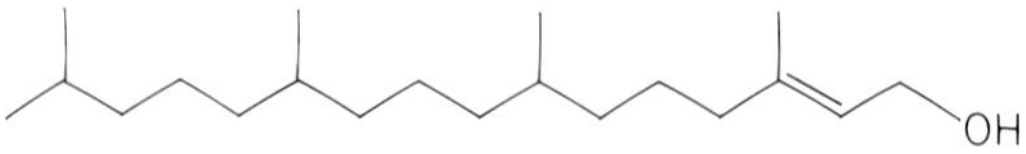

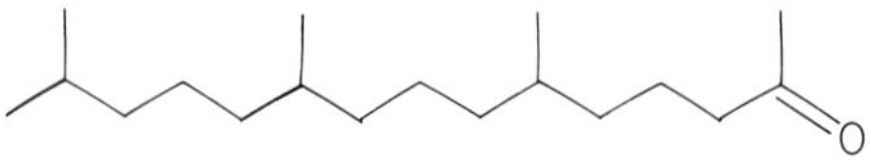

FIG. 2. (*continued*)

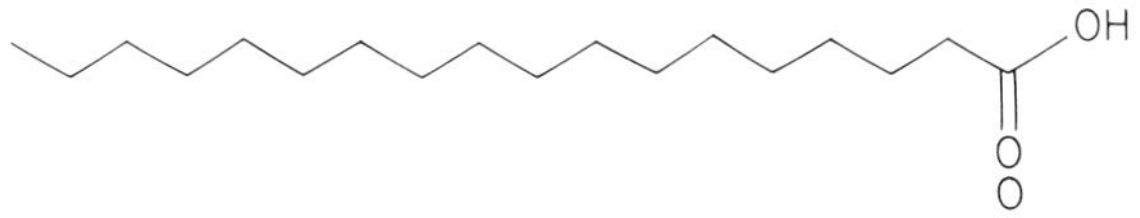

XX

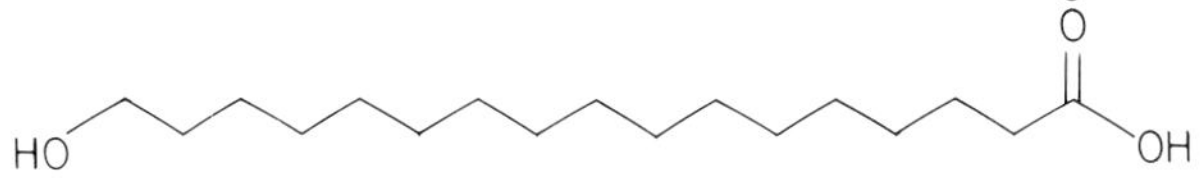

XXI

XXII

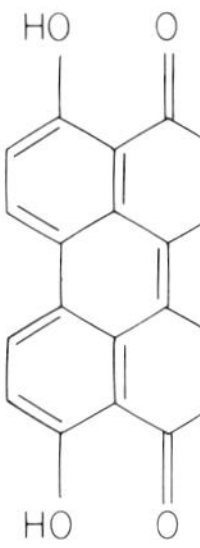

XXIII

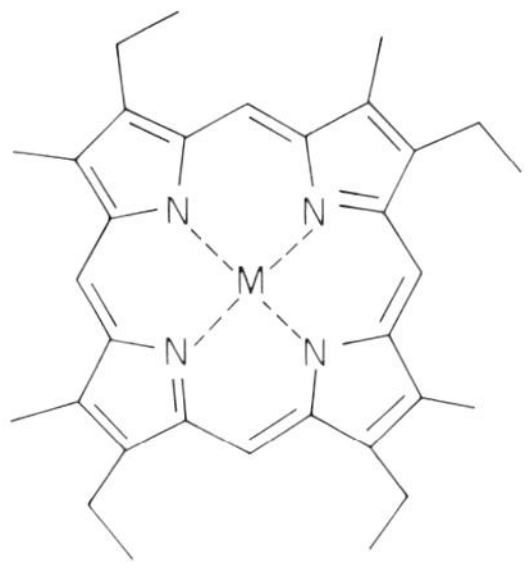

XXIV

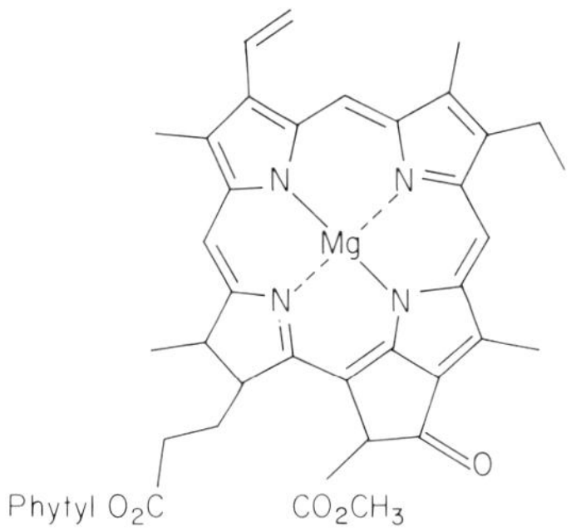

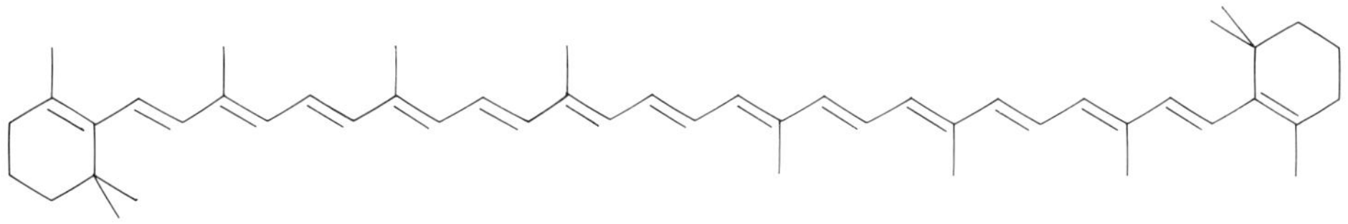

XXV

XXVI

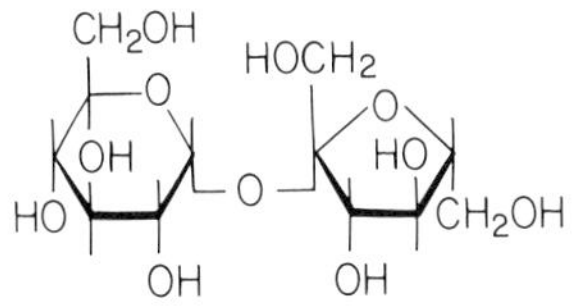

XXVII

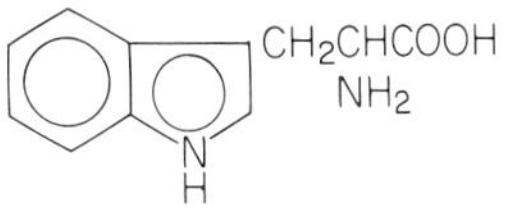

TABLE 3. *Classification of sedimentary organic matter using optical techniques (after Masran & Pocock 1981)*

1 Structured, terrestrially sourced, materials, e.g. cuticle[a], bark, etc.
2 Pollen and spores[b]
3 Charcoal[c]
4 Biodegraded, terrestrially sourced, materials[d]
5 Amorphous material (yellow-amber)[d]
6 Amorphous material (grey)[d]
7 Biodegraded, aqueous sourced, materials[d]
8 Structured, aqueous sourced, materials[e]

[a] Giving cutinite in older sediments.
[b] Giving exinite in older sediments.
[c] Giving fusinite in older sediments.
[d] Giving various forms of amorphous kerogen.
[e] e.g. tasmanites, acritarchs, dinoflagellates etc.

(5) Leads to the derivation of a series of units by which organic-rich rocks can be described and correlated in terms of their environment of deposition.

(6) Has phylogenetic meaning, i.e. reflects the evolutionary relations of the lipid donating organism.

The classification proposed here (Fig. 3) is a first attempt at integrating the above factors using a simple system of groups and sub-groups. Obviously it will need to be modified with time. In particular this classification is presently developed only to the level of 'blind taxonomy'. The actual evolutionary time sequence of lipid structural development has not yet been included, i.e. a lipid 'phylogeny' still needs to be developed. This is within the bounds of possibility but is not attempted here. Nevertheless the proposed classification marks an advance on simple structural summation.

The biosynthetic pathways

The biosynthetic hierarchy (see Fig. 3) forms a convenient starting point for the discussions of lipid classification. Lipids are generated by four major pathways:—

The acetate pathway

This leads to the formation of various fatty acids of differing carbon chain lengths, saturations and branch points. Hydroxy-derivatives produce the cuticle of leaves, similarly *n*-alkanes form the wax layer of leaves.

The mevalonate pathway

This leads to the formation of multiple, regularly branched carbon compounds, i.e. the isoprenoids; examples include phytol (part of chlorophyll a) the steroids and other terpenoids (including rubber and sporopollenin) (Templeton 1969).

The amino-laevulinic acid pathway

This leads to the development of the chlorophylls and porphyrins, i.e. heterocyclic, nitrogen-containing compounds.

The shikimate pathway

This leads to various lignins, and possibly some of the non-terpenoid aromatics found in sediments.

Most of the great range of compounds and biopolymers found in sediments (Brooks *et al.*

this volume) are generated by these four main pathways. This array of possibilities is illustrated in Fig. 2. The main structural classes within the acetate and mevalonate groups are discussed below in turn.

The acetates

Simple addition of carbon units leads to straight chain molecules of varying chain length. A branch point may develop at various carbon numbers in the chain. The commonest types include branch points at the 2 and 3 positions (iso and anteiso) (Structures I and II, Fig. 2) but branch points may also be found at positions 4 and 5; mid chain branching is also found. An unusual form of branching involves ring closure at the branch point, this mid chain branching gives a small strained ring (the cyclopropanoid) (Structure III, Fig. 2). Within this group may also be grouped the cyclohexanoid compounds which exhibit terminal ring closure to give an unstrained 6 membered ring (Structure IV, Fig. 2).

The mevalonates

The related pathway of mevalonate synthesis develops the branching aspect to give the isoprenoids. Isoprenoids contain a branch point every four carbon atoms. These compounds may be considered as polymers of isoprene (the C_5 precursor unit). A terpene is a compound composed of two or more isoprene units. Thus monoterpenes are C_{10} compounds; they have been found in many oils and sediments. These compounds are volatile and will not be discussed further here. Diterpenes (C_{20} compounds) contain four isoprene units. The simplest forms are phytol derivatives (the acyclic terpenoid alcohol esterified onto chlorophyll a). Other acyclic derivatives are also known e.g. the 'GX' series (Structure V, Fig. 2) (Yon *et al.* 1982; Rowland *et al.* in press). Here branching of the isoprenoid chain produces various unusual structures. Tricyclic diterpenoid skeletons are commonly found in sediments, especially those of the abietane structure (Structure VI, Fig. 2). Dehydroabietic acid and its various defunctionalized derivatives are of wide occurrence. Other tricyclic structures found in sediments include the kaurane beyerane and phyllocladane types (Noble *et al.*, in press). Much work remains to be done on diterpenoids and lower terpenoids in sediments.

Probably the most important isoprenoids present in sediments are the triterpenoids. The acyclic structure, squalane (as its polyunsaturated derivative, squalene) is the precursor for a multiplicity

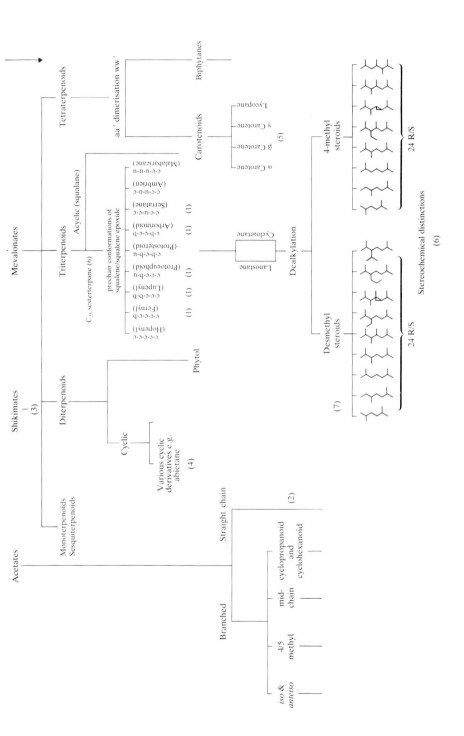

FIG. 3. Classification of sedimentary lipids by structure (Carbon skeleton taxonomy).

(1) This diverse range of triterpenoids are all found in sediments. The small amounts found in DSDP sediments necessitated 'overgrouping' into the non-specific 'taxon' of non-hopanoid triterpenoids. They are almost all higher plant (gammacerane excepted).

(2) Straight chain components can be subdivided into short (n–C_{10}–C_{20}): long (n–C_{21}–C_{36}): and very long (n–C_{37}–C_{39}). The subdivision has some chemotaxonomic validity (though essentially arbitrary) as short chain are often algal/bacterial in origin, long chain (plant wax); very long chain (Haptophyte lipids).

(3) Lignins, etc; maturation/pyrolysis of woody material would yield an extensive array of aromatic compounds (possibly related to those found in sediments).

(4) A considerable range of cyclic diterpenoids may be generated according to the prechain conformation of geranyl geraniol.

(5) Functional distinctions in the carotenoids have considerable chemotaxonomic significance.

of cyclic derivatives. Two major pathways exist for the biosynthesis of triterpenoids (Table 4).
(1) The aerobic pathway (via squalene epoxide).
(2) The anaerobic pathway (via squalene and water) (see review by Ourisson *et al.* 1979 also Howard 1980).

The two pathways each have their distinctive patterns of cyclization. The aerobic pathway produces the steroids and euphoids (tetracyclics), and pentacyclics with six membered E rings, such as the amyrin derivatives. (A–E, Table 4). The anaerobic pathway produces the hopanes (pentacyclics with five membered E rings), fernanes and arboranes. However hopanoids are also generated via the aerobic pathway.

The steroid pathways bifurcates into two major divisions based on the cycloartane and lanostane structures (Structures VII and VIII, Fig. 2) to give a range of dealkylated products. These naturally fall into two major categories, the 4-methyl steroids and desmethyl steroids and these may in turn be subdivided according to their side chains (Fig. 3). It is not possible at present to distinguish dealkylated steroids from cycloartane, with those derived from lanostane, and dealkylations of either precursor gives the same range of products.

The tetraterpenoids (C_{40}) compounds divide conveniently into two main sub-divisions, firstly those based on the carotane molecule (Structure XII, Fig. 2) have two geranyl geraniol units linked via a head to head linkage. The complete acyclic carotenoid molecule (lycopane structure; Structure XIII, Fig. 2) may exist in various cyclic modifications, in which the 'ends' of the molecules are closed to give a cyclohexane ring. Thus α and β carotane structures (Structure XII, Fig. 2) have two terminal rings, whereas γ carotene (Structure XI, Fig. 2) has only one. Secondly, tail to tail linkage geranyl-geraniol units leads to the biphytanyl structure (Structure X, Fig. 2). This may also be partially cyclized (but in a quite different manner) to give unusual 'intra chain' cyclopentane rings (Structure IX, Fig. 2).

Sedimentary lipid classification

Ruzicka's rules

The work of Ruzicka's group forms the basis for the classification of triterpenes by their original squalene conformation, i.e. the pre-chain folding preceding squalene cyclization, rather than using the multiplication of functional possibilities encountered in triterpene based natural products (Eschenmoser *et al.* 1955; Ruzicka 1959). Ruzicka's rules should form the basis of classification of sedimentary lipids as these are similarly characterized by a multiplicity of functional groups—not always similar to those commonly found in organisms (Tissot & Welte 1978; Devon & Scott 1972). This style of classification is now commonly extended to other terpenoids and acyclic compounds. Ourisson *et al.* 1979 have shown that the structure of the various isoprenoids play very specific roles in the reinforcement of cell membranes and this is clearly linked with

TABLE 4. *Classification of triterpenoids by conformation of the squalene and squalene epoxide precursor (after Howard 1980)*

Triterpanes derived from squalene epoxide, or presumptively from squalene epoxide: (Aerobic pathway)

A	Chair–boat–chair–boat–unfolded	sterols, steroids, phytosterols (e.g. lanosterol, cycloartenol)—ex. protosteroid cation: give steranes in sediments
B	Chair–chair–chair–boat–unfolded	euphol series (e.g. euphane)
C	Chair–chair–chair–boat–boat	lupanes, oleananes, ursenanes (e.g. lupeol)—ex. lupenyl cation
D	Chair–chair–unfolded–chair–chair	(e.g. onocerane)
E	Chair–chair–unfolded:unfolded–chair	(e.g. ambreane)

Tritarpanes derived from squalene, or presumptively from squalene directly: (Anaerobic pathway)

F	Chair–chair–chair–chair–chair	hopane series (e.g. diplotene; gammacerane)*—ex. hopenyl cation
G	Chair–chair–chair–chair–boat	fernene series (e.g. fernene)
H	Chair–boat–chair–chair–boat	arborane series (e.g. arborinol)

The terminology chain/boat/unfolded refers to the shape of folding of the isoprenoid chains. Every six carbon

atoms can be arranged either linearly (unfolded) i.e. ⌇⌇⌇ , or in a chair conformation

⌇ , or in a boat conformation ⌇ . This folding precedes carbon-carbon bonding.

N.B. Structures shown *after* carbon-carbon bonding.

terpenoid structure. Lastly, the role of lipids as extracellular protection agents also ensures that as a whole, lipids, (and/or terpenoids), are among the most stable of sedimentary products under reducing conditions. However, the functionality of a lipid is unstable to diagenesis and consequently (if for no other reason) *sedimentary lipid* classification must closely follow Ruzicka's rules. The implications are that the many hundreds of natural products in sediments can be legitimately grouped by structure into a few categories. It is these categories that form the basis of the present work.

Most sedimentary triterpenoids fall into three major groups based on Ruzicka's hypothetical cations (Table 4):

(1) the hopanoids (i.e. ex-hopenyl cation)
(2) the steroids (i.e. ex-protosteroid cation)
(3) non-hopanoid higher plant triterpenoids (i.e. mainly ex-lupenyl cation).

Additional sub-groups could be delineated for the multiplicity of steroids, i.e. 4,4-dimethyl (rare), 4-methyl and 4-desmethyl steroids; also the non-hopanoid triterpenoids can be sub-divided, i.e. lupanes, gammacerane, oleananes, fernanes, arboranes, etc. Euphanes appear not to have been reported commonly from sediments. The steroids can also be further sub-divided according to side chain substitution and 24 R/S stereochemistry. Thus, a hierarchy of groups and sub-groups based on the biosynthetic pathways provides the best means for simple 'information retrieval' system in 'filing' quantitative sedimentary lipid data. More than a hundred hopane-derived compounds are commonly encountered in sediments (Ourisson *et al.* 1979). The hopanoids might, therefore, all be grouped together in one unit. This unit could then be quantitatively compared with other units of similar 'weighting' i.e. steroids, non-hopanoid triterpenoids, etc.

This application of 'Ruzicka's rules' could be further extended to the monoterpenes, sesquiterpenes and diterpenes. The lower terpenes are commonly encountered in terrestrial sediments and oils (Richardson & Müller 1982).

Taxonomic distribution of structural groups

The major structural groups found in sediments are outlined in Table 5. Each structural group represents very many functionalized components added together and a 'blanket decision' of their biological origin, based on the literature surveys of Kimble (1972), Wardroper (1979), Brassell *et al.* (1980a and b) and references therein, as to the most likely origin of the particular summed group of compounds when found in sediments. Thus, the hopanoids, which are mostly found in aerobic organisms such as aerobic bacteria, cyanophyta and various ferns (Ourisson *et al.* 1979) are here taken as indicating an aerobic bacterial input since cyanophyte and fern input (which also contain these compounds) to most marine sediments can be considered minor. However, the problem of multiple sources for a single structural type or compound is a difficulty much encountered in environmental reconstructions based on organic geochemical data. The approach of grouping different compounds of related structure might be described as 'structural summation'. The total (expressed as ng/g dry weight sediment) summed structures may then be expressed in histogram form. The histograms for different environments may then be compared. This approach to some extent may be expected to minimize the confusion due to diagenetic over-printing. Environmental comparison based on the carbon skeleton would not be expected to be so gravely affected by diagenesis.

The steroids are particularly abundant and varied in most environments, and this reason justifies their further subdivision (Table 5b).

A matrix approach to dealing with organic geochemistry data

Using the sub-groups outlined in Fig. 3, a method of dealing with the lipid data can be obtained by placing the structural groups down one axis, and the functional possibilities down the other axis (Table 6b). The various sample quantifications and identifications can be easily 'slotted in'. This system allows the hundreds of individual compounds found in a sediment to be rapidly allocated and represented. A similar approach can be used with specific sub-groupings such as the steroids (see Table 6c).

The analysis of 30 DSDP samples were handled using the grid system of 'structural summations', in which the major structural types of any functionality (aliphatic hydrocarbons, aromatic hydrocarbons, ketones, acids and alcohols), are summed together (Table 6b). These data are supplemented by a detailed analysis of the steroid data. The steroids are handled in a similar way. They are separated into 4-methyl and 4-desmethyl steroids. These in turn are subdivided by their side chain, and functionality (i.e. double bond position and whether alcohol, ketone, hydrocarbon or acid). The results are easily expressed as histograms (Fig. 4) and these then visually compared with the geological data.

TABLE 5a. *Input indicators (grouped by structure and taxonomic affinities)*

Structural grouping	Higher plant lipids (terrestrial markers)	Algal lipids (mainly marine markers)	Bacterial markers and lipids	Others
Straight chain (Short) $n\text{-}C_{10}\text{-}n\text{-}C_{20}$	—	Not very specific marker compounds, common in many algae and bacteria.		
Straight chain (Long) $n\text{-}C_{21}\text{-}n\text{-}C_{36}$	Plant waxes[a] n-alkanes, n-acids n-alcohols, n-ketones	[b]	—	—
Straight chain (Very long) $n\text{-}C_{37}\text{-}C_{39}$	—	Nanoplankton lipids (coccoliths) polyunsaturated ketones and hydrocarbons	—	—
Branched chain (Short) $C_{10}\text{-}C_{20}$	—	—	iso and antesio compounds, acids, alcohols esp. C_{15} (C_{17} compounds)	—
Branched chain (Long) $C_{21}\text{-}C_{35}$	Alkanes and mono-methyl alcohols	—	Unusual mid-chain branched $C_{19}\text{-}C_{30}$ alkanes found in some Pre-Cambrian oils	—
Acyclic isoprenoid (Diterpenoid)	Phytol, C_{18} isoprenoid ketone, phytene, pristane, phytane, etc. are taxonomically non-specific productivity indicators			
Other acyclic	—	—	Squalane, lycopane, C_{25} sesterterpane, etc. are believed to be of archaebacterial origin	—
Carotenoids	Very diverse origins, found in great range of organisms. In sediments, taxonomic allocation depends on functionality.			
Cyclic diterpenoid	Dehydroabietic acid,[c] dehydroabietin, retene, fichtelite, simonellite	—	Extended diterpenoid[d]	—
Hopanoid	3-Keto hydroxy derivatives and degraded tetracyclic alkanes/alkenes/ aromatics		Diverse aerobic bacteria cyanobacteria	—
Non hopanoid triterpenoids	Lupane, etc. (about 20[f] different structural types)	—	Fernenes found in[g] photosynthetic anaerobic bacteria	Gammacerane (Tetrahymanol found in protoza)
4-methyl steroids	—	Dinosterol (ex-dino-flagellates) and possibly the other major 4-methyls in sediments	C_{28}-4-methyl steroids are found in methanotrophic bacteria	—
Desmethyl steroids	Sitosterol[i]	$C_{26}, C_{27}, C_{28}, C_{30}$ sterols	[h]	—
Polynuclear aromatics (PNA's)	Common in terrestrial[j] sediments, coals, etc.	—	—	—
Porphyrins and chlorins	Taxonomic and productivity indicators.			

[a] Certain bacteria biosynthesis n-acids/n-alkanes in this carbon number range, but with little or no carbon preference inde:
[b] Some marine sediments contain a considerable range of diols and keto-ols in this carbon number range, they are probab of 'algal' origin.
[c] Diagenetic derivatives of conifer resin.   [d] Possibly algal.
[e] The majority of hopanoids in sediments are probably bacterial.
[f] Those sediments containing a considerable range of non-hopanoid structures possibly contain an angiosperm input.
[g] Also in ferns.   [h]Desmethyl steroids are not biosynthesized by bacteria.
[i] Higher plants commonly contain 24-ethyl groups in the R position, marine algae in the 24 S position dependent on Λ unsaturation.
[j] Ex-coal maceral/oil seeps etc. (of indirect biological origin).

TABLE 5b. *Taxonomic distribution of steroid side chains*[a]
[a] See Table 5a.
(This table represents a breakdown of the steroid subsection of Table 5a).

PARENT STERANE CARBON NUMBER	DESMETHYL SIDE CHAIN	HIGHER PLANTS	ALGAE	INVERTEBRATES	OTHERS
C_{26}			This complete range of side chains found in various marine algae. However, usually only as simple distributions and 'unusual side chains' relatively uncommon.	Complex distributions of steroids, especially those with 'unusual side chains' are found in various invertebrates, e.g. sponges, which contain symbiotic dinoflagellates, etc. and filter feed.	Cholesterol dominant in carnivores and higher animals.
C_{27}					
C_{27}					
C_{28}		24 R found in higher plants			
C_{29}					
C_{29}					Gorgosterol particularly common in coelenterates
C_{30}					
C_{30}					
C_{30}					

	4-METHYL SIDE CHAIN	HIGHER PLANTS	ALGAE	INVERTEBRATES	OTHERS
C_{27}			This complete range of side chains found in various dinoflagellates		methanotrophic bacteria
C_{28}					
C_{29}					
C_{30}					
C_{30}					
C_{31}					

Examples of 'structural summation'

Thirty sediments were chosen (Table 1), spanning a wide range of inputs, with special emphasis on the deep sea as an area of interest.

Three examples are reported here, a typical deep-sea sediment, a lacustrine sediment and a more mature marine sediment in which the majority of lipid components are represented by hydrocarbons.

The chemical data were obtained by solvent extraction of thawed DSDP core samples, saponification of the extracts and TLC of the neutrals. GC and GC–MS were used in characterization of the differing TLC fractions. Manual identification, quantification and tabulation of the differing compounds completed the first and most laborious part of the study (see Barnes *et al.* 1979 for experimental details). Quantification was achieved by:

(1) Running a standard mix of known concentration for calibration, before GC of the rock extracts.
(2) Running GC's of total neutral extracts in which TLC has not been allowed to interfere with the concentrations of key components.
(3) Using computerized quantification files (QUAN) for each GC–MS run.

In this paper the basic geological data are laid out in tabular form and may be compared with the geochemical data, both in the form of data matrices and grouped histograms.

Except where stated otherwise, the geological data are obtained from the Initial Reports of the Deep Sea Drilling Project.

Percentages of fossils are not given, and only the order of abundance stated. Experience has shown that the lipid patterns do not vary (except in a purely qualitative way) with the percentage of fossil groups, also, for the most part the geological data available are of a qualitative nature, making quantitative comparisons impossible.

The format adopted is a geological summary drawn up in tabular form, followed by matrices of quantitative lipid data. These matrices are: (a) The total structural groups data; classified initially into major structural types found in sediments; thus straight chain, mono-branched chain, acyclic isoprenoids, carotenoids, cyclic diterpenoids, triterpenoids, steroids PNA's and porphyrins. Some of these categories are sufficiently abundant in sediments to make further structural sub-division convenient, e.g. straight chain components conveniently fall into short chain (n-C_{10}–C_{20}), long chain (n-C_{21}–C_{36}), very long chain (n-C_{37}–C_{39}) taxonomically useful sub-divisions etc. (Table 6b). This system is flexible and further sub-division of any structural group used here may prove valuable, e.g. the subdivided non-hopanoid triterpenoids, could perhaps be used, if sufficiently abundant, to classify peats, coals, and resinous oils. The second 'axis' is according to the traditional functional groupings of acids, alcohols, ketones and hydrocarbons. (b) The steroid data; classified initially into desmethyl and 4-methyl steroids, and then sub-divided according to side chain (e.g. Table 6c). These structural sub-groupings form one 'axis', the other axis being the range of functionalities commonly encountered in sediments, i.e. primary groupings into alcohols, ketones and hydrocarbons (steroid acids being uncommon in these sediments) and secondary groupings mainly according to double bond positions. Both axes could be extended as new side chains and/or functional groups are discovered.

This system permits rapid description of a wide range of lipid data by structure only; functionality becoming of secondary interest. The summations are then expressed as histograms, the major component being used as the 100% basis for calculation of the lipid patterns (e.g. Figs. 4A and 4B). Finally, the histogram data are discussed and compared.

Quantification is expressed as nanograms per gram of dry weight sediment for each sample, except where indicated otherwise.

Only three examples are given here, though the data from thirty samples were collated and used in overall assessment of palaeoenvironmental parameters (Tables 6 and 7; Figs 4 and 5). These samples were each typical of a particular depositional environment and were representative of lipid distributions of the other twenty-seven samples.

TABLE 6a. *East Mediterranean sapropel DSDP sample 42A–374–3–1 (125–129 cm) (from Hsü, Montadert* et al. *1978)*

Location	Ionian Sea
Age	Lower Pleistocene (NN 20)
Palaeodepth	Bathyal
Present depth of site	Abyssal
Sample sub-bottom depth	208 metres
Organic carbon	4.95% (wet weight)
Fossil content	Common nannoplankton and planktonic foraminifera
Lithology	Clay rich green calcareous sapropel
Sedimentation rate	High
Burial temperature	19°C

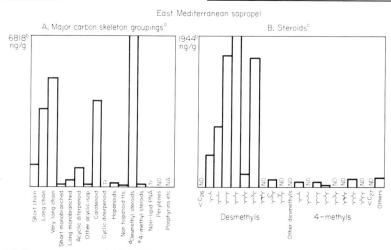

FIG. 4. East Mediterranean sapropel (42A–374–3–1) Lipid data.
[a] See Table 5a.   [b] Nannograms per gram dry weight sediment.   [c] See Table 5a.

TABLE 6b. *East Mediterranean sapropel 42A–374–3–1. Major carbon skeleton groupings*

Structure	Functional grouping						
	Carboxylic acids	Alcohols	Ketones	Alkanes	Alkenes	Aromatics	Total
Short straight chain[d]	318	433[a]	74	88	—	—	913
Long straight chain[e]	183	2431[a]	103	750	—	—	3467
Very long chains[f]	—	—	4764[b]	—	122[b]	—	4886
Short monobranched[g,j]	—	13	—	—	—	—	13
Long monobranched[h,k]	—	—	—	34	—	—	34
Acyclic diterpenoids[i]	—	700	110	2.5	18.5	—	831
Other acyclic isoprenoids[c]	—	—	—	10.5	—	—	11
'GX' Derivatives[l,n]	—	—	—	3.0	—	—	3
Partially cyclic tetraterp. (carotane)	—	940	290	—	890	1880	4000
Cyclic diterpenoids	Tr	—	—	—	—	—	Tr
Hopanoids	—	2	37	78	90	—	207
Non-hopanoid triterpenoids	—	—	—	2	23	—	25
Desmethylsteroids[m]	—	6563	75	—	180	—	6818
4-methyl steroids[m]	—	5	148	—	20	—	168
Non-lipid PNA's	—	—	—	—	—	Tr	Tr
Porphyrins	—	—	—	—	—	—	—

[a] Includes n-alkanols, n-alkenols (n-diols and n-ketols = 817 ng/g);
[b] Includes di and triunsaturated components;   [c] Includes squalane, C_{25} sesterpane, and lycopane;
[d] n-C_{19}–C_{36};   [e] n-C_{21}–C_{36};   [f] n-C_{37}–C_{39};   [g] C_{10}–C_{20};   [h] C_{27}–C_{30};   [i] ex phytol;
[j] iso + anteiso compounds;   [k] iso compounds;   [l] 2,6,10-trimethyl-7-(3-methyl butyl)-dodecane;
[m] See Table 6c;   [n] Not shown in Fig. 4.

The first example is of a Pleistocene sapropel from the Eastern Mediterranean (DSDP section 42A–374–3–1) (Tables 6). This sapropel is dominated by an amorphous gelatinous marine organic material, containing only a planktonic microfauna. The sapropels lack of benthos and absence of bioturbation may indicate deposition under anoxic conditions. Its structural distribution pattern (Fig. 4) is dominated by steroids, very long straight chain material (n-C_{37-39}) and carotenoids. It also contains some terrestrial input (long chain n-C_{21-35}) i.e. plant wax alkanes.

The steroids, in view of their variety and abundance, justified further sub-division. The sample was unusually low in 4-methyl steroids, particularly the dinosterol 'suite', but in the other sapropels and most other marine samples these compounds were normally dominant. Apart from the low abundance of 4-methyl steroids the sapropel showed a characteristic marine steroid distribution in which at least twelve side chains were represented.

The second example is of an Albian marine limestone from the N.W. Pacific 'black shale' facies (DSDP section 62–465A–38–3) (Table 7). The sample contained a relatively high content of fatty acids, small amounts of alcohols and ketones, a high hydrocarbon content and abundant porphyrins. In particular the polycyclic isoprenoid based compounds were mainly de-

functionalized to give alkanes (Tables 7b and 7c). Structural summation revealed striking similarities with the Mediterranean sapropels. In particular the steroids were again characterized by their multiplicity of side chains. In the 4-methyl series those steroids of the 'dinostane' skeleton were particularly prominent (Fig. 5A). Cholestane, 24-methyl cholestane and, 24-ethyl cholestane were the most prominent of the desmethyl steroids (Fig. 5B). This steroid side chain pattern matches the other marine sedimentary steroid analysis. The major carbon skeleton groupings were dominated by short straight chain components of probable algal derivation (Comet *et al.* 1981) and unusually large amounts of porphyrins of presumably a similar algal source.

A major difference from the sapropels and many of the other marine samples studied was the high hopane content. This may reflect an extensive bacterial contribution. The absence of terrestrial components is indicated by the minor amounts of plant wax (i.e. long chain material). Visual kerogen data supported the idea of an extensive marine contribution. The structural distribution patterns of this Albian limestone allowed easy comparison with the structural distribution of the much more immature sapropel. To compare sterane and sterene distributions with sterol distributions would not have been environmentally meaningful, as a single sterol

TABLE 6c. *East Mediterranean Sapropel 42A-374-3-1 Steroid Data* [e,f,g]

42A — 374 — 3 — 1

Steroid data	Sterols										Ketones				Hydrocarbons											Total
a Functionality / a Side chain	b Δ^0	Δ^5	$\Delta^{5,22}$	Δ^{22}	Δ^7	$\Delta^{5,7}$	Δ^{24}	$\Delta^{5,24}$	c $\Delta^{5,24(28)}$	c $\Delta^{24(28)}$	Other Ketones	b Stan-3-one	b Ster-4-enone	Ster-22-enone	d Sterene Δ^2	Sterene Δ^4	Sterene Δ^5	Sterene $\Delta^{3,5}$	Sterene $\Delta^{x,22}$	Sterene $\Delta^{x,24}$	Rearranged Steranes	Rearranged Sterenes	Ster-trienes	Sterane	Aromatics	Total
Desmethyl — Degraded																										
(side chain)	3	10	290	97								-1.4														401
(side chain)	96	604	77																							778
(side chain)	242	725	555	145					410	73		11.2	0.1		1	3			3	15						1703
(side chain)	97	73	966	242											15				13	50						1944
(side chain)	48	48	72												9											168
(side chain)	242	676	507	96	24				72	5		(42)			36				20	15						1663
Other desmethyl	5		–							10	10															87
4-Methyl — Degraded																										
(side chain)											5.6															6
(side chain)												5.6														6
(side chain)												16.8								10						27
Other												50	0.1	42						10						102
Degraded / Other	48	6	20	24					3		28															129

[a] n.b. No distinction between 24R and S side chains;   [b] Both 5α and 5β isomers;   [c] Both 24E and Z isomers;   [d] All isomers;
[e] ng/g dry wt. sed.;   [f] Δ refers to double bond position;   [g] The steroid data on this table is a breakdown of the steroid data of Table 6b.

may give rise to a whole suite of diagenetic derivatives of similar structure.

The final example comes from Rostherne Mere, a small freshwater lake in Cheshire which has been well studied for a number of years (Quirk 1978). Structural summation showed a very different pattern in the steroid side chains, thus only cholestane, methylcholestane and stigmastane (ethylcholestane) were detected (with a trace of C_{26} sterol). The variety of steroid side chains were considerably reduced. Long chain material (plant wax) was dominant in the major carbon skeleton groupings, though short chain (algal) lipid was also very important. Steroids were abundant, probably also reflecting a freshwater algal (as opposed to marine) input. This analysis appears to be fairly representative of those described in the literature.

Discussion

The sedimentary lipid analyses fell into three main groups, dependent more on the sources of organic matter deposited (cf. palynofacies) rather than watercolumn conditions. The groups are (1) marine dominated inputs, e.g. the Mediterranean sapropel 42A–374–3–1; (2) terrestrial dominated inputs, e.g. Rostherne Mere; (3) bacterial dominated inputs, e.g. the Albian limestone (62–465A–38–3) from the N.W. Pacific black shale

facies (Table 8). Drawbacks to this system are twofold. Firstly the lipid structures are not entirely stable to heat and do break down with increased geothermal stress. Secondly, kerogen binding is important, and is selective. As an

TABLE 7a. *Albian limestone—N.W. Pacific 'black shale' facies DSDP section 62–465A–38–3 (Data from Thiede, Vallier et al. 1981)*

Location	Hess Rise, N.W. Pacific
Age	Albian
Palaeodepth	Upper bathyal
Present depth of site	Lower bathyal
Sample sub-bottom depth	295 metres
Organic carbon	2.1% (dry weight)
Fossil content	Palynology—abundant amorphous kerogen, few spores, particles of vitrinite indicates immaturity ($R_0 = 0.33\%$). Numerous foraminifera linings. Restricted fauna of benthic forams. Diverse planktonics (nearby sections).
Lithology	Well lithified, finely laminated grey limestone (92% carbonate).
Sedimentation rate	High
Burial temperature	Not given

TABLE 7b. *Hess rise—leg 62—Albian limestone. Major carbon skeleton groupings (Comet et al. 1981) 62–465A–38–3*

Structure	Functional grouping						
	Carboxylic acids	Alcohols	Ketones	Alkanes	Alkenes	Aromatics	Total
Short straight chain[b]	263[a]	1.2	0.8	48.9	—	—	313.9
Long straight chain[c]	6.8	—	0.2	36.5	—	—	43.5
Very long straight chain	—	—	—	—	—	—	ND
Short monobranched[d]	10	—	—	—	—	—	10
Long monobranched	—	—	—	—	—	—	—
Acyclic diterpenoid[e]	0.5	—	0.2	6.2	—	—	6.9
Acyclic sesterterpenoid							
Other acyclic isoprenoids[f]	—	—	—	19.3	—	—	19.3
Partially cyclic tetraterp. (carotane)	—	—	—	—	—	—	ND
Cyclic diterpenoid	1.0	—	—	—	—	4.0	5.0
Hopanoid	1.0	—	6.2	52.4	92.3	26.4	178.4
Non-hopanoid triterpenoid	—	—	—	—	2.8	—	2.8
Desmethylsteroid[g]	—	4.2	7.5	13.2	36.8	Tr	61.7
4-methyl steroid[g]	—	0.8	6.1	0.3	8.8	Tr	16.0
Non-lipid PNA	—	—	—	—	—	1.4	1.4
Perylenes	—	—	—	—	—	4.6	4.6
Porphyrins + chlorins	—	—	—	—	—	600	600

[a] Includes unsaturated fatty acids;   [b] n-C_{10}–C_{20};   [c] n-C_{21}–C_{35};   [d] iso and anteiso C_{10}–C_{20};
[e] ex-phytol;   [f] C_{25} sesterterpane, squalane and (abundant) lycopane;   [g] See Table 7c.

TABLE 7c. *Albian limestone Hess rise 62–465A–38–3. Steroid data*[c,d,e] *(Comet et al. 1981)*

Steroid data

62—465A—38—3

c.d.e

Functionality / Side chain	Sterols Δ[0][f]	Δ[5]	Δ[5,22]	Δ[22]	Δ[7]	Δ[24]	Δ[5,24]	Δ[5,24(28)]	Δ[24(28)]	Other Ketones	Stan-3-one	Ster-4en-3one	Ster-22-enone	Sterene Δ[2]	Sterene Δ[4]	Sterene Δ[5]	Sterene Δ[3,5]	Sterene Δ[22]	Sterene Δ[2,4]	Rearr. Steranes	Rearr. Sterenes	Ster-trienes	Sterane	Aromatics[b]	Total
Desmethyl — Degraded																							1.36	—	1.36
	0.4	4.0									1.76	1.5			11.05	2.42					0.25		2.94	—	24.32
	0.4	0.6									0.66	0.3			4.86	0.69							1.64	—	9.13
														2.64				2.36					0.71	—	5.7
	0.4	1.0									2.28	1.1			10.35	2.32							5.1	—	22.55
																							1.35	—	1.35
Other desmethyl										3.0														—	3.3
										1.2														—	1.2
4-Methyl — Degraded	1.2												1.9					6.84	2.04					—	12.0
Degraded																							0.29	—	0.29
Other																									

[a] n.b. No distinction between 24R and S isomers;   [b] Traces only;   [c] ng/g dry weight sediment;
[d] The steroid data on this table is a breakdown of the steroid data on Table 7b;
[e] Δ refers to double bond position;   [f] Both 5 α and 5 β isomers.

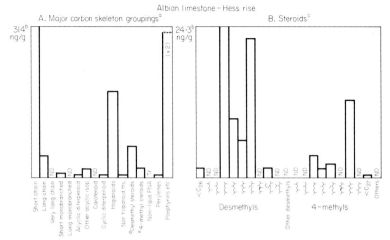

FIG. 5. Albian Limestone—Hess Rise (62–465A–38–3) Lipid data.
[a] See Table 7b.　　　　[b] Nannograms per gram dry weight sediment.　　　　[c] See Table 7c.

example, the hopane/sterane ratio is probably influenced by higher temperatures, i.e. oils sourced from a given source rock become relatively rich in hopanes and poor in steranes with increasing depth of burial (A. J. G. Barwise—personal communication). The hopane tetrol probably binds much more firmly into kerogen than do the sterols (with only one hydroxyl group). Kerogen cracking will initially yield oils rich in sterane and poor in hopane, further heating would liberate only hopanes, the steranes having

been already expelled (Comet 1984—unpublished results).

These problems may be circumvented in part by using natural product ratios of closely related structure and functionality in which differential thermal stability and ease of release from kerogen are minor problems (Table 9). Bearing in mind the above drawbacks it is possible, under favourable conditions, to identify different facies and to use organic geochemical parameters in facies description and correlation.

TABLE 8. *Characteristic[a] lipid assemblages from different kinds of sedimentary organic matter*

Aquatic phytoplankton organic matter

1 Relatively abundant polycyclic compounds compared with acyclic components.

2 Absence of strongly dominant n-alkanes ('plant wax') C_{21}–C_{35}, with a pronounced CPI (carbon preference index).

3 Abundant steranes.

4 Complex pattern of steroid side chains (C_{26}, C_{27}, nor steroids C_{28}, C_{29}) (two side chains), C_{30} etc.) for marine 'algal' distributions only[b]—for higher plants, side chain distribution pattern is much simpler.

5 Presence of algal markers, presence of gammacerane (from protozoa), 4, 23, 24-trimethylcholestane, presence of very long chain n-alkanes (C_{37}–C_{40})[b], carotanes, 'GX' (s) and botryococcane.

'Terrestrial' organic matter

1 Predominance (over the cyclics) of the heavier (C_{21}–C_{35}) n-alkanes (plant wax) with a pronounced C.P.I. (carbon preference index).

2 Abundant higher plant (non-hopanoid) triterpenoids and their degradation products (ex-resin).

3 Abundant diterpenoids, sesquiterpenoids and monoterpenoids (ex resin).

4 Abundant non-terpenoid aromatics.[c]

5 Steranes with a simple pattern of side chains, i.e. cholestane, ergostane, and stigmastane only.

6 Predominance of stigmastane.[d]

'Bacterial' organic matter

1 Predominance of hopanes (aerobic bacteria) over the steranes.

2 Predominance of C_{28} 4-methyl steranes (methanotrophs) within the 4-methyl series.

3 Abundant acyclic isoprenoids with ω,ω-linkage (C_{40}), as well as squalane, and possibly lycopane (methanogens).

4 Abundant iso and anteiso alkanes.

5 Absence of steranes.

6 Low abundance of n-alkanes.

---

[a] Note that these groups remain 'rather open' at present. Greater exactitude is not really possible at present with so few complete lipid analyses available in the literature.

[b] 'Brackish' lipid assemblages cannot at present be clearly distinguished from marine or terrestrial assemblages.

[c] Especially PNAs lacking extensive alkylation.　　　　[d] 24 R stereochemistry.

TABLE 9. *Parameters* proposed for the description of organic geochemical facies (i.e. source parameters)*

1 $\sum C_{26}/\sum C_{27}/\sum C_{28}/\sum C_{29}/\sum C_{30}$ desmethyl steranes
2 $\sum C_{28}/\sum C_{29}/\sum C_{30}$ 4-methyl steranes
3 $\sum$Desmethyl steranes $/\sum$4-methyl steranes
4 $\sum$Hopanes $/\sum$Non hopanoid triterpanes
5 $\sum$Hopanes $/\sum$Desmethyl steranes
6 $\sum$Diterpanes $/\sum$Steranes $/\sum$Triterpanes

* Parameters arranged in order of insensitivity to maturation. Parameters 5 and 6 are the most sensitive parameters to maturation: Parameters 1–4, the least sensitive (and most reliable).

All these parameters can be used in an analogous way to using the proportions of heavy minerals or quartz, clay and carbonate, in the description of a sedimentary rock. Though direct environmental information can be obtained by detailed lipid analysis, (Table 8) this table is tentatively intended to move *beyond* genetic explanations of the data (i.e. interpretation in terms of algal, bacterial and terrestrial environments), to purely formal description of a given source rock/oil etc. Eventually, based on these descriptive parameters, it may become possible to devise a nomenclature for particular organic geochemical associations, c.f. sedimentary facies nomenclature.

Overview

The present study has emphasized the value of lipids in sedimentary environmental studies. Progress has been made in the following areas:
(1) The recognition of the value of Ruzicka's biogenetic rules in classifying the numerous organic compounds in sediments into a few, clearly defined lipid sub-groups related to their biosynthetic origin.
(2) The application of the concept of a hierarchy of 'refined subsets' in demonstrating the relationships between the various lipid sub-groups. The hierarchy proposed represents a first, tentative attempt at delineating a 'geolipid family tree'.
(3) The carbon skeleton of a lipid structure is remarkably stable in sediments of different maturities. The proportions of the different structural types in a sediment have a strong environmental (rather than diagenetic) component.

(4) By cataloguing lipids in terms of their biological origin, i.e. making an attempt at a chemotaxonomic classification, sedimentary lipid distributions can be rationalized in terms of biota input.
(5) The use of structural summation as a technique in administering the data, i.e. to describe quantitatively the sediment or oil in terms of each structural grouping. The use of simple grids allows one to rapidly evaluate the proportions of each structural grouping.
(6) Alternatively, by monitoring with a grid the differing proportions of each functionalized component, a good idea of the maturation, or diagenetic zone that a sediment has reached may be obtained (J. McEvoy— unpublished data).
(7) Facies analysis can be attempted using histograms of the principal carbon skeleton groupings, and steroid sub-groupings. Marine, terrestrial and bacterial components of the sediments can be usually differentiated.
(8) Environmental sub-grouping can also be tentatively recognized. Thus marine sediments may be classifiable by their steroids. Terrestrial sediments possibly by their non-hopanoid triterpenoids. Bacterial input may also be capable of sub-division.
(9) Correlation studies using lipid groups show some promise, though a carefully selected suite of samples would be required to confirm the value of lipids in this type of work.
(10) Petroleum source studies may benefit from the application of the series of 'palaeoenvironmental rules' derived from the present studies. Thus petroleum may be classified according to its environment of deposition rather than by its physical properties or maturity. The principal terpenoid groups of an oil may provide significant clues as to its origin when compared with the embryonic 'data base' outlined in the present study.

ACKNOWLEDGEMENTS: We thank NERC (GR3/2951 and GR3758) for GC-MS facilities. We gratefully acknowledge Mrs A P Gowar for assistance with GC-MS analyses. Dr Robert Kidd and the National Science Foundation are thanked for provision of the sapronel samples. Drs P J McEvoy and J R Maxwell are thanked for useful discussions and critical comment.

References

BARNES, P. J., BRASSELL, S. C., COMET, P. A., EGLINTON, G., McEVOY, J., MARWELL, J. R., WARDROPER, A. M. K. & VOLKMAN, J. K. 1979. Preliminary lipid analyses of core sections 18, 24 and 30 from Hole 402A. *In:* MONTADERT, L., ROBERTS, D. G., *et al., Initial rep. deep sea drill proj.* **48**. Govt. Print. Off. Washington, D.C. 965–976.
BRASSELL, S. C., COMET, P. A., EGLINTON, G., McEVOY,

J., MAXWELL, J. R., QUIRKE, J. M. E., VOLKMAN, J. K. 1980a. Preliminary lipid analyses of Cores 14, 18 and 28 from Deep Sea Drilling Project Hole 416A. *In:* LANCELOT, Y., WINTERER, E. L. *et al., Initial Rep. Deep Sea drill proj.* **50**. U.S. Govt. Print Off. Washington, D.C. 647–664.

——, COMET, P. A., EGLINTON, G., ISAACSON, P. J., McEVOY, J., MAXWELL, J. R., THOMSON, I. D., TIBBETS, P. J. C. & VOLKMAN, J. K. 1980b. Preliminary lipid analyses of sections 440A–7–6, 440B–8–4, 440B–8–4, 440B–68–2 and 463–11–4. *In:* Scientific Party, *Initial Rep. Deep Sea drill Proj.* **56, 57** Part 2. U.S. Govt. Print. Off. Washington, D.C. 1367–1390.

BRASSELL, S. C., EGLINTON, G. & MAXWELL, J. R. 1981. Preliminary lipid analyses of two Quaternary sediments from the Middle America Trench, Southern Mexico transect. Deep Sea Drill. Proj. Leg 66. *In:* WATKINS, J. S., MOORE, J. C., *et al., Initial Rep. Deep Sea Drill. Proj.* **66**. U.S. Govt. Print. Off. Washington, D.C. 557–580.

COMET, P. A. 1982 *The use of lipids as facies indicators.* PhD Thesis, University of Bristol. (unpubl.)

——, McEVOY, J., BRASSELL, S. C., EGLINTON, G., MAXWELL, J. R. & THOMSON, I. D. 1981. Lipids of an upper Albian Limestone, section 465A–38–3. *In:* THIEDE, J., VALLIER, T. *et al., Initial Rep. Deep Sea drill proj.* **62**. U.S. Govt. Print. Off. Washington, D.C. 923–937.

DEVON, T. K. & SCOTT, A. I. 1972 *Handbook of Naturally Occurring Compounds II: Terpenes.* Academic Press, New York.

EGLINTON, G. 1973. Chemical fossils; a combined organic geochemical and environmental approach. *Pure and Applied Chemistry*, **34**, 611–632.

ESCHENMOSER, A. E., RUZICKA, L., JEGER, O. & ARIGONI, D. 1955. Zur kenntnis der triterpene. *Helv. Chim. Acta*, **38**, 1890.

HOWARD, D. L. 1980. Polycyclic triterpenes of the anaerobic photosynthetic bacterium *Rhodomicrobium vannielli.* PhD Thesis, University of California, Los Angeles (unpublished).

HSÜ, K., MONTADERT, L., *et al.* 1978. *Initial Rep. Deep Sea drill. Proj.* **42** (Part 1) U.S. Govt. Print. Off. Washington D.C. 1249 pp.

KIDD, R. B., CITA, M. B. & RYAN, W. B. F. 1978. Stratigraphy of Eastern Mediterranean sapropel sequences recovered during DSDP Leg 42A and palaeoenvironmental significance. *In:* HSÜ, K., MONTADERT, *et al.* 1978. *Initial Rep. Deep Sea drill. Proj.*, 42, Part 1. U.S. Government Printing Office, Washington, D.C. 421–444.

KIMBLE, B. J. 1972. *The geochemistry of triterpenoid hydrocarbons.* PhD Thesis, University of Bristol. (unpubl.).

MASRAN, T. C. & POCOCK, S. A. J. 1981. The classification of plant derived particulate organic matter in sedimentary rocks. *In:* BROOKS, J. (ed), *Organic Maturation studies and Fossil Fuel Exploration.* Academic Press. 441 pp.

McEVOY, J., EGLINTON, G. & MAXWELL, J. R. 1981. Preliminary lipid analyses of sediments from Sections 467–3–3 and 467–97–2. *In:* HAQ, B. U., YEATES, R. S. *et al., Initial Rep. Deep Sea drill. Proj.* 63. U.S. Government Printing Office, Washington, D.C. 763–774.

NOBLE, R., KNOX, J., ALEXANDER, R. & KAGI, R., in press. Identification of tetracyclic diterpanes in Australian crude oils and sediments. *Chem. Comm.*

OURISSON, G., ALBRECHT, P. & ROHMER, M. 1979. The hopanoids palaeochemistry and biochemistry of a group of natural products. *Pure and Applied Chemistry*, **51**, 709–729.

QUIRK, M. M. (1978). *Lipids of peat and lake environments.* PhD Thesis, University of Bristol (unpubl.).

RICHARDSON, J. S. & MÜLLER, D. E. 1982. Identification of dicyclic and tricyclic hydrocarbons in the saturate fraction of a crude oil by GC–MS. *Anal. Chem.* **54**, 765–768.

ROWLAND, S. J., YON, D. A., LEWIS, C. A. & MAXWELL, J. R., in press. Occurrence of 2,6,10-trimethyl-7(3-methylbutyl)-dodecane and related hydrocarbons in the green alga, *Enteromorpha prolifera* and sediments. *Org. Geochem.*

RUZICKA, L. 1959. History of the isoprene rule. *Proc. Chem. Soc.* 347.

TEMPLETON, W. 1969. An introduction to the chemistry of the terpenoids and steroids. Butterworths. Sevenoaks, Kent.

THOMSON, I. D., BRASSELL, S. C., EGLINTON, G. & MAXWELL, J. R. 1982. Preliminary lipid analysis of section 481–2–2. *In:* CURRAY, J. R., MOORE, D. G. *et al., Initial Rep. Deep Sea drill Proj.*, 64, Part 2. U.S. Government Printing Office, Washington, D.C. 913–919.

THIEDE, J., VALLIER, T. *et al.*, 1981. *Initial Rep. Deep Sea drill Proj. 62.* U.S. Government Printing Office, Washington, D.C. 1120 pp.

TISSOT, B. P. & WELTE, D. H. 1978. *Petroleum Formation and Occurrence.* Springer-Verlag. 538 pp.

YON, D. A., MAXWELL, J. R. & RYBACK, G. 1982. 2,6,10-trimethyl-7(3-methylbutyl)-dodecane, a novel biological marker compound. *Tetrahedron*, **23**, 2143–2146.

WARDROPER, A. M. K. 1979. *Aspects of the geochemistry of polycyclic isoprenoids.* PhD Thesis, University of Bristol. (unpubl.).

WARDROPER, A. M. K., MAXWELL, J. R. & MORRIS, R. J. 1978. Sterols of a diatomaceous ooze from Walvis Bay. *Steroids, 32*, 203–221.

P. A. COMET* and G. EGLINTON, Organic Geochemistry Unit, School of Chemistry, University of Bristol, Cantock's Close, Bristol, BS8 1TS.
Present address: Core Laboratories International Ltd, 24-A Lim Teck Boo Road, Singapore 1953.

Part II
Depositional Processes and Environments

The carbon cycle—tracking the path of organic particles from sea to sediment

E. T. Degens & V. Ittekkot

S U M M A R Y : Sedimentation of organic matter in the marine habitat represents a major link in the transfer of carbon from the hydrosphere to the geosphere. Evidence is presented that zooplankton and phytoplankton communities are actively involved in the fast removal of small-sized mineral and organic particles from the euphotic zone to the deep sea. For instance, copepods package detritus into faecal pellets which are jetted to the sea floor at velocities of about 500 m per day. Attention is also drawn to coccoliths. They excrete mucus which is instrumental in scavenging detritus and in forming macroflocs which rapidly sink. Time series sediment traps deployed in various shallow and deep-sea environments permit collection of such particles in mid-water. Variations in the distribution pattern of sugars, amino sugars, and amino acids indicate seasonality in the fluxes of 'fresh' materials. These data suggest that the bulk of small-sized particles presently suspended in surface waters of the open ocean is carried off by planktonic organisms to the sea floor. Prior to the advent of copepods or mucus-excreting nannoplankton in the stratigraphic record, the ancient sea must have looked different with respect to the content of suspended solids since settling velocities—according to Stoke's law—are only a few centimetres a day for clay-sized particles. Even at later geological times, environmental events that lead to unbalanced plankton communities should have found their echo in the sediment facies.

The assumption that anaerobic conditions combined with high primary productivity will in time generate a petroleum source bed explains the problem only superficially. In practice, a series of physical, chemical, biological, and geological factors must combine to yield a sediment of this distinction (Degens *et al.* 1981). Nevertheless, a *conditio sine qua non* is a substantial biological productivity in the aquatic environment be it fresh water or marine not only to secure an abundant supply of organic carbon but to dispatch clay-sized detritus and organic particles from the euphotic zone to the sediment-water interface. It is this transfer mechanism which will be the focal point of this article.

We were asked by the editors to present a brief overview on the global carbon cycle. It was felt that such background information could place the event of fossil fuel generation into its proper perspective and assist in judging the efficiency of hydrocarbon generation.

The global carbon cycle

From a rather elaborate scheme on the global carbon cycle recently presented (Bolin *et al.* 1979), we extracted the most critical parameters and arranged them into four major categories or compartments: air, sea, life and earth (Fig. 1). The pristine carbon cycle is characterized in that the four compartments are separated by distinct boundaries. Any carbon going from one box to

another has to pass through such an interface. The natural cycle reveals that we are dealing with a kind of steady state where input and output are balanced out. It is evident that most of the turnover of carbon is related to the activity of terrestrial and aquatic organisms and the chemical exchange at the air–sea interface. All in all 182×10^{15} g C y^{-1} is recycled between biosphere, hydrosphere and atmosphere. In contrast, the contribution from volcanic emanations represents about 0.2×10^{15} g C y^{-1}. The bulk of this carbon is recycled and derived from former sediments or sea water passing through the oceanic crust. It appears that biological activity is tuned to this rate of crustal carbon release. About three quarters of this carbon is returned to the geosphere as carbonate and one fourth in the form of organic matter. In short, the efficiency of the exogenic turnover is several orders higher than the release or uptake of carbon by the lithosphere.

Superimposed on the pristine carbon cycle is man's contribution (Fig. 1). Fossil fuel burning and changing land use has caused an increase in atmospheric CO_2 because the rate at which man-made carbon is presently emitted into the air is higher than the speed of its removal by natural processes. Oil, coal and gas combustion will release about 5×10^{15} g C y^{-1} into the atmosphere. Added to this are *ca.* 2×10^{15} g C y^{-1} from deforestation activities largely in tropical forests (Bolin *et al.* 1979). There is consensus with respect to the first figure, whereas the deforestation value

From: BROOKS, J. & FLEET, A. J. (eds) 1987, *Marine Petroleum Source Rocks*
Geological Society Special Publication No. 26 pp. 121–135.

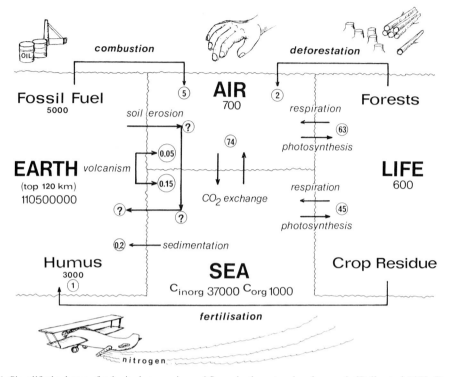

FIG. 1. Simplified scheme of principal reservoirs and fluxes in the natural carbon cycle (Bolin *et al.* 1979; Degens 1982). The sizes of the reservoirs are given in gigatons ($= 10^9$ t or 10^{15} g C); the magnitude of the fluxes (encircled numbers) is given in gigatons C y^{-1}. Man's input is depicted as combustion, deforestation, and fertilization. Wavy lines are drawn to emphasize that the individual compartments are separated by boundaries.

might be in error by $\pm 1 \times 10^{15}$ g C y^{-1}. Of that total amount, 2.5×10^{15} g C y^{-1} remains airborne and is the cause of the present increase of atmospheric CO_2 at a rate of about 1.5 ppm y^{-1} (e.g. Keeling *et al.* 1976; Freyer 1979). There is strong indication that about 2.5×10^{15} g C y^{-1} of human induced CO_2 is removed by the sea (Chen 1982). The remaining 2×10^{15} g C y^{-1} is temporarily stored in humus or is utilized by organisms (eutrophication effect). Eventually, however, the shallow sea becomes the final burying ground for the about 2×10^{15} g C y^{-1} of man-made CO_2 (Degens 1982).

At the present rate of fossil fuel burning, the reserves estimated at 5000×10^{15} g C will be exhausted in less than 1000 years. On the basis of carbon, the fossil fuel reserves are only about 10 times the amount contained in modern biota and 50 times the value annually generated by photosynthesis. In the sea, photosynthesis yields 45×10^{15} g C y^{-1}. It is the origin and fate of these 45 billion tons of annually produced carbon that we turn our attention to.

Organic carbon pools—overview

The major oceanic and land organic carbon pools are depicted in Figure 2. Soil organic carbon is by far the most substantial pool followed by dissolved organic carbon in the sea and by land biomass. In contrast, oceanic biomass is minimal. Turning to the oceanic organic carbon pool, the major role is played by the dissolved organic carbon of the deep-sea environment. Although this is a major sink quantitatively, it is rather inert, biologically, and appears to have originated mainly from inputs from rivers (Degens & Ittekkot 1983). Dissolved marine organic carbon is of low molecular weight (< 5000 daltons) and becomes slowly oxidized at a rate which is equal to the discharge rate of riverine organic carbon to the sea. Particulate carbon, plankton and bacteria contribute to the rest of the oceanic organic carbon pool. Riverine contribution of particulate organic carbon to the open sea is minimal, because it is mainly trapped in estuaries and deltas (Deuser 1979).

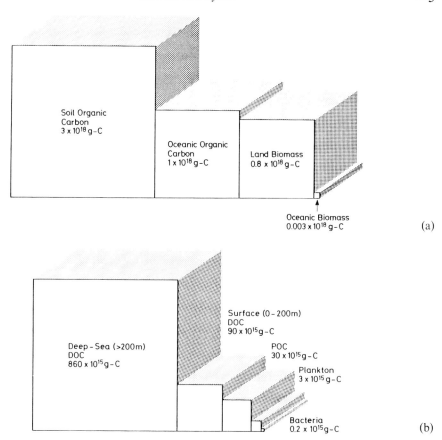

FIG. 2. (a) Comparison of oceanic and land organic carbon pools. (b) Distribution of organic carbon pools in the ocean.

Fig. 3 presents data on the distribution of water volume above the seafloor above different depth intervals, and the inputs of organic carbon to surface waters above the same depths. High inputs of organic matter to a small volume of water over the shelves are registered. This is due to input from rivers, not only of particulate organic carbon, but also of mineral nutrients which increase the primary productivity and organic input in these regions.

Tracking techniques by organic tracers

The method adopted here involved identification of specific groups of organic compounds and relating them to the source materials, and the probable transport and transformation processes. This method has been successfully used in gaining information on processes in a wide variety of

sedimentary environments (e.g. Degens & Mopper 1976; Didyk *et al.* 1978; Böhm *et al.* 1980).

Sugars and amino acids comprise 40–80% of organic matter of most organisms and, as a consequence, represent a large part of organic input to the aquatic sedimentary environment. They are primarily associated with structural components—biominerals—of these organisms. Biominerals are composed of an inorganic phase (mineral phase) and an organic phase. The organic phase acts as a template on which epitaxial growth of the mineral phase proceeds. Sugars and amino acids act as templates in the biomineralization of silicate, phosphate, and carbonate minerals (see Degens 1976 for a review). The utility of sugars and amino acids as biogeochemical tracers stems from the fact that species-specific patterns exist. Data collected over several years in the authors' laboratories, and those collected by colleagues (e.g. Parsons *et al.* 1961; King 1974; Müller & Suess 1977) further indicate that specific sugars and amino acids are

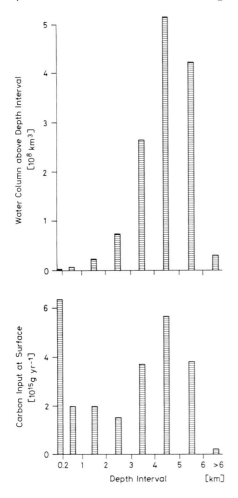

FIG. 3. Distribution of volume of water above different depth intervals of the sea floor and the input of organic carbon to the surface waters above the same depth intervals (after Deuser 1979).

fucose and aspartic acid:glycine in mineralized tissues are reversed, with arabinose and aspartic acid dominating the organic matter associated with carbonate producers.

The amino acid:hexosamine (AA/HA) ratios are indicators of the relative inputs from phytoplankton and zooplankton, especially crustaceans. Although bacteria, and the peritrophic membranes of faecal pellets of crustaceans contain minor quantities of hexosamine this is probably insignificant in comparison with the amount of chitin present in the whole crustacean (Raymont *et al.* 1969). A dominant input from crustacean remains will shift this ratio in favour of hexosamines.

A second group of indicators concerns the microbially and abiotically mediated transformation products of the organic matter within the water column and in sediments. The nonprotein amino acids: β-alanine, γ-aminobutyric acid and ornithine are products of decomposition of aspartic and glutamic acids and arginine respectively. Since microbial transformation of organic matter in the deep-sea environment (>1000 m) appears to be retarded (Jannasch *et al.* 1971), or minimal with respect to proteinaceous materials (Wefer *et al.* 1982), variations in the relative amounts of these amino acids in deep-sea tripton probably reflects the degree of microbial reworking of organic matter in the biologically active surface layers. Expressed differently, they mirror the relative 'freshness' of organic matter.

We have used these biochemical indicators in interpreting results of sugar and amino acid analyses of materials collected during time series sediment trap deployments from three marine environments—the North Sea, the Sargasso Sea and the Panama Basin. Details of the experiments can be found elsewhere (Deuser *et al.* 1981; Honjo 1982; Honjo *et al.* 1982).

potentially useful not only as indicators of the source but also of the transport and transformation processes operating within the water column, and in sediments.

The major input of organic matter in marine sediments is in association with shells, tests and frustules of calcareous and siliceous organisms. Relative inputs from the various sources can be ascertained by examining the distribution pattern of specific sugars and amino acids. For example, relative amounts of the sugars: arabinose and fucose, and those of the amino acids: aspartic acid and glycine, may be used to distinguish between inputs from silica and carbonate producers. Although they are constituents of both silica and carbonate producers, the ratios arabinose:

North Sea

Samples from the North Sea were collected during time series sediment trap deployments at three depths within the water column during the Fladenground Experiment (FLEX 1976). Sampling intervals were up to seven days, and the traps deployed were of the type described by Zeitschel *et al.* (1978). FLEX 1976 took place within a 100 km-side square and covered a three month period from mid-March to mid-June 1976. During the experiment a series of physical, chemical, and biological parameters were measured at a central station in Fladenground (58° 55′ N, 0° 32′ E) at intervals of two to six hours. Some critical data are depicted in Fig. 4. Briefly, the main spring bloom started with the

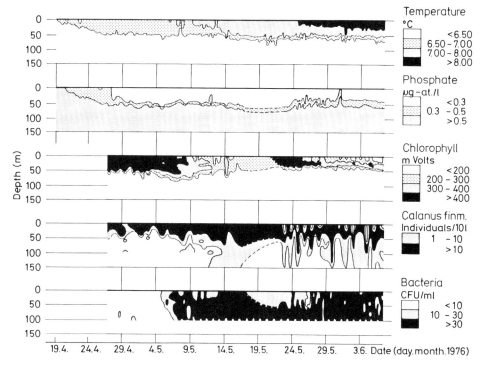

FIG. 4. Depth and time profiles of water temperature, phosphate, chlorophyll, *Calanus finmarchicus*, and colony-forming bacteria (CFU) at a central station, during FLEX 1976. For details see text (after Bolin *et al.* 1979).

formation of the thermocline in the second half of April and came to an end near May 4. This bloom (which was dominated by the diatoms of *Chaetoceros* sp.) was followed by a less intense bloom of dinoflagellates and small diatoms (Wandschneider 1980). With the development of the first bloom the level of dissolved nutrients was lowered in the upper layers. Following the *Chaetoceros* bloom, zooplankton—*Calanus finmarchicus*—and colony-forming bacteria appeared in large numbers (Krause 1981; Hentzschel 1980). These measurements gave the opportunity of correlating the nature of the sedimenting organic matter with specific biogenic input from the surface layers.

Fluxes of sugars varied in response to the development of the *Chaetoceros* bloom at 100 and 125 m (Fig. 5a). Amino acid fluxes showed a similar trend at 125 m, but increased steadily at 100 m with time. However, the nature of organic matter being sedimented is similar. This is seen from the AA/HA ratio (Fig. 5b), which indicates a predominant input from phytoplankton. The fluxes of sugars and amino acids increased after this period, and dramatically so, at 125 m. AA/HA ratio of this flux was lower than that of the

flux from the previous time increment, which indicates an additional input from zooplankton remains. It must, however, be noted that this large flux may be associated with actively swimming zooplankton entering the trap. Since the traps were poisoned it is difficult to distinguish between poisoned active swimmers and passive sinkers. Hence the flux measured during this period may not necessarily reflect the actual vertical flux. In addition, resuspension and redeposition of the sinking materials can also contribute to such a large flux. In fact, what appears to be a vertical 'upward' flux of faecal pellets was observed during this period (Krause 1981). The disintegration of these materials within the surface layers contributed partly to an increase in dissolved organic matter during this period (Ittekkot 1982). Such processes can complicate flux calculations made from a high energy environment such as the North Sea, unless detailed information on the hydrographic parameters is available. Stormy weather conditions leading to the breakdown of the main thermocline, vertical upward flux of sedimenting materials, and input from active swimmers could all have contributed to the large flux recorded.

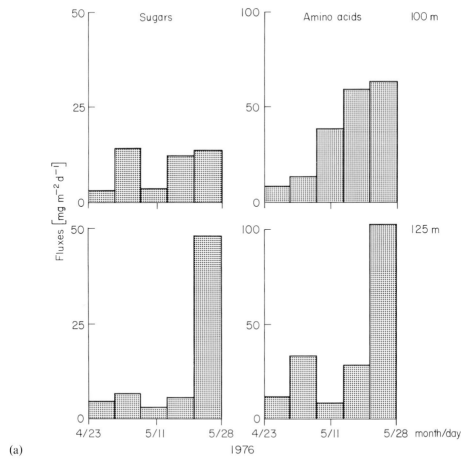

(a)

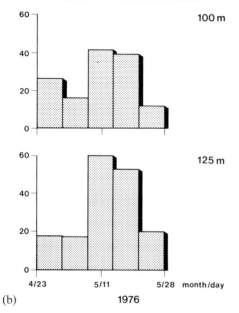

(b)

FIG. 5. (a) Fluxes of sugars and amino acids during time series sediment trap deployments in the North Sea during FLEX 1976; see also text. (b) Ratios of amino acids:hexosamines of the nitrogenous materials measured during time series sediment trap deployments in the North Sea during FLEX 1976; see also text.

Sargasso Sea

Particulate flux to the deep Sargasso Sea were sampled during successive two month sediment trap deployments from April 1978 to December 1981. The trap was moored 45 km southeast of Bermuda, 3200 ± 100 m below the sea surface and 1000 m above the seafloor. Studies on organic matter flux in the collected materials revealed seasonal fluctuations in pulse with primary productivity in the surface layers (Deuser & Ross 1980). This seasonality was also characteristic for the flux of materials in the $< 37 \mu m$ fraction. Analyses of sugars, amino acids and amino sugars showed a similar seasonality associated with the nature of organic input from the surface layers (Fig. 6) (Ittekkot *et al.*, 1984b).

Distribution patterns of sugars and amino acids were in general similar to those reported for biomineralized tissues of carbonate and silica producers and the cell walls of nonbiomineralizing organisms. However, the amounts of nonprotein amino acids, i.e. β-alanine, and γ-aminobutyric acid relative to aspartic and glutamic acids, and those of hexosamines relative to total amino acids varied seasonally (Fig. 7) and in phase with the flux of materials shown in Fig. 6. During high flux periods the amount of nonprotein amino acids is low in comparison to aspartic and glutamic acids. This implies that organic matter arriving at the trap during high flux periods—related to surface productivity peaks—is microbially less degraded than at other times. This shows materials collected in the trap during these periods have been rapidly transferred to the deep-sea environment from the surface layers. This transfer appears to have taken place on large aggregate particles such as faecal pellets or macroaggregates.

A major problem with the approach taken here is the uncertainty concerning the nature and extent of degradation of organic matter within the traps. A recent paper by Gardner *et al.* (1983) shows that loss of organic matter from the trapped materials can take place due to decomposition, cell lysis or leaching. However, a direct comparison between the results obtained by them and those presented here may not be realistic. By their very nature, the materials used by Gardner *et al.* (1983) in their experiments—lobster shells, squid pens and zooplankton—may not be representative of the natural particles reaching the deep-sea environment (Lee *et al.* 1983). Our data on sugars and amino acids show that the organic matter associated with settling particles is mainly in the form of structural components. At best the results obtained by Gardner *et al.* (1983) may be relevant for materials collected during periods of peak surface productivity, when there is a predominant input of 'fresh' materials.

The ratio of amino acids: hexosamines also shows a similar trend for the flux of materials from 1978 to 1980. However, for the anomalously large flux of 1981 (Fig. 6) they remained nearly constant. Hexosamines were present in higher amounts relative to amino acids compared to previous years. C/N ratios and the distribution pattern of the major sugars and amino acids showed no significant variations (Ittekkot *et al.* 1984b) in comparison with the fluxes of previous years. From the amino acid: hexosamine ratios it appears that there is a difference in the relative proportions of organic matter from different sources reaching the traps. The anomalously large flux of 1981 is associated with a discrete input. The abundance of phytoplankton remains (cell walls and biomineralized tissues) during 1979 and 1980 suggests that rapidly sinking faecal pellets or macroaggregates are probably the principal removal mechanisms of phytoplankton debris from the surface layers. In contrast, the low AA/HA ratios in the 1981 flux indicate that in addition to the above, crustacean remains also contribute significantly to the observed flux.

Results of the above study show that zooplankton populations through their active and passive products are instrumental in the transfer of materials into the deep ocean. Biochemical evidence for a different transport mechanism was obtained from studies from another deep-sea environment—the Panama Basin.

Panama Basin

Time series sediment trap deployments at three depths—860 m, 2590 m and 3560 m—in the Panama Basin (5° 22' N, 85° 35' W) during 1980 revealed seasonality in the fluxes of materials to deep ocean related to surface primary productivity (Honjo 1982). There were two peak fluxes: one in February–March, which was associated with a high productivity during regional upwelling, and the other with an unusual bloom of a single species of coccolithophorids, *Umbellicosphaera sibogae*. The peaks in mass flux were registered at all the three depths simultaneously. The samples from these experiments were analysed for sugars and amino acids, details of which are presented elsewhere (Ittekkot *et al.* 1984a).

The nature of organic input associated with the two peak fluxes showed distinct characteristics which were related to the source materials in the surface layers. The differences were manifested in the relative abundances of the sugars: ribose, arabinose and fucose, and those of the amino acids: aspartic acid and glycine (Fig. 8).

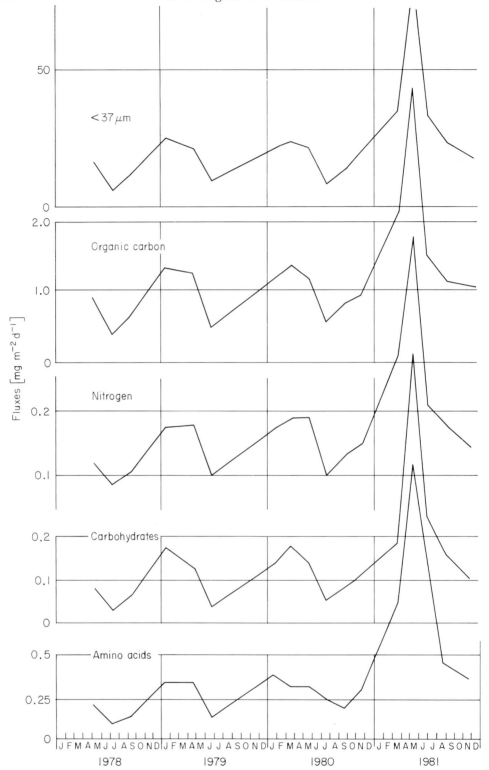

FIG. 6. Fluxes of organic carbon, nitrogen, amino acids and sugars in the < 37 μm fraction of materials arriving at a sediment trap set at 3000 ± 100 m in the Sargasso Sea; measured during continuous sediment trap deployments from April 1978 to December 1981; for details see Deuser *et al.* (1981) and Ittekkot *et al.* (1984b).

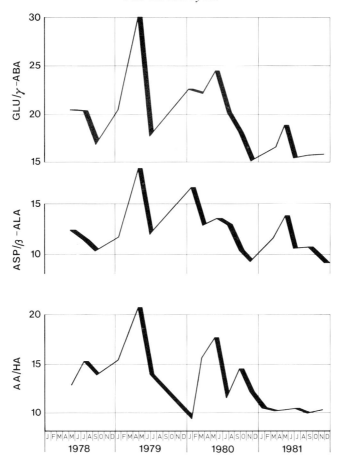

FIG. 7. Ratios of aspartic acid:β-alanine, glutamic acid:γ-aminobutyric acid, amino acids:hexosamines of the materials in the < 37 μm fractions; details as for Fig. 6.

Organic matter associated with the June–July flux was enriched in aspartic acid, ribose and arabinose. The ratios arabinose:fucose, and aspartic acid:glycine were highest during this period. Most remarkable is the fact that these characteristics were recorded at all depths simultaneously. This suggests that the materials were transported rapidly to the deeper layers, i.e. within the two months of the collection period, and that no significant transformation of the materials had taken place during transit. In contrast to transport mechanisms involving active or passive participation of zooplankton populations as was discerned for materials arriving at the deep-sea environment of the Sargasso Sea, the peak flux of June–July in the Panama Basin appears to have arrived via a different vehicle. What appears to have caused this mass transport is the formation of macroaggregates via

a polysaccharide-rich organic matter of the mucopolysaccharide type, released by the alga itself. Interestingly, macroaggregates of this type are found to be capable not only of transporting biogenic matter rapidly from the surface layers, but also of translating horizontally advected abiogenic particles in midwater into vertical flux (Honjo *et al*. 1982).

Seasonality in the sedimentation of organic matter in the open ocean environment as discerned from the data presented above, show that the present-day deep-sea environment is more dynamic and variable in nature than previously thought. One might expect the records of these to be smoothed out by burrowing organisms in a fully oxygenated ocean. However, such records may be well preserved in sediments taken in areas of restricted water circulation, such as the modern Black Sea basin.

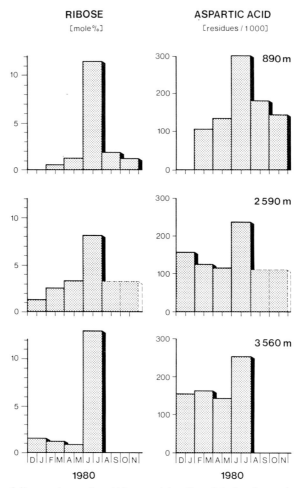

FIG. 8. (a) Distribution of ribose and aspartic acid in materials collected during time series sediment trap deployments in the Panama Basin; for details see Honjo (1982) and Ittekkot *et al.* (1984a).

Black Sea

Since the Black Sea sediments were deposited under varying environmental conditions, fluctuations in the nature of organic matter associated with these environmental changes can be clearly discerned (Degens & Stoffers 1980). For example, data on amino acids and hexosamines in sediments from the Black Sea (Fig. 9) show that during the period between 3500 and 7500 years B.P. the hexosamine content was negligible. Before and after this, hexosamine was a substantial fraction of the total nitrogenous organic matter. It appears that this sudden drop in hexosamine was due to the onset of conditions of extremely high productivity, perhaps eutrophic conditions, in the surface waters. During eutrophic conditions, the algal biomass which

contains little or no chitinous materials (hexosamines) overwhelms the zooplankton biomass, which generally contains significant quantities of chitinous materials, with the result that the sediment has a high amino acid/hexosamine ratio. The decline of zooplankton populations could have also been caused by the establishment of saline conditions around 7500 years B.P., with the pronounced influx of Mediterranean waters.

Only at times of balanced plankton communities is the transport of materials from the euphotic zone to the bottom of the sea secured. The formation of sapropels in the Black Sea environment which is linked to the stratification of the water body, should thus be regarded not only as a result of eutrophication but the lack of mechanisms to transfer clay-sized particles rapidly from surface to sediment.

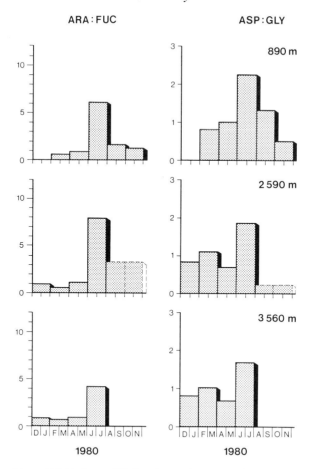

FIG. 8. (b) Ratios of arabinose (ARA):fucose (FUC) and aspartic acid (ASP):glycine (GLY) in materials collected during sediment trap deployments in the Panama Basin. Details as for Fig. 8a.

Discussion

Data presented above and those of previous workers suggest the existence of biological mechanisms in the rapid transport of materials to the deep ocean. This transfer appears to proceed on 'vehicles' such as faecal pellets (Schrader 1971; Honjo 1982), faecal matter (Bishop *et al.* 1977) and marine snow (Alldredge 1979; Shanks & Trent 1980), which are created at the sea surface. Remarkably these vehicles are involved not only in the transport of biogenic particles, but also of wind-transported abiogenic materials (Deuser *et al.* 1983) and horizontally advected suspended clays (Honjo *et al.* 1982). It appears that packaged in or on such vehicles particles even in the fine fractions reach the sea floor within weeks, which would have otherwise remained suspended for years (Fig. 10).

In the modern deep-sea environment, because of this biological control, the residence time of particles within the water column is short, and as a consequence, particle/sea water interaction is probably insignificant. This implies arrival at the sediment-water interface of biogenic and abiogenic particles which are not in equilibrium with seawater. With respect to organic matter, significant quantities of metabolizable organic matter may be expected to arrive at the seafloor. Significance of this organic flux for deep-sea benthic communities is apparent; seasonality in the reproductive pattern of benthic communities is probably triggered by a seasonality in the flux of metabolizable organic matter.

Comparison of the distribution pattern of sugars and amino acids of materials arriving at our deepest sedimentation traps with those in the underlying sediments reveal significant differ-

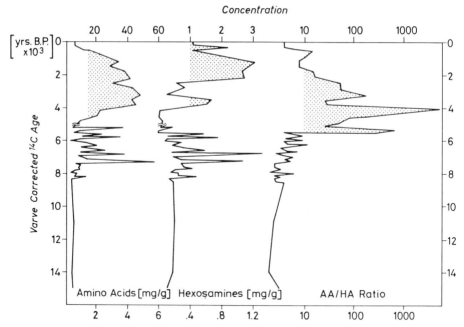

FIG. 9. Distribution of amino acids and hexosamines and the ratios amino acids:hexosamines in a Black Sea core (Degens & Mopper 1976).

ences. In materials collected in the traps the concentrations of amino acids and sugars are considerably higher. In contrast, non-protein amino acids, indicators of microbial decomposition of organic matter are higher in sediments (Whelan 1977). In the present-day deep-sea environment there appears to be at or near the sediment-water interface a zone of intense biochemical activity—the 'benthic transition layers' of Honjo et al. (1982)—where significant alteration of organic matter takes place. In fact, such alterations may also be expected to affect even the abiogenic input.

In ancient environments devoid of such mechanisms, before the advent of zooplankton communities and mucopolysaccharide-releasing algae—sedimentation processes must have been different, and for fine particles, more in agreement with Stoke's Law. This would result in a longer residence time for these particles, and as a consequence more intense particle–seawater interactions. The material reaching the seafloor would be more in equilibrium with seawater. Furthermore, intensive remineralization of organic matter should proceed within the water column, allowing only organic matter with refractory character to be buried in sediments. On the other hand, oxidation of organic matter will entail

removal of oxygen from the water column, making it prone to anoxic conditions. An excellent example of such an environment is the Precambrian sea. The mechanisms suggested above will imply that the environmental conditions that existed in the Precambrian were those bordering oxic and anoxic conditions, and that slight changes in the biogeochemical situation would have tilted it into the oxic or anoxic direction. The extensive occurrences of minerals formed in environments ranging from oxidizing to reducing at those times is probably related to such mechanisms (e.g. Floran & Papike 1975).

During the past 600 million years world oceans continued to oscillate between oxic and anoxic conditions (Degens & Stoffers 1976). Anoxic conditions were prevalent during definite geological periods, for example, during the Lower Paleozoic, Jurassic and Cretaceous (Schlanger & Jenkyns 1976; Ryan & Cita 1977; Jenkyns 1980; Leggett 1980; Morris 1980). The basic mechanism which led to world-wide anoxia is probably similar to the one which was encountered in the Precambrian, especially if one considers that these occurrences were during periods of large-scale global extinctions of planktonic communities (Tappan & Loeblich 1971), which would otherwise have influenced sedimentation proc-

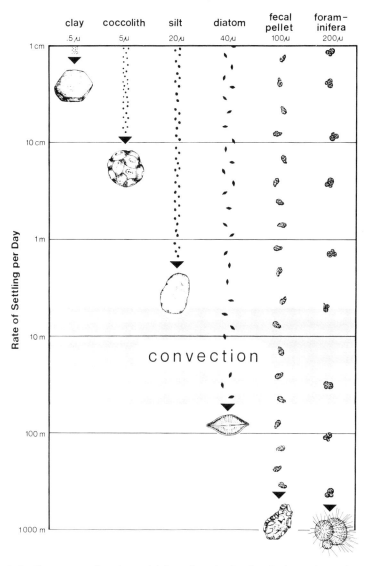

FIG. 10. Settling rates per day of materials in various size fractions in the marine environment.

esses. At those times, detritus content in the open ocean must have been more substantial because the convenient transfer vehicle for suspended particles: faecal pellets, macroaggregates or macroflocs were retarded on the global scale. On the other hand, particles with high specific density generated in the water columns, such as sulphides, would rapidly sink and accumulate at the sediment surface. The same applies to airborne particles derived from sand storms or cosmic dust. Geochemical anomalies in sediments would be the consequence.

ACKNOWLEDGEMENTS: Samples from sediment trap experiments in the North Sea, Sargasso Sea and the Panama Basin were provided, respectively by Drs U. Brockman, W. G. Deuser and S. Honjo. Mrs I. Jennerjahn provided secretarial assistance. Financial support for the study was obtained through grants from the German Ministry for Science and Technology (BMFT Grant MFG 0034) and from the Shell Grants Committee, London.

DEDICATION: This paper is dedicated to Friedhelm Korte, on the occasion of his 60th birthday.

References

ALLDREDGE, A. L. 1979. The chemical composition of macroscopic aggregates in two neritic seas. *Limnol. Oceanogr.* **24**, 855–866.

BISHOP, J. K. B., EDMOND, J. M., KETTEN, D. R., BACON, M. P. & SILKER, W. B. 1977. The chemistry, biology, and vertical flux of particulate matter from the upper 400 m of the equatorial Atlantic Ocean. *Deep-Sea Res.* **24**, 511–548.

BÖHM, L., DAWSON, R., LIEBEZEIT, G. & KAMINSKI, E. 1978. Suitability of monosaccharides as markers for particle identification in carbonate sediments. *Sedimentology,* **27**, 167–177.

BOLIN, B., DEGENS, E. T., KEMPE, S. & KETNER, P. (eds) 1979. *The Global Carbon Cycle.* SCOPE Report **13**, John Wiley & Sons, Chichester, 491 pp.

CHEN, C. T. 1982. On the distribution of anthropogenic CO_2 in the Atlantic and southern oceans. *Deep-Sea Res.* **29**, 563–580.

DEGENS, E. T. 1976. Molecular mechanisms on carbonate, phosphate and silica deposition in the living cell. *Topics in Curr. Chem.,* **64**, 1–112.

DEGENS, E. T. 1982. Riverine carbon—an overview. *In:* DEGENS, E. T. (ed), *Transport of Carbon and Minerals in Major World Rivers,* Part 1, Mitt. Geol.-Paläont. Inst. Univ. Hamburg, SCOPE/UNEP Sonderband, **52**, 1–12.

—— & ITTEKKOT, V., 1983. Dissolved organic carbon—an overview. *In:* DEGENS, E. T., KEMPE, S. & SOLIMAN, H. (eds), *Transport of Carbon and Minerals in Major World Rivers,* Part 2, Mitt. Geol.-Paläont. Inst. Univ. Hamburg, SCOPE/UNEP Sonderband, **55**, 21–38.

——, MICHAELIS, W. & PALUSKA, A. 1981. Principles of petroleum source bed formation. *In:* MERRICK, D. & MARSHALL, R. (eds), *Energy—Present and Future Options, 1,* John Wiley & Sons, Chichester, New York, Brisbane, Toronto. 93–186.

—— & MOPPER, K. 1976. Factors controlling the distribution and early diagenesis of organic material in marine sediments. *In:* RILEY, J. P. & CHESTER, R. (eds), *Chemical Oceanography,* 2nd Edition, **6**, 60–114.

—— & STOFFERS, P. 1976. Stratified waters as a key to the past. *Nature,* **263**, 22–27.

—— & STOFFERS, P. 1980. Environmental events recorded in Quaternary sediments of the Black Sea. *J. geol. Soc. London,* **137**, 131–138.

DEUSER, W. G. 1979. Marine biota, nearshore sediments and the global carbon balance. *Org. Geochem.* **1**, 243–247.

—— & ROSS, E. H. 1980. Seasonal changes in the flux of organic matter to the deep Sargasso Sea. *Nature,* **283**, 364–365.

——, ROSS, E. H. & ANDERSON, R. F. 1981. Seasonality in the supply of sediment to the deep Sargasso Sea and implications for the rapid transfer of matter to the deep ocean. *Deep-Sea Res.* **28**, 495–505.

——, BREWER, P. G., JICKELLS, T. D. & COMMEAU, R. D. 1983. Biological control of the removal of abiogenic particles from the surface ocean. *Science,* **219**, 388–391.

DIDYK, B. M., SIMONEIT, B. R. T., BRASSELL, S. C. & EGLINTON, G. 1978. Organic geochemical indicators of palaeoenvironmental conditions of sedimentation. *Nature,* **272**, 216–222.

FLORAN, R. J. & PAPIKE, J. J. 1975. Petrology of the low-grade rocks of the Gunflint Iron-Formation, Ontario-Minnesota. *Geol. Soc. Amer. Bull.* **86**, 1169–1190.

FREYER, H. D. 1979. Variations in the atmospheric CO_2 content. *In:* BOLIN, B., DEGENS, E. T., KEMPE, S. & KETNER, P. (eds), *The Global Carbon Cycle,* SCOPE Report **13**, John Wiley & Sons, Chichester. 79–99.

GARDNER, W. D., HINGA, K. R. & MARRA, J. 1983. Observations on the degradation of biogenic material in the deep ocean with implication on accuracy of sediment trap fluxes. *J. Mar. Res.* **41**, 195–214.

HENTZSCHEL, G. 1980. Wechselwirkungen bakteriolytischer und saprophytischer Bakterien aus der Nordsee. *Mitt. Inst. Allg. Bot. Hamburg,* **17**, 113–124.

HONJO, S. 1982. Seasonality and interaction of biogenic and lithogenic particulate flux at the Panama Basin. *Science,* **218**, 883–884.

——, SPENCER, D. W. & FARRINGTON, J. W. 1982. Deep advective transport of lithogenic particles in Panama Basin. *Science,* **216**, 516–518.

ITTEKKOT, V. 1982. Variations of dissolved organic matter during a plankton bloom. Qualitative aspects, based on sugar and amino acid analyses. *Mar. Chem.* **11**, 143–158.

——, DEGENS, E. T. & HONJO, S. 1984a. Seasonality in the fluxes of sugars, amino acids and amino sugars to deep ocean. Panama Basin. *Deep-Sea Res.* **31**, 1071–1083.

——, DEUSER, W. G. & DEGENS, E. T. 1984b. Seasonality in the fluxes of sugars, amino acids and amino sugars to deep ocean. Sargasso Sea. *Deep-Sea Res.* **31**, 1057–1069.

JANNASCH, H. W., EIMHJELLEN, K., WIRSEN, C. O. & FARMANFARMIAN, A. 1971. Microbial degradation of organic matter in the deep sea. *Science,* **171**, 672–675.

JENKYNS, H. C. 1980. Cretaceous anoxic events: from continents to oceans. *J. geol. Soc. London,* **137**, 171–188.

KEELING, C. D., BACASTOW, R. B., BAINBRIDGE, A. E., EKDAHL, C. A., GUENTHER, P. R., WATERMAN, L. S. & CHIN, J. F. S. 1976. Atmospheric carbon dioxide variations at Mauna Loa Observatory, Hawaii. *Tellus,* **28**, 538–551.

KING, K., jr., 1974. Preserved amino acids from silicified protein in fossil radiolaria. *Nature,* **252**, 690–692.

KRAUSE, M. 1981. Vertical distribution of fecal pellets during FLEX 1976. *Helgoländer wiss. Meeresunters.* **34**, 313–327.

LEE, C., WAKEHAM, S. G. & FARRINGTON, J. W. 1983. Variations in the composition of particulate organic matter in a time series sediment trap. *Mar. Chem.* **13**, 181–194.

LEGGETT, J. K. 1980. British Lower Paleozoic black

shales and their palaeo-oceanographic significance. *J. geol. Soc. London*, **137**, 139–156.

MORRIS, K. A. 1980. A comparison of major sequences of organic rich shales in the British Jurassic. *J. geol. Soc. London*, **137**, 157–170.

MÜLLER, P. J. & SUESS, E. 1977. Interaction of organic compounds with calcium carbonate: III. Amino acid composition of sorbed layers. *Geochim. Cosmochim. Acta*, **41**, 941–949.

PARSONS, T. R., STEPHEN, K. & STRICKLAND, J. D. 1961. On the chemical composition of eleven species of marine phytoplankters. *J. Fish. Res. Bd. Canada*, **18**, 1001–1016.

RAYMONT, J. E. G., SREENIVASAGAM, R. T. & RAYMONT, J. K. B. 1969. Biochemical studies on marine zooplankton. VII. Observations of certain deep sea zooplankton. *Int. Rev. ges. Hydrobiol.* **54**, 357–365.

RYAN, W. B. & CITA, M. B. 1977. Ignorance concerning episodes of ocean-wide stagnation. *Mar. Geol.* **23**, 197–215.

SCHLANGER, S. O. & JENKYNS, H. C. 1976. Cretaceous oceanic anoxic events, causes and consequences. *Geol. Mijnbouw*, **55**, 179–184.

SCHRADER, H. J. 1971. Fecal pellets in sedimentation of pelagic diatoms. *Science*, **201**, 371–373.

SHANKS, A. L. & TRENT, J. D. 1980. Marine snow: sinking rates and potential role in vertical flux. *Deep-Sea Res.* **27**, 137–143.

TAPPAN, H. & LOEBLICH, A. R., jr. 1971. Geological implications of fossil phytoplankton evolution and time-space distribution. *In*: KOSANKE, R. M. & CROSS, E. T. (eds) *Symp. Palynology of Late Cretaceous and Early Tertiary*, East Lansing, Michigan State University. 247–340.

WANDSCHNEIDER, K. 1980. Die Artensukzession des Phytoplanktons während der Frühjahrsblüte 1976 im Fladengrundgebiet (nördliche Nordsee). *Mitt. Inst. Allg. Bot. Hamburg*, **17**, 39–48.

WEFER, G., SUESS, E., BALZER, W., LIEBEZEIT, G., MÜLLER, P. J., UNGERER, C. A. & ZENK, W. 1982. Fluxes of biogenic components from sediment trap deployment of circumpolar waters of the Drake Passage. *Nature*, **299**, 145–147.

WHELAN, J. K. 1977. Amino acids in a surface sediment core of the Atlantic abyssal plain. *Geochim. Cosmochim. Acta*, **41**, 803–810.

ZEITSCHEL, B., DIEKMANN, P. & UHLMANN, L. 1978. A new multisample sediment trap. *Mar. Biol.* **45**, 285–288.

E. T. DEGENS and V. ITTEKKOT, Geological and Paleontological Institute and Museum, University of Hamburg, Bundesstrasse 55, D-2000 Hamburg 13, Federal Republic of Germany.

Oceanographic controls on the accumulation of organic matter in marine sediments

S. E. Calvert

SUMMARY: The concentration of organic matter in marine deposits depends on the relative rates of accumulation of the various sedimentary components and the ease with which these components are preserved after burial. The supply of organic matter to any area of sea floor is controlled by the primary production rate in the surface ocean and the depth through which particulate material must settle. The accumulation of organic matter in sediments depends on the primary setting flux and on the bulk sedimentation rate, more carbon surviving decomposition where it is buried rapidly.

The preferential preservation of organic matter under anoxic conditions, a widely-accepted explanation for the formation of sapropels, black shales and petroleum source beds, is considered to be of secondary importance in governing the accumulation of carbon in marine deposits. The modern sediments of the Black Sea, a widely-used analogue of the environment of black shale formation, do not have exceptionally high carbon contents, although an earlier sapropel is known to have formed during the change from an oxic lake to an anoxic marine basin. Likewise, the available information on modern anoxic fjords shows that they do not have sediments containing more carbon than their oxic counterparts. And finally, the inverse correlation between the carbon content of slope sediments and the oxygen content of the near-bottom waters in areas where the oxygen minimum intersects the sea floor is shown to be one of coincidence and understandable on the basis of the relationship between sedimentary carbon levels and other sediment properties.

The supply of organic matter to marine deposits, controlled by the primary production rate, and the bulk sedimentation rate appear to be the most important factors which determine the organic content of sediments. Recent work on the location of former upwelling centres suggests that variations in palaeoproductivity may be responsible for the formation of many organic-rich rocks and may provide a better basis for predicting the location of petroleum source beds in the geological record.

Organic material is generally a minor, but variable, component of most marine sediments, reaching concentrations of a few percent by weight in most nearshore, fine-grained deposits. Its importance in the geochemistry of marine sediments, however, is out of all proportion to its abundance since it is the energy source for diagenetic reactions; the microbial degradation of deposited organic matter leads to the production of certain metabolites which establish various interstitial chemical environments within sediments. A series of post-depositional chemical reactions proceed in these environments, some of which may lead to the formation of authigenic mineral phases. Hence, the organic matter content of sediments directly influences the bulk mineralogical and chemical composition of sediments.

The composition of a sediment is controlled, in a simple fashion, by the relative rates of accumulation of individual sediment components, the ease with which these components are preserved and the diagenetic reactions which proceed after deposition. In some cases, the importance of accumulation rate differences and preservation can be estimated, but in many other situations the balance of these processes is not clear. This difficulty applies especially to many organic-rich sediments and sedimentary rocks, some of which have been identified as petroleum source beds. The identification of the environment of formation of such deposits has been of interest for some considerable time. Thus, an extensive literature appears to suggest that the accumulation of large quantities of organic matter takes place under anoxic conditions. Such conditions are developed in hydrographically-restricted basins and, as discussed in recent work on black shales recovered by drilling in the deep ocean areas, in oceanic oxygen minima. The prevailing view appears to be that preferential preservation of organic matter under anoxic conditions is a critical factor in the formation of organic-rich sediments and sedimentary rocks.

The purpose of this paper is to review the processes controlling the distribution and concentration of organic matter in modern marine sediments using some of the results of recent oceanographic research. This will involve discussion of the variations in the flux of organic matter to sediments, the burial rates of this organic matter and the conditions under which particu-

From: BROOKS, J. & FLEET, A. J. (eds) 1987, *Marine Petroleum Source Rocks* Geological Society Special Publication No. 26 pp. 137–151.

larly organic-rich deposits are accumulating today. Particular attention will be devoted to the available information on anoxic basins and oceanic oxygen minima in view of the perceived importance of anoxic conditions in the formation of organic-rich facies.

The production of organic matter in the ocean

Primary organic production by photosynthesis in the ocean is limited by nutrient supply and solar radiation (Ryther 1963). Well-known relationships between light intensity and photosynthesis of some marine algae show that the amount of incident radiation reaching the surface is often insufficient for sustained production at high latitudes but is not a critical factor in the tropics. In addition, the amount of light available to photosynthesizing organisms is affected by the transparency of the water. Light attenuation by absorption and scattering essentially limits plant growth (where photosynthesis exceeds respiration) to a thin surface layer of the ocean, the euphotic zone. This zone varies in thickness from 100–120 m in clear, open ocean waters to a few metres in turbid, nearshore waters.

The two principal factors determining phytoplankton production in the ocean must be considered together because plant nutrients can only be effectively utilized in the euphotic zone. Nutrients are generally in very low concentration in the euphotic zone because they are consumed by the growing phytoplankton; they are returned

to the water below the euphotic zone because settling particulate organic debris is remineralized by decomposing bacteria. Hence, a vertical profile of a nutrient, say inorganic phosphate, shows a minimum at the surface, sharply increasing concentrations with depth below the euphotic zone, and a maximum at around 1000 m depth which is a layer of minimal water movement.

Sustained production in the ocean can therefore only occur if the surface illuminated layers are continuously supplied with nutrients. This can only happen if the vertical stability of the water column allows upward mixing, either by turbulence or by upwelling, the latter signifying wholesale vertical flow of water in response to a surface divergence.

The regional variation of the primary production in the ocean (Fig. 1) reflects these physical controls. The centres of the mid-latitude gyres are sites of relatively low production, although solar radiation is high at all times, because the warm surface layers are very stably separated from the deep water; the only means of nutrient replenishment in the euphotic zone is by turbulent mixing across the thermocline. In equatorial regions, a surface divergence, induced meteorologically, causes upwelling of subsurface water so that sustained production takes place year-round at a moderate rate. In high latitudes, convective winter mixing fertilizes the surface layers and high rates of production are a feature of the spring and summer months when the euphotic zone has thickened and the surface has been stabilized by solar heating. Finally, very high rates of production are a feature of eastern boundary currents where the trade winds drive

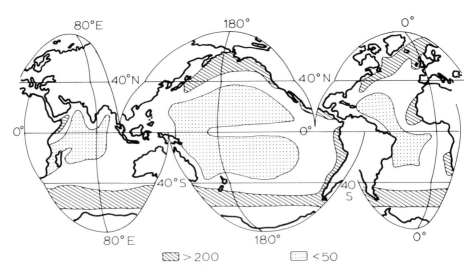

FIG. 1. Primary organic production (g m^{-2} y^{-1}) in the ocean. Redrawn from Riley & Chester (1971).

surface water away from coastlines and cause coastal upwelling.

Primary organic production in the ocean is therefore basically controlled by nutrient supply to the surface of the ocean and this in turn is governed by vertical stability in the water column. The latter is responsible for replenishing nutrients stripped from the surface and for maintaining dividing phytoplanktonic cells in nutrient replete, illuminated conditions above a critical depth where photosynthesis and respiration are equal.

Primary production by phytoplankton represents the base of the marine food chain. Secondary and tertiary production is accomplished by herbivorous and carnivorous zooplankton, fish and mammals. This production is limited in turn by the distribution of the primary food sources.

Organic matter fluxes

Organic debris from the surface layers of the ocean, produced by grazing, fragmentation and excretion, settles to the sea floor through a variably deep water column. Part of it is oxidized during settling, liberating organic and inorganic constituents that were stripped from the surface layers; part of it is used as food by benthic organisms; part undergoes further degradation in the sediments, the remainder being buried. The relative importance of these processes varies from place to place in the ocean depending on the level of production, the water depth and the rate of sedimentation.

Bogdanov *et al.* (1979) first established that the amount of settling organic carbon at any level can be predicted from the production rate and the water depth. More recently, Suess (1980) has provided a synthesis of the information on settling fluxes from particle interceptor traps (Soutar *et al.* 1977) deployed at several locations in the open ocean which has allowed the first quantitative estimate of the flux of organic matter into deep water and hence the primary input to the sediments. As established by McCave (1975), the dominant mechanism of vertical transport in the oceanic water column is by means of large, rapidly-settling particles (faecal pellets, carapaces, etc.) produced by grazing organisms in the surface layers. The flux of carbon by this means, relative to the production rate, decreases in a predictable way with increasing water depth (Fig. 2). At a given production rate, the settling flux decreases by a factor of ten for every 10-fold increase in water depth; it is approximately 10% of the surface production at around 400 m and only 1% of the surface production at around 4000 m depth. This relationship therefore allows

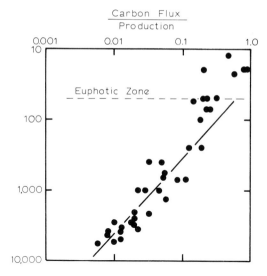

FIG. 2. Relationship between the settling flux, normalized to the primary production rate, and water depth in metres (ordinate) in the ocean. Redrawn from Suess (1980).

one to predict the organic input to a given area (depth) of sea floor from a knowledge of the primary production and can be used to examine possible controls on the accumulation of carbon in sedimentary deposits.

Organic matter in marine sediments

The concentration of organic carbon in marine deposits is controlled by the interplay between the processes of supply and preservation of the various components in any given deposit. Hence, it is necessary to pay attention to the variations in supply rates of carbon and other materials which will dilute the carbon input as well as other processes which, independently of the influxes, promote differential preservation of the accumulated organic material. In addition, the organic content of a sediment is related to its texture, finer-grained deposits in any given area invariably containing more organic carbon (Trask 1953), presumably because particulate organic matter acts as the hydraulic equivalent of fine sediment particles.

The distribution of organic carbon in modern marine sediments can be conveniently examined with reference to the Pacific Ocean where reasonable sample coverage is available. Premuzic *et al.* (1982) have produced the latest compilation of the data (Fig. 3). Sediments with organic carbon concentrations greater than 0.5% by weight are confined to the marginal areas close to

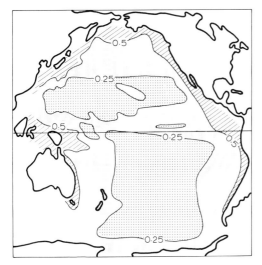

FIG. 3. Distribution of organic carbon (% dry weight) in the surface sediments of the Pacific Ocean. Values exceeding 0.5% are confined to the areas shoreward of the 0.5% contours. Redrawn from Premuzic *et al.* (1982).

the continents. In the open ocean, carbon values are less than 0.25% in the central, poorly productive gyres and only slightly higher in the more productive equatorial, sub-Arctic and sub-Antarctic deep-water areas.

In nearshore basins and on some continental shelf areas, organic carbon contents of sediments are much higher than 0.5% by weight. Some information on these environments is summarized by Calvert (1976) and Summerhayes (1983), and will be further discussed in more detail below.

The distribution depicted in Fig. 3 is explained by a combination of the depth-controlled settling flux and the sedimentation rate. The marginal areas of the ocean are generally more productive than the open ocean, as described earlier, so that a higher flux of carbon to the sediments is expected in these areas. The higher flux occurs where the burial rate of the deposited carbon is also higher because the bulk sedimentation rate of sediments is higher closer to the continents. Müller & Suess (1979) have established a clear relationship between the carbon content of a sediment and its bulk accumulation rate (Fig. 4). Thus, at a constant production rate, porosity and bulk density, the carbon content doubles with each 10-fold increase in the sedimentation rate. This relationship is interpreted as a reflection of the preservation of the settled carbon when it is buried below the sediment/water interface. The carbon that survives settling remains at or close to the sediment surface for a much longer period

than that taken to settle to the sea floor. Hence, there is a much greater chance for further degradation of organic matter at the sediment surface by microbes and deposit feeders (microbial biomass is much higher at the sediment surface than at depth because the more recently settled particles are more readily metabolized). Faster burial will remove a given particle, containing a higher proportion of labile organic compounds, from the site of the highest metabolic rate and thereby promote its preferential preservation. Consequently, as emphasized by Müller & Suess (1979), the carbon contents of different bodies of sediments can only be directly compared if their sedimentation rates are taken into account.

Anoxic basins

In the open ocean, the oxidation of organic matter is accomplished by aerobic microbes which use dissolved oxygen as an electron-acceptor. Where the rate of replenishment of oxygen is less than its utilization rate, other oxidants are used by different microbial communities to continue the decomposition process. After oxygen is exhausted, other micro-organisms degrade the organic substrate using other available oxidants, first nitrate, then sulphate and finally CO_2. The sequence of oxidations is controlled by the physiology of the particular organisms, oxygen being toxic to nitrate- and sulphate-reducing bacteria and nitrate inhibiting sulphate-reducers (McCarty 1972). Purely thermodynamic arguments have also been made to explain the sequence (Goldhaber & Kaplan 1974). Sulphate-reducing bacteria metabolize organic detritus and produce hydrogen sulphide (or HS^- ion at sea water pH) as a by-product. This is toxic to almost all other forms of life and sulphide-bearing waters are therefore environments devoid of higher plant or animal communities. For convenience, I shall refer to anoxic systems as those in which oxygen *and* nitrate are absent and, consequently, where free sulphide is present in the water body.

The rate of replenishment of oxygen will be lower than its consumption under two different circumstances. In the first, a body of water with a stable vertical density structure is isolated from the open ocean by a physical barrier which restricts free exchange between the basin and the open ocean. Hence, regardless of the oxygen demand of the deep water in the basin, oxygen is exhausted below a strong pycnocline (density gradient) because it cannot be replenished at a sufficient rate and other oxidants are used in the degradation of settling organic detritus. Exam-

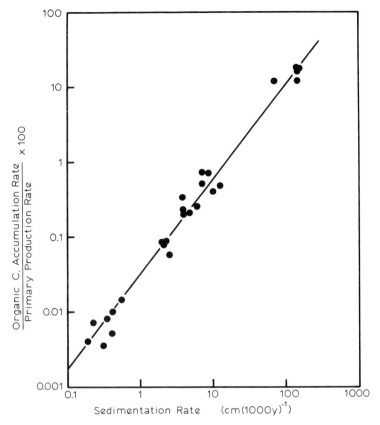

FIG. 4. Relationship between the organic carbon accumulation rate, normalized to the surface primary production rate, and sedimentation rate of selected oceanic and nearshore sediments. Redrawn from Müller & Suess (1979).

ples of such basins are some of the well-known fjords of Norway and British Columbia (Strøm 1936; Richards 1965), the Black Sea (Andrusov 1890; Caspers 1957) and the Cariaco Trench (Richards & Vaccaro 1956). In the fjords and the Black Sea, the stability of the water column is due to salinity stratification, because a fresher surface layer from run-off overlies a more saline water mass. In the Cariaco Trench, the surface layers are much warmer, and hence less dense, than the deeper water mass so that stability is maintained even though the trench is in contact with open Caribbean waters above a relatively deep sill. The same control operates in the anoxic lakes of equatorial east Africa.

The second situation which promotes the formation of anoxic conditions is where the rate of consumption of oxygen is very high because organic production is high. This occurs in some regions of coastal upwelling (coastal Peru and Namibia) where the flux of settling carbon lowers the oxygen content of the water even though

there is no barrier to exchange with the open ocean (Calvert & Price 1971a). One of the effects of the formation of anoxic conditions in these circumstances is spectacular mass fish kills (Hart & Currie 1960; but see Brongersma-Sanders 1957 for another explanation).

Information on the organic carbon content of the sediments of anoxic basins is meagre. The Black Sea is frequently identified as containing particularly carbon-rich modern sediments. The information given by Glagoleva (1961), Strakhov (1962) and Shimkus & Trimonis (1974), however, shows that the modern deep-water sediments have a maximum organic carbon content of around 5% by weight. Thus, the stratigraphy of the sediments of the central Black Sea (Fig. 5) shows a relatively low carbon facies overlying sapropelic sediments which formed 1000–5000 years ago under conditions quite different from those now prevailing. These will be discussed more fully later.

Within any given basin, it is difficult to prove

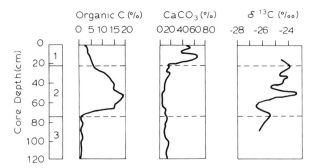

FIG. 5. Carbon and carbonate stratigraphy in a core from the central Black Sea [data from Deuser (1972) and Ross & Degens (1972)]. The stratigraphic units on the left are: 1, modern coccolith ooze; 2, sapropel; 3, lacustrine silts. Boundaries between the units are dated at approximately 1,000 yrs and 5,000 yrs B.P., respectively (Degens *et al.* 1980).

that anoxic sediments contain more carbon than oxic deposits accumulating above the oxygen/sulphide boundary in view of the clear relationship between sedimentary carbon and other sediment properties discussed earlier. Thus, it is not valid to conclude that the anoxic sediments of Saanich Inlet show preferential preservation of carbon compared with the oxic sediments at sill depth, even though the basin sediments have three to four times the carbon contents of the shallower sediments (Gucluer & Gross 1964), because the latter deposits are significantly coarser-grained and would be expected to have less carbon. Valid comparisons can only be made between deposits of similar texture accumulating at similar depths and at similar rates. Such a comparison shown in Fig. 6 shows little difference in the carbon contents of the deep-water sediments in two neighbouring fjords.

Richards (1970), in reviewing the available evidence, has concluded that the waters of anoxic basins do not appear to contain more dissolved organic carbon than their oxygenated counterparts. He further suggests that the sediments of some anoxic basins may appear to contain more carbon simply because the sediments accumulate more rapidly and thereby quickly remove the deposited carbon from the sediment surface where the microbial biomass is highest (see Kriss 1963).

Some of the highest sedimentary carbon contents in modern environments are found in areas of coastal upwelling (Fig. 7), and the factors causing this enrichment have been reviewed by Summerhayes (1983). The highest primary production rates are often recorded in such environments (Platt & Subba Rao 1975) and the flux of detrital carbon to the rather shallow shelf and slope areas is exceptionally high. In addition, run-off from the neighbouring arid land areas is

very small so that the deposited carbon suffers very little dilution (Calvert & Price 1971b). The resulting facies, organic-, diatom- and minor metal-rich ooze, is characteristic of modern coastal upwelling environments (Calvert & Price 1983). These systems usefully illustrate the neces-

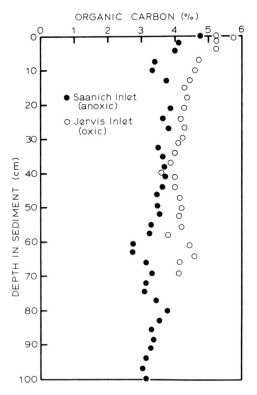

FIG. 6. Distribution of organic carbon in sediment cores from the central parts of Saanich and Jervis Inlets, British Columbia. Analytical method given in Calvert & Price (1971a) and data salt-corrected.

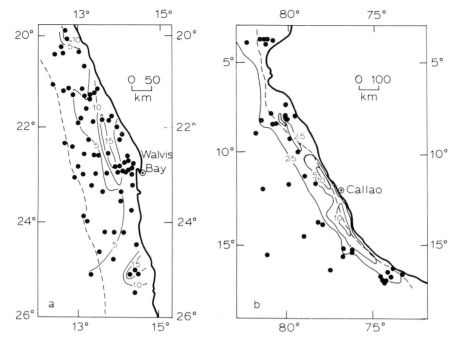

FIG. 7. Distribution of organic carbon (% dry weight) in the surface sediments of (a) coastal Namibia (after Calvert & Price 1983), and (b) the continental margin of Peru (after Reimers, 1981). Dashed lines represent the edge of the continental shelf. Dots are sample locations.

sity of understanding the complex interplay between the supply rates of the various sedimentary components in order to explain the composition of a given sediment.

The oxygen minimum

In addition to restricted basins and marginal marine environments where primary production is high, low oxygen conditions are also found at intermediate depths in some areas of the open ocean. The oxygen minimum in the water column occurs where the concentration of dissolved oxygen has been reduced by the microbial decomposition of settling organic debris in a layer which advects slowly and has been out of contact with the atmosphere for a long period (Richards 1957; Wyrtki 1962). The intensity of the oxygen minimum therefore varies with the age of the water mass and with the primary production of the overlying waters. The eastern tropical Pacific is an area where the intermediate oxygen minimum often has vanishingly small oxygen concentrations and where nitrate reduction is intense (Brandthorst 1959). Sulphate reduction has been reported in the oxygen minimum zone of the Arabian Sea (Ivankenkov & Rozanov 1961).

The bottom waters in some areas of the open ocean may therefore be nearly or completely anoxic where the oxygen minimum intersects the continental slope. Such an environment has been suggested in several recent models for the formation of some intermediate-depth, organic-rich black shales recovered by the Deep Sea Drilling Project (Schlanger & Jenkyns 1976; Thiede & van Andel 1977). Dean and Gardner (1982) give details of some of the features of such black shales suggesting deposition under oxygenated conditions.

A clear inverse correlation between the sedimentary organic carbon content and the near-bottom oxygen content was discovered in the northwestern Gulf of Mexico by Richards & Redfield (1954). In this area, the oxygen minimum is relatively weakly developed, concentrations being fully half the saturation levels near the sea surface (Fig. 8). The carbon content of the surface sediment shows a maximum between 200 m and 1000 m, roughly coincident with the zone where the oxygen minimum intersects the slope. This relationship is, however, misleading. The depth distribution of sedimentary carbon in the Gulf of Mexico can be understood very simply by the interplay between sediment texture and accumulation rate; sediments in shallow water (100–200 m) are coarser-grained and represent the basal transgressive facies which is widely distributed on the outer shelf and upper slope (Curray

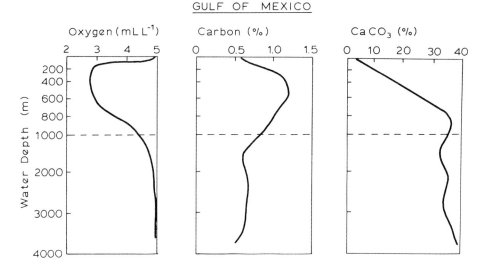

FIG. 8. Distribution of organic carbon and calcium carbonate in surface sediments of the NW Gulf of Mexico in relation to the oxygen content of the near-bottom water. Data obtained from Trask (1953) and Redfield & Richards (1954).

1960). The organic carbon content of this facies is very low. The grain-size decreases in the modern silts and muds in deeper water and the carbon content consequently rises to levels which are characteristic of this facies and of the prevailing production. The decrease in the carbon content in deeper water is due to the decrease in the settling flux of carbon and the decrease in the bulk sedimentation rate (cf. Müller & Suess 1979). The sedimentary carbon maximum is therefore *induced* by the interrelationship between the factors which control the bulk composition of sediments. Similar sedimentary carbon maxima on slopes, described by Gross (1967) and Premuzic *et al.* (1982), can be explained by the same reasoning.

In contrast to the examples given above, there appears to be no relationship between sedimentary carbon and the oxygen content of the bottom water in the Gulf of California. Here, an intense oxygen minimum in the eastern tropical Pacific is further intensified by the high primary production in the Gulf itself. On the slopes of the Gulf, where the oxygen minimum intersects the sea floor, the sediments are distinctively laminated (Calvert 1964a) because a benthos is absent in the highly oxygen-depleted bottom waters and the seasonally pulsed sediment supply (Calvert 1966; Donegan & Schrader 1982) is not homogenized by bioturbation. The carbon contents of the nearly anoxic, laminated sediment are, how-

ever, indistinguishable from those of the oxic, homogenized sediment above and below the oxygen-minimum zone (Fig. 9). Hence, whatever process is deemed effective in preserving carbon under oxygen-deficient conditions, it does not operate in this basin.

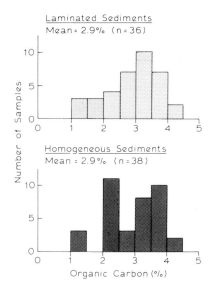

FIG. 9. Organic carbon (% dry weight) contents of homogeneous and laminated sediments from the central Gulf of California (data from Calvert 1964b).

Preservation of organic matter in marine sediments

From the foregoing discussion, it seems clear that:

(a) modern anoxic basins do not contain exceptionally organic-rich sediments

(b) oxygen-minimum zones are not necessarily sites of preferential preservation of deposited carbon

(c) the highest fluxes and accumulations of organic matter in the modern ocean are found in areas of coastal upwelling.

The concept of preferential preservation of organic matter in marine sediments which accumulate under anoxic conditions is widely accepted in the geological literature. Early work on the identification of the environment of deposition of petroleum source rocks concluded that so-called euxinic conditions were necessary for the accumulation of the quantities of organic matter deemed necessary to generate petroleum. The Black Sea, which has generally been considered to contain exceptionally organic-rich contemporary sediments, has been used as a modern analogue of an environment where petroleum source beds are formed, as in the barred basin model of Woolnough (1937). More recently, the discovery of black shales in Cenozoic and Mesozoic sections in the deep ocean by the Deep Sea Drilling Project has revived interest in this problem. Almost without exception, the idea that wholesale stagnation of the deep ocean is required to explain some of the occurrences has been reiterated (Fischer & Arthur 1977; Dow 1978; Arthur 1979a,b; Arthur & Schlanger 1979; Weissert *et al.* 1979; Demaison & Moore 1980; Jenkyns 1980; Leggett 1980; Morris 1980; Tissot *et al.* 1980; Summerhayes 1981; Cool 1982; Peters & Ekweozor 1982). The notable exception to this consensus is the paper by Gardner *et al.* (1977) who contend that Lower Cretaceous black shales in the northwestern Atlantic are the result of increased productivity in the ocean or a higher rate of supply of terrigenous organic material rather than wholesale stagnation of the bottom waters. With the recent understanding of the factors governing the accumulation of carbon in modern sediments, detailed oceanographic work in the Black Sea and the modern work on the general compositional variability of marine sediments, it is appropriate to reconsider some of the well-established concepts about the formation of black shales, sapropels and petroleum source beds.

Arguments concerning the role of anoxic conditions in preserving organic material in marine sediments invariably ignore the fact that *all* fine-grained nearshore, shelf and hemipelagic (slope) sediments are anoxic below a surface oxic layer (Klenova 1938; Gorshkova 1957). This layer is very thin (a few millimetres) in rapidly accumulating muds and several tens of centimetres thick in more slowly accumulating deep-water muds (Bezrukov 1960; Lynn & Bonatti 1965). At a particular horizon, the rate of consumption of dissolved oxygen in the sediment pore waters by the aerobic degradation of deposited organic matter is higher than its replenishment by diffusion from the overlying water, and microbial sulphate-reduction ensues below this level (Fenchel & Riedl 1970). Hence, even though organic matter may initially accumulate in oxygenated surface sediments, it is eventually destined to be buried in an anoxic environment. Recent work suggests that in many aquatic environments a main part of the mineralization of organic matter seems to take place after the material has reached the anoxic zone (Fenchel & Jørgensen 1977).

Murray *et al.* (1978) have shown that the concentration of organic carbon in the sediments of anoxic Saanich Inlet decreases below the sediment surface by roughly 25% (see also Fig. 6) and interpret this as the breakdown of organic matter by sulphate-reducing microbes. This value is identical with that obtained by Martens *et al.* (1984) in a nearshore lagoonal environment where the anoxic sediment is capped by a very thin oxygenated layer. Jørgensen (1977; 1982a) has shown that the intensity of sulphate reduction depends on the influx of organic matter and that the maximal sulphate-reduction rate is found in the uppermost part of the sulphide zone where the buried organic matter is more easily metabolized than that deeper in the sediment. Furthermore, employing simultaneous measurements of oxygen and sulphate depletion in nearshore marine sediments, Jørgensen (1982b) has demonstrated that the breakdown of organic matter by aerobes and by sulphate-reducers is roughly equal. Newly-discovered strains of sulphate-reducers can potentially completely mineralize the deposited organic matter in such sediments. Although anaerobic bacteria are known to be less efficient that aerobes in converting detrital carbon compounds into bacterial biomass, they nevertheless mineralize the organic material as readily as aerobic bacteria and evidently produce larger quantities of low molecular weight metabolites which provide substrates for other classes of bacteria (Jørgensen 1977; Fenchel & Blackburn 1979). Hence, organic matter degradation certainly proceeds in anoxic sediments, and one would not expect that organic material would be preferentially preserved under these conditions.

The perceptive observations of Richards (1970) and the recent work of Müller & Suess (1979) suggest that the preservation of labile organic matter is controlled by its rate of burial. It is therefore necessary to consider the sedimentation rate as well as the availability of carbon oxidants in order to unravel the possible controls on preferential preservation of carbon in marine sediments.

Sapropels

Black, organic-rich mud horizons in normal deep-water nannofossil oozes were discovered in the eastern Mediterranean during the Swedish Deep Sea Expedition (Fig. 10) and are briefly described by Kullenberg (1952). Several horizons are now known to occur, ranging in age from Holocene to Pliocene (Kidd *et al.* 1978). By analogy with black shales, the sapropels are considered to represent sedimentation under anoxic conditions. Calvert (1983) has argued, however, that this correlation is not valid because modern black sediments are not the analogues of black shales; the black pigmentation of modern anoxic sediments is due to the presence of finely-divided, unstable FeS, whereas the colour of black shales (and sapropels) is due to the presence of carbonized organic matter.

Using the results of Müller & Suess (1979), it can be shown that under the present-day primary production rate in the eastern Mediterranean (Platt & Subba Rao 1975) and assuming a sedimentation rate of the most recent sapropel of 2 cm $(1000 \text{ y})^{-1}$ (Mangini & Dominik 1979), the organic carbon content of a resulting sediment would be 0.5%, within a factor of three of the values in the associated marls and oozes reported by Calvert (1983) and Sutherland *et al.* (1984). Likewise, at a depth of 3000 m, using the results of Suess (1980), the potential carbon accumulation rate, assuming no loss in the sediments, is less than that necessary to account for carbon contents of up to 20% by weight observed in some of the sapropels. Since we know that organic matter is mineralized within sediments, it must be concluded that sapropels are unlikely to have formed under the prevailing production and sedimentation rates in this basin (Calvert 1983).

As outlined at the beginning of this paper, the second factor which governs the bulk composition of a sediment is the supply rate of individual components. The possibility that the settling flux of organic matter in the eastern Mediterranean was much higher during sapropel formation has not been considered. As already discussed, some coastal upwelling areas are sites of intense primary production and the bottom sediments are very rich in organic matter. Moreover, the bottom waters in these areas have very low oxygen contents (Calvert & Price 1971a) because of the high oxygen demand of the settling carbon. The sediments here are not organic-rich because of the nearly anoxic conditions; low oxygen conditions are the *result* of the high production.

Conditions in the eastern Mediterranean during the formation of sapropels were quite different from those of today. During the deposition of the youngest sapropel (8–12,000 yr. B.P.), there was greatly increased rainfall in equatorial Africa which led to exceptionally high flood water discharge via the Nile (Rossignol-Strick *et al.* 1982). The water balance in the Mediterranean would therefore have been changed and it is likely that estuarine circulation in the deep water would have ensued (Berger 1976; Calvert 1983) resulting in deep-water renewal rather than the present deep-water loss. Under these changed conditions, the eastern Mediterranean would have been a more productive basin and localized

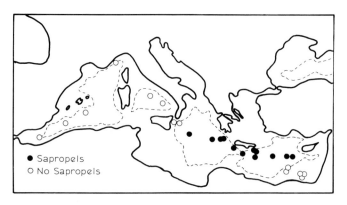

FIG. 10. Distribution of piston cores containing sapropel units recovered during the Swedish Deep Sea Expedition in the Mediterranean Sea (data from Olausson 1960).

upwelling could have further increased the carbon flux into deep water. Different sapropel horizons actually contain distinctive microfossil assemblages (diatoms, silicoflagellates) which could reflect the occurrence of localized upwelling centres (Schrader & Matherne 1981; Calvert 1983).

In the Black Sea, a sapropel, containing 20% organic carbon, was formed 1000–5000 years ago (Degens *et al.* 1980). Prior to its formation, the Black Sea was an oxic lake, being isolated from the Mediterranean by the lowered Pleistocene sea level. The beginning of sapropel formation roughly coincides with the time when this connection was re-established and saline water entered the basin through the Bosporus. The end of sapropel deposition, on the other hand, occurred when the present stable density stratification was established and anoxic conditions became a permanent feature of the deep water. As emphasized previously, the modern sediments of the Black Sea contain much less organic carbon (Fig. 5). Conditions during the transition period from the oxic lake phase to the anoxic marine phase were evidently unusual. During the post-Pleistocene sea level rise, the supply rate of terrestrial sediment was almost certainly greatly reduced because of river aggradation so that the sedimentation rate of inorganic materials was relatively low. Moreover, Boon *et al.* (1979) discovered that a distinctive sterol, dinosterol, is abundant in the sapropel and suggested from this that dinoflagellate blooms were common during this period. Simoneit (1977) found that the organic matter in some sapropel samples was predominantly terrestrial, although the stable carbon isotope data of Deuser (1972) show that it does become progressively more marine in the upper part of the sapropel unit (Fig. 5). Hence, a combination of an increased supply of terrestrial organic material relative to inorganic sediment, variable overall sedimentation rates and a high primary production rate could explain the formation of the sapropel. The anoxicity of the basin appears to play a minor role. In both the Black Sea and the eastern Mediterranean, sapropels were formed when the hydrographic balances were changing markedly and it is probable that the production levels were quite different from those prevailing today.

Oceanic fertility

As argued previously, the bulk chemical and mineralogical composition of marine sediments are controlled by the relative rates of accumulation of the various sediment components and the ease with which these components are preserved after deposition. Hence, it is not possible to select a single causative factor to explain the abundance or otherwise of a particular component unless the inter-relationships between these factors are understood. The formation of organic-rich sediments and rocks, sapropels as well as black shales, have generally been ascribed to preferential preservation without recognition of the many other factors which can influence the make-up of sediments.

Variations in the extent and intensity of primary production in the modern ocean are now well understood. This process, which controls the settling fluxes of organic matter in the ocean, together with the marked regional variations in the bulk accumulation rate of sediments, are the primary determinants of the organic matter content of marine sediments.

The importance of increased primary production rates in explaining the occurrence of organic-rich sediments in the open ocean has recently been identified using somewhat different approaches by Müller & Suess (1979) and Pedersen (1983). Off north-west Africa and in the eastern equatorial Pacific, respectively, the latest Pleistocene sediments contain as much as 3 to 6 times the organic carbon content of the Holocene sediments. Müller & Suess (1979) were unable to reconstruct the carbon profile off NW Africa from the modern production rate and the accumulation rates of the sediments, and concluded that the influx of carbon, and hence the production rate, must have been higher during the late Pleistocene. Müller *et al.* (1983) have established that there are cycles of high and low organic carbon, corresponding to glacial and interglacial periods, respectively, over a 500,000 year interval in the sediments of the northeastern Atlantic. Likewise, Pedersen (1983), arguing from the relationship between iodine and sedimentary organic carbon, concluded that production was higher during the late Pleistocene in the equatorial Pacific, as suggested earlier on the other grounds by Arrhenius (1952). In addition, the higher level of organic carbon in the sediments of Orca Basin, a hypersaline, anoxic basin on the continental slope of the northern Gulf of Mexico, is explained by Sheu (1983) as the consequence of increased primary production in the overlying waters rather than enhanced preservation. The interplay between production levels and bulk sedimentation rates would therefore appear to provide a better basis for understanding the occurrence of ancient sapropels and perhaps some black shales and petroleum source beds rather than the frequent formation of truly anoxic conditions or expanded oxygen minima in the deep ocean. A critical requirement now is detailed work on individual sapropel and black shale sequences in order to increase the very meagre amount of information on their bulk compositions, accumulation rates and organic geochemistries.

Recent work by Parrish (1982) and Parrish and Curtis (1982) is a welcome attempt to consider primary organic production as one of the important variables in explaining the occurrence and distribution of petroleum source rocks. They find, for example, that ancient upwelling zones, predicted from plate tectonic reconstructions and atmospheric circulation models, coincide with the locations of many organic-rich rocks. This potentially fruitful approach requires further work as it may provide a sounder basis for predicting the occurrence of petroleum source rocks.

Conclusions

The concentration of organic matter in marine sediments, in common with other compositional features of such deposits, depends upon the relative rates of supply of all sedimentary components and the preservation of each component after burial. In the modern ocean, the abundance of sedimentary organic carbon appears to be governed by the regional and depth-dependent settling flux of carbon and the bulk accumulation rate of the sediment. The wide variations in the concentration of carbon in marine sediments are readily understood, therefore, with reference to two basic factors, namely primary productivity and sedimentation rate.

From the available information, modern an-oxic basins and oxygen minima do not appear to be sites of accumulation of particularly organic-rich sediments. The sediments of many nearshore basins, where productivity and sedimentation rates are both relatively high, generally have organic carbon contents of a few per cent by weight, whether they form in oxic or anoxic environments. The extent of degradation of organic matter via aerobic and anaerobic metabolic pathways appears to be similar. The role of macro-benthonic organisms in degrading organic matter in aerobic environments is thought to be relatively small (Nedwell 1984).

In view of these considerations, it is proposed that a coherent explanation for the occurrence of black shales in the geological record may be provided by variations in the rate of primary production, and hence the flux of carbon to the sea floor, in the past. There is clear evidence that this factor is responsible for the formation of some Pleistocene organic-rich, deep-sea sediments, some of which could be called sapropels based on their carbon contents. A variable production rate, modulated by climatic variations, appears to the writer to be a more generally applicable explanation for the observed variations in sedimentary carbon content than the widely accepted notion that large parts of the deep ocean were totally anoxic or that the oceanic oxygen minimum was greatly intensified in the past. We need considerably more ancillary information on both modern and ancient organic-rich sediments and their associated facies in order to provide critical tests of these two contrasting views.

ACKNOWLEDGEMENTS: Preparation of this paper was supported by the Natural Sciences and Engineering Research Council of Canada.

References

ANDRUSOV, N. I. 1890. Preliminary account of participation in the Black Sea deepwater expedition of 1890. *Izv. Russk. Geogr. Obshch.* **26**, 398–409.

ARRHENIUS, G. O. S. 1952. Sediment cores from the East Pacific. *Rep. Swedish Deep-Sea Exped.*, **5**, Fasc. 1, 227 pp.

ARTHUR, M. A. 1979a. Paleoceanographic events—recognition, resolution, and reconsideration. *Rev. Geophys. and Space Phys.* **17**, 1474–1494.

—— 1979b. North Atlantic Cretaceous black shales: The record at Site 398 and a brief comparison with other occurrences. *In:* SIBUET, J-C, RYAN, W. B. F. *et al., Initial Rep. Deep Sea drill. Proj.*, **47**, Part 2, U.S. Government Printing Office, Washington, DC. 719–738.

—— & SCHLANGER, S. O. 1979. Cretaceous 'oceanic anoxic events' as causal factors in development of reef-reservoired giant oil fields. *Bull. Am. Assoc. Petrol. Geol.* **73**, 870–885.

BERGER, W. H. 1976. Biogenous deep sea sediments: production, preservation and interpretation. *In:* RILEY, J. P. and CHESTER, R. (eds), *Chemical Oceanography*, 2nd Edition, **5**, Academic Press. 265–388.

BEZRUKOV, P. L. 1960. Sedimentation in the north-western Pacific Ocean. *21st. Intern. Geol. Congress, Copenhagen, Rept.* **X**, 39–49.

BOGDANOV, Y. A., GURVICH, Y. G. & LISTSIN, A. P. 1979. A model of organic carbon accumulation in bottom sediments of the Pacific Ocean. *Geokhimiya*, **6**, 918–927.

BOON, J. J., RIJPSTRA, W. I., DE LANGE, F. & DELEEUW, J. W. 1979. Black Sea sterol—a molecular fossil for dinoflagellate blooms. *Nature*, **227**, 125–127.

BRANDHORST, W. 1959. Nitrification and denitrification in the eastern tropical North Pacific. *J. Conseil. Explor. Mer.* **25**, 3–20.

BRONGERSMA-SANDERS, M. 1957. Mass mortality in the sea. *Mem. geol. Soc. Am.* **67**, Volume 1, 941–1010.

CALVERT, S. E. 1964a. Factors affecting distribution of laminated diatomaceous sediments in the Gulf of California. *In*: VAN ANDEL, Tj. H. and SHOR, G. G. (eds), *Marine Geology of the Gulf of California, Mem. Assoc. Petrol. Geol.* **3**, 311–330.

—— (1964b). Diatomaceous sediments of the Gulf of California. *Ph.D. Dissertation*, Univ. of California, San Diego, 245 pp.

—— 1966. Origin of diatom-rich, varved sediments from the Gulf of California. *J. Geol.* **74**, 546–565.

—— 1976. The mineralogy and geochemistry of nearshore sediments. *In*: RILEY, J. P. and CHESTER, R. (eds), 2nd Edition, *Chemical Oceanography*, **6**, Academic Press, London. 187–280.

—— 1983. Geochemistry of Pleistocene sapropels and associated sediments from the Eastern Mediterranean. *Oceanologica Acta*, **6**, 255–267.

—— & PRICE, N. B. 1971a. Upwelling and nutrient regeneration in the Benguela Current, October 1968. *Deep-Sea Research*, **18**, 505–523.

—— & PRICE, N. B. 1971b. Recent sediments of the Southwest African shelf. *In*: DELANY, F. M. (ed), *Geology of the East Atlantic Continental Margin, Institute of Geological Sciences, Report 70/16*. 171–185.

—— & PRICE, N. B. 1983. Geochemistry of Namibian shelf sediments. *In*: SUESS, E. and THIEDE, J. (eds), *Coastal Upwelling: Its sediment record, A.* NATO Conf. Ser. IV, **10A**. Plenum Press, New York. 337–375.

CASPERS, H. 1957. Black Sea and Sea of Azov. *Mem. geol. Soc. Am.* **67**, 803–889.

COOL, T. E. 1982. Sedimentological evidence concerning the palaeoceanography of the Cretaceous western north Atlantic Ocean. *Palaeogeog., Palaeoclimat. Palaeoecol.* **39**, 1–35.

CURRAY, J. R. 1960. Sediments and history of Holocene transgression, continental shelf, northwest Gulf of Mexico. *In*: SHEPARD, F. P., PHELEGER, F. B. and VAN ANDEL Tj. H. (eds), *Recent Sediments, Northwest Gulf of Mexico*, Spec. Publ. Am. Assoc. Petrol. Geol. **1**, 221–226.

DEAN, W. E. & GARDNER, J. V. 1982. Origin and geochemistry of redox cycles of Jurassic to Eocene age, Cape Verde Basin (DSDP Site 367), continental margin of North-West Africa. *In*: SCHLANGER, S. O. and CITA, M. B. (eds), *Nature and Origin of Cretaceous Carbon-rich Facies*, Academic Press. 57–78.

DEGENS, E. T. & ROSS, D. A. (1972). Chronology of the Black Sea over the last 25,000 years. *Chemical Geol.* **10**, 1–16.

——, MICHAELIS, W., GARRASI, C., MOPPER, K., KEMPE, S. & ITTEKKOT, V. A. 1980. Warven-Chronologie und fruhdiagenetische umsetzungen organischer Substanzen holozäner Sedimente des Schwarzen Meeres. *Neu. Jahrb. Geol. Palaeontol. Monatsh.* **2**, 65–86.

DEMAISON, G. J. & MOORE, G. T. 1980. Anoxic environments and oil source bed genesis. *Organic Geochem.* **2**, 9–31.

DEUSER, W. G. 1972. Late-Pleistocene and Holocene history of the Black Sea as indicated by stable-isotope studies. *J. Geophys. Res.* **77**, 1071–1077.

DONEGAN, D. & SCHRADER, H. (1982) Biogenic and abiogenic components of laminated hemipelagic sediments in the central Gulf of California. *Marine Geol.* **48**, 215–237.

DOW, W. G. 1978. Petroleum source beds on continental slopes and rises. *Bull. Am. Assoc. Petrol. Geol.* **62**, 1584–1606.

FENCHEL, T. & RIEDL, R. J. 1970. The sulfide system: a new biotic community underneath the oxidized layer of marine sand bottoms. *Mar. Biol.* **7**, 25–268.

—— & BLACKBURN, T. H. 1979. *Bacteria and Mineral Cycling*. Academic Press, London. 225 pp.

—— & JØRGENSEN, B. B. 1977. Detritus food chains of aquatic ecosystems: the role of bacteria. *In*: ALEXANDER, N. (ed), *Advances in Microbial Ecology*, **1**, Plenum Press. 1–58.

FISCHER, A. G. & ARTHUR, M. A. 1977. Secular variations in the pelagic realm. *Spec. Publ. Soc. econ. Paleontol. Mineral.* **25**, 19–50.

GARDNER, J. V., DEAN, W. E. & JANSA, L. 1977. Sediments recovered from the northwest African continental margin, Leg 41, Deep Sea Drilling Project. *In*: LANCELOT, Y., SEIBOLD, E. *et al.*, *Initial Rep. Deep Sea drill. Proj.*, **41**, U.S. Government Printing Office, Washington, DC. 1121–1134.

GLAGOLEVA, M. A. 1961. On the geochemistry of the sediments of the Black Sea. *In*: STRAKHOV, N. M. (ed), *Recent Sediments of Seas and Oceans*, Izd. Akad. Nauk SSSR, Moscow. 448–476.

GOLDHABER, M. B. & KAPLAN, I. R. 1974. The sulfur cycle. *In*: GOLDBERG, E. D. (ed), *The Sea*, **5**, John Wiley, New York. 569–655.

GORSHKOVA, T. I. 1957. Sediments of the Kara Sea. *Trudy, Vsesoyuzn. Gidrobiol. Obsh. Akad. Nauk SSSR*, **8**, 68–99.

GROSS, M. G. 1967. Organic carbon in surface sediment from the northeast Pacific Ocean. *Int. J. Oceanol. and Limnol.* **1**, 46–54.

GUCLUER, S. M. & GROSS, M. G. 1964. Recent marine sediments in Saanich Inlet, a stagnant marine basin. *Limnol. and Oceanogr.* **9**, 359–376.

HART, T. J. & CURRIE, R. I. 1960. The Benguela Current. *Discovery Reports*, **31**, 123–298.

IVANENKOV, V. N. & ROZANOV, A. G. 1961. Hydrogen sulphide contamination of the intermediate layers of the Arabian Sea and the Bay of Bengal. *Okeanol.* **1**, 443–449.

JENKYNS, H. C. 1980. Cretaceous anoxic events: from continents to oceans. *J. geol. Soc. London*, **137**, 171–188.

JØRGENSEN, B. B. 1977. The sulfur cycle of a coastal marine sediment (Limfjorden, Denmark). *Limnol. and Oceanogr.* **22**, 814–832.

—— 1982a. Ecology of the bacteria of the sulphur cycle with special reference to anoxic-oxic interface environments. *Philos. Trans. R. Soc. London, B*, **298**, 543–561.

—— 1982b. Mineralization of organic matter in the sea

bed—the role of sulphate reduction. *Nature,* **296,** 643–645.

KIDD, R. B., CITA, M. B. & RYAN, W. B. F. 1978. Stratigraphy of eastern Mediterranean sapropel sequences recovered during Leg 42A and their paleoenvironmental significance. *In:* HSU, K. J., MONTADERT, L. *et al., Initial Rep. Deep Sea drill. Proj.* **42A,** U.S. Government Printing Office, Washington D.C. 421–443.

KLENOVA, M. B. 1938. Colouring of the deposits of the Polar Seas. *Dolk. Akad. Nauk, SSSR,* **19,** 8.

KRISS, A. E. 1963. *Marine Microbiology,* Oliver and Boyd, Edinburgh. 536 pp.

KULLENBERG, B. 1952. On the salinity of the water contained in marine sediments. *Goteborgs Kungl. Vetenskaps. Vitt-Samhal. Handlingar,* B., **6,** 3–37.

LEGGETT, J. K. 1980. British Lower Palaeozoic black shales and their palaeo-oceanographic significance. *J. geol. Soc. London,* **137,** 139–156.

LYNN, D. C. & BONATTI, E. 1965. Mobility of manganese in diagenesis of deep-sea sediments. *Mar. Geol.* **3,** 457–474.

McCARTY, P. L. 1972. Energetics of organic matter degradation. *In:* MITCHELL, R. (ed), *Water Pollution Microbiology,* John Wiley, New York. 91–118.

McCAVE, I. N. 1975. Vertical flux of particles in the ocean. *Deep-Sea Res.* **22,** 491–502.

MANGINI, A. & DOMINIK, J. 1979. Late Quaternary sapropel on the Mediterranean Ridge: U-budget and evidence for low sedimentation rates. *Sedim. Geol.* **23,** 113–125.

MARTENS, C. S. & KLUMP, J. V. 1984. Biogeochemical cycling in an organic-rich coastal marine basin. 4. An organic carbon budget for sediments dominated by sulfate reduction and methanogenesis. *Geochim. et Cosmochim. Acta,* **48,** 1987–2004.

MORRIS, K. A. 1980. Comparison of major sequences of organic-rich mud deposition in the British Jurassic. *J. geol. Soc. London,* **137,** 157–170.

MÜLLER, P. J. & SUESS, E. 1979. Productivity, sedimentation rate and sedimentary organic matter in the oceans—I. Organic carbon preservation. *Deep-Sea Res.* **27A,** 1347–1362.

——, ERLENKEUSER & R. VON GRAFENSTEIN 1983. Glacial-interglacial cycles in oceanic productivity inferred from organic carbon contents in eastern north Atlantic sediment cores. *In:* THIEDE, J. and SUESS, E. (eds), *Coastal Upwelling: its sediment record, B.* NATO Conf. Ser. IV, **10B,** Plenum Press, New York. 365–398.

MURRAY, J. W., GRANDMANIS, V. & SMETHIE, W. M. 1978. Interstitial water chemistry in the sediments of Saanich Inlet. *Geochim. et Cosmochim. Acta,* **42,** 1011–1026.

NEDWELL, D. B. 1984. The input and mineralization of organic carbon in anaerobic aquatic sediments. *In:* MARSHALL, K. C. (ed), *Advances in Microbial Ecology,* 7, Plenum Press. 93–131.

OLAUSSON, E. 1960. Description of sediment cores from the Mediterranean and Red Sea. *Rep. Swedish Deep-Sea Exped.* **8,** Fasc. 5, 287–334.

PARRISH, J. T. 1982. Upwelling and petroleum source beds, with reference to Paleozoic. *Bull. Am. Assoc. Petrol. Geol.* **66,** 750–774.

PARRISH, J. T. & CURTIS, R. L. 1982. Atmospheric circulation, upwelling, and organic-rich rocks in the Mesozoic and Cenozoic eras. *Palaeogeog., Palaeoclimat., Palaeoecol.,* **40,** 31–66.

PEDERSEN, T. F. 1983. Increased productivity in the eastern equatorial Pacific during the last glacial maximum (19,000 to 14,000 yr. B.P.). *Geology,* **11,** 16–19.

PETERS, S. W. & EKWEOZAR, C. M. 1982. Origin of mid-Cretaceous black shales in the Benue Trough, Nigeria. *Palaeogeog., Palaeoclimat., Palaeoecol.* **40,** 311–319.

PLATT, T. & SUBBA RAO, D. V. 1975. Primary production of marine microphytes, *Photosynthesis and Productivity in Different Environments,* Intern. Biol. Prog., **3,** Cambridge University Press. 249–280.

PREMUZIC, E. T., BENKOVITZ, C. M., GAFFREY, J. S. & WALSH, J. J. 1982. The nature and distribution of organic matter in the surface sediments of world oceans and seas. *Organic Geochem.* **4,** 63–77.

REIMERS, C. E. 1981. *Sedimentary organic matter: distribution and alteration processes in the coastal upwelling region off Peru.* Ph.D. Dissertation, Oregon State University, Corvallis, Oregon. (unpubl.).

RICHARDS, F. A. 1957. Oxygen in the ocean, *Mem. geol. Soc. Am.* **67,** Volume **1,** 185–238.

—— 1965. Anoxic basins and fjords. *In:* RILEY, J. P. and SKIRROW, G. (eds), *Chemical Oceanography,* **1,** Academic Press, London. 611–645.

—— 1970. The enhanced preservation of organic matter in anoxic marine environments. *In:* HOOD, D. W. (ed), *Organic Matter in Natural Waters, Inst. Mar. Sci. Univ. of Alaska Occas. Publ.* **1,** 399–422.

RICHARDS, F. A. & REDFIELD, A. C. 1954. A correlation between the oxygen content of sea water and the organic content of marine sediments. *Deep-Sea Res.* **1,** 279–281.

RICHARDS, F. A. & VACCARO, R. F. 1956. The Cariaco Trench, an anaerobic basin in the Caribbean. *Deep-Sea Res.* **3,** 214–228.

RILEY, J. P. & CHESTER, R. 1971. *Introduction to Marine Chemistry,* Academic Press, London. 465 pp.

ROSS, D. A. & DEGENS, E. T. 1974. Recent sediments of Black Sea. *In:* DEGENS, E. T. & ROSS, D. A. (eds), *The Black Sea—Geology, Chemistry and Biology, Mem. Am. Assoc. Petrol. Geol.* **20,** 183–199.

ROSSIGNOL-STRICK, M., NESTEROFF, W., OLIVE, P. & VERGNAUD-GRAZZINI, C. 1982. After the deluge: Mediterranean stagnation and sapropel formation. *Nature,* **295,** 105–110.

RYTHER, J. H. 1963. Geographic variations in productivity. *In:* HILL, M. N. (ed), *The Sea,* Volume **2,** Wiley Interscience, New York. 347–380.

SCHLANGER, S. O. & JENKYNS, H. C. 1976. Cretaceous oceanic anoxic events: causes and consequences. *Geologie en Mijubouw,* **55,** 179–184.

SCHRADER, H. & MATHERNE, A. 1981. Sapropel formation in the eastern Mediterranean: evidence from preserved opal assemblages. *Micropaleontology,* **27,** 191–203.

SHEU, D.-D. 1983. *The geochemistry of Orca Basin sediments.* Doctoral dissertation, Texas A&M University, 135 pp. (unpubl.).

SHIMKUS, K. M. & TRIMONIS, E. S. 1974. Modern

sedimentation in the Black Sea. *In*: DEGENS, E. T. & ROSS, D. A. (eds), *The Black Sea, Mem. Am. Assoc. Petrol. Geol.* **20**, 249–278.

SIMONEIT, B. R. T. 1977. The Black Sea, a sink for terrigenous lipids. *Deep-Sea Res.* **24**, 813–830.

SOUTAR, A., KLING, S. A., CRILL, P. A., DUFFRIN, E. & BRULAND, K. W. 1977. Monitoring the marine environment through sedimentation. *Nature,* **277**, 136–139.

STRAKHOV, N. M. 1962. *Principles of Lithogensis,* **I**, Oliver and Boyd, Edinburgh. 245 pp.

STRØM, K. M. 1936. Land-locked waters. *Skifter Norsk. Viden-Akad, Oslo I*, 1–84.

SUESS, E. 1980. Particulate organic carbon flux in the oceans—surface productivity and oxygen utilization. *Nature,* **288**, 260–263.

SUMMERHAYES, C. P. 1981. Organic facies of middle Cretaceous black shales in deep north Atlantic. *Bull. Am. Assoc. Petrol. Geol.* **65**, 2364–2380.

—— 1983. Sedimentation of organic matter in upwelling regimes. *In*: THIEDE, J. & SUESS, E. (eds), *Coastal Upwelling: Its Sediment Record B.* NATO Conf. Ser. IV, **10B**, Plenum Press, New York. 29–72.

SUTHERLAND, H. E., CALVERT, S. E. & MORRIS, R. J. 1984. Geochemical studies of the Recent sapropel and associated sediment from the Hellenic Outer Ridge, eastern Mediterranean Sea. I. Mineralogy and chemical composition. *Mar. Geol.* **56**, 79–92.

THIEDE, J. & VAN ANDEL, Tj. H. 1977. The paleoenvironment of anaerobic sediments in the late Mesozoic south Atlantic Ocean. *Earth and Planet. Sci. Letters,* **33**, 301–309.

TISSOT, B., DEMAISON, G., MASSON, P., DELTEIL, J. R. & COMBAZ, A. 1980. Paleoenvironment and petroleum potential of middle Cretaceous black shales in Atlantic Basins. *Bull. Am. Assoc. Petrol. Geol.* **64**, 2051–2063.

TRASK, P. D. 1953. Chemical studies of the sediment of western Gulf of Mexico. *Papers in Physical Oceanography and Meteorology, Mass. Inst. Technol.* **12**, 49–120.

WEISSERT, H., MCKENZIE, J. & HOCHULI, P. 1979. Cyclic anoxic events in the early Cretaceous Tethys Ocean. *Geology,* **7**, 147–151.

WOOLNOUGH, W. G. 1937. Sedimentation in barred basins, and source rocks of oil. *Bull. Am. Assoc. Petrol. Geol.* **21**, 1101–1157.

WYRTKI, K. 1962. The oxygen minimum in relation to ocean circulation. *Deep-Sea Res.* **9**, 11–23.

S. E. CALVERT, Department of Oceanography, University of British Columbia, Vancouver, B.C., V6T 1W5, Canada.

The formation of organic-rich deposits in two deep-water marine environments

R. J. Morris

SUMMARY: Organic-rich sediments have been collected from deep-water core sites in the Eastern Mediterranean (6500–9000 years BP) and the Guinea Basin (50,000–250,000 years BP estimated). The results of geochemical analyses suggest that similar processes may have been involved in their formation. The same processes are known to give rise to present day organic-rich oozes on the continental shelves off Peru and Namibia. The deep-water organic deposits are believed to have been a direct result of periods of greatly increased productivity in the overlying water column. Their formation is not thought to have involved the development of widespread stagnant conditions in the associated body of water, conditions which are often taken to be essential for the preservation of organic matter in deep water.

Enormous quantities of organic matter are formed in the high productivity areas of the world ocean (Demaison & Moore 1980). Indeed the sources of many present day oilfields and deposits of bituminous shales are generally thought to have once lain under such marine areas (Colombo 1967; Tissot & Welte 1978; Tissot 1979). Sedimentary conditions presumably favoured the preservation of the natural product organic matter produced in these water columns thus subsequently producing the organic-rich oil-source sediments.

The continental shelves off S.W. Africa and Peru are two particular areas of the world ocean where conditions today are probably similar to those that have given rise to some of the existing continental shelf oil deposits. Intense seasonal upwelling occurs at both sites (Hart & Currie 1960; Gunther 1936) giving rise to periods of exceptionally high primary productivity (Steemann-Nielsen & Jensen 1957; Ryther *et al.* 1970), the dense phytoplankton blooms which occur being apparently dominated by diatoms (Neaverson 1934; Hart & Currie 1960; Kollmer 1963; Ssaidova 1971; Jouse 1972).

A detailed analysis of the organic-rich oozes which underlie these highly productive water columns has indicated that a large proportion of the biomass produced during the periodic phytoplankton blooms is rapidly deposited onto the shelf surface. The sediments off S.W. Africa and Peru are strongly anoxic, including the interfacial deposits, and are dominated mineralogically by opaline silica (Morris & Calvert 1977; Smith *et al.* 1982, 1983a; Poutanen & Morris 1983a) while a microscopic analysis of the surface sediments indicates the presence of many intact diatoms some with pigments in their chloroplasts. Large amounts of recognizable phytoplankton pigments

(Brongersma-Sanders 1951; Morris & Calvert 1977; Cronin & Morris 1982; Poutanen & Morris 1983a) fatty acids (Morris & Calvert 1977; Smith *et al.* 1983b, c) and sterols (Wardoper *et al.* 1978; Smith *et al.* 1982, 1983a) have been reported in these sediments, evidence of rapid sedimentation and burial of virtually intact phytoplankton cells.

From the results of these studies it appears that in such marine areas sedimentation of phytoplankton blooms occurs in a series of discrete 'events', giving pulses of biological material which sediment out rapidly (Cronin & Morris 1982), blanketing the underlying sediment surface. The very high rates of sedimentation which result ensure the burial of large quantities of the organic debris. The greatly increased flux of organic material to the sediment/water interface stimulates microbial activity with a concomitant development of anoxic conditions in the near surface sediments and pore waters. The anoxic conditions limit bacterial degradation by all but the anaerobic species and prevent auto-oxidative breakdown. Other studies have indicated that in such sedimentary environments the natural product organic compounds present in the phytoplankton detrital material, together with the contribution of organic matter from the interfaunal bacterial community, rapidly interreact to give rise to high molecular weight humic compounds (Cronin & Morris 1982; Poutanen & Morris 1983a). It has been suggested that the formation of high molecular weight moieties may well protect the organic matter against chemical and biological attack.

Work on experimental enclosed ecosystems has largely supported these hypotheses. The end of the spring phytoplankton bloom in northern Scottish waters appears to occur when growth conditions (i.e. nutrients) become limiting (Mor-

From: BROOKS, J. & FLEET, A. J. (eds) 1987, *Marine Petroleum Source Rocks*
Geological Society Special Publication No. 26 pp. 153–166.

ris *et al.* 1983). At this stage the massed phytoplankton cells drop rapidly out of the euphotic zone. Upon sedimentation anoxic conditions are quickly developed in the phytoplankton detrital material and high molecular weight compounds start to form (Cronin & Morris 1983; Poutanen & Morris 1983b).

The above discussions relate to geochemical processes which are thought to occur in marine water columns of a few hundred metres depth at most. For preservation of organic material to occur in sediments underlying oceanic water columns of several thousands of metres depth it has often been assumed that very different mechanisms operate with the development of a stagnant water column as the primary factor. In the bottom waters of certain marine basins with a restricted water circulation, dissolved oxygen is used up in the decomposition of organic matter and is not readily replenished from the surface layers. Under such conditions the degradation of organic matter might be expected to be restricted to the action of reducing bacteria and, as a result be much slower, leading to better preservation of the sedimentary organic material (see discussion in Morris & Culkin (1975) and references therein). Richards (1972) however could find no clear evidence for a relationship between preservation of organic matter and anoxic conditions resulting from restricted circulation, and suggested that the raised levels of organic matter in anoxic basins such as the Black Sea and Cariaco Trench may represent faster rates of sedimentation rather than slower rates of decomposition. Müller & Suess (1979) went further and postulated a relationship between the fraction of primary produced organic carbon preserved in the oceanic sediments and the bulk sedimentation rate. Clearly, as Calvert (1983) points out, the case for anoxic conditions being responsible for the formation of organic-rich deposits has not been adequately proven.

The belief that stagnation of a water column is a necessary prerequisite for the formation of organic-rich deposits in deep-water marine sediments is best exemplified by studies on the East Mediterranean sapropels. Indeed the term sapropel has for many years been used to refer to organic-rich sediment formed under anoxic conditions (the terms sapropel and sapropelic deposits as used in this work follow the recommendations of Kidd *et al.* 1978). Most workers are generally agreed that, following the hydrological isolation of the deep waters, stagnation of the Eastern Mediterranean basins and the concomitant formation of anoxic conditions occurred prior to the deposition of the sapropelic layers (Olausson 1960, 1961; Ryan 1972; Nesterhoff

1973; McCoy 1974; Cita *et al.* 1977; Ryan & Cita 1977; Thunnel *et al.* 1977; Vergnaud-Grazzini *et al.* 1977; Stanley 1978; Rossignol-Strich *et al.* 1982). The arguments have tended to centre on the likely events which might have triggered such hydrological conditions, rather than whether they were in fact always the primary factor involved in the preservation of the organic material.

In this paper I have attempted to investigate the likely origins of organic deposits at two deep water core sites. The results of a number of related studies on a recent sapropel from Hellenic ridge, East Mediterranean, are summarized, and preliminary results are given of studies on sapropelic layers recently found in sediments from the Guinea Basin (South Atlantic). Results are compared with those from shallow water organic deposits and possible similarities in the processes leading to their formation are discussed. The specific problem of the primary cause of the deep water organic-rich deposits is addressed, and, in particular, the likely role of anoxic conditions in their formation.

Materials and methods

Collection

Samples were collected using a Kastenlot corer (Kogler 1963), equipped with a 2 m or 4 m long 15×15 cm section barrel, from RRS Discovery during cruises to the Eastern Mediterranean (Discovery Cruise 104) and South Atlantic (Discovery Cruise 128).

Location of core sites

(a) Eastern Mediterranean

Samples of the recent S_1 sapropel were required from an area which had suffered as little post-depositional disturbance as possible and which had received as little lateral input as possible from bottom currents, i.e. a site which would mainly mirror the sedimentary input from the overlying water column. To this end a site was chosen on the northern arm of the Hellenic Outer Ridge (Fig. 1). It was protected from lateral influences to the north, east and west by deep water basins and to the south by the east–west ridge system. Narrow and wide beam echo sounders revealed the site to have a fairly complex local topography. A local high spot (2900 m depth) was then chosen to minimize the danger of post-depositional slumping and ponding. Whilst the loss of part of the sediment to deeper lying areas by the winnowing action of deep

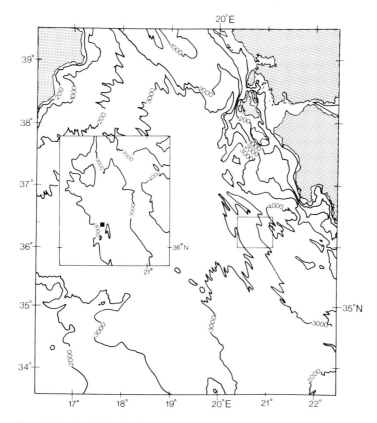

FIG. 1. Core site (■) in the Eastern Mediterranean.

currents had to be expected it was considered that at least the remainder should be in the original time sequence of deposition.

(b) Guinea Basin

The objective was to study a deep-water sediment underlying an area of high biological productivity whose sources of input were mainly restricted to marine components. A core site was chosen on the flat abyssal plain (4735 m depth) of the Guinea Basin (Fig. 2). It was considered that the area would be far removed from any significant terrigenous influence and, it was hoped, turbidite action originating on the continental shelves of Africa.

Core description

(a) E. Mediterranean

A light brown marl ooze, 28 cm thick, overlaid a black sapropel, 73 cm thick, containing well preserved pteropod tests throughout, which in turn overlaid a stiff light grey calcareous clay (Fig. 3).

(b) Guinea Basin

The core consisted of alternating marls and oozes. The oozes were grey to black in colour and occurred between 55–110 cm, 190–140 cm and 320–350 cm depth. Distinct black-grey bands were found in each of the ooze deposits (Fig. 4).

Sampling

Samples were recovered immediately from the open core on deck and immediately preserved under nitrogen at −20°C in specially cleaned (acid-washed, $CHCl_3$—CH_3OH rinsed), sealed containers. All possible precautions were taken to avoid contamination.

Analysis

In the laboratory sub-samples for bulk mineralogical and inorganic chemical analysis were dried at 110°C and ground to fine powders in a tungsten carbide and agate swing mill. Organic carbon and carbonate were determined gravimetrically using a Leco carbon analyser following methods given in Gaskell *et al.* (1975).

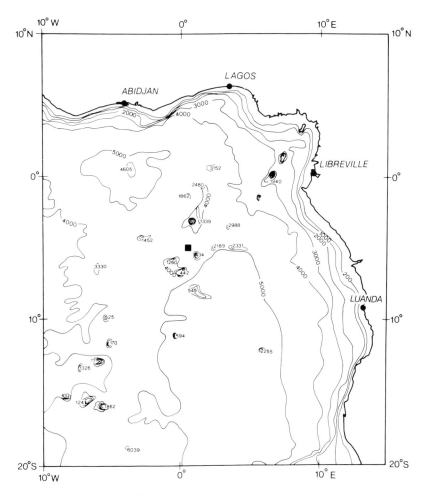

FIG. 2. Core site (■) in the Guinea Basin.

Mineralogy was determined by conventional X-ray diffraction methods (Calvert 1966; Eisma & Van der Gaast 1971) and inorganic chemical analysis carried out by X-ray emission spectrometry (Calvert & Morris 1977; Sutherland *et al.* 1984).

The extraction and fractionation of humic substances was carried out on undried subsamples using methods described previously (Poutanen & Morris 1983a).

Total lipids were extracted from undried subsamples using chloroform-methanol (Morris & Calvert 1977) and the major lipid classes separated. Detailed analyses of the total component fatty acids and sterols were carried out by GC and GC-MS techniques (Smith *et al.* 1982, 1983a, b).

Sub-samples were also taken from the East Mediterranean core for radiocarbon and stable carbon isotope measurements at the Scottish Universities Research Reactor Centre, East Kilbride, Scotland.

Results and discussion

(a) E. Mediterranean core

Smear slide analysis

A microscopic analysis showed the presence of pteropods, planktonic foraminifera, coccoliths, plant debris, siliceous spines and shell fragments. Pteropod tests were particularly abundant both in the sapropel and the overlying marl ooze often in an excellent state of preservation. The two predominant species found were *Clio pyramidata* and *Cavolinia tridertata*. These species generally

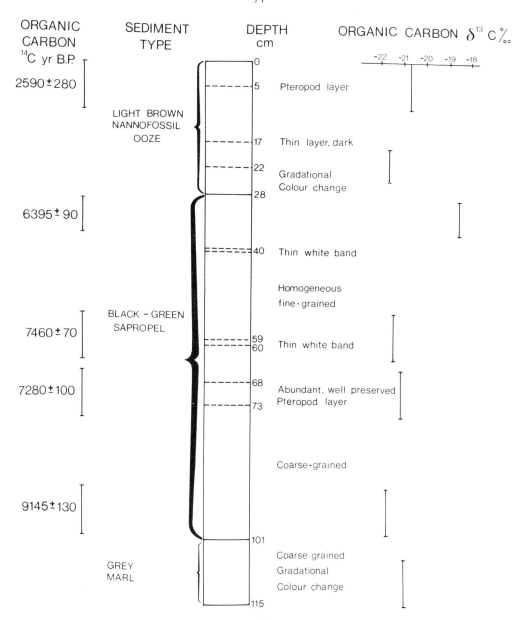

10103 # 8K

FIG. 3. Core description of Mediterranean sediment and ^{13}C values.

occur in open Mediterranean waters in the upper 2000 m (Menzies 1958) and the upper 1000 m (Tesch 1946) respectively. Their presence in large numbers in this sapropel indicates that during the formation of the sapropel the overlying water was fully oxic.

Diatoms, silicoflagellates and dinoflagellates were not present in the sapropel, neither was

evidence of any benthic fauna. The absence of benthic fauna is certainly an indicator that the bottom sediments were anoxic during sapropel formation. Furthermore following the work of Deelman (1975) who investigated the effect of low redox potentials produced by sulphate reducing bacteria on the dissolution of carbonate, the excellent preservation of the aragonite pteropod

R. J. Morris

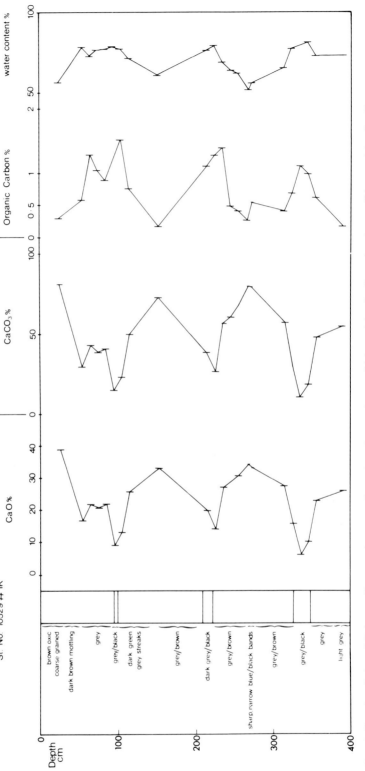

Fig. 4. Core description of Guinea sediment and content of organic carbon, carbonate (% dry weight of sediment) and water (% wet weight of sediment)

tests may be further evidence of anoxic conditions in the sediments. This suggestion is further supported by the observation that aragonite shells are preserved in an anaerobic basin off California (Berger & Soutar 1970).

Mineralogy and inorganic chemistry

The results of the mineralogical and inorganic chemical analyses will be reported in detail elsewhere (Sutherland *et al.* 1984). Only those results of immediate relevance to this study will be discussed.

The sapropel contains an order of magnitude more organic carbon than the overlying or underlying sediments (Fig. 5). There were however no major differences between the different sediment types in their general mineralogy or major element chemistry, indicating that radical changes in the inorganic inputs to the sediment had not occurred during sapropel formation.

The radiocarbon data (Fig. 6) give age limits of about 6500–9000 yrs BP to the sapropel unit, identifying it as S_1 (Cita *et al.* 1977). Sedimentation rates derived from these dates give the sapropel around 23 cm/1000 y and the upper marl ooze and lower clay between 4 and 7 cm/1000 y. The sapropel appears to have been formed under conditions of much more rapid sedimentation than the surrounding sediments, although a

contribution by local slumping cannot be ruled out.

The stable carbon isotopic composition of the organic material throughout the core (Fig. 3) strongly indicates a predominantly marine planktonic source (see discussion in Gaskell *et al.* 1975). If terrestrial organic material is present in the sapropel it can only be a minor constituent as the $\delta^{13}C$ value is much lower than the mean value of $-20.6°$ determined here ($\delta^{13}C$ values are expressed per ml relative to the PDB standard). This conclusion is supported by the organic C/N ratios of about 10 found in the sapropel (Sutherland *et al.* 1984). Allowing for preferential loss of N during diagenesis (Müller 1977) this would give the original C/N ratio of the sedimenting organic matter to be close to the value of 7 found in marine plankton (Redfield *et al.* 1963).

Using Rb as an index of the relative abundance of aluminosilicate phases the contents of the minor elements Ba, Cr, Cu, Mo, Ni and Zn are all higher relative to Rb in the sapropel whilst Mn is lower (Sutherland *et al.* 1984). Cr, Cu, Mo, Ni and Zn are all essential trace metals for living organisms and their raised levels in the sapropel may be indicative of a higher biogenic input. The enrichment of Ba in the sapropel (Fig. 5) contrasts with the lack of enrichment in diatom oozes from the Namibian shelf (Calvert & Price 1983) and may be evidence for a non-diatom

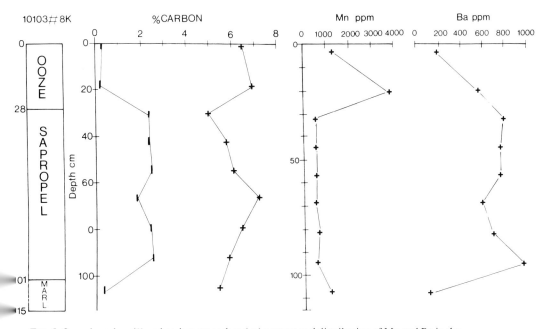

FIG. 5. Organic carbon (**I**) and carbonate carbon (**+**) content and distribution of Mn and Ba in the Mediterranean sediment.

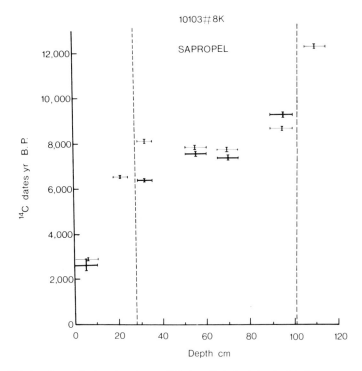

FIG. 6. Organic ^{14}C data (heavy line) and carbonate ^{14}C data (light line) for the Mediterranean sediment.

planktonic input, possibly flagellates (e.g. Fresnel *et al.* 1979).

The depletion of Mn in the sapropel (Fig. 5) and the high levels found near the base of the overlying marl ooze can be readily explained by mobilization of this element under reducing conditions and reprecipitation in oxidizing conditions (Sutherland *et al.* 1984). These data strongly suggest that anoxic conditions occurred

in the sediment during sapropel formation, oxic conditions being restored at the end of this period.

Humic chemistry

The molecular size distribution of humic and fulvic acids at one depth horizon (41–48 cm) in the sapropel is shown in Fig. 7. A more detailed description of the humic chemistry of this core

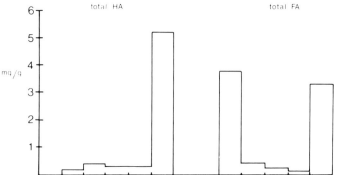

FIG. 7. Molecular weight distribution (mg/g dry sediment) of humic (HA) and fulvic (FA) acid fractions in the Mediterranean sapropel.

will be published later (Poutanen & Morris in preparation). From these preliminary data over 20% of the organic carbon present in the sapropel appears to be present as extractable humic and fulvic acids. The high molecular weight moieties ($>300,000$) make up over 60% of the total humics. The pattern of humic compounds in the Mediterranean sapropel is remarkably similar to that reported previously for the diatomaceous oozes of the Namibian Shelf (Cronin & Morris 1982) and the Peruvian Shelf (Poutanen & Morris 1983a). A typical distribution for the humics in these sediments is shown in Fig. 8; the three samples range in age from modern to 1000 y BP. The conclusion from the humic studies on the diatomaceous oozes was that in such sediments receiving a high biogenic input, the humic and fulvic acids were formed directly and rapidly *in situ* from the biogenic organic compounds. The humic data for the East Mediterranean sapropel indicate that a similar large planktonic input may have occurred during its formation.

Lipid chemistry

The detailed lipid analyses of the sapropel will be published later (Smith *et al.* in preparation) but some preliminary data on the component fatty acids and sterols in the 29–36 cm horizon are presented here.

Over 80% of the component fatty acids were in the C_{12}–C_{22} range. Major acids present were 16:0, 18:0/18:1 and 14:0. The dominance of the low molecular weight, even chain, fatty acids in the sapropel indicates a mainly marine planktonic source (Morris & Culkin 1975 and references therein; Morris & Calvert 1977 and references therein), acids in the carbon range C_{24}–C_{34} being generally taken as terrestrially derived. That this planktonic source is mainly phytoplankton can be further predicted from the distribution of the major acids (Morris & Calvert 1977 and references therein; Smith *et al.* 1983b and references therein), the high levels of 18:0/18:1 w9 acids suggesting a non-diatomaceous input, possibly flagellates.

The level of bacterial activity in the sediment during sapropel formation may also be inferred from the acid data (see review by Joint & Morris 1982). Branched chain *iso-* and *anteiso-*C_{13}–C_{17} fatty acids and 18:1 w7 (vaccenic) acid are commonly taken as bacterial indicators. In this sapropel sample *iso* 15:0, *anteiso* 15:0 and 18:1 w7 acids are certainly present but at fairly low levels (1–4% total fatty acids). This suggests that there was limited bacterial activity during the formation of the sapropel, possibly as a result of

anoxic conditions being established in the sediment.

A range of C_{26}–C_{31} sterols was found, the distribution being somewhat similar to those previously reported for diatomaceous oozes on the Namibian Shelf (Smith *et al.* 1982) and the Peruvian Shelf (Smith *et al.* 1983a). Such sterol distributions in sediments are typical of a phytoplanktonic source of organic material. The major difference between the diatomaceous oozes and the sapropel was in the levels of dinosterol (4,23,24-trimethyl-5-choles-22-en-3-ol) which, on a percentage basis, was present in much higher amounts in the sapropel. This sterol is generally regarded as a dinoflagellate marker (Smith *et al.* 1982 and references therein) but no dinoflagellate cysts were found in the sediment. It may be that the dinosterol in the sapropel results from an as yet chemically uncharacterized biological source (see discussion in Smith *et al.* 1982) such as small flagellates. High levels of dinosterol have also been reported in the recent sapropel from the Black Sea (Boon *et al.* 1979).

(b) Gulf of Guinea core

Detailed analyses of this material is only at an early stage therefore only very preliminary data will be presented here.

Smear slide analysis

Abundant coccoliths, radiolarians, foraminifera and diatoms were found throughout the core. The oozes were particularly noteworthy in that they contained much greater numbers of radiolarian and diatom remains, the latter including very large cell fragments $>100\,\mu m$ across. Some of these fragments have been tentatively identified as coming from *Ethmodiscus* (Mikkelsen 1977). The coccolith stratigraphy for the core suggests continuous deposition to beyond 250,000 years (P. Weaver, personal communication) and a lack of turbidite action.

Mineralogy and inorganic chemistry

The ooze deposits are characterized by raised levels of organic carbon (Fig. 4) and opaline silica (Fig. 9) and much reduced values for calcium carbonate (Fig. 4). This could be explained either by dissolution or dilution of the carbonate fraction. Visually there appeared to be no consistent relationship between dissolution of carbonate tests and the ooze deposits which suggests that the peaks in organic carbon and opaline silica reflect periods of increased productivity of siliceous organisms superimposed upon

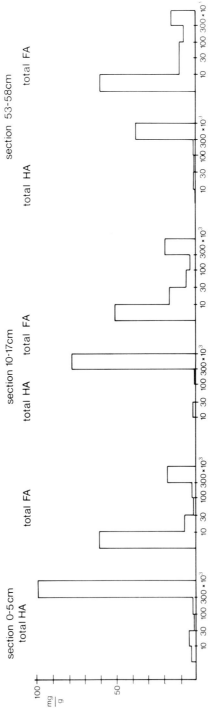

Fig. 8. Molecular weight distributions (mg/g dry sediment) of humic (HA) and fulvic (FA) acid fractions in a sediment core from the Peru continental shelf.

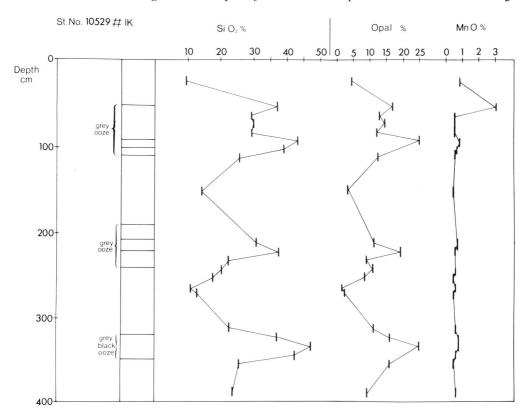

FIG. 9. Distribution of total silica, opaline silica and Mn in the Guinea sediment.

the more steady production of calcareous organisms. The raised water contents of the ooze deposits (Fig. 4) could relate to periods of increased sedimentation, although in this case changes in sediment texture may be the explanation.

On a ppm dry weight basis the trace metals Cr, V, Co, Ni, Zn, Cu all appear to be significantly enriched in the oozes compared to the rest of the core, an observation which could be explained by an enhanced planktonic input.

As for the sapropel, Mn is depleted in the majority of the core, showing a definite enrichment at the base of the marl layer which overlies the most recent ooze deposit (Fig. 9). We believe this profile is explained by re-mobilization of the Mn under reducing conditions and re-precipitation in oxidizing conditions (see earlier discussion). If correct this would suggest that the sediment and pore waters were anoxic at least during the formation of the most recent dark layer.

Lipid chemistry

The preliminary data on the extractable lipids from the most recent dark band show a fatty acid profile dominated by C_{14}–C_{18} even chain acids (*ca* 80% total fatty acids) with 16:0, 18:0 and 14:0 as the major components. As discussed earlier this suggests that the organic carbon in this deposit had mainly a marine phytoplanktonic origin of possibly both diatoms and flagellates. The presence of a considerable monounsaturated component (11–12% total fatty acids) points to a good preservation of this organic source. From the levels of *iso*- and *anteiso*-C15:0 acids (<1.5%) and vaccenic acid (<3.0%) there appears to have been a limited bacterial activity in the sediments during the deposition of the most recent sapropellic layer (see earlier discussion), a result possibly of the anoxic conditions predicted by the Mn data.

A range of C_{27}–C_{30} sterols are present and dinosterol is a major component. As discussed for the Mediterranean sapropel, this type of sterol profile is indicative of a phytoplankton input which includes dinoflagellates. The absence of dinoflagellate cysts in the sample suggests that this is yet another organic-rich sediment formed partly as a result of an as-yet uncharacterized biological input (see earlier discussion and Smith *et al*. 1982).

General discussion

A number of conclusions can be drawn from the various related studies on the Eastern Mediterranean sapropel. The abundance of well preserved pteropod tests points to an oxic water column and anoxic sediments during the deposition of the sapropel. The distribution of Mn in the core and the apparent lack of a large bacterial contribution to the sapropel lipids is further support for there being anoxic conditions in the sediment at this time. Sedimentation rates appear to have been higher during this period than for the adjacent sediment layers although the pattern of minerals supplied were not dramatically altered. The supply of organic material to the sediments appears to have been much higher however, and this organic material seems to have a marine phytoplanktonic origin which is non-diatomaceous but could be composed primarily of small flagellates. The similarity in the humic chemistry of the sapropel and continental shelf organic-rich oozes suggests that not dissimilar organic inputs and post-depositional changes are involved in these areas.

Hence the sapropel appears to have been formed at a time when there was a general increase in sedimentation and a considerable increase in marine phytoplankton production in the area. Possible hydrographic conditions which might have been involved in such a scenario have been discussed previously by Calvert (1983) and Sutherland *et al*. (1984). Of immediate relevance to this work is that the phytoplankton blooms have left a record in the inorganic and organic chemistry of the underlying deep water sediments. The preservation of many of the lipid components suggest a fairly rapid flux of the planktonic detrital material to sediment with the initial stimulation of bacterial activity and the rapid development of anoxic conditions in the sediments and pore waters. Diagenetic processes leading to the formation of high molecular weight humic compounds then appear to have taken place in a similar manner to that already described for organic-rich sediments underlying shallow water areas of high productivity.

Although work on the Guinea Basin core is still at an early stage I believe there is sufficient data to draw some preliminary conclusions. It is considered most unlikely that anoxic conditions could prevail in the water column at this core site. The microscopic and mineralogical data indicate that the sapropelic layers are associated with periods of greatly increased productivity in the overlying ocean. This productivity appears to have included blooms of large-celled diatoms and possibly an increase in radiolarian production. The trace metal data and the lipid analyses support this suggestion and further indicate that small-celled flagellates may also have formed a significant input. The development of anoxic conditions in the sediment during the formation of the sapropelic layers is indicated by the Mn distribution and the apparent lack of a large bacterial contribution to the component lipids.

As for the sapropel, this is a deep water area where past events involving periods of high productivity have resulted in the formation of organic-rich sediments in the underlying sediments. A rapid flux of the detrital material to the sediments appears to have occurred with a concomitant development of anoxic conditions and preservation of many of the organic compounds for subsequent burial.

Conclusions

Two deep-water depositional environments are described where phytoplankton productivity in the overlying waters has apparently been directly responsible for the formation of organic-rich deposits. A fast sedimentation of the phytoplankton blooms, subsequent development of anoxic conditions in the sediment and rapid burial of a considerable part of the detrital material appear to be the processes involved, processes which are all known to be important in the formation of some shallow-water organic-rich deposits. As found in the shallow-water sedimentary environments, anoxic conditions in the deep-water sediments are thought to be a direct result of an increased supply of organic matter. A major weakness in the argument is the lack of experimental evidence to support the suggestion that pulses of planktonic organic material could sink through 5000 m of an oceanic water column fast enough and in a discrete 'event' to allow such sedimentary processes to occur. However the recent report of a seasonal pulse of organic detrital material to bathyal and abyssal depths being derived directly from the surface primary productions (Billett *et al*. 1983) clearly supports our hypothesis.

ACKNOWLEDGEMENTS: This paper summarizes a number of related studies at present in progress, which will be the subject of more detailed publications. The collaboration of Mr M. J. McCartney, Mrs E. Poutanen and Dr D. Smith in this work is acknowledged. Thanks are due to Dr S. E. Calvert and Dr P. Weaver for helpful discussion, Professor G. Eglinton for use of departmental facilities and Dr D. D. Harkness of the Scottish Universities Research and Reactor Centre for kindly providing ^{14}C dates and $\delta^{13}C$ values.

References

BERGER, W. H. & SOUTAR, A. 1970. Preservation of plankton shells in an anaerobic basin off California. *Bull. geol. Soc. Am.*, **81**, 275–282.

BILLET, A. S. M., LAMPITT, R. S., RICE, A. L. & MANTOURA, R. F. C. 1983. Seasonal sedimentation of phytoplankton to the deep-sea benthos. *Nature*, **302**, 520–522.

BOON, J. J., RIJPSTRA, W. I., DE LANGE, F. & DE LEEUW, J. W. 1979. Black Sea sterol—a molecular fossil for dinoflagellate blooms. *Nature*, **277**, 125–127.

BRONGERSMA-SANDERS, M. 1951. On conditions favouring the preservation of chlorophyll in marine sediments. *Proceedings of the 3rd World Petroleum Congress, Section I*, 401–413.

CALVERT, S. E. 1966. Accumulation of diatomaceous silica in the sediments of the Gulf of California. *Bull. geol. Soc. Am.*, **77**, 569–596.

—— 1983. Geochemistry of Pleistocene sapropels from the eastern Mediterranean, *Oceanologica Acta*, **6**, 255–267.

—— & MORRIS, R. J. 1977. Geochemical studies of organic-rich sediments from the Namibian shelf. II. Metal-organic associations. *In:* ANGEL, M. (ed.) *A voyage of Discovery*, Pergamon Press, Oxford. 667–680.

—— & PRICE, N. B. 1983. Geochemistry of the recent sediments of the Namibian shelf. *In:* SUESS, E. & THIEDE, J. (eds) *Coastal Upwelling: its Sediment Record, A*, NATO conf. Ser. IV **10A**. Plenum Press, New York. 337–375.

CITA, M. B., VERGNAUD-GRAZZINI, C., ROBERT, C., CHAMLEY, H., CIARANFI, N. & DONOFRIO, S. 1977. Paleoclimatic record of a long deep-sea core from the eastern Mediterrranean. *Quaternary Research*, **8**, 205–235.

COLOMBO, V. 1967. Origin and evolution of petroleum. *In:* NAGY, B. & COLOMBO, V. (eds) *Fundamental aspects of Petroleum Geochemistry*, Elsevier, Amsterdam. 331–369.

CRONIN, J. R. & MORRIS, R. J. 1982. The occurrence of high molecular weight humic material in recent organic-rich sediment from the Namibian shelf. *Estuarine, Coastal and Shelf Science*, **15**, 17–27.

—— & MORRIS, R. J. 1983. Rapid formation of humic material from diatom debris. *In:* SUESS, E. & THIEDE, J. (eds) *Coastal Upwelling: Its Sediment Record, A*, NATO conf. Ser. IV, **10A**. Plenum Press, New York. 485–496.

DEELMAN, J. C. 1975. Bacterial sulphate reduction affecting carbonate sediments. *Soil Science*, **119**, 73–80.

DEMAISON, G. J. & MOORE, G. T. 1980. Anoxic environments and oil source bed genesis. *Organic Geochem.*, **2**, 9–31.

EISMA, D. & VAN DER GAAST, S. J. 1971. Determination of opal marine sediments by X-ray diffraction. *Netherlands J. Sea Res.*, **5**, 382–389.

FRESNEL, J., GALLE, P. & GAYRAL, P. 1979. Resultats de la microanalse des cristeaux vacuolaires chez deux chromophytes unicellulaires marines: *Exanthemachrysis gayraliae, Pavlova* sp. (Prymnesiophycees, Pavlovacees). *C.R. Academy Science Paris D*, **228**, 823–825.

GASKELL, S. J., MORRIS, R. J., EGLINTON, G. & CALVERT, S. E. 1975. The geochemistry of a recent marine sediment off north-west Africa. An assessment of source input and early diagenesis. *Deep-Sea Research*, **22**, 777–789.

GUNTHER, E. R. 1936. A report on oceanographical investigations in the Peru coastal current. *Discovery Report*, **13**, 107–276.

HART, T. J. & CURRIE, R. I. 1960. The Benguela Current. *Discovery Report*, **31**, 123–298.

JOINT, I. R. & MORRIS, R. J. 1982. The role of bacteria in the turnover of organic matter in the sea. *Oceanography and Marine Biology Annual Review*, **20**, 65–118.

JOUSE, A. P. 1972. Diatoms in the surface sediment layer of the Chilean–Peruvian region of the Pacific Ocean. *Oceanologia*, **12**, 831–841.

KIDD, R. B., CITA, M. B. & RYAN, W. B. F. 1978. Stratigraphy of eastern Mediterranean sapropel sequences recovered during DSDP Leg 42A and their paleoenvironmental significance. *In:* HSU, K. J., MONTADERT, L. *et al.* (eds) *Initial Reports of the Deep Sea Drilling Project*, **42**, Part 1, U.S. Govt. Print. Off. Washington DC. 421–443.

KOGLER, F. C. 1963. Das Kastenlot. *Meyiana*, **13**, 1–7.

KOLLMER, W. E. 1963. The pilchard of South West Africa (*Sardinops ocellata* Pappe): notes on zooplankton and phytoplankton collections made off Walvis Bay. *Investigational Report, Marine Research Laboratory, South West Africa*, **3**, 1–78.

MCCOY, F. W. 1974. *Late Quaternary sedimentation in the eastern Mediterranean Sea*. Ph.D. Thesis, Harvard University, Cambridge, Mass., 132 pp. (unpubl.)

MENZIES, R. J. 1958. Shell-bearing pteropod gastropods from Mediterranean plankton (Cavoleniidae). *Publicazioni Della Stazione Zoologica di Napoli*, **30**, 381–401.

MIKKELSEN, N. 1977. On the origin of Ethmodiscus ooze. *Marine Micropaleontology*, **2**, 35–46.

MORRIS, R. J. & CULKIN, F. 1975. Environmental organic chemistry of oceans, fjords and anoxic basins. *In:* EGLINTON, G. (ed.) *Environmental Chemistry, 1*. The Chemical Society, London. 81–108.

—— & CALVERT, S. E. 1977. Geochemical studies of

organic-rich sediments from the Namibian Shelf I. The organic fractions. *In:* ANGEL, M. (ed.) *A Voyage of Discovery*, Pergamon Press, Oxford. 647–665.

——, MCCARTNEY, M. & ROBINSON, G. in press. Studies of a spring phytoplankton bloom in an enclosed experimental ecosystem. I. Biochemical changes in relation to the nutrient chemistry of the water. *Journal of Experimental Marine Biology and Ecology.*

MÜLLER, P. J. 1977. C/N ratios in Pacific deep-sea sediments: Effect of inorganic ammonium and organic nitrogen compounds sorbed by clays. *Geochim. et Cosmochim. Acta,* **41**, 765–776.

—— & SUESS, E. 1979. Productivity, sedimentation rate, and sedimentary organic matter in the oceans. I. Organic carbon preservation. *Deep-Sea Research,* **26**, 1347–1362.

NEAVERSON, E. 1934. The sea-floor deposits I. General characters and distribution. *Discovery Report,* **9**, 295–350.

NESTEROFF, W. D. 1973. Petrography and mineralogy of sapropels. *In:* RYAN, W. B. F. & HSU, K. J. *et al., Initial Reports of the Deep Sea Drilling Project, 13, Part 2,* U.S. Government Printing Office, Washington, D.C. 713–720.

OLAUSSON, E. 1960. Description of sediment cores from the Mediterranean and the Red Sea. *Reports of the Swedish Deep-Sea Expedition 8,* **5**, 287–334.

—— 1961. Studies of deep-sea cores. *Reports of the Swedish Deep-Sea Expedition 8,* **6**, 337–391.

POUTANEN, E.-L. & MORRIS, R. J. 1983a. The occurrence of high molecular weight humic compounds in the organic-rich sediments of the Peru continental shelf. *Oceanologica Acta,* **6**, 21–28.

—— & MORRIS, R. J. 1983b. A study of the formation of high molecular weight compounds during the decomposition of a field diatom population. *Estuarine, Coastal and Shelf Science,* **17**, 189–196.

REDFIELD, A. C., KETCHUM, B. H. & RICHARDS, F. A. 1963. The influence of organisms on the composition of sea water. *In:* HILL, M. N. (ed.), *The Sea,* 2, Wiley, Interscience, London. 26–77.

RICHARDS, F. A. 1972. The enhanced preservation of organic matter in anoxic marine environments. *In:* HOOD, D. W. (ed.), *Organic Matter in Natural Waters,* Institute of Marine Science, University of Alaska Occasional Publication 1. 399–411.

ROSSIGNOL-STRICK, M., NESTEROFF, W., OLIVE, P. & VERGNAUD-GRAZZINI, C. 1982. After the deluge: Mediterranean stagnation and sapropel formation. *Nature,* **295**, 105–110.

RYAN, W. B. F. 1972. Stratigraphy of Late Quaternary sediments in the eastern Mediterranean. *In:* STANLEY, D. J. (ed.), *The Mediterranean Sea,* Dowden, Hutchinson & Ross, Stroudsbury, Penn. 149–169.

—— & CITA, M. B. 1977. Ignorance concerning episodes of ocean-wide stagnation. *Mar. Geology,* **23**, 197–215.

RYTHER, J. H., MENZEL, D. W., HULBURT, E. M., LORENZEN, C. J. & CORWIN, N. 1970. Production and utilization of organic matter in the Peru coastal current. *Anton Bruun Report,* **4**, 4.3–4.12.

SMITH, D. J., EGLINTON, G., MORRIS, R. J. & POUTANEN, E. L. 1982. Aspects of the steroid geochemistry of a recent diatomaceous sediment from the Namibian Shelf. *Oceanologica Acta,* **5**, 365–378.

——, ——, —— & —— 1983a. Aspects of the steroid geochemistry of an interfacial sediment from the Peruvian upwelling. *Oceanologica Acta,* **6**, 211–219.

——, —— & —— 1983b. The lipid chemistry of an interfacial sediment from the Peru Continental Shelf: Fatty acids, alcohols, aliphatic ketones and hydrocarbons. *Geochimica et Cosmochimica Acta,* **47**, 2225–2232.

——, —— & —— 1983c. Interfacial sediment and assessment of organic input from a highly productive water column. *Nature,* **304**, 259–262.

SSAIDOVA, H. M. 1971. Recent sediments off the Pacific coast of South America. Academy of Science USSR. *Investigation P. P. Shirschov—Institute of Oceanologie,* **89**, 139–145.

STANLEY, D. J. 1978. Ionian Sea sapropel distribution and Late Quaternary paleoceanography in the eastern Mediterranean. *Nature,* **274**, 149–152.

STEEMANN-NIELSEN, E. & JENSEN, A. E. 1957. Primary oceanic production. The autotrophic production of organic matter in the oceans. *Galethea Report,* **1**, 49–136.

SUTHERLAND, H. E., CALVERT, S. E. & MORRIS, R. J. 1984. Geochemical studies of the Recent sapropel and associated sediment from the Hellenic Outer Ridge, Eastern Mediterranean Sea. I. Mineralogy and chemical composition. *Mar. Geology.* **56**, 79–92.

TESCH, J. J. 1946. The thecostomatous pteropods I. Atlantic. *Dana Reports,* **28**, 1–82.

TISSOT, B. 1979. Effects on prolific petroleum source rocks and major coal deposits caused by sea-level changes. *Nature,* **277**, 463–465.

TISSOT, B. & WELTE, D. 1978. *Petroleum Formation and Occurrence,* Springer Verlag, Heidelberg. 538 pp.

THUNELL, R. C., WILLIAMS, D. F. & KENNETT, J. P. 1977. Late Quaternary paleoclimatology, stratigraphy and sapropel history in the eastern Mediterranean deep-sea sediments. *Marine Micropaleontology,* **2**, 371–388.

VERGNAUD-GRAZZINI, C., RYAN, W. B. F. & CITA, M. G. 1977. Stable isotopic fractionation, climate change and episodic stagnation in the eastern Mediterranean during the Late Quaternary. *Marine Micropaleontology,* **2**, 353–370.

WARDROPER, A. M. K., MAXWELL, J. R. & MORRIS, R. J. 1978. Sterols of a diatomaceous ooze from Walvis Bay. *Steroids,* **32**, 203–221.

R. J. MORRIS, Institute of Oceanographic Sciences, Wormley, Godalming, Surrey, U.K.

A model of organic sedimentation on present-day continental margins

R. Pelet

SUMMARY: A very general mathematical formalism describing biological degradation in either the water column or in sediments is proposed. Coupled with considerations of sedimentary processes, it permits the qualitative description of organic sedimentation. It is found that a simple, general relationship relating the organic-carbon content of sediments and sedimentation rates cannot exist, and that any apparent relationship is caused by the covariation of factors which are not logically linked. Consideration of the rates of degradation of organic matter in different oceanic environments leads to the conclusion that, in aerobic environments, meio- and macro- benthos are more efficient biological consumers than the free bacterial community.

Organic matter is a normal component of sedimentary rocks. If this is sometimes forgotten, it is because the average organic content of rocks is low and because the inorganic remains of living beings—the usual fossils—are so spectacular and can be used in so many ways that the study of the organic fraction itself seems superfluous. And yet, even for the broadest geological purposes, its study can be fruitful. A part can be recognized, with more or less sophisticated optical means, as organic fossils; the amorphous remainder can be studied by chemical means—which is the scope of what can be termed general organic geochemistry. Obviously, these considerations do not apply to workers in the petroleum and coal industries who are directly involved in the fate of sedimentary organic matter, but if these researchers remain isolated from the geological community, this will result in losses for both groups.

Classical textbooks on sedimentology say little about organic matter. Not only is the difficult problem of organomineral interactions avoided but even the simpler and fundamental question of organic sedimentation is not dealt with. Some indications can be found in the best treatises on coal, but they are often rather simplistic (an exception is Stach *et al.* 1982) and in any case highly specialized. Recently oceanographers have shown some interest in these questions, because organic sedimentation represents escape from biological recycling.

These studies (e.g. Romankevic 1977) have shown that biological recycling is indeed very efficient, the escape being on the average a few parts per thousand of the organic matter produced at the oceanic surface (but see below). This recycling—termed 'degradation', 'alteration', etc. by organic geochemists—is thus the first control on organic sedimentation. But the second is even more obvious, it is the organic supply. I write here supply, and not production, because, for oceanographers, production means marine (planktonic) production, whereas terrestrial vegetal production is of equivalent magnitude and its products can be transported to the sea; therefore one must be prudent on the ultimate origin of the organic matter sedimented.

Of the two fundamental controls distinguished—supply and alteration—which is the most important? Logically, the best candidate appears the supply—one cannot alter something which does not exist, and the rate of alteration must be more or less dependent on the quantity of organic matter initially present. Fig. 1 is a map of the organic productivity of the world ocean, apart from the equatorial convergence, the zones of high oceanic productivity are always in the vicinity of continents. Similarly, the main zones of continental input are evidently close to the continents, and generally distinct from the zones of high oceanic productivity: e.g. the Gulf of Guinea or the Gulf of Bengal. Fig. 2 is a map of the organic content of surficial oceanic sediments. It displays a striking similarity to Fig. 1, if the input of riverborne organic matter is also taken into consideration. This is another argument for the main control resting on supply. Finally, geochemical considerations (e.g. Pelet 1983)

From: BROOKS, J. & FLEET, A. J. (eds) 1987, *Marine Petroleum Source Rocks*
Geological Society Special Publication No. 26 pp. 167–180.

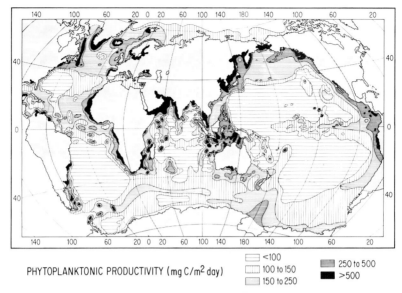

PHYTOPLANKTONIC PRODUCTIVITY (mg C/m² day)

☐ <100
☐ 100 to 150
☐ 150 to 250
▨ 250 to 500
■ >500

FIG. 1. Global phytoplankton productivity (mg C m^{-2} day^{-1}).

show that even extreme environmental conditions, such as anoxia, claimed to be the cause of very high organic matter concentrations and accumulations, are in fact themselves a consequence of high organic input, coupled with particular topographic or oceanographic conditions.

The organic supply is largely independent of what occurs in the sedimentary column. Alteration, similarly, takes place essentially in the water column and is thus relatively insensitive to depositional and diagenetic phenomena. On the other hand, the organic carbon content of a sediment, i.e. the ratio of organic to mineral matter, obviously depends on this latter control, and, from it, on the

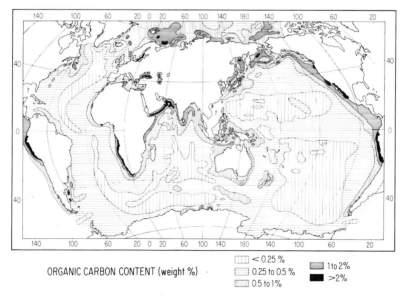

ORGANIC CARBON CONTENT (weight %)

☐ < 0.25 %
☐ 0.25 to 0.5 %
☐ 0.5 to 1%
▨ 1 to 2%
■ >2%

FIG. 2. Global organic carbon content (weight %) of seafloor sediments.

sedimentation rate. However, all these factors—organic supply, mineral supply, biological alteration—are not strictly independent. To disentangle their relations is to elucidate the first and simplest problem of the sedimentology of organic matter: what are the quantities and concentrations deposited? This is the scope of this paper.

Development of the models

Two extreme sedimentological models will be described, termed respectively 'marine pelagic' and 'continental detrital'. Any actual situation will be considered as a combination, in various proportions, of these two end-members.

General

The basic data for the determination of sedimentation rates are ages, either palaeontological or absolute, determined at various depths in cores. Rates are given in length per unit time, e.g. cm/1000 y. These rates are therefore apparent, because they do not take into account the compaction which, with the evolution of time, will inevitably lower the initial values. However, the determination of the actual rates would involve the knowledge of the distribution of porosity along the whole core sections under investigation. This parameter is, as a rule, ignored, thus making the apparent rates the only available.

I shall consider separately the initial organic and mineral supplies as two functions R and P, kg $m^{-2}s^{-1}$, attached to a certain element of sediment which after a time T is found at a depth H in the sedimentary column, thus defining a mean apparent sedimentation rate $V = H/T$. If, at the same time T, $\mathcal{Q}_c$ and $\mathcal{Q}_m$ are the quantities of organic and mineral matter deposited on height H and surface S, with densities ρ_c and ρ_m, then by definition:

$$V(1-\phi) = \frac{\mathcal{Q}_c}{ST\rho_c} + \frac{\mathcal{Q}_m}{ST\rho_m}$$

As mineral matter is considered to suffer no change, $\mathcal{Q}_m/ST \equiv P$ where ϕ is porosity. We can abbreviate $\mathcal{Q}_c/ST = R'$

so

$$V(1-\phi) = \frac{R'}{\rho_c} + \frac{P}{\rho_m} \tag{1}$$

and if θ is the mass fraction of the organic matter,

$$\theta = \frac{R'}{R'+P} \tag{2}$$

θ and τ, the organic carbon content expressed in weight %, are related by $\theta = 10^{-2}\alpha\tau$ where α is a conversion factor, which is about 1.5 for freshly sedimented organic matter (for the basis for this estimation see Pelet 1983a) and decreases with the time. I shall consider it is a constant for present purposes.

From equation (2) P can be expressed as a function of θ and this value introduced in (1), hence:

$$V = \frac{R'}{1-\phi}\left(\frac{1-\theta}{\theta\rho_m} + \frac{1}{\rho_c}\right) \tag{3}$$

This equation can be used to estimate R'.

I shall take two examples of deep-sea surficial sediments, with low carbon contents and low sedimentation rates, to have an idea of the range of R' values (the pertinent data are given in Table

1), together with the values of R, surface organic productivity of the ocean above the sampling points, which give a minimum estimate of the organic supply.

The conclusion is clear: there is a tremendous change in R' compared to R. The effect of alteration (which is believed to be entirely biological) in the water column and in the sedimentary column is to decrease organic input by factors well below 10^{-2}. This conclusion must be considered as general, as the two samples being used here are by no means exceptional.

It is possible to go further. The organic content along a core usually does not show great variations. When this organic content decreases orderly—which is not always the case—this variation can be interpreted as the effect of alteration in the sedimentary column. It is very rare to see more than a four-fold decrease from the surficial layer (0–2 cm) to the quasi-constant values in the depth of the cores. Even if some processes in the 0–2 cm interval result in a final tenfold decrease (a factor of 10^{-1}) the part remaining is still always high relative to the presedimentary organic content. For the two samples of Table 1, the decreases actually observed are 7×10^{-1} for the ORGON sample— meaning a 4×10^{-3} decrease occurred during presedimentary alteration—and 3.5×10^{-1} for the VALVIDIA sample—meaning a 1.4×10^{-4} decrease during presedimentary alteration.

The alteration formalism

We shall assume that this alteration is entirely biological, for reasons not discussed here. The altering agents, whether biological or not, are diverse and do not necessarily work on distinct substrates. The function, D, specifying this alteration will be a sum of elementary functions, each one relative to a given agent acting on a given substrate.

$$D(t) = \sum_{ij} \alpha_{ij} D_{ij}(t) \quad \sum_{ij} \alpha_{ij} = 1$$

The properties of the D function must be as follows. At time 0, there is no alteration, so $D(0) = 1$. As time $\to \infty$ D tends towards a finite limit, which is the non-metabolizable fraction of the organic matter.

$$D_{t \to \infty} \to d < 1$$

$D(t)$ must be continually decreasing so $\delta D / \delta t < 0$. Now, considering the usual shape of curves describing the concentration of various substrates versus depths—very smooth with convexity towards the origin—it is advisable that $\delta^2 D / \delta t^2 > 0$ and, more generally, that D be infinitely derivable, with odd rank derivatives < 0 and even rank > 0. Examples of such functions:

$$(1-d)\,e^{-kt} + d; \quad \frac{1-d}{1+t} + d; \quad \text{Log} \frac{e+t\,e^d}{1-t} \quad \text{etc.}$$

TABLE 1. *Data for two examples of deep-sea sediments with low total organic carbon contents and low sedimentation rates*

Sample	Carbon content τ	Porosity ϕ	Sedimentation rate (cm 10^{-3} y^{-1})	R' (g C m^{-2} y^{-1})	R (g C m^{-2} y^{-1})	R'/R	Source
ORGON III KR 10–1	0.5	0.52	5	0.3	100	3×10^{-3}	Pelet 1983
VALVIDIA 10147–2	0.23	0.8	0.4	0.005	100	5×10^{-5}	Müller & Suess 1979

From the definition, it is clear that a D function sum of elementary D_{ij} obeying the requirements described above itself obeys the same requirements. Now if we admit that the set of the D_{ij} functions covers the entire range of possible reactions, the difference between the D function expressing a specific process (e.g. sulphate reduction in open sea, uptake of aminocompounds by copepods, etc.) lies in the set of α_{ij}. We shall label D_α, D_β etc. such functions D possessing a distinct α_{ij} set.

Now, in some cases, there is a correspondence between t in the D functions and z, depth, in the sediment: this occurs when the mean free displacement of organisms is very small compared to the scale of study of the core, which is at best the cm. This is the case of microorganisms, and to some extent of meiobenthos, but not at all of macrobenthos. In that case, which is the rule in oxic sediments, a layer of 5–10 cm thickness is continually reworked by burrowing or filter feeding organisms, resulting in an enhanced degradation compared to the case of the motionless ecosystem. It is extremely difficult to model this enhanced degradation. The formalism of diffusion mixing (e.g. Billen 1982) is quite satisfactory, but does not appear especially realistic; in any instance, the true problem is to define and measure in the cores, or better *in situ*, parameters representative of the processes invoked. For my purposes, I shall simply specify a distinct set D_β of D functions for those processes.

We consider now a layer of sediment accumulating on the sea floor, during a time dt on area S, it contains a quantity dq_0 of organic matter.

After burial to a depth h, attained in a time $t = h/V$, V being the sedimentation rate considered as time independent, it remains:

$$dq = dq_0 . D(t)$$

More precisely, we shall consider that, down to a depth B, only benthos is important (with D_β) and beyond B, only microorganisms are active (with D_μ).

If $t_B = B/V$

then for $t \le t_B$ $\quad dq = dq_0 D_\beta(t)$

$t > t_B \quad dq = dq_0 D_\beta(t_B) D_\mu(t - t_B)$

Now, the sampling is being done with a finite thickness H. The total quantity of organic matter contained in the sample is thus

$$\mathcal{Q}_c = \int_0^H dq$$

if dq_0 is written $dq_0 = R_0 S \, dt$,

$$\mathcal{Q}_c = \int_0^{H/V} R_0 S D_\beta(t) \, dt \quad \text{for } H \le B$$

$$\mathcal{Q}_c = \int_0^{B/V} R_0 S D_\beta(t) \, dt + \int_{B/V}^{H/V} R_0 S D_\beta(t_B) D_\mu(t - t_B) \, dt \quad \text{for } H > B$$

if we put

$$\mathcal{D}_\lambda(A) = \int_0^A D_\lambda(t) \, dt$$

and as R_0 is independent of the time t in the core (since it is the value attained by some parameter at time $= 0$ for the core) we have

$$\mathcal{Q}_c = R_0 S \mathcal{D}(V)$$

with

$$
\mathbb{D}(V) =
\begin{cases}
\mathscr{D}_\beta\!\left(\dfrac{H}{V}\right) & \text{for } H \le B \\[2ex]
\mathscr{D}_\beta\!\left(\dfrac{B}{V}\right) + D_\beta\!\left(\dfrac{B}{V}\right)\mathscr{D}_\mu\!\left(\dfrac{H-B}{V}\right) & \text{for } H > B
\end{cases}
$$

with the notations of p. 169

$$
R' = \frac{\mathscr{D}_c}{ST} = \frac{R_0 V}{H}\mathbb{D}(V) \tag{4}
$$

R' will be termed accumulation rate (kg/m² s). It is a fraction of the input rate R_0, $(V/H)\mathbb{D}(V)$ being dimensionless. Now equation (3) can be solved in θ, organic mass fraction,

$$
\theta = \frac{R'}{V\rho_m(1-\phi)+R'(1-\rho_m/\rho_c)}
$$

if we replace R' by its value from (4)

$$
\theta = \frac{R_0\mathbb{D}(V)}{H\rho_m(1-\theta)+R_0(1-\rho_m/\rho_c)\mathbb{D}(V)}
$$

With our hypotheses on D functions, $\mathbb{D}(V)$ is a slightly decreasing function of V (decreasing less rapidly than $1/V$). ρ_m, ρ_c and by definition here H and ϕ are independent of V. If R_0 is independent of V, then θ is a slightly decreasing function of V (decreasing less rapidly than $\mathbb{D}(V)$), and consequently R' is a slightly increasing function of V, increasing less rapidly than V.

These relations are readily understandable from a physical standpoint. R_0 being independent of V, the quantity of organic matter originally supplied depends only on time; the shorter the time elapsed to deposit H (the greater V), the smaller this quantity; the effect of the alteration is only to reduce further this quantity. So θ decreases, and this is the so-called 'dilution effect'. But now the reduction due to alteration is itself the smaller, the shorter the time of deposition (the greater V); the original accumulation rate is the constant input rate, it has to be multiplied by this reduction factor increasing with V: therefore, contrary to θ, R', the accumulation rate, increases with V.

We have a means to test the validity of this approach. H and V play a reciprocal role in $\mathbb{D}$. If V is constant, then $\mathbb{D}(H)$ is a slightly increasing function of H, increasing less rapidly than H; therefore θ is a slightly decreasing function of H (because of the term in $H\rho_m(1-\phi)$). In a given core, V can be considered as constant for the first 30 cm, R_0 is constant as well as ρ_m and ρ_c, $1-\phi$ increases with H: θ measured on a 0–2 cm or 0–5 cm slice must be therefore greater than θ measured on 0–30 cm slice. This comparison has been done for the τ value of ORGON cores where it was possible. Table 2 shows the results. It can be seen that generally $\tau_{0-5} > \tau_{0-30}$. The few exceptions are for cores where τ varies irregularly along the core.

The pelagic (planktonic) model

In this model, the organic supply is created by surface productivity R, kg m⁻² s⁻¹; the mineral matter is partly allochthonous, essentially airborne, and partly made of the planktonic skeletons, and thus linked to R:

$$
P = P_0 + \alpha R \tag{6}
$$

During the descent of the protosediment in the water column, organic matter is destroyed by biological recycling, with a set D_θ of functions D. For the sake of simplicity I shall assume that P is

TABLE 2. *Comparison of the organic carbon content (weight %) in KR samples (0–2 cm, except for ORGON I, 0–5 cm) and KL samples (0–30 cm)*

Station		KR	KL
I	2	2.16	1.80
	5	2.27	1.77
	8	0.99	0.44
	10	0.56	1.01
	14	0.41	0.40
II	1	3.07	3.02
	12	1.20	0.56
	17	0.93	1.27
III	10	0.50	0.43
	11	0.90	0.91
	14	2.45	2.28
	15	2.20	2.08
	16	0.45	0.34
	17	0.50	0.57
IV	1	2.58	2.75
	2	1.88	1.76
	4	3.20	2.67
	5	2.06	1.52
	6	1.32	0.95
	7	5.52	4.20
	8	1.44	1.62
	9	6.88	6.05
	10	2.70	2.66

unchanged. At the bottom of the sea, an initial quantity of organic matter $dq_0 = RS \, dt$ becomes

$$dq = RSD_0(T) \, dt$$

T being the time of descent. If we suppose the speed of descent U to be approximately constant, then if Z is the height of the water column:

$$T = \frac{Z}{U}$$

From the above definitions, $R_0 \equiv RD_0(Z/U)$. But the new fact is that now, due to the relation $P = P_0 + \alpha R$, we must carefully distinguish which parameters covary with V, and which are independent. In the previous section, I have implicitly assumed that P was covarying with V, and explicitly that R_0 was independent (physically, it means that V varies by variation of the mineral supply only). If we now make the same assumptions, the same results will apply, meaning that now we are transferring on P_0 the covariation with V. Obviously, this assumption cannot hold for $P_0 = 0$, where we are obliged to consider R (hence R_0) as covarying with V.

If we write now $1/\theta$ (its expression is simpler than θ) we have

$$\frac{1}{\theta} = 1 + \frac{P}{R'} = 1 + \frac{\alpha R}{R'} + \frac{P_0}{R'}$$

after some calculation

$$\frac{1}{\theta} = 1 + \frac{\alpha H}{V \mathbb{D}(V) D_0(Z/U)} + \frac{P_0 H}{V \mathbb{D}(V) R_0}$$

The case of the former section is $\alpha = 0$, and therefore $1/\theta$ reduces to

$$1 + \frac{P_0 H}{V\mathbb{D}(V)R_0}$$

which is, as we saw, an increasing function of V (since θ is a decreasing function of V). Consequently,

$$\frac{P_0 H}{V\mathbb{D}(V)R_0}$$

increases, and as H and R_0 are independent of V,

$$\frac{P_0}{V\mathbb{D}(V)}$$

is an increasing function of V.

Now, if we suppose P_0 independent and P_0 covariable with V, and $\alpha \neq 0$, we must consider the entire equation (7). The term

$$\frac{\alpha H}{V\mathbb{D}(V)D_\theta(Z/U)}$$

decreases with V, since $V\mathbb{D}(V)$ is an increasing function of V. The term

$$\frac{P_0 H}{V\mathbb{D}(V)R_0}$$

is now also decreasing, since $P_0 H$ is independent of V and R_0 must be, physically, increasing with V. Formerly, the expression of R_0 drawn from equation (1) is now

$$R_0 = \frac{H\rho_c[V\rho_m(1-\phi) - P_0]D_\theta(Z/U)}{\alpha H\rho_c + \rho_m V\mathbb{D}(V)D_\theta(Z/U)}$$

where only V and $\mathbb{D}(V)$ are functions of V, and which is increasing since V increases more rapidly than $V\mathbb{D}(V)$. Finally, $1/\theta$ decreases with V and correspondingly θ increases.

An apparent inconsistency appears if one makes $\alpha \to 0$, since now the term $P_0 H/V\mathbb{D}(V)/R_0$ is decreasing, but once again this is only a consequence of our hypotheses on P_0 and R_0, or, physically speaking, on the reasons, mineral or organic, for the variation of V.

The accumulation rate R' is now, after some calculations,

$$R' = \frac{\rho_c[\rho_m V(1-\phi) - P_0]V\mathbb{D}(V)D_\theta(Z/U)}{\alpha H\rho_c + \rho_m V\mathbb{D}(V)D_\theta(Z/U)}$$

which is an increasing function of V, increasing more rapidly than V but less rapidly than V^2.

We can now conclude. For pelagic environments, two extreme situations can occur:

• The organic productivity is constant, and the variation of V is therefore induced by variations in mineral (aeolian, or other allochthonous) supply. In that case, θ is a slightly decreasing function of V ('dilution effect') and the accumulation rate a slightly increasing function of V.

• The mineral supply is constant, and the variation of V is therefore due to variations in the organic productivity. Now θ is a slightly increasing function of V and the accumulation rate a function of V increasing more rapidly than V.

Real situations will certainly lie in between those two extremes. It is, therefore, very difficult to resolve their influences, since everything depends on the ratio P_0/R_0 and on the value of α. Without any further discussion, we shall say that on the whole, θ will tend to increase (very slightly) rather than to decrease (very slightly).

All these conclusions are valid for the other parameters being constant. In any situation the variation of H will have an effect greater than the variation of V. It means that doubling the thickness H of a sample compensates more than doubling, or halving, the value of V. The value of $D_\theta(Z/U)$ varies largely with Z, i.e. with the geographic location, as well as can do α, P_0 and R_0. It is therefore extremely risky to compare samples from different locations.

The continental (detrital) model

In this model, the organic matter is supplied by detrital input, and there is no admixture with any marine autochthonous material, either organic or mineral. It is impossible to define areal productivities P and R, since the geometry of sedimentation is entirely different. I shall, therefore, consider that the sediments issue from one point on the coastline, at a rate of $\mathscr{P}$ kg s^{-1} and $\mathscr{R}$ kg s^{-1} for mineral and organic matter respectively, and are spread on the shelf, slope, rise and abyssal plain of the margin with a density maximum on the slope-rise and decreasing to zero in the abyssal plain. This density function must obviously depend on Λ, horizontal distance from the origin, and on the steepness of the slope. I shall approximate this last value to the water depth Z. The third space coordinate naturally will be the azimuth ψ, the sea floor being described by an equation $Z = Z(\psi, \Lambda)$. If the surface element on the sea floor is dS, our density function δ will obey

$$\delta(Z, \Lambda) \to 0 \quad \text{when } \Lambda \to \infty \text{ whatever } Z$$

$$\frac{\partial \delta}{\partial Z} > 0 \quad \text{(slope effect: at a given } \Lambda, \delta \text{ increases with } Z\text{)}$$

$$\iint_{\text{sea floor}} \delta(Z, \Lambda) \, dS = 1 \quad \text{(mass conservation)}$$

(unit: $\delta(Z, \Lambda)$ is in m^{-2}).

But this is for the supply only, the organic matter will suffer alteration during this transportation, the longer the time involved the greater this alteration. I shall consider that the residence time is proportional to and inversely linked to slope effect:

$$T_R = \omega \frac{\Lambda}{Z + Z_0}$$

ω and Z_0 are specific constants. Finally, the function representing the alteration will be once again from the D set, let us say $D_\gamma(T_R)$.

At a given location (Λ, Z) attained in a time T_R the organic supply without alteration would have been $\mathscr{R} \, \delta(Z, \Lambda) \, dS$; with the alteration it is $\mathscr{R} \, \delta(Z, \Lambda) D_\gamma(T_R) \, dS$. Formally, $\mathscr{R} \, \delta(Z, \Lambda)$ is equivalent to R and $\mathscr{R} \, \delta(Z, \Lambda) D_\gamma(T_R)$ to R_0, but now the change is that $\mathscr{P} \, \delta(Z, \Lambda)$, formal equivalent of P is no longer constant; on the other hand, we have always $\mathscr{P} = \beta \mathscr{R}$. If we now write equation (7), then $P_0 = 0$ and finally

$$\frac{1}{\theta} = 1 + \frac{\beta H}{V \mathbb{D}(V) D_\gamma(T_R)}$$

which shows that θ is a slightly increasing function of V, with exactly the same limitations as in the previous section: variations of H have a greater effect than variations of V; and D_γ varies locally, which makes the practical use of this relation rather delicate.

The rate of accumulation is now

$$R' = \frac{\mathscr{R}\,\delta(Z, \Lambda)D_\gamma(T_R)V\mathbb{D}(V)}{H}$$

but here there is a relation between $\mathscr{R}\,\delta(Z, \Lambda)$ and V which can be drawn from equation (1)

$$\mathscr{R}\,\delta(Z, \Lambda) = \frac{\rho_c\rho_m HV(1-\phi)}{\beta H\rho_c + \rho_m D_\gamma(T_R)\mathbb{D}(V)}$$

Hence

$$R' = \frac{\rho_c\rho_m V^2(1-\phi)D_\gamma(T_R)\mathbb{D}(V)}{\beta H\rho_c + \rho_m D_\gamma(T_R)V\mathbb{D}(V)}$$

which is a function of R' increasing more rapidly than V and less rapidly than V^2, with the same validity as for θ.

General case

The general case applies when the two extreme processes described in the previous section are both operative. This is the domain of hemipelagic sedimentation. In this case we can again write equation (7):

$$\frac{1}{\theta} = 1 + \frac{H}{V\mathbb{D}(V)}\left[\frac{\alpha}{D_\theta(Z/U)} + \frac{\beta}{D_\gamma(T_R)} + \frac{P_0}{R_0}\right]$$

The discussion is exactly the same as for the general case of pelagic sedimentation: if, on the average, at a given location, θ is a slightly increasing function of V, variations of H overcome variations of V and changing locations can obscure completely any relationship. However, it should be noticed that, often in hemipelagic sedimentation, although true direct physical and mathematical links do not exist between Z, T_R, R_0 and V, V is small for high Z, high T_R and low R_0 (this is only the formal translation of the effect of increasing distance offshore). Consequently, when V increases, R_0 tends to increase, Z and T_R to decrease and hence $D_\theta(Z/U)$ and $D_\gamma(T_R)$ to increase. The net effect will be to statistically enhance the tendency for θ to increase with V.

We shall use the same technique of the inverse to examine the accumulation rate, in order to have simpler formulae:

$$\frac{1}{R'} = \frac{1}{\rho_m V(1-\phi) - P_0}\left[\frac{\rho_m}{\rho_c} + \frac{H}{V\mathbb{D}(V)}\left(\frac{\alpha}{D_\theta(Z/U)} + \frac{\beta}{D_\gamma(T_R)}\right)\right]$$

which shows that R' is an increasing function of V; for the same reasons as above, it will statistically increase more than V and less than V^2.

At this point, it must be stressed once again that the practical use of all the formalism derived up to now is highly questionable. In addition to all the reasons discussed above there is another very important fact: the measurement of V itself is by no means straightforward. We know nearly nothing about the values to be given to α, β, P_0. We know very little about the values of the primary productivity, R, because they vary considerably during the year, or about how to take this variation into consideration simply. Finally, even an apparently simple parameter such as the porosity ϕ is generally never measured.

Nevertheless, we can try to test all these mathematics against real measurements (or estimations?) for hemipelagic sedimentation. The only ones which provide the necessary parameters are those of ORGON (1977), ORGON (1978), ORGON (1979), ORGON (1981) and ORGON (1983) and of

Müller and Suess (1979). They are displayed for θ (or rather τ) and R' on Fig. 3 in the linear scale, and on Fig. 4 in the bilogarithmic scale. At first sight, the points of Fig. 3 do not show any relationship. However Fig. 4 shows some elongation of the cloud of points, witness of a vague direct relationship. Of course the situation is better for accumulation rates (Fig. 5). The following comments can be made. Bilogarithmic representation introduces an artificial compression of representative points in the high values zone, and an artificial dispersion in the low values zone. The result is an artificial homogenization of the global dispersion—at a very high level. Such a representation has to be avoided as far as possible. On the other hand, the vague direct relationship thus 'revealed'—and which corresponds to a significant, although low, linear correlation coefficient, is only the quantitative expression of the covariation of some influential parameters (sedimentation rate, water depth, distance from the shore) which I have already noted. A more interesting point is the sort of maximum which appears in Fig. 3. This could simply indicate that beyond some sedimentation rate, the dilution effect becomes predominant, whatever the origin of organic matter.

In conclusion, even if a direct relationship can, in some instances, be found, it cannot be linked to one or two simple controlling factors, but to the covariation of factors which by their nature are widely different. It is therefore impossible to derive from these empirical correlations any quantitative relation permitting the prediction of the values of simple factors (e.g. surface organic productivity), even for present day samples, not to speak of the past.

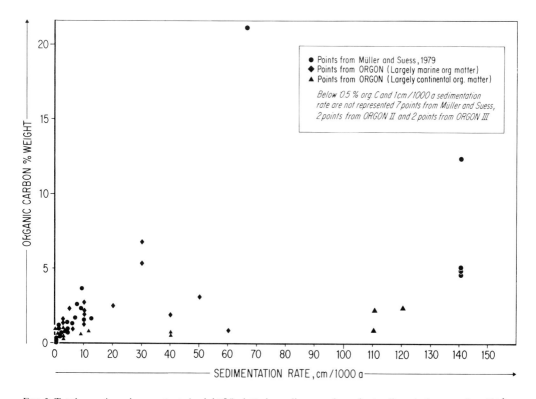

FIG. 3. Total organic carbon contents (weight %) plotted on a linear scale against sedimentation rates (cm 10^{-3} y^{-1}) of some marine sediments (ORGON 1977; ORGON 1978; Muller & Suess 1979; ORGON 1979; ORGON 1981; ORGON 1983).

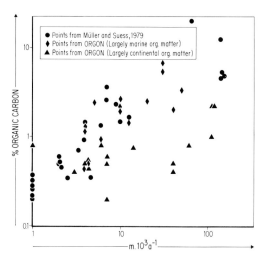

FIG. 4. Total organic carbon contents (weight %) plotted on a log–log scale against sedimentation (cm 10^{-3} y^{-1}): data as Fig. 3.

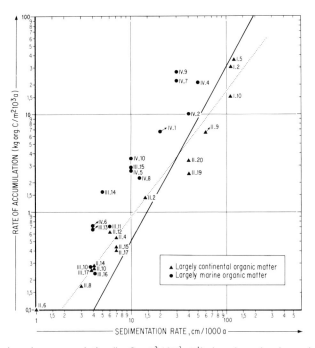

FIG. 5. Rates of organic carbon accumulation (kg C m^{-2} 10^{-3} y^{-1}) plotted on a log–log scale against sedimentation rate (cm 10^{-3} y^{-1}) of some ORGON sediments (ORGON 1977; ORGON 1978; ORGON 1979; ORGON 1981; ORGON 1983).

Biological considerations

In the preceding sections, I did not consider the nature of the biological agencies through which alteration took place. Very often, microorganisms are claimed to be the most active of these agencies. However, this poses a problem of terminology. A cow has a complex nutritional system: it swallows grass and other vegetation, but does not feed on them; its digestive tractus is a microbiological reactor, where a bacterial ecosystem feeds on this cellulosic stock, the cow itself finally digesting the bacteria. But this bacterial ecosystem is completely unable to thrive on a meadow without the mandatory presence of the cow. In this section, we shall consider that a cow is not bacteria, and that a reaction will be attributed to microorganisms if, and only if, they are free-living in the environment under consideration.

Apparent degradation rates

Up to now, I have characterized biological degradation by some function $D(t)$ obeying very general conditions, but did not choose any particular formalism. We must choose one now, in order to go further. Although a Michaelis–Menten formalism would be physically better, I shall choose first-order formalism because it is simpler, it is equivalent to the former for low rates, and the data I shall use are so uncertain as to make illusory any apparent gain in precision. I shall assume that temperature does not vary, and consequently write

$$q = q_0 \, e^{-Kt}$$

where q is the quantity of a given substrate at time t, q_0 the same at time 0 and K the rate constant. Now, to simplify further we shall suppose that total organic matter is a simple unique substrate, and that the ecosystem feeding on it is reduced to a single form. Once again, given the quality of original data, any refinement would be entirely illusory. This approach has been followed by Toth and Lermann (1977) and Müller and Mangini (1980). The calculation of K involves fitting the observed curve of organic carbon decrease in a core with the theoretical curve, provided by the time scale along the core, i.e. the knowledge of sedimentation rate. This is not always possible, because it is frequently impossible to fit the observed curves to an exponential—it is especially in that sense that I spoke of the low quality of data. But this is also not possible, when sedimentation rates are unknown, or known with great uncertainties. For ORGON samples, we could estimate K for 11 cores of ORGON II, III and IV cruises.

As it is computed, K depends not only on the intrinsic activity of the biota, but also of their number. For ORGON III and IV, we have counts of the aerobic heterotrophic microflora and of the anaerobic sulfate reducers in those same cores, and we can therefore take these numbers into consideration.

The points from ORGON samples, and two zones regrouping the results of Toth and Lermann (1977) and Müller and Mangini (1980), are plotted versus sedimentation rates in Fig. 6. The first remark to be made is that an error on sedimentation rates displaces a point, on this type of diagram, on a 45° line; thus it is possible to compare values of K corresponding to various values of the sedimentation rate by projecting the corresponding points along a 45° line onto the same vertical. If this is done, it appears that K values for Müller and Mangini are higher than for ORGON, the latter being higher than for Toth and Lerman. Toth and Lerman reported anaerobic microbial degradation, and Müller and Mangini sedimentary aerobic degradation. The latter authors explained the difference by the higher efficiency of aerobic microbial degradation. It is possible to go further. On Fig. 6 the number of bacteria per ml of sediment, expressed as logarithms, have been placed by the ORGON points. No correlation appears with the K-value. The simplest interpretation is that if aerobic degradation is more efficient than anaerobic, it is because the main agency in aerobic degradation is not the bacterial, but the macro- and meio-benthic community. This interpretation is reinforced by the consideration that benthic consumption is strongly depth-dependent within the sediment: benthos are active only in a 10–15 cm layer; it is therefore natural that the sediments studied by Müller and Mangini, which have by far the lowest sedimentation rates and therefore the longest residence times in the benthic activity zone, show the highest K.

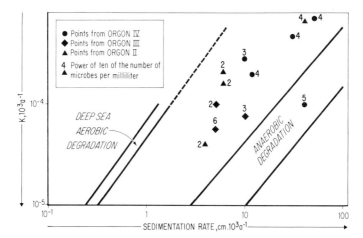

FIG. 6. K, the rate constant for biological degradation plotted against the sedimentation rate (cm 10^{-3} y^{-1}) of some ORGON sediments (ORGON 1977; ORGON 1978; ORGON 1979; ORGON 1981; ORGON 1983) and of sediments (Toth & Lehrman 1977; Müller & Mangini 1980) in which anaerobic degradation occurs, plotted as two zones.

Conclusions

A very general formalism of biological degradation, in either the water or the sedimentary column, has been proposed. Coupled with considerations of sedimentary processes, it permits the qualitative description of organic sedimentation. The conclusion is that a simple, general relationship relating the organic-carbon content of sediments and sedimentation rates cannot exist, and that any apparent relationship is caused by the covariation of non-logically linked factors.

An examination of the apparent degradation rate coefficients in different oceanic situations leads to the conclusion that in aerobic environments meio- and macrobenthos are more efficient biological consumers of sedimentary organic matter than the free bacterial community.

References

BILLEN, G. 1982. Modelling the processes of organic matter degradation and nutrients recycling in sedimentary systems. In: NEDWELL, D. B. & BROWN, C. M. (eds) *Sediment Microbiology*, Academic Press. 15–52.

MÜLLER, P. J. & SUESS, E. 1979. Productivity, sedimentation rate and sedimentary organic matter in the oceans. I—Organic matter preservation. *Deep-Sea Res.*, **26A** 1347–1362.

—— & MANGINI, A. 1980. Organic carbon deposition rates in sediments of the Pacific manganese nodule belt dated by ^{230}Th and ^{231}Pa. *Earth planet. Sci. Lett.*, **51** 94–114.

ORGON 1977. I *Mer de Norvège*, Editions du CNRS, Paris, 296p.

ORGON 1978. II *Atlantique Nord-Est, Brésil*, Editions du CNRS, Paris, 390p.

ORGON 1979. III *Mauritanie, Sénégal, Iles su Cap Vert*, Editions du CNRS, Paris, 441p.

ORGON 1981. IV *Golfe d'Aden, Mer d'Oman*, Editions du CNRS, Paris, 547p.

ORGON 1983. D'ORGON à misedor, Editions du CNRS, Paris, 479p.

PELET, R. 1983. Preservation and alteration of present-day sedimentary organic matter. In: BJOROY, M. (ed.) *Advances in Geochemistry 1981*. John Wiley. 241–250.

ROMANKEVIC, E. A. 1977. *Geochemistry of Organic Matter in the Ocean*. Nauka, Moscow (in Russian) 256p.

STACH, E., MACKOWSKY, M. TH., TEICHMÜLLER, M., TAYLOR, G. H., CHANDRA, D. & TEICHMÜLLER, R. 1982. *Stach's Textbook of Coal Petrology*, 3rd edition, Gebrüder Borntraeger, Berlin–Stuttgart. 535p.

TOTH, D. J. & LERMAN, A. 1977. Organic matter reactivity and sedimentation rates in the ocean. *Am. J. Sci.*, **277**, 465–485.

R. PELET, Institut Français du Pétrole, B.P. 311, 92506 Rueil-Malmaison, France.

Coastal upwelling and a history of organic-rich mudstone deposition off Peru

E. Suess, L. D. Kulm & J. S. Killingley

SUMMARY: The present-day upwelling circulation off Peru, the regional pattern of organic matter in surface sediments and the stable carbon isotope characteristics of Neogene and Quaternary carbonate lithologies suggest a unique feedback mechanism in continental margin deposition and subsequent alteration after burial. In such a scenario, the high bio-productivity, the position of a poleward flowing undercurrent and the rate of subsidence of margin basins appear to be the principal variables controlling this mechanism.

Transfer of organic matter from the sea surface to the sea floor is particularly efficient in the upwelling ecosystem off Peru. Preservation and burial are enhanced by high bulk sedimentation rates along the upper continental slope (between $11°$–$15°$S) at depths where the subsurface current velocities decrease below those normally associated with the poleward flow. Burial and preservation are diminished, however, where shallow water depths promote continuous reworking of the bottom sediments by onshore flows and alongshore water movement (between $6°$–$10°$S). The resulting sedimentary facies are distinctly different from each other in that the former process yields an organic-rich (>5 wt % C_{org}) and the latter process yields a calcareous (>15 wt % $CaCo_3$) mud facies. The bulk sediment accumulation and individual component fluxes are estimated for both portions of the margin situated between $6°$ and $15°$S latitude and lying in <500 m of water depth. Furthermore, the chemical environment of organic-matter decomposition in the rapidly accumulating carbonate-poor facies is dominated by microbial fermentation and methanogenesis, whereas, the muds containing lesser amounts of organic matter are dominated by microbial sulphate reduction. These differences in facies composition persist throughout the subsequent stages of compaction and diagenesis. Most prominent among these is the formation of 'organic' dolomites with distinctly different isotopic signatures and mineral assemblages. The original upwelling facies (i.e., organic-rich muds or calcareous muds), the extent of reworking by subsurface currents, and the subsidence history of the margin basins may be inferred from these sedimentary signatures.

The Nazca plate passes beneath the Peruvian continental margin and forms a well-known subduction plate boundary within the Peru Current, as eastern boundary current regime, off the west coast of South America. These two long-standing and extraordinary features have become cornerstones for developing our understanding of global tectonics of subducting plate boundaries and for developing our knowledge of the dynamics of coastal upwelling circulation, respectively. Important scientific contributions, too numerous to cite here, have dealt with almost all aspects of Peru margin tectonics and coastal upwelling. At present, several volumes are available which summarize and synthesize tectonic, sedimentological, biological, and oceanographic concepts of continental margins. Studies of the Peruvian margin between about $6°$ and $17°$S latitude have contributed significantly to this general understanding (Kulm *et al.* 1981a; Richards 1981, Suess & Thiede 1983; Thiede & Suess 1983).

With this wealth of information as a background, we show how the tectonically controlled margin morphology interacts with eastern boundary coastal upwelling to produce either an organic-carbon-rich mud facies, or a calcareous mud facies, and finally, demonstrate that the mineralogy and stable isotope compositions of certain Neogene and Quaternary lithologies may reflect such interaction in the past tectonic history, even though the primary sedimentological signatures of the mud facies have become severely overprinted by diagenesis.

Data base

In many ways, this overview of organic carbon-rich mudstone formation off Peru is a step towards the synthesis of an interdisciplinary project on continental margin sedimentation initiated by Oregon State University in 1977. Numerous contributions have since appeared in print, several of which contain data collections used here (Müller & Suess 1979; Krissek *et al.* 1980; Kulm *et al.* 1981b; Suess 1981; Thornburg & Kulm 1981; Reimers & Suess 1983a).

In addition, several theses completed in the course of this project, were particularly important and we would like to acknowledge them here.

From: BROOKS, J. & FLEET, A. J. (eds) 1987, *Marine Petroleum Source Rocks* Geological Society Special Publication No. 26 pp. 181–197.

The organic carbon and calcium carbonate analyses of slope sediments, on which Figs 2 and 3 are based, are from Reimers (1981). They have been supplemented by a large set of data from the Peru shelf area which C. C. Delgado, Instituto del Mar del Peru, Callao, generously made available to us. When combined, this sample coverage is the most complete available to date. The sediment budget is partly based on estimates of terrigenous input compiled by Krissek (1982) and Krissek and Scheidegger (1983), on bulk physical properties of sediments compiled by Busch (1980), on sedimentation rates obtained by Reimers (1981) and DeVries (1979), and on palaeoceanographic information supplied by Schuette (1980). Our interpretation of margin tectonics and subsurface facies distribution has greatly benefitted from the work by Thornburg (1981) and Jones (1978).

Finally, stable isotope and mineral parameters of lithified Neogene and Quaternary rocks represent the first results from an ongoing project on the dolomitization of Peru margin deposits (Suess *et al.* 1982; Kulm *et al.* 1982).

Patterns of sediment distribution

Two prominent sedimentary bodies presently characterize the upper continental slope and shelf region off Peru (Fig. 1), extending for more than 1200 km between 6° and 17°S latitude. An organic carbon-rich mud facies accumulates at water depths largely between 50 and 500 m from 11° to 15°S. The regional extent is well-constrained by our sample coverage (Fig. 2) and it contains $\gg 5$ wt % organic carbon. A different facies, calcareous mud, lower in organic carbon and coarser in texture (Fig. 3), forms between 6° and 10°S and at a much smaller area, around 16°S. The description used here for both facies refers to a fine-grained, diatomaceous, hemipelagic mud high in organic carbon and a coarse-grained, hemipelagic, calcareous mud, respectively. The terms, organic carbon-rich muds and calcareous muds are quite relative, and, as such, apply to the Peru margin deposits. The actual values can be gleaned from the contour intervals of the maps (Figs 2, 3).

The vertical extent of both facies is likewise quite different. Based on 3.5 kHz acoustic profiling, the organic carbon-rich facies forms a continuous lens-shaped body extending from the outer shelf platform to upper slope depths (between 11.31°S and 13.61°S; Fig. 4). Its depositional centre is well-defined and located just seaward of the shelf break. One hundred metres is the apparent maximum thickness of

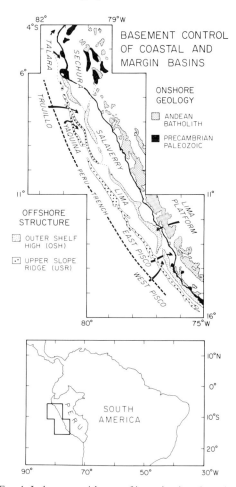

FIG. 1. Index map with area of investigation along the Peru continental margin.

this acoustically transparent deposit. On the other hand, the calcareous facies forms a thin (a few metres), discontinuous sediment blanket over the shallow inner shelf (8.85°S; Fig. 4). A substantially thicker deposit of the same facies accumulates at 15°–17°S behind an outer shelf ridge. No sediment presently accumulates between 6°–10°S or 15°–17°S at the shelf break.

Processes of sediment accumulation

The coastal waters over the Peruvian margin are subject to one of the best developed and most persistent upwelling regimes that is initiated in response to the southeast trade winds (Smith 1983, and many others). One prominent feature

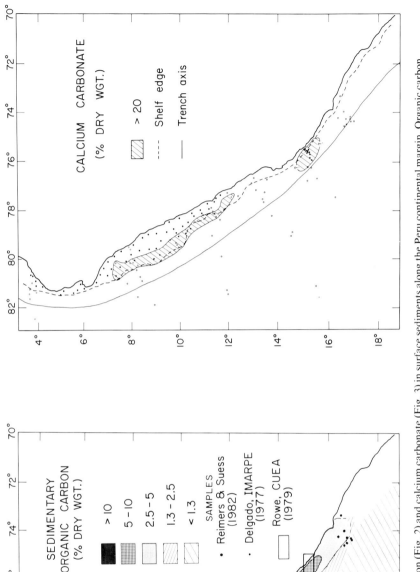

FIGS. 2 and 3. Distribution of organic carbon (Fig. 2) and calcium carbonate (Fig. 3) in surface sediments along the Peru continental margin. Organic carbon concentrations <2.5 wt-% north of 11°S and >5.0 wt-% south of this latitude characterize two contrasting facies. The distribution of calcium carbonate also reflects this difference between a northern and a southern facies. Position of trench axis is indicated in Fig. 3 (inset); data compilation from many sources.

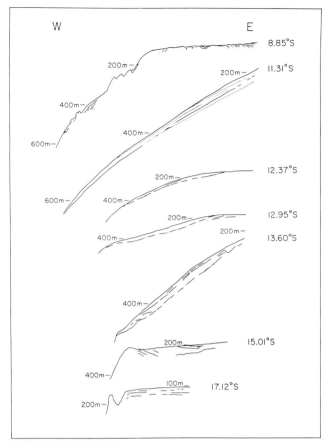

FIG. 4. High-resolution 3.5-kHz reflection profiles at selected latitudes perpendicular to the Peruvian margin; water depths in (m). Profiles between 11.31°–13.60° delineate shelf and slope morphology, the distribution and thickness of organic carbon-rich mud facies along upper slope; profiles at 8.85°S (thin sediment cover) and between 15.01°–17.12°S (thicker basin fillings) are typical for calcareous mud facies; modified from Krissek et al. (1980); the length scale and vertical exaggeration vary for each profile.

of this upwelling circulation system is a southward flowing subsurface current, the Peru poleward undercurrent (Smith 1981). Flow is observed over the entire area between 6° and 17°S, and a coherent pattern shows mean current velocities of 6–16 cm/s at the flow core depth of approximately 90 m. At 10°S, the core of this flow is strongly deflected eastward towards the inner shelf region, whereas at the remainder of the margin, it is situated above the shelf break and upper slope region. Shaffer (1982), and others before him, have shown a much swifter flow for this deflected portion of the undercurrent. Mean velocities as high as 25 cm/s have been recorded, and Shaffer speaks of this phenomenon as a poleward flowing subsurface 'jet'. In turn, this 'jet' appears responsible for setting up a stronger upwelling cell over the wide, shallow shelf region than over the narrow, deeper shelves (Fig. 5).

Dividing the poleward movement of subsur-

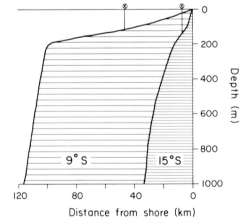

FIG. 5. Contrast in shelf-slope morphology and water depths at 9°S and 15°S; such differences strongly affect position of poleward undercurrent with respect to sea floor and hence sites of deposition and non-deposition; see also Smith (1983).

face water into its alongshore and onshore current components, the following general picture emerges according to Brockmann *et al.* (1980) and Shaffer (1982): in the region of coarse-grained, calcareous muds between 6°–10°S, the maximum current velocities are found in the waters above the shelf (Fig. 6a). By extrapolating the current vectors to the sea floor it appears that, essentially, the entire shelf is affected by strong bottom currents, the inner shelf by a maximum

alongshore component of ∼5 cm/s, and the outer shelf by a maximum onshore component of ∼15 cm/s. Only in a narrow band along the coast at 40–60 m depth does the poleward flow drop to zero velocity before reversing its direction in a wind-driven surface flow.

In contrast, the sea floor in the region of preferential organic matter deposition (11°–14°S) is out of reach of the alongshore and onshore current components (Fig. 6b). Indeed, the extrap-

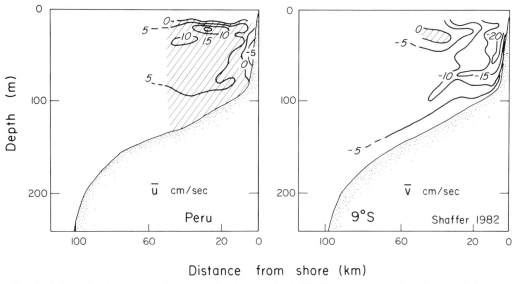

FIG. 6a. Poleward undercurrent; subsurface velocities over the shelf at 9°S; ū = mean onshore flow (shaded area = positive velocities) and v̄ = alongshore flow (negative velocities = southward) extend down to the shelf floor; note different scale from Fig. 6b.

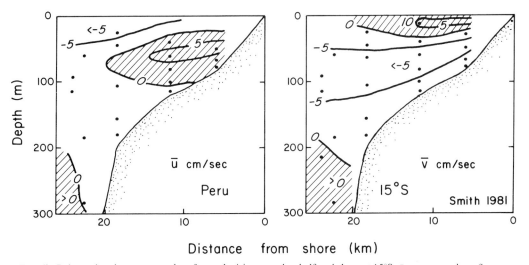

FIG. 6b. Poleward undercurrent; subsurface velocities over the shelf and slope at 15°S; ū = mean onshore flow (shaded area = positive velocities) and v̄ = alongshore flow (positive velocities = northward) are well off the bottom; between 100–200 m the bottom is exposed to minimal flow; note different scale from Fig. 6a.

TABLE 1. *Short-term sedimentation rates from ^{210}Pb activity-depth profiles of organic-rich mud facies between 11° and 15°S latitude*

Core	Latitude (°S)	Longitude (°W)	Water depth (m)	Sedimentation rate* (mm y^{-1})
7706–39[a]	11° 15.1'	77° 57.5'	186	1.6
7408–2312[b]	12° 02.1'	77° 43.0'	200	3.4
7706–36[a]	13° 37.3'	76° 50.5'	370	0.66
7408–1909[b]	14° 38.9'	76° 10.3'	366	3.2
WHOI[c]	15° 04'	75° 30'	92	11.0
WHOI[c]	15° 09'	75° 34'	268	12.0
FSU BX4[d]	15° 15.7'	75° 23.5'	133	4.3
FSU BX3[d]	15° 16.9'	75° 23.9'	387	2.3

* The variability between ∼0.7 and 12 mm y^{-1} reflects the distance of the coring sites from the depositional centre of the respective margin transect (see Fig. 4). Periods of non-deposition, alternating with periods of rapid sedimentation, as shown here, reduce the integrated rates over a time frame of ∼10,000 y (Fig. 7) by more than an order of magnitude (i.e., 0.1–0.2 mm y^{-1}). Such rates are comparable to long-term subsidence rates of the Lima Basin (i.e., 0.5 m $(10^6 y)^{-1}$).

a = DeMaster (1981), b = Koide & Goldberg (1982), c = Henrichs (1980), d = Froelich *et al.* (1983).

olated velocities for bottom currents here are all close to zero. At 16°–17°S, where a rather narrow but shallow shelf platform extends upward into the reach of the undercurrent, conditions similar to those at 9°S might again favour accumulation of coarse calcareous muds, although the high sedimentation rates (Table 1) indicate a much more rapid accumulation and less reworking.

Reworking and export of sediments from the shelf and upper slope region by components of the poleward undercurrent is, therefore, one important mechanism by which material is supplied to a prominent particle maximum identified in a light-scattering profile associated with the oxygen-minimum layer off the 9°S area (Pak *et al.* 1980) and even to seaward areas across the Peru–Chile trench. Winnowing of the upper slope-shelf edge by waters of the undercurrent also plays a role in supplying sediments to the lower slope and trench basins along the Peru margin.

Past patterns of sediment distribution

A high-resolution chronostratigraphic record of deposition over the last 15,000 years shows two hiatuses at upper slope depths which may reflect past interaction between the poleward undercurrent and the shelf-slope morphology (Fig. 7; Table 1). Interestingly, the most prominent period of non-deposition, between 10,000 and 6,000 years ago, does not coincide with a lower global

sea level stand (Vail *et al.* 1977) but instead, with a general warming trend in global climate (Mercer 1976; Heuser & Streeter 1980; Salinger 1981). Shaffer (1982) and others observed that during El Niño years, when warm equatorial waters inundate the coastal region off Peru and cause disaster to the ecology and local fishing industry, the poleward undercurrent intensifies significantly. Hence it is likely that non-deposition of the organic-rich mud facies may be linked to periods of increasing frequency and strength of El Niño events. Such a coupling between sediments and poleward flow suggests a promising approach to 'tracking that crazy weather' back in time that presently captures so much attention (Golden 1983).

Source and fluxes of sediment components

The difference in facies composition on the Peruvian upper slope and shelf is all the more remarkable when considering that the entire margin is long known to be affected by strong and persistent upwelling and associated high bioproductivity. The long-term integrated primary production over the continental margin compiled by Zuta and Guillén (1970) clearly delineates these centres well (Fig. 8). The authors and others have subsequently refined productivity estimates (Guillén *et al.* 1973; Guillén & Calienes 1981; von Bröckel 1981) and suggest for large-

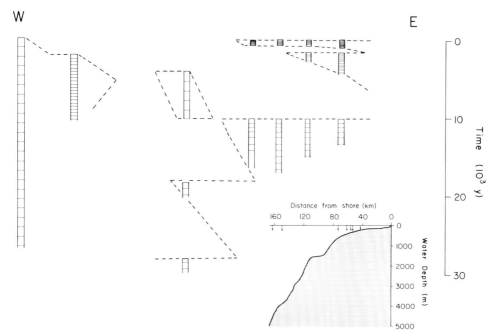

FIG. 7. High-resolution chronostratigraphic record of 5 sediment cores from the upper slope and 2 from the lower slope region off Peru at ∼11°S latitude (arrows on inset indicate relative position of cores). Two extensive periods of non-deposition, at ∼2000 years ago and between 6000–10,000 years ago, characterize the past sedimentation pattern on the upper slope. These and similar correlatable hiatuses might be caused by shifts in water depth and position of the poleward undercurrent relative to the upper slope and shelf morphology. Sites at lower slope receive sediments from strong offshore flow caused by undercurrent; modified from Reimers & Suess (1983b).

scale assessment and cycling of carbon an annual mean production rate of 400 g m^{-2} y^{-1} (=1.1 g m^{-2} d^{-1}) over a strip 50 km wide along the coastal waters. Local centres of upwelling such as at ∼9°, at ∼11°, and at ∼15°S latitude produce well in excess of 2 g m^{-2} d^{-1}. Further offshore an additional strip of varying width, for simplicity the area landward of the 500 m depth contour, produces another 200 g m^{-2} y^{-1}, so that all the water masses over the margin <500 m in depth yield about 2.2 × 10^{13} g of carbon annually (see Table 3).

Preservation of organic carbon

The fraction of the gross production which eventually becomes buried is the subject of intense debate (Calvert, this volume; Pelet, this volume) and has been variously estimated. At present a number of factors have emerged that control preservation and burial: bulk sedimentation rate (Heath *et al.* 1977; Müller & Suess 1979), water column oxygen (Demaison & Moore 1980), water depth (Suess 1980), benthic regeneration (Reimers & Suess 1983a), and ecology (Walsh 1981;

von Bröckel 1981; Staresinic *et al.* 1983). Incidentally, most of these concepts presently being debated have relied to a large extent on sedimentological, biological, chemical, and geological data from the very same area off Peru and even from the very same samples and cores discussed here.

Generally, the carbon fraction buried is an exponential function of the sedimentation rate, i.e., $F = 0.03S^{1.3}$, according to Müller & Suess (1979) where F = fraction of organic carbon buried and S = sedimentation rate. This empirical relationship yields a range of between 7 and 80% preserved carbon depending on the sedimentation rates encountered in the organic carbon-rich mud facies. The best mean value of preservation using this approach seems to be about 15%.

Walsh (1981) presents an interesting comparison of carbon fluxes through the entire food web of the Peruvian region, assuming both 'normal' upwelling and 'El Niño' conditions (Table 2). The decline in anchovy population during El Niño is reflected in a staggering increase in the pre-burial flux of detrital organic carbon to the sea floor from 11 to 70%. This fraction escapes

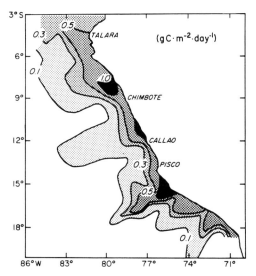

FIG. 8. Mean annual primary productivity along the Peru margin; values are integrated over the photic zone and represent an average over ~ 10 years (Zuta & Guillén 1970; Guillén & Calienes 1981). Short-term rates of production of 3–5 g m^{-2} y^{-1} of carbon at three prominent upwelling centres, ~ 9°, ~ 11°S, and ~ 15°S, significantly exceed the long-term mean. The biogenous sediment input should be uniformly high over the entire strip of coastal water (50 km wide) and gradually drop off seaward.

biological cycling in the water column during El Niño because of the virtual absence of plankton-feeding anchovy. At the benthic interface Walsh estimates a further reduction, primarily by micro-organisms, such that the eventual burial flux amounts to 8% of the initial amount produced under 'normal' upwelling conditions but increases to 59% under 'El Niño' conditions. The estimate of 8% is corroborated independently by Reimers & Suess (1983a) who showed that benthic respiration and early diagenesis combine to remove enough organic carbon from the sediment/water interface that only ~ 6% of the primary input is buried (Table 2). The huge increase of organic deposition and burial as a consequence of El Niño conditions, according to Walsh (1981), has not been further substantiated but seems an intriguing lead to follow in future studies, particularly in light of the erosional nature of the undercurrent during El Niño as discussed above.

Existing measurements of organic carbon flux rates from the Peru upwelling regime at ~ 15°S, however, do not unambiguously support the above estimates on carbon preservation. Staresinic et al. (1982) and von Bröckel (1981) in repeated measurements and with different sediment trap designs were able to show that only about 10% of the surface-produced organic

carbon actually seems to escape the photic zone, largely in the form of anchovy fecal pellets (Fig. 9) and not ~ 40% as Walsh (1981) and Suess (1980) suggested. On the other hand, Knauer & Martin (1981) and Karl & Knauer (1984) have measured between 25 and 45% of the production rate of carbon descending to ~ 100 m of water depth. It is possible that the sediment traps of Staresinic et al. (1982) and von Bröckel (1981) which were deployed during night-time and at very shallow depths (~ 14–50 m) intercepted only part of the anchovy faecal detritus because an equally significant part was actually secreted during the day time but at greater depths and out of reach of the sediment traps. Without really satisfactorily explaining this discrepancy in pre-burial flux estimates, we will assume that for a typical site of organic-rich mud deposition in ~ 100 m of depth at the Peru margin 22% of the primary-produced carbon reaches the sediment/water interface, 14% is regenerated by benthic activity, and about 8% is buried. Accordingly, for the Peru margin mud facies which underlies the strip of water of highest productivity, the above carbon flux partitioning implies a mean burial rate of 32 g m^{-2} y^{-2}. This translates into 22 × 10^{10} g for the total area receiving sediments. For the continental shelf within the influence of the undercurrent, however, a pre-burial flux of 88 g m^{-2} y^{-1} and a benthic regeneration rate of > 50 g m^{-2} y^{-1} result in a net export of organic matter of ~ 25 × 10^{12} g y^{-1} (Table 3). It would be redundant now to compare these mean estimates to actual rates of carbon accumulation because they are not independently derived. In summary, though, the biological, sedimentological, and geological evidence give a coherent picture of organic matter partitioning over the margin as detailed in Table 2 below.

Input of terrigenous detritus

Based on an initial attempt by Scheidegger and Krissek (1983) to quantify the terrigenous input to the margin and expanding the area to include the shallow margin between 6°–10°S, we present a revised budget for the distribution of terrigenous detrital components. The crucial parameters here are fluvial transport rates by Peruvian rivers onto the margin. Scheidegger and Krissek estimated that the 50 largest streams carry ~ 5 × 10^{12} g of detritus annually to each of the two areas considered for the sedimentary budget; i.e., between 6°–10°S and between 10°–15°S. Since the latter area is roughly one half the size of the former, 28 × 10^{9} m^2 and 50 × 10^{9} m^2, respectively, an even distribution of detritus would result in an accumulation of ~ 100 g m^{-2} y^{-1} for

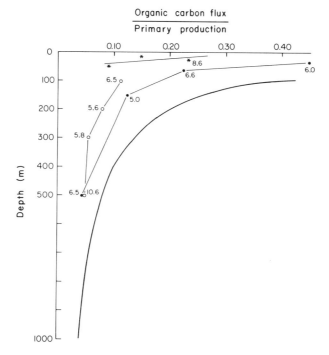

FIG. 9. Change in organic carbon flux as a function of depth and the rate of primary production in regions of strong coastal upwelling. (○) and (●) were measured by sediment traps off Monterey, California (Karl & Knauer 1984; Knauer & Martin 1981), (*) was measured off Peru (Staresinic *et al.* 1982), the latter is believed to represent only $\sim\frac{1}{2}$ of the actual flux (for discussion see text). The number for each data point is the C/N wt-ratio, with values between 5.0–6.6 indicating high proportions of biomass and values >6.6 high proportions of detritus. The solid line indicates empirical relationship described by Suess (1980). The difference in predicted and measured flux rates might indicate the higher ecological efficiency of particles removed in an upwelling system.

TABLE 2. *Partitioning of organic carbon fluxes in the Peru upwelling regime during sedimentation and burial of organic matter. Numbers refer to % of gross production and pertain to a variety of ecological and sedimentological conditions listed in columns a–d.*

	Walsh 1981		Reimers & Suess 1983a	
	a	b	c	d
Water column cycling	89	30	78*	89*
Pre-burial flux	11	70	22	11
Benthic respiration ⎫	3	11	13	7
Early diagenesis ⎬			3	2
Burial ⎭	8	59	6	2

a = normal upwelling, b = El Niño,
c = at 200 m water depth and 1.6 mm y^{-1} sedimentation rate
d = at 400 m water depth and 0.7 mm y^{-1} sedimentation rate
* Predicted from empirical relationship described by Suess (1980).

the northern margin and ~ 180 g m^{-2} y^{-1} for the southern margin (Table 3). The higher estimate, as Scheidegger and Krissek have shown, essentially agrees with the measured mean rate of detritus accumulating in the area of the organic-rich mud facies deposition. This leaves none of the detritus to be exported much beyond the continental slope. On the other hand, the northern margin retains perhaps as little as 10% of the input and thus close to 5×10^{12} g annually escape down-slope as seen in numerous organic carbon-rich mud patches at water depths >3000 m. This quantity of detritus along with 25 g m^{-2} y^{-1} of organic carbon and an as yet undetermined amount of biogenous silica are the principal annual fluxes of material accumulating in down-slope structural basins and the Peru–Chile trench.

Skeletal calcium carbonate

Estimates of production, fluxes, burial rates (= preservation), and regenerative loss by disso-

TABLE 3. *Sediment budget for the Peru continental margin between*
6°S and 14°S latitude and < 500 m water depth

	6°–10°S	10°–14°S
Area of continental margin	(10^9 m^2)	
Coastal waters, 50 km wide	20.7	15.5
Offshore waters, variable width	29.0	13.0
Total area, < 500 m water depth	78.2	
Production of biogenous components	$10^{12}(\text{g y}^{-1})$	
Organic carbon		
Coastal waters, 400 g m^{-2} y^{-1}	7.6	6.2
Offshore waters, 200 g m^{-2} y^{-1}	5.8	2.6
Gross production	22.1	
Calcium carbonate	11.6	
Terrigenous detritus		
Total input	5.0*	4.9*
Terrigenous detrital fluxes	$(\text{g m}^{-2}\text{ y}^{-1})$	
Even distribution	100	180
Measured burial	< 10	175*
Export	> 90	none
Biogenous detrital fluxes	$(\text{g m}^{-2}\text{ y}^{-1})$	
Calcium carbonate†		
Even distribution	150	150
Measured burial	< 1 ?	8
Export ⎫	150 ?	none
Dissolution loss ⎭		142
Organic carbon required for		
dissolution of CaCO$_3$		34
Benthic organic carbon loss		52
Organic carbon‡		
Pre-burial flux	88	88
Benthic regeneration ⎫	> 50	52
Early diagenesis ⎭		9
Measured burial	< 2 ?	24
Export	~ 25 ?	none

* Based on estimates by Scheidegger & Krissek (1983).
† Neglecting difference between high-productivity coastal waters and less
productive offshore waters.
‡ Only for area of sedimentation rates of 1.5 mm y^{-1} and maximum bioproduction (case c of Table 2).

lution for biogenous calcium carbonate are much more sketchy than for organic matter and terrigenous detritus. However, including calcium carbonate as one of the components will tie together the sediment budget unexpectedly well. The typical composition of suspended matter from the surface water of the upwelling centre at ~11°S is 34 wt % organic carbon, 38 wt % calcium carbonate, and 8 wt % opal (Reimers 1981). Such proportions of carbonate-to-organic-carbon may be coupled with mean primary productivity estimates (400 and 200 g m^{-2} y^{-1}) to yield a gross calcium carbonate production of 11.6×10^{12} g over the entire area or 210 g m^{-2} y^{-1} for the most productive strip of upwelled water. The accumu-

lation rates measured in the organic-rich muds, however, are no more than 8–10 g m^{-2} y^{-1}. The deficit between the amounts produced and pre-served after burial is ~200 g m^{-2} y^{-1}, which may reflect a loss of calcium carbonate from dissolution at the benthic interface (i.e., lysocline effect; Emerson & Bender 1982). Since no significant export of material beyond the upper slope edge occurs, physical loss of skeletal CaCO$_3$ is unlikely. From the stoichiometry of calcium carbonate dissolution by metabolic CO$_2$, we calculate that aerobic regeneration of between 35–50 g m^{-2} y^{-1} of organic matter are required to dissolve the amount of carbonate causing the deficit in the budget. Hereby the high estimate refers to centres of maximum production and the low estimate to the strip of water farther offshore where productivity is 200 g m^{-2} y^{-1}.

Most interestingly, the annual loss of organic carbon due to 'preburial' respiration was independently estimated to be between 27 and 52 g m^{-2} y^{-2}. We like to believe, at this point, that the close agreement for calcium carbonate loss estimated by two independent approaches reflects the internal consistency of the sedimentary budget and lends credibility to the whole approach.

Tectonic control

The present pattern and processes of sediment facies accumulating on the margin appear to be controlled by source, overwhelmingly from high bioproduction, and by interaction of continental margin morphology and upwelling current regime. The morphology in turn reflects the style of large-scale tectonics of the Peru forearc region. Elongate basement ridges and basins within the continental massif occupy the shelf and upper slope off Peru (Thornburg & Kulm 1981; Kulm *et al.* 1981c). The inner portion of the wide, shallow shelf between 6° and 10°S represents the main part of the Salaverry Basin and the outer shelf and upper slope portions of the Trujillo Basin. Both basins are separated by an outer shelf

high (OSH) consisting of metamorphic rocks of the continental massif, and an upper slope ridge (USR) of similar terrain apparently forms the seaward flank of the latter basin (Fig. 10). The depositional centre of the Salaverry Basin is situated at about the mid-shelf position at 9°S. To the south and farther seaward lies the Lima Basin whose landward and seaward flanks are underlain by the outer shelf and upper slope ridge, respectively (Fig. 11). The depositional centre of the basin is located at about 1500 m water depth, but its landward flank extends to the outer edge of the shelf at 12°S where the Lima Basin deposits overlap with those of the Salaverry Basin to the east.

The Salaverry, Trujillo and Lima basins have contrasting tectonic histories, especially since late Miocene time. The Lima Basin has been subsiding continuously at the rapid rates of 275 m per 10^6 y during Pliocene to middle Pleistocene time and 500 m per 10^6 y during the late Pleistocene with little internal disruption of the basin deposits (Kulm *et al.* 1981b). The Trujillo Basin and presumably the Salaverry Basin have been more stable, with respect to vertical movements during a comparable period of time, although the Trujillo Basin deposits have experienced considerable faulting and folding (Figs 10, 11; Thornburg & Kulm 1981). These tectonic movements are expressed in the continental shelf and upper slope morphologies that we observe today and

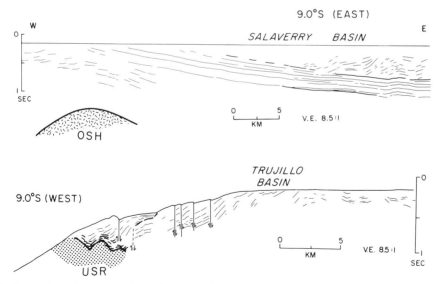

FIG. 10. Proposed stratigraphic section and structural interpretation of seismic reflection profile across the shelf and upper slope at ~9°S. The outer shelf high (OSH) consists of metamorphic rocks of the continental massif and separates the margin into the inner shelf Salaverry Basin and outer shelf/upper slope Trujillo Basin. The upper slope ridge (USR) forms the seaward flank of the Trujillo Basin. Coarse-grained, calcareous mud accumulates as a reworked upwelling facies in these basins. From Thornburg & Kulm (1981).

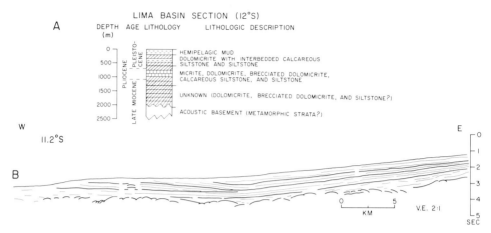

FIG. 11. Proposed stratigraphic section and structural interpretation of seismic reflection record for Lima Basin at ∼12°S. The easternmost flank of the basin extends to upper slope depth where the organic carbon-rich mud facies is presently forming. The depositional centre is at ∼1500 m of water depth. The Lima Basin has continuously subsided since Late Miocene times. From Kulm *et al.* (1981b).

are recorded in the sediments accumulating over this specific period of basin history. Because the structurally controlled margin morphologies directly affect the near bottom currents which then may modify the incoming source material as discussed previously, we are seeing here the chemical and physical fractionation of an 'upwelling facies' ultimately controlled by the tectonics of this convergent margin. For example, the generally slow subsidence inferred near the depositional centre of the Salaverry Basin (central and inner shelf) limits the volume of sediment that can accumulate, and winnowing by bottom currents selectively preserves skeletal calcium carbonate with little organic matter being included in the matrix of the terrigenous detritus. Thus, a calcareous mud facies develops in this area. Post-Oligocene uplift of the outer shelf high and subsequent truncation of the Neogene and Quaternary strata of the Trujillo Basin, at the outer shelf and uppermost slope, produce a similar facies with perhaps an even smaller total volume, primarily due to less terrigenous input and correspondingly higher contents of skeletal calcium carbonate.

Subsidence of the Lima Basin essentially accommodates all sedimentary components of the upwelling organic-rich mud facies without significant modification, and its entire volume is allowed to accumulate. Chemical fractionation at the benthic interface removes organic matter and calcium carbonate at a molar ratio of 2:1 prior to burial. The actual amounts removed by benthic regeneration, and hence the amounts preserved, are a function of the rates of bioproduction and sedimentation.

Diagenetic overprinting during dolomitization

The contrasting tectonic styles of the Lima Basin and the Trujillo–Salaverry Basin deposits continue to amplify their differences in the Neogene and Quaternary deposits during diagenesis. The driving mechanism for diagenesis in both facies is microbial anaerobic decomposition of organic matter. Based on a limited sampling of Neogene and Quaternary lithologies by dredgings from both basins (Kulm *et al.* 1981b), we tentatively deduce a series of different diagenetic pathways that are consistent with the processes and history of sedimentation (Suess *et al.* 1982; Kulm *et al.* 1982). Dredge sites in the basins yielded dark, laminated dolomicrite and brecciated dolomicrite lithologies. Their fabric in many instances is reminiscent of that observed in recent organic-rich mud facies (Reimers & Suess 1983c) with added dolomitic cement pervading the original pore space. Perhaps as little as 30 vol % compaction during dolomitization can be estimated from fabric and residue analyses (Kulm *et al.* 1982, 1984). In addition to a first dolomitization event affecting the groundmass, there are other, later, events as evidenced in vein filling and breccias, but for the discussion here only, the dolomitized groundmass will be considered.

The dolomite mineralogy and stable carbon-isotope composition from both basin lithologies are quite different from each other (Figs 12, 13). The Lima Basin dolomites yielded two distinct groups, one deficient in calcium (46–50 mole %) and the other enriched (50–54 mole %). Both

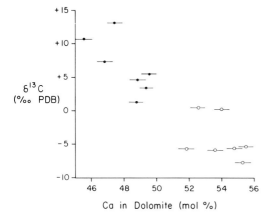

FIG. 12. Composition of dolomites from the Lima Basin (7706–46 and DR-series) and Trujillo Basin (7706–54 and 7706–59). Rocks, representing dolomitized groundmass only, differ significantly in their mineralogy and stable carbon isotope composition.

were isotopically 'heavy' ($\delta^{13}C = +2$ to $+15\%$ PDB). The Trujillo Basin dolomites contained an excess of calcium (52–56 mole %) and were isotopically 'light' ($\delta^{13}C = -2$ to -10% PDB). Within each regional population there is a gradual change rather than a clear end-member type separation between calcium contents and $\delta^{13}C$ signature.

Very large carbon-isotope differences, as meas-

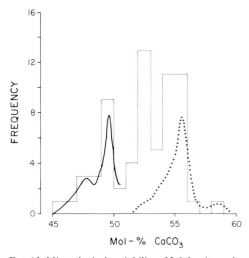

FIG. 13. Mineralogical variability of 3 dolomite rocks dredged from the Peru continental margin (histogram) and grouping of Lima Basin samples (7706–46 and DR-series) and Trujillo Basin samples (7706–54 and 7706–59).

ured here for dolomites, have long been known to result from decomposition of organic matter by either sulphate reduction or carbonate reduction/fermentation pathways (Russell *et al.* 1967; Murata *et al.* 1969; Hathaway & Degens 1969; Deuser 1970; Irwin *et al.* 1977; Suess 1979; Dickson & Coleman 1980; Irwin 1980; Pisciotto 1981; Pisciotto & Mahoney 1981; Kelts & McKenzie 1982; McKenzie & Bernoulli 1982). In general, sulphate reduction (reactions 1 and 2) preserves the $^{13}C/^{12}C$ ratio of the organic substrate undergoing decomposition, whereas, carbonate reduction (reaction 3) strongly fractionates ^{12}C from ^{13}C in the resulting methane and the residual carbon dioxide.

$$CH_4 + SO_4^{2-} \rightarrow H_2S + HCO_3^- + OH^- \quad (1)$$
$$2(CH_2O) + SO_4^{2-} \rightarrow 2HCO_3^- + H_2S \quad (2)$$
$$HCO_3^- + 4H_2 \rightarrow CH_4 + 2H_2O + OH^- \quad (3)$$

As a consequence, either isotopically 'light' or isotopically 'heavy' carbonates may precipitate. In the case of sulphate reduction, the organic substrate may be detrital organic matter (reaction 2) with $\delta^{13}C \sim -22$ parts/10^3 PDB or methane (reaction 1) with $\delta^{13}C \sim -60$ parts/10^3 PDB such that the carbonate pool of the subsequently precipitated carbonate has approximately the same isotopic composition as the substrates did (Fig. 14).

In the case of carbonate reduction, the residual carbon dioxide pool generally is $\sim 50\%$ heavier than the starting carbonate pool (Reeburgh 1982) assuming steady-state conditions in an open system, a uni-directional reaction and large isotopic fractionation factors typical for low temperatures. However, Claypool and Kaplan (1974) and others since then have postulated carbonate reduction in a closed system. In such a case, isotopic fractionation from the increasingly smaller but 'heavier' carbon dioxide reservoir would generate a whole range of 'heavy' carbonates. These values would be more in accord with the actually observed $\delta^{13}C$ signatures of 'heavy' organic dolomites but would require first a build-up of a metabolic carbon dioxide reservoir in the pore space of sediments followed by gradual reduction. We presently think that a closed system might not yield enough carbonate for pervasive dolomitization of the host rock and are, therefore, more inclined to favour the open system model. In such a case, the range of $\delta^{13}C$ values of 'organic' carbonates would result from mixing inorganic carbon dioxide from dissolution of, or isotopic exchange with skeletal calcium carbonate and carbon dioxide from the organic matter reservoir (Fig. 14). The detailed arguments in favour of this approach need to be examined more closely but, in general, they would help

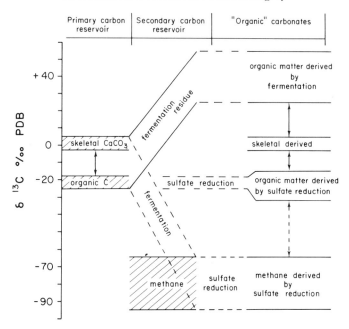

FIG. 14. Preliminary interpretation of $\delta^{13}C$ variability of Peru continental margin 'organic' dolomites. Although the primary carbon reservoirs are significantly different in their $\delta^{13}C$ signatures, mixing between them and introduction of transient reservoirs (methane and residual carbon dioxide from carbonate reduction) opens up numerous possibilities for 'broadening' of the carbon isotope signature of the four end-member organic carbonates.

support the different pathways by which lithification proceeds within the contrasting facies of Lima Basin and Trujillo Basin deposits.

Conclusions

The upwelling circulation system, the pattern of organic matter in surface sediments, and the stable carbon-isotope characteristics of Neogene and Quaternary dolomites from the Peru margin suggest that the following processes may control organic carbon-rich mud deposition and reaction pathways after burial:

Bioproductivity and the resulting initial input of detrital organic matter and skeletal calcium carbonate is uniformly high over the Peru continental margin; yet the sedimentary facies accumulating on the upper slope and shelf areas are distinctly different in the North (6°–10°S) and the South (11°–16°S). We suggest that the poleward flowing undercurrent, whose maximum velocities are measured close to the bottom, physically and chemically fractionates the biogenous detritus such that skeletal calcium carbonate and generally coarse-grained hemipelagic sediments low in organic carbon are deposited on

the shallow, wide northern margin. On the narrow and relatively steep southern margin the poleward flow is largely within the water column, it thereby permits undisturbed deposition of an upwelling facies on the bottom.

Past patterns of sediment accumulation on the upper slope show distinctive time-concordant hiatuses which may be related to shifting positions of the poleward undercurrent rather than to sea level fluctuations.

A sediment budget for the Peru continental margin also reflects this difference between the northern and southern parts. Between 6°–10°S latitude much of the biogenous and terrigenous input is exported from the upper slope and shelf region, whereas, between 11°–15°S almost all components remain on the margin. The accumulation deficit of calcium carbonate and benthic organic carbon on the southern margin suggests strong dissolution of calcium carbonate by aerobic organic matter decomposition at the interface.

Sediment accumulation on the margin appears to be controlled by interaction of morphology and upwelling current regime. In this case the morphology reflects the different styles of tectonism of the northern and southern Peru forearc region, in particular the continuous, rapid subsidence of the Lima Basin in the south, which promotes rapid accumulation of organic carbon-rich muds, and the more stable history of the Salaverry–Trujillo Basin in the north causing changes in the poleward undercurrent pattern that rework the sediments which produce the calcareous hemipelagic muds.

Tectonically controlled low sedimentation rates (<15 cm 10^{-3} y) and organic carbon contents ~ 2 wt% support sulphate reduction as the main decomposition mechanism of organic matter after burial on the northern margin. This reaction is maintained because diffusion from the sediment/water interface is sufficient to continuously supply sulphate and because the relatively low organic-matter contents yield slow overall sulphate reduction rates. The main product of organic diagenesis along the northern margin are dolomites with 'light' carbon-isotope signatures. The style of tectonism of the Salaverry and Trujillo basins is likely to support and maintain

this type of chemical environment during diagenesis.

High sedimentation rates (>15 cm 10^{-3} y) and organic-carbon contents above certain threshold values ($\gg 5\%$) can no longer support sulphate reduction at any depth more than a few tens of centimetres below the sediment/water interface because diffusive sulphate supply does not keep up with increased sulphate reduction rates. Therefore, microbial fermentation becomes the dominant decomposition mechanism of organic matter and, in the process, yields isotopically 'heavy' organic dolomites. Subsidence of the Lima Basin and its deposits are likely to support this type of chemical environment during diagenesis. Different ratios of inorganic ($=$ biogenic skeletal) and organic carbon pools in the source material undergoing diagenesis tend to shift and 'broaden' the $\delta^{13}C$ signatures of the end-member 'organic' dolomites by mixing and isotope exchange.

References

BROCKMANN, C., FAHRBACH, E., HUYER, A. & SMITH, R. L. 1980. The poleward undercurrent along the Peru coast: 5–15°S. *Deep-Sea Res.*, **27**, 847–856.

BUSCH, W. H. 1980. *The physical properties, consolidation behavior, and stability of the sediments of the Peru–Chile continental margin*, Ph.D. dissertation, Corvallis, Oregon State University. 149 pp. (unpublished).

CLAYPOOL, C. E. & KAPLAN, I. R. 1974. The origin and distribution of methane in marine sediments. *In:* KAPLAN, I. R. (ed.) *Natural Gases in Marine Sediments*, Plenum Press, New York. 99–140.

DEMAISON, G. J. & MOORE, G. T. 1980. Anoxic environments and oil source bed genesis. *Organic Geochemistry*, **2**, 9–31.

DEMASTER, D. J. 1981. The supply and accumulation of silica in the marine environment. *Geochim. Cosmochim. Acta*, **45**, 1715–1732.

DEVRIES, T. J. 1979. *Nekton remains, diatoms, and Holocene upwelling off Peru*, M.S. thesis, Corvallis, Oregon State University. 85 pp (unpublished).

DEUSER, W. G. 1970. Extreme $^{13}C/^{12}C$ variations in Quaternary dolomites from the continental shelf. *Earth planet. Sci. Lett.*, **8**, 118–124.

DICKSON, J. A. D. & COLEMAN, M. L. 1980. Changes in carbon and oxygen isotope composition during limestone diagenesis. *Sedimentology*, **27**, 107–118.

EMERSON, S. & BENDER, M. 1981. Carbon fluxes at the sediment water interface of the deep sea: calcium carbonate preservation. *J. Marine Res.* **39(1)**, 139–162.

FROELICH, P. N., KIM, K.-H., JAHNKE, R., BURNETT, W. C., SOUTAR, A. & DEAKIN, M. 1983. Pore water fluoride in Peru continental margin sediments: Uptake from seawater. *Geochim. Cosmochim. Acta*, **47**, 1605–1612.

GOLDEN, F. 1983. Tracking that crazy weather. *Time Magazine* April 10, **67**.

GUILLÉN, O. & CALIENES, R. 1981. Upwelling off Chimbote. *In:* RICHARDS, F. A. (ed.) *Coastal Upwelling*, American Geophysical Union, Washington D.C. 312–328.

——, DE MENDIOLA, B. R. & DE RONDÁN, R. I. 1973. Primary productivity and phytoplankton in the coastal Peruvian waters. *In: Oceanography of the South Pacific*, 1972 New Zealand National Commission for UNESCO, Wellington. 405–418.

HATHAWAY, J. C. & DEGENS, E. T. 1969. Methane-derived marine carbonates of Pleistocene age. *Science*, **165**, 690–692.

HEATH, G. R., MOORE, T. C. & DAUPHIN, J. P. 1977. Organic carbon in deep-sea sediments. *In:* ANDERSEN, N. R. & MALAHOFF, A. (eds) *The Fate of Fossil Fuel CO₂ in the Oceans*. Plenum Press, New York. 605–625.

HENRICHS, S. M. 1980. *Biogeochemistry of Dissolved Free Amino Acids in Marine Sediments*, Ph.D. dissertation, Woods Hole Oceanographic Institution, WHOI 80–39. 253 pp. (unpublished).

HEUSER, C. J. & STREETER, S. S. 1980. A temperature and precipitation record of the past 16,000 years in southern Chile. *Science*, **210**, 1345–1347.

IRWIN, H. 1980. Early diagenetic carbonate precipitation and pore fluid migration in the Kimmeridge Clay of Dorset, England. *Sedimentology*, **27**, 577–591.

——, CURTIS, C. D. & COLEMAN, M. L. 1977. Isotopic evidence for source of diagenetic carbonates formed during burial of organic-rich sediments. *Nature*, **269**, 209–213.

JONES, P. R. 1978. *Seismic ray trace techniques applied*

to the determination of crustal structures across the Peru continental margin and Nazca Plate at 9°S latitude, Ph.D. dissertation. Oregon State University, Corvallis. 156 pp. (unpublished).

KARL, D. M. & KNAUER, G. A. 1984. Vertical distribution, transport and exchange of organic matter in the Northeast Pacific Ocean: evidence for multiple zones of biological activity. Deep-Sea Res. 31, 221–244.

KELTS, K. & McKENZIE, J. A. 1982. Diagenetic dolomite formation in Quaternary anoxic diatomaceous muds of Deep Sea Drilling Project Leg 64, Gulf of California. In: CURRAY, J. R., MOORE, D. G. et al. (eds) Initial Reports of the DSDP, Leg 64, Part 2, U.S. Govt. Printing Office, Washington, D.C. 553–570.

KNAUER, G. A. & MARTIN, J. H. 1981. Primary production and carbon-nitrogen fluxes in the upper 1500 m of the northeast Pacific. Limnol. & Oceanogr. 26, 181–186.

KOIDE, M. & GOLDBERG, E. D. 1982. Transuranic nuclides in two coastal marine sediments off Peru. Earth and Planet. Sci. Lett. 57, 263–277.

KRISSEK, L. A. 1982. Sources, dispersal, and contributions of fine-grained terrigenous sediments on the Oregon and Washington continental slope, Ph.D. dissertation, Oregon State University, Corvallis. 226 pp.

—— & SCHEIDEGGER, K. F. 1983. Environmental controls on sediment texture and composition in low oxygen zones off Peru and Oregon. In: THIEDE, J. & SUESS, E. (eds) Coastal Upwelling: Its Sediment Record, Part B, NATO conf. Ser. IV, 10B, Plenum Press, New York. 163–180.

——, —— & KULM, L. D. 1980. Surface sediments of the Peru–Chile continental margin and the Nazca plate. Bull. geol. Soc. Amer. 91, 321–331.

KULM, L. D., DYMOND, J., DASCH, J. E. & HUSSONG, D. M. (eds) 1981a. Nazca Plate: Crustal Formation and Andean Convergence, Mem. geol. Soc. Amer. 154, 824 pp.

——, SCHRADER, H., RESIG, J. M., THORNBURG, T. M., MASIAS, A. & JOHNSON, L. 1981b. Late Cenozoic carbonates on the Peru continental margin: Lithostratigraphy, biostratigraphy, and tectonic history. In: KULM, L. D. et al. (eds) Nazca Plate; Crustal Formation and Andean Convergence, Mem. geol. Soc. Amer. 154, 469–508.

——, PRINCE, R., FRENCH, W., JOHNSON, S. & MASIAS, A. 1981c. Crustal structure and tectonics of the central Peru continental margin and trench. In: KULM, L. D. et al. (eds) Nazca Plate: Crustal Formation and Andean Convergence, Mem. geol. Soc. Amer. 154, 445–468.

——, SUESS, E. & THORNBURG, T. 1982. Mechanism of dolomitization of Peru convergent margin sediments: Depositional and tectonic history. EOS, Trans. Amer. geophys. Union, 63(45), 1000.

——, SUESS, E. & THORNBURG, T. M. 1984. Subduction zone tectonics and the evolution and distribution of organic-rich sedimentary facies: the Cenozoic Peru forearc region. In: GARRISON, R. E. et al. (eds) Dolomites in the Monterey Formation and other

organic-rich units, SEPM Special Publication, Bakersfield, California.

McKENZIE, J. A. & BERNOULLI, D. 1982. Geochemical variations in Quaternary hardgrounds from the Hellenic trench region and possible relationship to their tectonic setting. Tectonophysics, 86, 149–157.

MERCER, J. H. 1976. Glacial history of southernmost South America. Quaternary Research, 6, 125–166.

MÜLLER, P. J. & SUESS, E. 1979. Productivity, sedimentation rate, and sedimentary organic matter in the oceans—I. Organic carbon preservation. Deep-Sea Res. 26, 1347–1362.

MURATA, K. J., FRIEDMAN, I. & MADSEN, B. M. 1969. Isotopic composition of diagenetic carbonates in the marine Miocene formations of California and Oregon. Prof. Pap. U.S. geol. Surv. 614, 24.

PAK, H., CODISPOTI, L. A. & ZANEVELD, J. R. V. 1980. On the intermediate particle maxima associated with oxygen-poor water off western South America. Deep-Sea Res. 27, 783–798.

PISCIOTTO, K. A. 1981. Review of secondary carbonates in the Monterey Formation California. In: GARRISON, R. E. & DOUGLAS, R. G. (eds) The Monterey Formation and Related Siliceous Rocks of California, Spec. Publ. Soc. econ. Paleontol. Mineral. Tulsa, Oklahoma. 273–284.

—— & MAHONEY, J. J. 1981. Isotopic survey of diagenetic carbonates, Deep Sea Drilling Project Leg 63. In: YEATS, R. S., HAQ, B. U. et al. Initial Reports of the DSDP, Leg 63. U.S. Govt. Printing Office, Washington, D.C. 595–610.

REEBURGH, W. S. 1982. A major sink and flux control for methane in marine sediments: anaerobic consumption. In: FANNING, K. A. & MANHEIM, F. T. (eds) The Dynamic Environment of the Ocean Floor, Lexington Books, Lexington, Mass. 203–218.

REIMERS, C. E. 1981. Sedimentary organic matter: Distribution and alteration processes in the coastal upwelling region off Peru, Ph.D. dissertation, Oregon State University, Corvallis. 219 pp. (unpublished).

—— & SUESS, E. 1983a. The partitioning of organic carbon fluxes and sedimentary organic matter decomposition rates in the ocean. Mar. Chem. 13, 141–168.

—— & SUESS, E. 1983b. Spatial and temporal patterns of organic matter accumulation on the Peru continental margin. In: THIEDE, J. & SUESS, E. (eds) Coastal Upwelling: Its Sediment Record, NATO conf. Ser. IV, 10B, Plenum Press, New York. 311–346.

—— & SUESS, E. 1983c. Late Quaternary fluctuations in the cycling of organic matter off central Peru: A proto-kerogen record. In: SUESS, E. & THIEDE, J. (eds) Coastal Upwelling: Its Sediment Record, NATO conf. Ser. IV 10A, Plenum Press, New York. 497–526.

RICHARDS, F. A. (ed.) 1981. Coastal Upwelling, Coastal and Estuarine Sciences, 1, Amer. Geophys. Union, Washington, D.C. 529 pp.

RUSSELL, K. L., DEFFEYE, K. S. & FOWLER, G. A. 1967. Marine dolomites of unusual isotopic compositions. Science, 155, 189–191.

SALINGER, M. J. 1981. Paleoclimates north and south. Nature, 291, 106–107.

SCHEIDEGGER, K. F. & KRISSEK, L. A. 1983. Zooplankton and nekton: natural barriers to the seaward transport of suspended terrigenous particles off Peru. *In:* SUESS, E. & THIEDE, J. (eds) *Coastal Upwelling: Its Sediment Record, A,* NATO conf. Ser. IV **10A**, Plenum Press, New York. 303–336.

SCHUETTE, G. 1980. *Recent marine diatom taphocoenoses off Peru and off Southwest Africa: Reflection of coastal upwelling,* Ph.D. dissertation, Oregon State University, Corvallis. 114 pp. (unpublished).

SHAFFER, G. 1982. On the upwelling circulation over the wide shelf off Peru: 1. Circulation. *J. Marine Res.* **40**, 293–314.

SMITH, R. L. 1981. A comparison of the structure and variability of the flow field in three coastal upwelling regions: Oregon, Northwest Africa, and Peru. *In:* RICHARDS, F. A. (ed.) *Coastal Upwelling,* American Geophysical Union, Washington D.C. 110–118.

—— 1983. Circulation patterns in upwelling regimes. *In:* SUESS, E. & THIEDE, J. (eds) *Coastal Upwelling: Its Sediment Record, A,* NATO conf. Ser. IV, **10A**. Plenum Press, New York. 13–36.

STARESINIC, N., VON BRÖCKEL, K., SMODLAKA, N. & CLIFFORD, C. H. 1982. A comparison of moored and free-drifting sediment traps of two different designs. *J. Marine Res.* **40**, 273–292.

——, FARRINGTON, J. W., GAGOSIAN, R. B., CLIFFORD, C. H. & HULBURT, E. M. 1983. Downward transport of particulate matter in the Peru coastal upwelling: Role of the anchoveta, *Engraulis ringens. In:* SUESS, E. & THIEDE, J. (eds) *Coastal Upwelling: Its Sediment Record, A,* NATO conf. Ser. IV, **10A**. Plenum Press, New York. 225–240.

SUESS, E. 1979. Mineral phases formed in anoxic sediments by microbial decomposition of organic matter. *Geochim. Cosmochim. Acta,* **43**, 339–352.

—— 1980. Particulate organic carbon flux in the ocean: surface productivity and oxygen utilization. *Nature,* **288**, 260–263.

—— 1981. Phosphate regeneration from sediments of the Peru continental margin by dissolution of fish debris. *Geochim. Cosmochim. Acta,* **45**, 577–588.

—— & THIEDE, J. (eds) 1983. *Coastal Upwelling: Its Sediment Record, A: Responses of the Sedimentary Regime to Coastal Upwelling,* NATO conf. Ser. IV, **10A**. Plenum Press, New York. 608 pp.

——, KULM, L. D. & KILLINGLEY, J. S. 1982. Mechanisms of dolomitization of Peru convergent margin sediments: isotope and mineral record. *EOS, Trans. Am. geophys. Union,* **63(45)**, 1000.

THIEDE, J. & SUESS, E. (eds) 1983. *Coastal Upwelling: Its Sediment Record, B: Sedimentary Records of Ancient Coastal Upwelling,* NATO conf. Ser. IV, **10B**. Plenum Press, New York. 617 pp.

THORNBURG, T. M. 1981. *Sedimentary basins of the Peru continental margin: Structure, stratigraphy, and Cenozoic tectonics from 6°S to 16°S latitude,* M.S. thesis, Oregon State University, Corvallis. 60 pp. (Unpublished.)

—— & KULM, L. D. 1981. Sedimentary basins of the Peru continental margin: structure, stratigraphy, and Cenozoic tectonics from 6°S to 16°S latitude. *In:* KULM, L. D. *et al.* (eds) *Nazca Plate: Crustal Formation and Andean Convergence, Mem. geol. Soc. Amer.* **154**, 393–422.

VAIL, P. R., MITCHUM, R. M. & THOMPSON, S. 1977. Seismic stratigraphy and global changes of sea level. *Mem. Amer. Assoc. Petrol. Geol.* **26**, 63–97.

VON BRÖCKEL, K. 1981. A note on short-term production and sedimentation in the upwelling region off Peru. *In:* RICHARDS, F. A. (ed.) *Coastal Upwelling,* American Geophysical Union, Washington D.C. 291–297.

WALSH, J. J. 1981. A carbon budget for overfishing off Peru. *Nature,* **290**, 300–304.

WYRTKI, K. 1975. El Niño—the dynamic response of the Equatorial Pacific Ocean to atmospheric forcing. *J. of Physical Oceanog.* **5**, 572–584.

ZUTA, S. & GUILLÉN, O. 1970. Oceanografia de las aguas costeras del Peru. *Instituto del Mar del Peru, Boletin* **2**, 161–323.

E. SUESS and L. D. KULM, College of Oceanography, Oregon State University, Corvallis, Oregon 97331 U.S.A.

J. S. KILLINGLEY, Scripps Institute of Oceanography, University of California, San Diego, La Jolla, California 92093 U.S.A.

Palaeo-upwelling and the distribution of organic-rich rocks

J. T. Parrish

S U M M A R Y: As many as half the world's organic-rich rocks may have been deposited in upwelling zones.

This paper alludes to the way in which ancient upwelling zones may be predicted and the criteria by which such areas may be recognized from the sedimentary record. The predicted distribution of upwelling sites is compared with the distribution of organic-rich rocks, and the other probable indicators of upwelling, notably phosphatic rocks, glauconite and biogenic siliceous sediments. A correspondence is shown. This correspondence is consistent with not all upwelling zones being underlain by organic-rich sediments and with not all organic-rich sediments originating beneath areas of upwelling.

The notion that petroleum source beds were deposited in coastal upwelling zones has been in the literature at least since Trask (1932) published his work on the distribution of organic matter in modern marine sediments. Coastal upwelling zones are regions of exceptionally high biological productivity in the world's oceans, 6–14 times as productive as the least productive parts of the oceans and about 3 times as productive as normal shelf waters (Ryther 1969; Koblentz-Mishke et al. 1970). The equatorial and subpolar open ocean upwelling zones are 3–8 times as productive as the least productive areas (Koblentz-Mishke et al. 1970; Bunt 1975 Fig. 8.1). Upwelling zones are a small fraction of the surface area of the world ocean. Coastal upwelling zones constitute about a tenth of one percent of the surface area (Ryther 1969) and open-ocean upwelling areas constitute about 25% (Koblentz-Mishke et al. 1970).

The high productivity in the water column in upwelling zones is frequently (but not always) accompanied by a high rate of supply of organic matter to the sediments, a high organic-carbon content in the sediments, and a very low oxygen content in the water column (e.g., Smith 1968). The low oxygen content is considered a consequence of the high rate of supply of organic matter, which consumes oxygen as it decays. The preservation of the large amounts of organic carbon in the sediments is, then, a consequence of the low oxygen content of the overlying water column.

The purpose of this report is to summarize and present revisions of some recent work on the relationship between organic-rich rocks and palaeo-upwelling and to present preliminary results of investigations into the associations of additional upwelling indicators. The approach to ancient upwelling taken in this work is palaeo-geographic—the locations of ancient upwelling zones are predicted and compared with the distributions of organic-rich rock and other possible upwelling indicators. The work has relevance to two topics of particular concern to the participants in this symposium. One of the topics is the general one of patterns in time and space of the distribution of organic-rich rocks (Arthur et al.; Hallam; Schlanger et al.; Stoneley; Summerhayes; Thickpenny & Leggett, all this volume). The other topic is the relative importance of organic productivity, stagnation (oxygen depletion independent of productivity), and sedimentation rate in the preservation of abundant organic carbon (Calvert, Morris, Pelet, Stow, Suess, Summerhayes, all this volume). Some workers believe that high productivity is the most important key to the preservation of large amounts of organic matter. Others emphasize the role of oxygen depletion under conditions of stagnation, independent of productivity. The extent to which deposits with high organic carbon content can be related to regions of high biologic productivity is pertinent to the solution of this controversy.

Methods

Atmospheric circulation and upwelling

The most persistent upwelling currents in the modern oceans are driven by the winds that constitute the major features of atmospheric circulation. Therefore, in order to predict where ancient upwelling zones occurred, one must first predict the general circulation of the atmosphere. The method for reconstructing ancient atmospheric circulation patterns has been discussed at length elsewhere (Parrish 1982a, Parrish & Curtis 1982); only a brief explanation is given here. Two underlying assumptions are the basis for constructing the palaeo-circulation maps:

(1) the pattern of zonal circulation characteristic of present-day circulation was the same in the past, and

From: BROOKS, J. & FLEET, A. J. (eds) 1987, *Marine Petroleum Source Rocks*
Geological Society Special Publication No. 26 pp. 199–205.

(2) changes in geography, primarily the placement of continents, created the greatest changes in circulation.

The present zonal circulation consists of six general wind systems, parallel to latitude, three in each hemisphere. These wind systems are the equatorial easterlies (trade winds), between the equator and latitudes 20°N and 20°S; the westerlies, between latitudes 40°N and 55°N and 40°S and 55°S; and the polar easterlies, poleward of latitudes 65°N and 65°S. The corresponding pressure regime consists of high pressure (descending air) at the poles and at about latitudes 30°N and 30°S and low pressure (ascending air) at the equator and at about latitudes 60°N and 60°S. The zonal pattern is created by the rotation of the Earth and by the equator-to-pole temperature contrast.

The zonal pattern is modified by the temperature contrast between land and sea. Where the contrast is greatest, the disruption of the zonal pattern is greatest. At high mid-latitudes, land areas tend to be cold relative to the adjacent ocean; at low mid-latitudes, land tends to be warm relative to the adjacent ocean. The effect of these contrasts is to intensify the oceanic pressure regimes and to establish contrasting pressure regimes on the adjacent land. For example, in the Northern Hemisphere summer, a low-pressure cell develops over the hot Great Basin of North America, whereas the high pressure expected at that latitude in the Pacific Ocean is intensified, in response to the adjacent relatively warm continent. Large continents, whose interiors are isolated from the ameliorating effects of the surrounding oceans, can become still hotter or colder than the adjacent water. This is part of the reason for the extremely intense high- and low-pressure cells that develop over Asia during the northern winter and summer, respectively. Finally, mountains can modify the general circulation by further isolating the interiors of the continents or, in the case of large plateaux, by functioning as high-altitude heat sources.

A palaeocirculation map can be constructed using these principles by starting with a zonal circulation and then modifying it, building high- and low-pressure cells where appropriate for the palaeogeography, taking into account the size and latitudinal positions of the continents. See Parrish (1982a) for a step-by-step explanation of the map construction process.

Major upwelling currents are driven by winds associated with large-scale features of atmospheric circulation, those that are predicted for past geographies by the above methods. Upwelling currents are either coastal or oceanic. Persist-ent oceanic upwelling is under low-pressure belts or cells. This type of upwelling has generally been ignored as a setting for the deposition of organic-rich rocks because, in the modern oceans, it is found only over abyssal depths; consequently, the organic matter produced in modern oceanic upwelling zones is not preserved. However, the high sea levels that characterized many geological periods permitted the possibility that oceanic upwelling could take place over the shelf, thus greatly enhancing the potential for the preservation of organic matter.

In the Northern Hemisphere, coastal upwelling occurs where the coastline is to the left of the prevailing wind, facing in the direction of flow; in the Southern Hemisphere, the coastline must be to the right of the wind for upwelling to occur. Persistent coastal upwelling is confined to regions with exceptionally steady winds, which, in the modern oceans, are along the west coasts of the continents, along east–west coasts that lie in zonal wind paths (e.g., northern Venezuela; Corredor 1979), and along the east coast of Africa during the northern summer (Swallow 1980, *et seq.*).

Base maps of global palaeogeography are from Scotese *et al.* (1979) and Ziegler *et al.* (1983). Each palaeogeographic map was for a single geologic stage (Table 1). The maps were equal-area, making it possible to measure directly the area of shelf and the area of predicted upwelling zones. The percentage of shelf area covered by predicted upwelling was used as a measure of the proportion of the examined rock types that would correspond to predicted upwelling by chance alone. This measure was used, in turn, in statistical calculations (P and chi-square) that determined the significance of the observed correspondence.

Data

Data on glauconite, phosphate, and chert were collected on a presence/absence basis from the literature. Data on organic-rich rocks were taken from the literature and from industry source-rock geochemistry files. For samples from most localities, only TOC (total organic carbon) was available and only those with 1 percent TOC or higher were used. For some samples, however, the results of elemental or other kerogen-type analyses were available. In these cases, a cut-off of 0.4% TOC was used and samples containing Type I and Type II kerogen were used. Samples that contained Type III kerogen and samples that contained Type I or Type II kerogen, but which were clearly from terrestrial (presumably lacustrine) areas, were not included. Deposits

TABLE 1. *Global palaeogeographic reconstructions used as base maps for the atmospheric circulation reconstructions and upwelling predictions*

Period and Epoch	Stage	Reference
Miocene, middle	Vindobonian[1]	Ziegler *et al.* (1983)
Eocene, middle	Lutetian	,,
Cretaceous, late	Maestrichtian	,,
Cretaceous, late	Cenomanian	,,
Jurassic, late	Volgian[2]	,,
Jurassic, early	Pliensbachian	,,
Triassic, early	Induan[3]	,,
Permian, late	Kazanian	Scotese *et al.* (1979)
Carboniferous, late	Westphalian CD	,,
Carboniferous, early	Visean[4]	,,
Devonian, early	Emsian[4]	,,
Silurian, late	Wenlock	,,
Ordovician, late	Llandeilo-Caradoc	,,
Cambrian, late	Franconian[4]	,,

[1] *sensu* Vinogradov (1967)
[2] late Kimmeridgian–Portlandian
[3] = Scythian
[4] These reconstructions have been revised since the original studies comparing the distribution of organic-rich rocks and predicted upwelling (Parrish 1982a; Parrish & Curtis 1982); the revisions will be in Parrish *et al.* (in press, Franconian Stage); Raymond *et al.* (1982, 1985, Tournaisian and Namurian Stages). Rowley *et al.* (1985, Visean Stage); Barrett (1982 and in prep., Emsian Stage and other Devonian maps used in the comparisons in Table 2). However, the revisions are such that they affect only the middle Devonian statistics in Table 2.

characterized solely as 'black shales' were not considered.

Because some regions have been studied for organic-rich rocks much more intensively than others, and because the most persistent upwelling zones usually are at least a few hundred kilometres long, aggregates of closely spaced localities were used in the geographic analysis. Each aggregate data point consists of all the analyses within a 5° latitude–longitude square.

Results and discussion

The results are presented in Table 2. Owing to revisions in the palaeogeographic reconstructions (see Table 1), the statistics comparing the distributions of predicted upwelling and organic-rich rocks for the middle Devonian have been revised from those presented in Parrish (1982a). Overall, 55% of the organic-rich rocks corresponded geographically with predicted upwelling

TABLE 2. *Organic-rich rocks and upwelling. First number is the number of deposits corresponding with predicted upwelling. Number in parentheses is the total number of deposits. The upwelling areas were extrapolated between times for which the palaeogeography was reconstructed. (From Parrish 1982a, Parrish & Curtis 1982, and this study)*

Time	Organic-rich rocks
Cenozoic	
Late Miocene	7 (14)*
Middle Miocene	6 (8)*
Oligocene	0 (3)
Middle Eocene	5 (7)*
Paleocene	1 (3)
Mesozoic–Cretaceous	
Maestrichtian	3 (5)
Santonian–Campanian	16 (23)*
Turonian–Coniacian	15 (23)*
Cenomanian	12 (21)*
Aptian–Albian	21 (28)*
Barremian	10 (20)*
Berriasian–Hauterivian	4 (13)
Mesozoic–Jurassic	
Volgian	1 (15)
Oxfordian	3 (9)
Bathonian–Callovian	2 (8)
Aalenian–Bajocian	1 (1)
Pliensbachian	1 (1)
Sinemurian	4 (6)
Hettangian	1 (1)
Mesozoic–Triassic	
Norian–Rhaetian	0 (1)
Karnian	6 (7)*
Ladinian	0 (1)
Induan	3 (3)*
Palaeozoic	
Late Permian	4 (11)*
Early Permian	3 (4)*
Late Pennsylvanian	2 (2)*
Early Pennsylvanian	3 (3)*
Late Mississippian	4 (4)*
Early Mississippian	3 (5)*
Late Devonian	13 (17)*
Middle Devonian	3 (7)†
Early Devonian	3 (8)
Silurian	1 (4)
Ordovician	3 (6)
Cambrian	2 (6)
Phanerozoic	166 (301)*

* Indicates statistically significant correspondence.
† Indicates value revised from Parrish 1982a.

zones. Statistically, this is a highly significant result (p. ≪0.001). However, the correspondence between organic-rich rocks and predicted upwelling is not uniform through the Phanerozoic.

A correspondence was found for the late Devonian to the late Triassic, most of the Cretaceous, and the later part of the Tertiary. Two-thirds of the organic-rich rocks fall into these time intervals and two-thirds of these corresponded with predicted upwelling zones.

The results in Table 2 are presented in graphic form in Figure 1. For comparison, the times of significant source rock deposition (Tissot 1979) and black shale deposition (Leggett *et al.* 1981; Jenkyns 1980) also are presented. According to these workers, black shales and/or source rocks predominated in the early Palaeozoic, late Devonian to early Mississippian, late Pennsylvanian to early Permian, middle Jurassic to early late Cretaceous, and Neogene. The major discrepancy between the distributions of black shales and source rocks is in the early Palaeozoic, for which Leggett *et al.* (1981) described widespread black shales of Ordovician age that apparently became source rocks in only a few places. Upwelling was potentially an important factor in the deposition of the source rocks in the late Palaeozoic to Triassic, Cretaceous, Eocene, and Miocene. Only a few Jurassic source rocks and early Palaeozoic black shales are explained by the upwelling predictions.

Several points, which indicate that the statistical results should be used only as a guide, must be emphasized about the relationship between upwelling and the distribution of organic-rich rocks. First, present-day upwelling zones are not all underlain by very organic-rich sediments. The most notable exception is the Northwest African upwelling zone, where sediments contain at most 2.6% TOC, compared with over 10% off Southwest Africa and 4–5% off southwestern North America (Summerhayes 1983). The upwelled waters off Northwest Africa are lower in nutrients than the waters of other upwelling zones and productivity is consequently lower (although still higher than ocean water in general). Moreover, mechanical reworking of the sediments is more severe, owing to a combination of a very shallow shelf and relatively variable winds, which favour turbulence over stable upwelling circulation.

Second, not all upwelling zones are wind-driven. However, the so-called dynamic upwellings, which occur in strong currents such as the Gulf Stream, do not at present have much effect on the underlying sediments, although they may have done in the past. For example, productivity in the palaeo-Gulf Stream, when that current flowed over the continental shelf, may have been responsible for the phosphate deposits in the southeastern United States (Riggs 1984).

Third, upwelling zones clearly are not the only setting for the deposition of organic-rich rocks (Demaison & Moore 1980). Detailed stratigraphic and palaeogeographic analysis of the area of each predicted upwelling zone is required to test each individual prediction. Such analyses have been made for the Permian Phosphoria Formation (e.g. McKelvey *et al.* 1967) and the Miocene Monterey Formation (e.g. Bramlette 1946; Garrison *et al.* 1981) of the United States and the Cretaceous rocks of the Tarfaya Basin, Morocco (Wiedmann *et al.* 1978). Many workers also have studied the sediments in modern upwelling zones (Bremner & Rogers 1981; Bur-

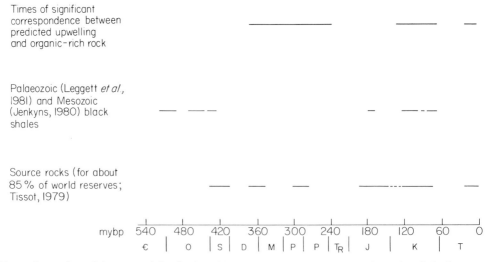

FIG. 1. Comparison of the temporal distribution of black shales, petroleum source rocks, and statistically significant correspondence between predicted upwelling and organic-rich rocks.

nett 1980; numerous papers in Suess & Thiede 1983). Many of these studies have revealed rock types, in addition to organic-rich rocks, that appear to be characteristic of upwelling deposits and which also might be used as indicators for the recognition of other ancient upwelling deposits. These indicators include phosphatic rock, glauconite, and biogenic siliceous rock. The studies of modern upwelling zones suggest that the organic-rich sediments, phosphate, and glauconite are deposited in different areas of the upwelling zone. Organic-rich sediment is deposited under anoxic water in the region of highest productivity, phosphate is precipitated in a halo of slightly oxic waters around the anoxic zone, and glauconite forms in still more oxic waters around the phosphate zone. Similar patterns are seen in ancient rocks. For example, in the Phosphoria Formation, especially in Meade Peak and equivalent rocks, the phosphorite is interbedded with and slightly shoreward of the most organic-rich rocks and glauconite is common in the still farther shoreward carbonate facies (Sheldon 1963; Cressman & Swanson 1964; McKelvey *et al.* 1967; Wardlaw 1981; Parrish 1983). A similar offshore-onshore distribution of organic-rich rock, phosphate, and glauconite is found in the Middle Cambrian rocks of the Georgina Basin, Australia (Russell & Trueman 1971; Howard 1972; Cook 1982) and in the Lower Cambrian rocks of South China (Bushinskii 1969; Xu *et al.* 1982; Lu 1982; Parrish 1983).

Under the Southwest African upwelling zone, biogenic siliceous sediment constitutes a distinct facies nearshore (Bremner 1983); chert also forms a distinct facies in ancient deposits. In the Phosphoria Formation, the chert is between the phosphate and carbonate facies, interbedded in places with the glauconite-carbonate facies. The same distribution is found in South China as in the Phosphoria, but in the Georgina Basin, the chert commonly occurs between the organic-rich rock and phosphate facies.

Subjecting all the organic-rich rocks used in this study to a detailed analysis of associated lithologies was beyond the scope of the study. However, the distribution of the organic-rich rocks in space and time was compared with that of phosphatic rocks, from a data set on phosphate deposits compiled for Parrish *et al.* (1983) and Parrish (1982b) and from the literature on the individual organic-rich rock deposits. The associated lithologies of many of the organic-rich rock deposits could not be determined; these were deposits that were sampled in boreholes from unnamed units. However, 137 of 301 units were surveyed; of these, 58 were associated with phosphatic rock. Significantly, all but seven of the organic-rich deposits that were associated with phosphatic rock also fell in or near predicted upwelling zones. No systematic search of chert and glauconite association was made, but in the course of determining the phosphate association, it was found that another ten organic-rich deposits, all of which fell in or near predicted upwelling zones, were associated with chert or glauconite. In summary, half the surveyed organic-rich deposits were associated with rocks that also can be upwelling indicators and nearly all of the deposits containing these associations corresponded with predicted upwelling. These results compare favourably with the original ones, that half of organic-rich rocks correspond with predicted upwelling.

In conclusion, as many as half of organic-rich rocks may have been deposited in upwelling zones. If subsequent basin-level studies, designed to provide a detailed analysis of associated lithologies and palaeogeographic setting, confirm this conclusion, the upwelling models will be helpful in predicting the locations in time and space of as yet undiscovered source rocks.

References

BARRETT, S. F. 1982. Biogeographic evidence for Devonian continental positions and climate: a framework for phytogeography. *North American Paleontological Convention* **III** *Abstracts*, p. 2.

—— 1985. Early Devonian continental positions and climate: a framework for paleophytogeography. *In:* TIFFNEY, B. H. (ed) *Geological Factors and the Evolution of Plants.* Yale University Press, New Haven, 93–127.

BRAMLETTE, M. N. 1946. The Monterey Formation of California and the origin of its siliceous rocks. *Prof. Pap. U.S. geol. Surv.* **212**, 57 pp.

BREMNER, J. M. 1983. Biogenic sediments on the South West African (Namibian) continental margin. *In:* THIEDE, J. & SUESS, E. (eds), *Coastal Upwelling: Its Sediment Record, B, NATO Conf. Ser. IV, **10B**, Plenum Press, New York. 73–103.

—— & ROGERS, J. 1981. Major lithofacies of the Namibian continental margin. *Program and Abstracts, NATO ARI Conference on Coastal Upwelling: Its Sediment Record,* Villanouva, Portugal, Sept. 1981.

BUNT, J. S. 1975. Primary productivity of marine ecosystems. *In:* LIETH, H. & WHITTAKER, R. H. (eds), *Primary Productivity of the Biosphere.* Springer-Verlag, New York. 169–184.

BURNETT, W. C. 1980. Apatite-glauconite association off Peru and Chile: palaeo-oceanographic implication. *J. geol. Soc. Lond.*, **137**, 757–764.

BUSHINSKII, G. I. 1969. *Old Phosphorites of Asia and Their Genesis.* Geol. Inst., Akademie Nauk SSSR, Moscow (Translation by Israel Program of Science Translations). 266 pp.

COOK, P. J. 1982. The Cambrian palaeogeography of Australia and opportunities for petroleum exploration. *J. Australian Petrol. Exploration Assoc.*, **22**, 42–64.

CORREDOR, J. E. 1979. Phytoplankton response to low level nutrient enrichment through upwelling in the Columbian Caribbean Basin. *Deep-Sea Res.*, **26A**, 731–741.

CRESSMAN, E. R. & SWANSON, R. W. 1964. Stratigraphy and petrology of the Permian rocks of southwestern Montana. *Prof. Pap. U.S. geol. Surv.*, **313 C**, 275–569.

DEMAISON, G. J. & MOORE, G. T. 1980. Anoxic environments and oil source bed genesis. *Bull. Am. Assoc. Petrol. Geol.*, **64**, 1179–1209.

GARRISON, R. E., DOUGLAS, R. G., PISCIOTTO, K. E., ISAACS, C. M. & INGLE, J. C. 1981. *The Monterey Formation and Related Siliceous Rocks of California.* Society of Economic Paleontologists and Mineralogists, Pacific Section, Los Angeles, 327 pp.

HOWARD, P. F. 1972. Exploration for phosphorite in Australia—a case history. *Econ. Geol.*, **67**, 1180–1192.

JENKYNS, H. C. 1980. Cretaceous anoxic events: from continents to oceans. *J. geol. Soc. Lond.*, **137**, 171–188.

KOBLENTZ-MISHKE, O. J., VOLKOVINSKY, V. V. & KABANOVA, J. G. 1970. Plankton primary production of the world ocean. *In:* WOOSTER, W. S. (ed), *Scientific Exploration of the South Pacific.* National Academy of Science, Washington, D.C. 183–193.

LEGGETT, J. K., MCKERROW, W. S., COCKS, L. R. M. & RICHARDS, R. B. 1981. Periodicity in the early Palaeozoic marine realm. *J. geol. Soc. Lond.*, **138**, 167–176.

LU, Y. 1982. Genesis, geologic and geographic distributions of the Cambrian phosphate deposits in China—a biostratigraphic view. International Geological Correlation Programme, Project 156, *Abstracts of the Fifth International Field Workshop and Seminar on Phosphorite*, Kunming, China, November 17–24, 1982, pp. 22–23.

MCKELVEY, V. E., WILLIAMS, J. S., SHELDON, R. P., CRESSMAN, E. R., CHENEY, T. M. & SWANSON, R. W. 1967. The Phosphoria, Park City, and Shedhorn Formations in Western Phosphate Field. *In:* HALE, L. A. (ed.), *Anatomy of the Western Phosphate Field,* IAG Fifteenth Annual Field Conference, Salt Lake City. 15–34.

PARRISH, J. T. 1982a. Upwelling and petroleum source beds, with reference to the Paleozoic. *Bull. Am. Assoc. Petrol. Geol.*, **66**, 750–774.

—— 1982b. Phanerozoic paleoceanography and phosphorites. International Geological Correlation Programme, Project 156, *Abstracts of the Fifth International Field Workshop and Seminar on Phos-*

phorite, Kunming, China, November 17–24, 1982, pp. 101–104.

—— 1983. Upwelling deposits: nature of association of organic-rich rock, chert, chalk, phosphorite, and glauconite. *Bull. Am. Assoc. Petrol. Geol.*, **67**, 529.

—— & CURTIS, R. L. 1982. Atmospheric circulation, upwelling, and organic-rich rocks in the Mesozoic and Cenozoic Eras. *Palaeogeog., Palaeoclimat., Palaeoecol.*, **40**, 31–66.

—— ZIEGLER, A. M. & HUMPHREVILLE, R. G. 1983. Upwelling in the Paleozoic Era. *In:* THIEDE, J. & SUESS, E. (eds), *Coastal Upwelling: Its Sediment Record,* B, NATO Conf. Ser. IV, **10B**, Plenum Press, New York, 553–578.

—— ZIEGLER, A. M., SCOTESE, C. R., HUMPHREVILLE, R. G. & KIRSCHVINK, J. L., in press. Early Cambrian paleogeography, paleoceanography, and phosphorites. *In:* SHERGOLD, J. H. & COOK, P. J. (eds), *Proterozoic and Cambrian Phosphorites.* Cambridge University Press, Cambridge.

RAYMOND, A., PARKER, W. C. & PARRISH, J. T. 1982. Implications of paleoclimatic reconstructions for phytogeography. *J. Paleontol.*, **56**, Supplement 2, 21.

——, —— & —— 1985. Phytogeography and paleoclimate of the early Carboniferous. *In:* TIFFNEY, B. H. (ed) *Geological Factors and the Evolution of Plants,* Yale University Press, New Haven, 169–222.

RUSSELL, R. T. & TRUEMAN, N. A. 1971. The geology of the Duchess phosphate deposits, northwestern Queensland, Australia. *Econ. Geol.*, **66**, 1186–1214.

ROWLEY, D. B., RAYMOND, A., PARRISH, J. T., LOTTES, A. L., SCOTESE, C. R. & ZIEGLER, A. M. 1985. Carboniferous paleogeographic phytogeographic and paleoclimatic reconstructions. *Int. Journ. Coal Geol.* **5**, 7–42.

RIGGS, S. R. 1984. Paleoceanographic model of Neogene phosphorite deposition, U.S. Atlantic continental margin. *Science,* **223**, 123–131.

RYTHER, J. H. 1969. Photosynthesis and fish production in the sea. *Science,* **130**, 72–76.

SCOTESE, C. R., BAMBACH, R. K., BARTON, C., VAN DER VOO, R. & ZIEGLER, A. M. 1979. Paleozoic base maps. *J. Geol. Chicago,* **87**, 217–277.

SHELDON, R. P. 1963. Physical stratigraphy and mineral resources of Permian rocks in western Wyoming. *Prof. Pap. U.S. geol. Surv.*, **313 B**, 49–273.

SMITH, R. L. 1968. Upwelling. *Oceanography and Marine Biology Annual Review,* **6**, 11–46.

SUMMERHAYES, C. P. 1983. Sedimentation of organic matter in upwelling regimes. *In:* THIEDE, J. & SUESS, E. (eds), *Coastal Upwelling: Its Sediment Record,* B. NATO Conf. Ser. IV, **10B**, Plenum Press, New York. 29–72.

SUESS, E. & THIEDE, J. (eds) 1983. *Coastal Upwelling: Its Sediment Record,* Parts A and B, NATO Conf. Ser. IV, 10A and 10B, Plenum Press, New York. 604 pp (A), 610 pp (B).

SWALLOW, J. C. 1980. The Indian Ocean experiment: introduction. *Science,* **209**, 588.

TISSOT, B. 1979. Effects on prolific petroleum source rocks and major coal deposits caused by sea-level changes. *Nature,* **277**, 463–465.

TRASK, P. D. 1932. *Origin and Environment of Source*

Sediments of Petroleum. Gulf Publishing Company, Houston. 322 pp.

VINOGRADOV, A. P. (ed) 1967. *Atlas of the Lithological-Paleogeographical Maps of the USSR, Volume IV: Paleogene, Neogene, and Quaternary.* Ministry of Geology, Academy of Science, Moscow.

WARDLAW, B. R. 1981. Middle-Late Permian paleogeography of Idaho, Montana, Nevada, Utah, and Wyoming. *In:* FOUCH, T. D. & MAGATHAN, E. R. (eds), *Paleozoic Paleogeography of West-Central United States.* Society of Economic Paleontologists and Mineralogists, Rocky Mountain Section, Denver. 353–361.

WIEDMANN, J., EINSELE, G. & IMMEL, H. 1978. Evidence faunistique et sèdimentologique pour un upwelling dans le bassin côtier de Tarfaya/Maroc dans le Crétacé supérieur. *Annales des Mines et de la Géologie,* **2** (28), 415–441.

XU, W., XIONG, R., LI, G. & WU, Y. 1982. Sedimentary facies and paleogeographic features of Early Cambrian phosphorites in Sichuan. International Geological Correlation Programme, Project 156, *Abstracts of the Fifth International Field Workshop and Seminar on Phosphorite,* Kunming, China, November 17–24, 1982, pp. 6–10.

ZIEGLER, A. M., SCOTESE, C. R. & BARRETT, S. F. 1983. Mesozoic and Cenozoic paleogeographic maps. *In:* BROSCHE, P. & SÜNDERMANN, J. (eds), *Tidal Frictions and the Earth's Rotation.* Springer-Verlag, Berlin. 240–252.

J. T. PARRISH, Branch of Oil and Gas Resources, Office of Energy and Marine Geology, U.S. Geological Survey, Box 25046, M.S. 971, Denver Federal Center, Denver, Colorado 80225, U.S.A.

The significance of carbonate ooids in petroleum source-rock studies

J. Ferguson

S U M M A R Y: Study of carbonate ooids from areas of present day ooid production in the Arabian Gulf and the Bahama Banks has shown that they contain significant amounts of light hydrocarbon gases. It is concluded that these gases are generated within the ooids themselves by the bacterial degradation of the contained algal proto-kerogen, in an anaerobic environment. Continuation of the degradation of the contained organic matter by artificial maturation, using enhanced temperature and pressure, in the presence of natural sea-water, has shown that an evolutionary series of kerogen and soluble hydrocarbons exist, which can be related to material isolated from British Jurassic oolitic limestones.

Two principal conclusions arise from these studies. Firstly, that carbonate ooids might provide a model for evaluating the potential of carbonates generally, as source rocks. Secondly, because the reactants and products are frequently isolated by the emplacement of the first phase of calcite cement early during diagenesis, thus trapping and possibly 'fossilizing' them, detailed studies of suitable oolitic limestone might lead to better understanding of organic reactions at different stages in diagenesis.

Very little is known of the possible role of carbonates as source rocks, in spite of a number of well argued papers such as those of Owen (1964) and Hunt (1967). A reluctance to accept this possibility has led to much speculation and disagreement concerning the source of some oils in carbonate dominated provinces; indeed a recent paper by Bockmeulen *et al.* (1983), although not specifically concerned with source rock studies, has questioned the origin of oil in the Bolivar coastal fields of Venezuela, which had previously been considered to be sourced from the La Luna and Logollo Limestones (Hedberg 1964). However there is an increasing acceptance of carbonate source rocks and two recent examples serve to emphasize this trend. Thus in a discussion of hydrocarbon habitat in Saudi Arabia, Ayres *et al.* (1982) suggested that the oils in the large southern area are derived from organic rich Jurassic carbonates (*ibid.* pp. 3–5); while Ala (1982), suggested that oil of the Zagros area of south west Iran is sourced from the largely calcareous Kazhdumi Formation (ibid. p. 1538).

Interest in the relationship between hydrocarbons and ooids was stimulated as a result of work carried out in the early 1970s by British Gas, on the onshore use of organic geochemical exploration for oil and gas. During this work, samples of rock were taken from a depth of 3–4 m and analysed for their contained light hydrocarbons (methane, ethane and propane). The samples from the middle Jurassic rocks of north Yorkshire, showed remarkable variations in their contained light hydrocarbons, which was found to be related to lithology. Of particular interest, is the significantly higher amounts of gases in the oolites (Table 1).

TABLE 1. *Light hydrocarbon gas analysis of some British Middle Jurassic rocks from north Yorkshire. Values in ppm w/w, sample size in brackets, acid extraction technique*

	Gas	Mean	Standard deviation
All rocks sampled (80)	Methane	22.7	28.9
	Ethane	3.2	6.1
	Propane	2.7	5.9
Oolitic limestone (15)	Methane	71.9	28.9
	Ethane	19.0	5.0
	Propane	17.5	5.3
Non-oolitic limestone (14)	Methane	16.9	11.9
	Ethane	3.8	2.4
	Propane	3.6	2.5

Following this finding, samples of Recent ooids from the Arabian Gulf were analysed and were also found to contain these gases. This work was complemented by a detailed study of Bahama Bank ooids by Ibe (1980), some of the results of which have been published (Ferguson & Ibe 1981 and 1982). In all cases examined, the most important constituent gases are methane, ethane and propane, and the levels detected have led to speculation as to the origin of these gases. Normal biogenic hydrocarbon gas, such as that generated by sewage sludge (ignoring carbon dioxide) is typically 99.9% methane with a maximum of 0.1% higher hydrocarbons, whereas gas in the Recent ooids can be about 60% methane, 25% ethane and 15% propane. Three possible explanations for these differences have been proposed (Ferguson & Ibe 1981, p. 105):

(i) Contamination—cannot be entirely ruled out, but it is unlikely that similar contam-

From: BROOKS, J. & FLEET, A. J. (eds) 1987, *Marine Petroleum Source Rocks* Geological Society Special Publication No. 26 pp. 207–215.

ination could occur in two widely separated areas.

(ii) Gas generated chemically—the reactions required to produce these hydrocarbons are not known at S.T.P.

(iii) Biogenic generation with some loss due to diffusion—this is the most likely explanation, requiring methane and carbon dioxide to escape, thus concentrating the other products.

Some confirmation of this latter proposal has now been obtained experimentally, by passing natural gas over present day ooids and then extracting and analysing the adsorbed gases. The results showed that although the gas used was around 99% methane, the three light hydrocarbon gases were adsorbed in the ratio 100:24:11; indicating that differentiation had taken place. This is probably due to the gas entering the ooids via minute pores, or perhaps algal borings, which are a characteristic of many of the ooids examined (Ferguson & Ibe 1982, p. 270 and Plates 1, C & D).

Another approach to the problem of the role of carbonate ooids is through experiments simulating early diagenesis and analysing the various products and comparing them with geological examples. The results of several experiments, designed to test the feasibility of this approach, have been published (Ferguson *et al.* 1981, 1984). Changes in the amounts of gaseous hydrocarbons as well as in the physical and chemical nature of the proto-kerogen and changes in the carbonate phase were recorded. The results for the organic matter, correlate closely with published examples of artificial and natural maturation of kerogen and proto-kerogen (Peters *et al.* 1981). This experimental work is continuing and the relevant aspects are summarized later.

Recent ooids

Inorganic materials

Much has been written on the formation of ooids and on their internal structure, covering both recent and ancient examples (see for example Bathurst 1975 and Loreau 1982). The most important factor in the context of this work, is the large pore space and internal surface area within individual ooids, which is largely occupied by algal material of one form or another. Thus in scanning electron micrographs of etched surfaces of individual ooids, the concentric voids between layers or aragonite needles and the smaller voids between intermeshing needles (Plate 1A), are normally filled with algal material. Similar structures are seen in Jurassic ooids (Plate 1B & 1C). Chemical and microprobe analysis show that the recent ooids examined, commonly contain around 0.8% Sr and 0.4% Mg, whereas the nuclei are often low magnesium calcite with 2.5–3.0% Mg (Plate 2A). Many ooids are heavily bored by endolithic algal species and these borings are frequently infilled with low magnesium calcite.

Although present-day marine carbonate ooid formation is more restricted than at some periods in the geological past, the evidence suggests that they have been formed in one environment only, that is, on a warm shallow sea floor which is well oxygenated.

Organic materials

Arabian Gulf and Bahama Bank ooids contain between 1.23 and 4.13 wt. per cent of organic carbon (Ferguson & Ibe 1982, p. 279), principally of algal origin. Separation of this organic material by acid extraction shows it to be formed largely of algal mucilage and filaments (*ibid.* p. 275 and Plates 2 & 3), some of which are recognizable and exhibit original pigmentation. Elemental analysis of the algal material shows, as expected, that it is a hydrogen rich (6.49%, *ibid.* p. 277) Type I kerogen.

Also trapped within the ooids are light hydrocarbon gases, principally methane, ethane and propane (Ferguson & Ibe 1981, Table 2). Butane has also been detected along with a number of unsaturated gases such as ethene, propene and butene. Soluble organic extracts have been prepared, by extracting with dichloromethane, and examined using gas chromatography (*ibid.* p. 279 & Fig. 1) and infra-red spectroscopy. The results of those examinations show that the soluble hydrocarbons are immature and particularly noteworthy is the infra-red absorption peak at 3450 cm^{-1}, indicating the presence of OH groups (Fig. 1).

Experimental evidence

Evidence for biogenic methane formation in Recent ooids has been deduced indirectly. Thus it has been suggested that the observed patterns of light hydrocarbon occurrence are due to biogenic activity, with enhancement of ethane and higher gases due to the effects of diffusion of methane and carbon dioxide. Further evidence has come as the result of experiments in which Recent Bahaman ooids were sealed into glass bottles along with oxygenated sea-water and air and exposed to sunlight (Ferguson 1983b). In

PLATE 1. Aspects of ooid microstructure. (A) S.E.M. photograph of the internal structure of a typical Bahamian ooid. Section polished and etched with 2% HCl before coating. Bar length 1 micron. (B + C) S.E.M. photographs of the internal structure of ooids from the Jurassic, Lincolnshire Limestone, Cowthick Quarry, nr. Corby, Northants. Sections polished and etched. Note: concentric structure (B) and infilled radial algal boring (C). Bar lengths 10 and 20 micron respectively. (D) Photomicrograph of ultra-thin section, showing the high magnesium calcite cement rim, after simulation experiment. Bar length 50 micron.

these experiments, carbon dioxide, methane and traces of higher hydrocarbons were produced and it is concluded that the detected hydrocarbons must have been generated within the ooids by bacterial activity (*ibid.* p. 220). Therefore, as methanogenic bacteria are obligate anaerobes (Rice & Claypool 1981), it is concluded that the interior of the ooids must be anaerobic.

Simulated early diagenetic changes in the organic matter contained within the ooids has been produced by enclosing mixtures of sea-water and Recent carbonate ooids in steel cells, and holding them at constant temperature and pres-

sure for some predetermined time (Ferguson *et al.* 1981, 1984). The original experiments, carried out at 120°C/25 bars and 140°C/48.25 bars for 3 and 6 months respectively (Ferguson *et al.* 1981) were followed by a series of 1 month experiments, carried out at 10° intervals in the temperature range 110–210°C. Full details of this work are given in Ferguson *et al.* (1984). These experiments have shown that maturation of the protokerogen occurs (*ibid.*, p. 260), accompanied by considerable changes in the inorganic material. For example, cementation occurs at temperatures in excess of 180°C, and is the result of the formation

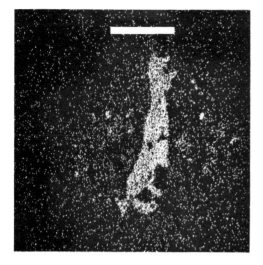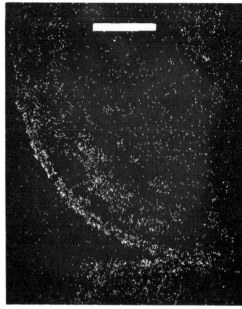

PLATE 2. X-ray maps for magnesium, of Recent Bahamian ooids. (A) Typical ooid, note high magnesium calcite 'core'. Bar length 100 micron. (B) Typical ooid after simulation experiment (Test 4). Note particularly the concentration of magnesium in the outer rim of cement and the generally more uneven distribution of the element, when compared with 2A. Bar length 100 micron.

of tabular crystals of low magnesium calcite around individual ooids (Plate 1D and 2B). This is accompanied by the formation of anhydrite crystals up to 2 mm in length, in the voids between the ooids.

Although a full description of the experiments and results has been published the principal changes are summarized as follows:

(i) Gaseous phase
Under the conditions of the experiments, most of the gases generated are dissolved in the water and come out of solution on cooling, although some gas remains trapped within the ooids. Analysis of the free gas show that it is principally carbon dioxide and methane, however other saturated and unsaturated hydrocarbons up to C_5 have been identified. This phase has proved to be difficult to quantify.

(ii) Liquid phase
The most important changes in the liquid phase are enrichment in calcium and strontium, and depletion in magnesium and sulphur. In several tests an 'oily slick' has been noted on the top of the liquid in the cell after it is opened. In one case, this 'slick' was separated and analysed. From duplicate analysis carried out at Imperial College and BP Research Laboratories, Sunbury

it was concluded that this material was most closely allied to organic soluble extracts, prepared from Recent algal matter (M. J. Gibbons, *pers. comm.*). The implication is that this material had not been greatly altered by the conditions of the experiment (210°C, 75.84 bars, 1 month).

Experiments carried out since this paper was written, indicate that organic matter outside the ooids does not mature to the same degree as that enclosed within them, under the same experimental conditions.

(iii) Solid phase
Changes in the inorganic solids corresponding to those in the liquid phase, have been noted above. More important in the context of this paper, are the changes in the organic materials. The separated proto-kerogen is in all cases structureless and the elemental analysis shows that, compared with the starting material, maturation had occurred, with both the atomic hydrogen/carbon, oxygen/carbon ratios decreasing (Ferguson *et al.* 1984, Table 9). Infra-red spectra of the dichloromethane soluble extract (Fig. 1, Cell Extract curve) show that the OH groups have disappeared, when compared with the Arabian Gulf and Bahamian ooid curves. Another significant change, is formation of humic acids and possibly humin. These substances are released when the

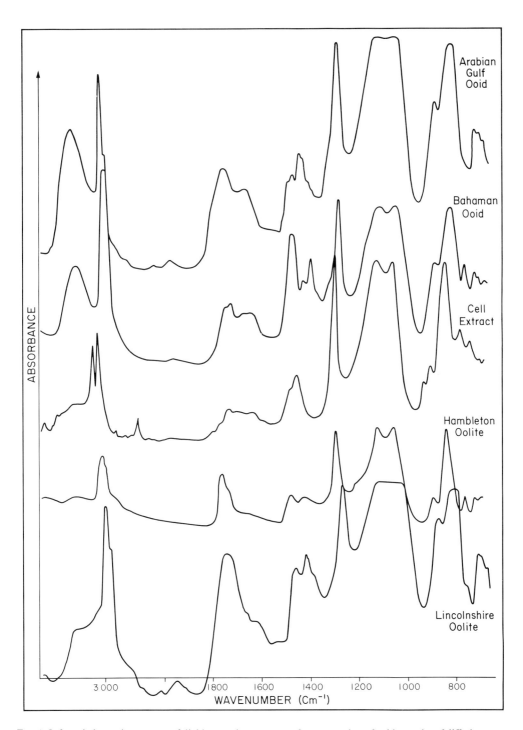

FIG. 1. Infrared absorption spectra of dichloromethane extracts from a number of ooid samples of differing ages. Spectrum labelled Cell Extract is from simulation experiments, Test 4.

ooids are dissolved in diluted HCl, and appear as a spectacular brown oily looking sludge, floating on the surface of the acid. Examination of this material showed that it is very rich in hydrogen and oxygen and is soluble in dilute alkali. It is thought to be similar in nature to the 'kerogen-like' material reported by Shimoyama and Johns (1972, p. 90), resulting from heating fatty acids in the presence of calcium carbonate.

An important conclusion which follows from these experiments is that maturation occurs only within the ooids and follows a pathway similar to clastic source rock maturation. It is likely that the 'oily slick' referred to earlier, represents organic matter flushed out of the ooids at an early stage in the experiments.

Geological evidence

Samples of oolitic limestone from four stratigraphic levels in the British Jurassic have been examined petrologically and chemically. In particular the organic components and inorganic, acid insoluble, residue have been examined. A summary of the relative amounts of these components is given in Table 2.

Petrological evidence

Although the oolites are now preserved as low magnesium calcite (Plate 1B+C), the features described relating to Recent ooids can still be identified, however the traces of boring endolithic algae and the concentric rings of algal mucilage are now largely infilled with calcite. Examination of slides of the Hambleton Oolite under ultraviolet light, shows a marked fluorescence of the ooids relative to the sparry calcite matrix, which is interpreted as indicating the presence of organic material, and in particular the light hydrocarbon gases, in the ooids rather than the matrix.

Soluble organic extract

The amounts recorded (Table 2) for these Jurassic oolitic limestones are the average of a small number of different samples. They contain slightly more extractable hydrocarbons than the present day ooids (Ferguson & Ibe 1982, Table 3, p. 280). Examination of these extracts by infra-red spectrometry shows similarities with those from Recent samples and artificially matured material from the experimental work. Two points are significant, the absence of a peak at 3430 cm^{-1}, indicating the lack of OH groups and an 'M' shaped peak between $1200–1000 \text{ cm}^{-1}$ (Figure 1, Hambleton and Lincolnshire Oolite curves). This peak appears to be characteristic of ooid extracts and is absent from extracts of rocks from other stratigraphic levels in the British Jurassic, not containing ooids. A series of spectra, representing various levels in the Jurassic of southern England is shown in Fig. 2, and it is evident that the peak at $1200–1000 \text{ cm}^{-1}$, differs significantly from peaks in the same frequency range, in non-ooid examples.

Gas chromatographic analyses of the extracts show that the ratio of nC_{17}/pristane indicates an anaerobic environment during maturation. The distribution of the n-alkanes does not appear to be significant.

Total organic carbon

The values obtained for total organic carbon are relatively low (0.21–0.37%) and less than values

TABLE 2. *Analyses of a number of British Jurassic oolitic limestones. Values as mean wt. %, based on whole rock analyses of the stated number of samples (in brackets)*

Stratigraphic horizon	Location	Soluble organic extract	Total organic carbon	Kerogen	Insoluble inorganic residue
Lincolnshire Limestone (6)	Cowthick Quarry, nr. Corby, Northamptonshire	0.03	0.37	0.06	2.99
Great Oolite Limestone (3)	Kirtlington Quarry, Oxfordshire	0.10	0.23	—	3.70
Hambleton Oolite (4)	Dalby Forrest, nr. Pickering, north Yorkshire	0.07	0.35	0.02	3.69
Osmington Oolite (3)	Osmington Mill, Dorset	0.12	0.21	—	12.60

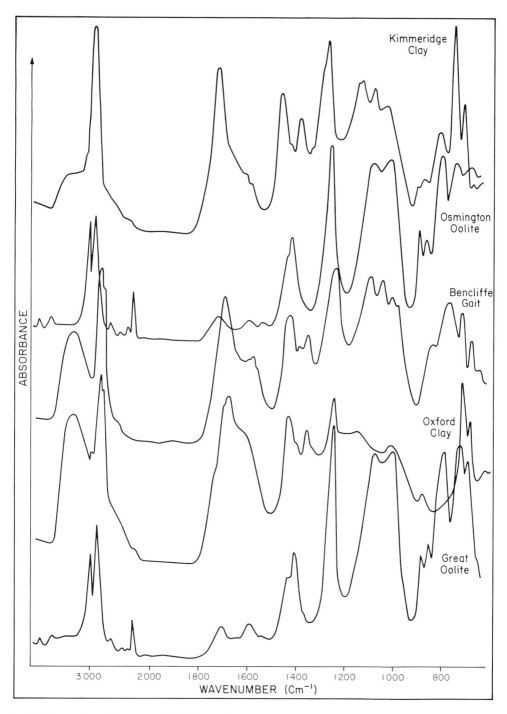

FIG. 2. Infrared absorption spectra of dichloromethane extracts comparing horizons of differing lithologies in the Jurassic of southern England.

J. Ferguson

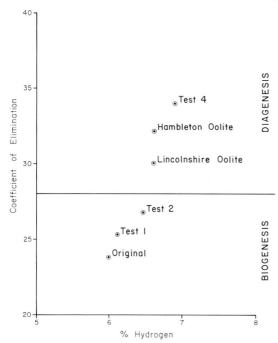

FIG. 3. Coefficient of elimination plot, comparing the elemental analysis (C-H-O) of three artificially matured proto-kerogens, with two Jurassic kerogens.

obtained from modern ooids, which have a mean total organic carbon content of 2.33% (Ferguson & Ibe 1982, Table 2, p. 279).

Kerogen

Small amounts of kerogen have been isolated from samples of the Hambleton and Lincolnshire Oolites and the elemental analyses of these kerogens (Table 3) indicate that they are relatively immature. A Coefficient of Elimination plot (Ferguson 1983a), Fig. 3, which compares these results with some of those obtained from the

TABLE 3. *Elemental analyses of two kerogens from British Jurassic, oolitic limestones. Localities as Table 2.*

		Lincolnshire limestone	Hambleton oolite
	C	58.49	56.62
	H	5.42	5.12
	O	18.56	16.17
	N	2.39	4.02
Atomic	H/C	1.112	1.085
Atomic	O/C	0.238	0.214

diagenesis experiments, confirms this, and suggests that the naturally occurring kerogens are less mature than that isolated from the experiment carried out at 210°C.

Insoluble inorganic residue

The insoluble inorganic residue is principally a mixture of quartz and clay minerals, with illite and kaolinite dominating the clay mineral assemblage. Minor amounts of a mixed layer clay mineral have been recognized, but the mineral species not identified. These results are similar to those for Recent Bahaman ooids and it is suggested that these insoluble minerals are largely derived from the cores of the original ooids.

Conclusions

The results of the study of Recent aragonite ooids suggest that significant quantities of algal organic matter is incorporated into their structure during growth. The material may be available for the formation of natural gas and oil related substances if they are deposited under the correct physico-chemical conditions. It is also deduced that although ooids form in aerobic environments, they are internally anaerobic. Further, there are sufficient spaces within the ooids to provide micro-sites for bacteria, and the internal surface area is sufficiently large to provide suitable sites for reactions to take place.

Experiments simulating diagenesis have shown that under the right physical conditions, the contained organic matter will mature, giving rise to further simpler hydrocarbons. Observations based on the examination of the products of these experiments and some British Jurassic oolitic limestones, suggest that once the first phase of cement has been emplaced, the organic materials are isolated and trapped within the individual ooids. It is difficult to see how these substances might escape, unless there is later creation of secondary porosity, which would raise a serious question as to the possibility of oolitic limestones acting as source rocks. Indeed there is an apparent negative correlation, between the number of broken ooids and the amount of contained hydrocarbons, in examples examined from the Hambleton Oolite of North Yorkshire. Unfortunately there are insufficient data available on this matter at present, to be more certain.

A comparison of the soluble and insoluble organic residues from Recent ooids, with those that have been subjected to varying temperature/pressure regimes experimentally and with geological examples, show that a related series of extracts and kerogens exist. In particular it is noted that the organic soluble material originating from ooid sources, is characterized by an 'M' shaped I.R. absorption peak at between 1200 and 1000 cm^{-1}.

Finally it is suggested that studies of carbonate ooids might make a major contribution to the understanding of the potential of carbonates as source rocks. In particular, it may prove possible to study natural situations of differing degrees of maturity and compare these with experimental data such as those discussed earlier.

ACKNOWLEDGEMENTS: This study has come about as the result of team-work and to mention by name, all those who have contributed, would produce a very long list, so to all those who have helped in any way I record my grateful thanks. I also acknowledge that the gas analyses for the North Yorkshire area given in Table 1 are published with permission of the British Gas Corporation. I must however, acknowledge my indebtedness to Professor D. J. Shearman who, as always, has given freely of his time and knowledge during this work and which has allowed refinement and improvement of the study. Finally I am grateful to Miss Gabriele Rothardt, for her patience in typing the various drafts of the manuscript.

References

ALA, M. A. 1982. Chronology of trap formation and migration of hydrocarbons in Zagros Sector of Southwest Iran. *Bull. Am. Assoc. Petrol. Geol.* **66**, 1535–1541.

AYRES, M. G., BILAL, M., JONES, R. W., SLENTZ, L. W., TARTIR, M. & WILSON, A. O. 1982. Hydrocarbon habitat in main producing areas, Saudi Arabia. *Bull. Am. Assoc. Petrol. Geol.* **66**, 1–9.

BATHURST, R. G. C. 1975. Carbonate sediments and their diagenesis. *Developments in Sedimentology*, **12**, Elsevier, Amsterdam. 658 pp.

BOCKMEULEN, H., BARKER, C. & DICKEY, P. A. 1983. Geology and geochemistry of crude oils, Bolivar coastal fields, Venezuela. *Bull. Am. Amer. Petrol. Geol.* **67**, 242–270.

FERGUSON, J. 1983a. The analysis of C-H-O data in kerogen studies using a Coefficient of Elimination. *Journ. Petrol. Geol.* **5**, 401–408.

—— 1983b. Evidence for in-situ generation of methane in carbonate ooids. *Journ. Petrol. Geol.* **6**, 217–220.

——, BUSH, P. R. & CLARKE, B. A. 1981. A note on the simulation of the early diagenesis of Recent carbonate ooids. *Journ. Petrol. Geol.* **4**, 191–193.

——, —— & —— 1984. The role of organic matter in the early diagenesis of carbonate ooids—an experimental study. *Journ. Petrol. Geol.* **7**, 245–266.

—— & IBE, A. C. 1981. Origin of light hydrocarbons in carbonate oolites. *Journ. Petrol. Geol.* **4**, 103–107.

—— & IBE, A. C. 1982. Some aspects of the occurrence of proto-kerogen in Recent ooids. *Journ. Petrol. Geol.* **4**, 267–285.

HEDBERG, H. D. 1964. Geologic aspects of the origin of petroleum. *Bull. Am. Assoc. Petrol. Geol.* **48**, 1755–1803.

HUNT, J. M. 1967. Origin of petroleum in carbonate rocks. *In:* CHILINGAR, G. V., BISSELL, H. J. & FAIRBRIDGE, R. W. (eds) *Carbonate Rocks, Physical and Chemical Aspects.* Elsevier, Amsterdam. 225–251.

IBE, A. C. 1980. *Origin of light hydrocarbons in Recent carbonate oolites in relation to the problem of petroleum genesis in carbonate rocks.* PhD Thesis. University of London. (Unpubl.)

LOREAU, J.-P. 1982. Sédiments aragonitiques et leur genèse. *Mem. Muséum National D'Hist. Nat., Novelle Série, Série C, Géologie*, **97**, Paris. 312 pp.

OWEN, E. W. 1964. Petroleum in carbonate rocks. *Bull. Am. Assoc. Petrol. Geol.* **48**, 1727–1730.

PETERS, K. E., ROHRBACK, B. G. & KAPLAN, I. R. 1981. Geochemistry of artificially heated humic and sapropelic sediments. I: Protokerogen. *Bull. Am. Assoc. Petrol. Geol.* **65**, 688–705.

RICE, P. D. & CLAYPOOL, G. E. 1981. Generation, accumulation, and resource potential of biogenic gas. *Bull. Am. Assoc. Petrol. Geol.* **65**, 5–25.

SHIMOYAMA, A. & JOHNS, W. D. 1972. Formation of alkanes from fatty acids in the presence of CaCO$_3$. *Geochim. et Cosmochim. Acta*, **37**, 87–91.

J. FERGUSON, Department of Geology, Imperial College, Prince Consort Road, London, S.W.7, U.K.

Hydrothermal petroleum from diatomites in the Gulf of California

B. R. T. Simoneit & O. E. Kawka

SUMMARY: The plate boundary zone within Guaymas Basin, Central Gulf of California, is a set of spreading axes offset by a central transform fault and covered by a thick sedimentary sequence. The high heat flow and concurrent hydrothermal circulation cause extensive thermal alteration and leaching of the organic and mineral matter covering the rift graben. The rapid vertical migration of the leach and subsequent quenching by colder sea-water results in the precipitation of hydrothermal deposits rich in sulphides and organic pyrolysates at the sediment surface. Deposits from the northeastern half of the Basin's Southern Trough have been sampled using the D.S.R.V. *Alvin*, to examine the organic condensate character and regional patterns, from which fractionation processes during hydrothermal fluid migration may be inferred.

With the characterization of the bitumen, three major patterns are resolved:
(1) Hydrocarbons with *n*-alkane predominance and no carbon number preference are the most common pattern;
(2) branched and/or unsaturated hydrocarbon predominance relative to *n*-alkanes mainly within the kerosene-diesel range;
(3) biodegraded material, dominated by a naphthenic hump, with a minor contribution of resolved compounds. Samples with predominant *n*-alkanes are further defined by their molecular weight range into distinct subgroups. Waxy condensates versus kerosene-range *n*-alkanes are found at different localities and may reflect regional differences in hydrothermal fluid exit temperatures.

It is postulated that variable pyrolytic temperatures and selective fractionation of pyrolysates during migration, with differential condensation and precipitation under varied thermal regimes, induce the observed general patterns. In addition, post-depositional processes such as biodegradation and removal of low molecular weight components by water solubilization can affect the bitumen character.

Hydrothermal activity is occurring at various spreading ridges where new oceanic crust is being formed (Edmond & Von Damn 1983). Guaymas Basin, in the Gulf of California, is one such area (Fig. 1). It differs from other locations such as the 21°N system of the East Pacific Rise (Spies *et al.* 1980; Ballard *et al.* 1981) and the Galapagos rift area (Corliss *et al.* 1979; Edmond *et al.* 1979; Honnorez *et al.* 1981) in that the rift area has a thick sedimentary cover, due to a high sedimentation rate and its central location within the basin. The accretionary process at the spreading ridge occurs by dyke and sill intrusion into the sediments. The hydrothermal activity associated with such plate growth alters the organic character of the sediments by pyrolysing and leaching the immature material.

Hydrothermal activity in the Gulf of California was first reported during dives of the DSV-4 *Seacliff* in 1977 (Lonsdale 1978). Subsequent reports dealt with the geological structures (Lonsdale & Lawver 1980) and associated mineralogical assemblages (Lonsdale *et al.* 1980) along the Guaymas Basin spreading centre. The effects of the hydrothermal activity on organic matter within the Basin have also been studied. The analysis of a gravity core from northern Guaymas Basin for lipids, humates, kerogens, and gasoline-range hydrocarbons found significant concentrations of petrogenic C_2 to C_8 hydrocarbons at greater depths of the core and thermally unaltered sediments of, primarily, marine origin throughout the bulk of the core (Simoneit *et al.* 1979). Additional evidence for the hydrothermal alteration of organic matter within the Basin was provided by dredge samples (Simoneit & Lonsdale 1982) and coring by the Deep Sea Drilling Project (DSDP) Leg 64 (Galimov & Simoneit 1982; Simoneit 1982a, b; Simoneit & Philp 1982).

Samples of hydrothermally altered material have been collected from the hydrothermal patches in the Southern Trough of Guaymas Basin using a deep submersible and were subsequently analysed for their bitumen (extractable organic matter) content. The characterization of the leach has indicated that some form of selective fractionation of the pyrolysate during hydrothermal removal from the source region is occurring. Correlation of these results with those obtained from previous studies leads us to enumerate various factors which may effect such a process.

Geological setting

The Guaymas Basin is located along the axis of the Gulf of California approximately midway

From: BROOKS, J. & FLEET, A. J. (eds) 1987, *Marine Petroleum Source Rocks*
Geological Society Special Publication No. 26 pp. 217–228.

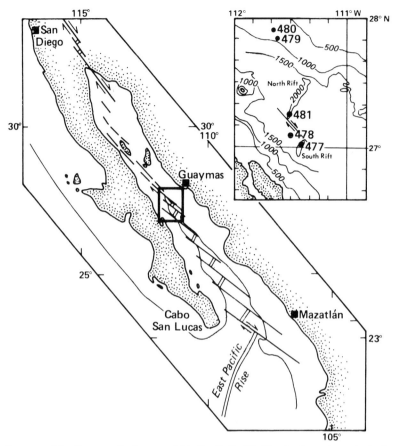

FIG. 1. Location map of the Guaymas Basin area within the Gulf of California. Inset shows the bathymetry (in meters) of the Basin, the location of the Northern and Southern Troughs (North and South Rifts) and the locations of the DSDP Sites 477, 478, 479, 480, and 481. (Adapted from Simoneit 1982c.)

between the southern extent of the San Andreas Fault and the northern section of the East Pacific Rise (Fig. 1). The axis of the Gulf is a series of short spreading ridges offset by a number of longer transform faults and is the boundary between the Pacific and North American Plates. The opening of the Gulf by 300 km of motion along the major fractures is supported by geological correlations across the San Andreas Fault and palaeogeographic reconstruction of the Gulf (Moore & Curray 1982a). Assuming a constant relative motion between the two plates of 5.6 cm/y (Minster & Jordan 1978), Moore and Curray (1982a) developed an hypothesis describing the chronological evolution of the Gulf. They postulated that the formation of the Gulf occurred as the result of a two-phase process (Moore & Curray 1982a, b). The rifting and dilation of continental crust with concomitant variable dike injection, referred to as diffuse extension (Coch-

ran 1981), began about 5.5 Ma and led to the initial opening of the Gulf and transform motion between the two plates along the present-day San Andreas Fault. At approximately 3.5 Ma, the localization of a spreading axis at the mouth of the Gulf began the generation of the linear magnetic anomalies in that area. The concurrent evolution of oceanic crust within the Gulf occurs at both discrete and diffuse spreading centres by basaltic intrusions into soft sediments.

Guaymas Basin, an area of active sea floor spreading, is composed of a set of spreading axes separated by a transform fault approximately 20 km long. The Northern and Southern Troughs so formed are rift valleys approximately 3–4 km wide and 200 m deep at their maximum (Lonsdale & Lawver 1980), (Fig. 1). The postulated tectonic model and rift dimensions require that the sediments in the Troughs be limited in age to approximately 50,000 years (Moore & Curray

1982b). The biostratigraphy at Site 477, DSDP Leg 64 (Fig. 1), within the Southern Trough, supports this (Moore & Curray 1982b). Sediments within the Basin are primarily diatomaceous oozes and mud turbidites (Curray *et al.* 1982). Radio carbon dating to 40,000 years by Spiker and Simoneit (1982) obtained sedimentation rates of 4.8, 0.92, and 1.4 m/10^3y at DSDP Sites 477, Southern Trough; 478, Basin floor; and 481, Northern Trough, respectively (Fig. 1). Biostratigraphy indicates much lower sedimentation rates of 0.18, >1.2, and >0.13 m/10^3yr, respectively (Aubry *et al.* 1982).

Highest heat flow values in Guaymas Basin are associated with the two rift grabens and range from 0.025 to >1.3 W/m^2 (0.6 to >30 HFU) (Williams *et al.* 1979). The highest heat flows in the Southern Trough were measured in the most northeastern portion near DSDP Site 477 (Fig. 2) and tended to decrease with distance from the Trough axis. The southern portion of the Northern Trough displayed highest heat flow near the western boundary and lower values at the rift floor. It has been postulated that either heat advection towards the fault area or hydrothermal recharge is occurring from the rift floor, which further implies close control of the spatial flow pattern by tectonic structures (Curray *et al.* 1982).

The mineralogical and isotope studies of Guaymas Basin have led to the identification of two separate hydrothermal systems within the Basin (Kastner 1982). The major system is similar to that of ridge crests and is maintained by relatively shallow magma chambers and fluid recharge. The secondary system results from sill intrusions into the diatomaceous muds of high porosity (70–90%, Einsele 1982) without the necessity of fluid recharge. Both recharge and discharge of the fluids occur along fault zones with intrusive sills acting to divert the flows (Gieskes *et al.* 1982).

Experimental details

The bulk of the samples described herein were obtained from the Southern Rift of Guaymas Basin with the D.S.R.V. Alvin (Fig. 2). The hand-collected samples were subsampled at the surface and sealed in glass containers with methylene chloride to preserve the volatiles and minimize biodegradation effects. The larger samples were subsequently extracted by sonication with addition of methanol to remove water. The extracts were then washed with commercially available distilled-in-glass pure water to remove the inorganics. Aqueous layers were back-extracted with methylene chloride. Sulphur was

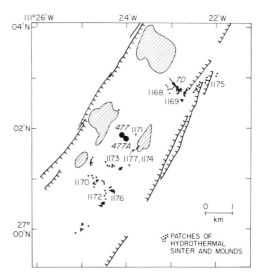

FIG. 2. Map of a portion of the Southern Trough of Guaymas Basin with locations of the *Alvin* dive sites, dredge sample 7D (Simoneit & Lonsdale 1982), and DSDP Sites 477 and 477A. Cross-hatched areas are elevated regions above the rift plain.

removed from a few samples containing large amounts using a silver and mercury amalgam. Total extract weights were obtained by weighing the residues of aliquots removed from known volumes of extracts. Select samples were separated by thin layer chromatography using silica gel coated plates and 9:1 hexane/ethyl ether as a developing solvent. Visualization of bands was obtained by ultraviolet light and iodine vapour.

Analyses were performed on a Varian Vista 44 gas chromatograph equipped with a 30 m × 0.25 mm i.d. fused silica capillary column coated with DB-5 (J & W Scientific Inc.). Helium carrier gas and flame ionization detection were used. Instrument conditions controlled by the Varian Vista 401 data system were as follows: detector 300°C; injection port 300°C; column temperature programmed at a rate of 4°C/min from 38°C to 290°C and held isothermally for 1 hour. Identification was accomplished by retention time comparison with known standards. Additional supportive evidence was obtained by gas chromatography/mass spectrometry using a Finnigan 9610 gas chromatograph interfaced directly with a Finnigan 4000 quadrupole mass spectrometer. Separation was accomplished with column and operating conditions identical to those above except the initial column temperature was set at 50°C. Mass spectra were analysed using the Finnigan Incos Model 2300 data system with compound identification by comparison with known mass spectra and retention times whenever possible. The subsampling and analysis of the Dredge 7D (Fig. 2) is described elsewhere (Simoneit & Lonsdale 1982). Samples 7D–3B and 7D–5A, previously analysed for the gasoline-range hydrocarbons, were subsequently freeze-dried and analysed for total hydrocarbons.

Results and discussion

The total extracts from the samples collected during the *Alvin* dives were analysed by gas chromatography to determine their general bitumen character. Sample and extract descriptions along with total extract yields are listed in Table

1. The concentrations of extractable organic matter obtained range from a high of 350 mg/g sediment for rock fragments of sample 1172–4 to trace amounts of bitumen at Sites 1174–5 and 1174–8 where the major soluble compounds appeared to be various sulphur derivatives of either primary or secondary origin. This group with low organic matter is one extreme of the patterns observed. The large variation in concentrations attests to the spatial inhomogeneity of the hydrothermal pyrolysis discharges. The evidence for a hydrothermal origin of the surface bitumen is multi-faceted and will be compiled later in this report. Within the Southern Trough of the Basin, the organic exudate has been observed as both an oily, diffuse seep at the

TABLE 1. *Summary of total extracts*

Sample		Description	Total yield mg/g-Sediment	Pattern*	Bitumen character dominance	Range	Pristane/ Phytane	C_{17}/ Pristane
1168–1	1	Large rock	—	N	—	—	—	—
	2	Large rock	81	N	—	—	—	—
	3B	Small rock	19	N	—	—	—	—
1170–1		Iridescent rock	—	A	C24	C11–32	1.24	0.89
	1	Inside	—	A	C26	C11–34	1.34	1.40
	1	Outside	—	N	—	—	—	—
	BC6	Box core, crust	—	N	—	—	—	—
	6	Crust fragment	—	A	C27	C15–32	1.06	2.35
	20–1	Ruby wax, crystals	—	A/B	C23	C20–30/< C20	1.11	0
	20–2	Microbes + ruby Wax	—	A/B	C23	C20–30/< C20	0.98	0
	20–3	Surface rock, tar	—	N	—	—	—	—
1172–1		Rock fragment	150	B,O/A	—	C10–18	1.80	0.40
	1A	Crust bulk, oily	—	A/B,O	C18	C12–26	1.29	1.03
	2	Interior pooled fragments	80	A/B,O	C15	C11–31	1.16	1.42
	2A	Red wax	—	A	C24	C10–35	1.11	1.33
	3	Crustal fragments	12	A/B,O	C20	C12–24	0.92	0.71
	4	Fragments	350	A/B,O	C19	C11–30	1.30	1.15
1173–2		Crust, vent spire	—	A/B,O	C12	C10–19	1.44	0.45
	3	Fragments	—	A	C18	C15–24	1.13	1.09
	8	Bottom of spire	97	A/B,O	C17	C10–23	1.33	0.56
	9	Sill, light green oil	—	AR/N	—	—	—	—
1174–5		Weathered barite	Trace	S	—	—	—	—
	8	Tall, inside chimney	Trace	S	—	—	—	—
1175–1		Claystone	—	A	C20	C15–34	0.30	0.93
1177–2C		Oily crust	63	B,O/A	—	C12–21	1.36	—
	2D	Oily crust	71	A/B,O	C16	C10–23	1.46	0.73
	3	Oily crust	—	A/B,O	C13	<C12–19	2.49	0.79
	4B	Oily crust, interior	10	A	C19	C13–31	1.13	0.19
7D–5A		Dredge	90	N	—	—	—	—
	2B†	Dredge	—	A	C22	C13–31	0.73	2.75
	3B	Dredge	32	N	—	—	—	—

* Naphthenes; A—*n*-Alkanes; B—Branched; O—Olefins (alkenes); S—Organo/sulphur compounds; AR—Aromatics
/ indicates order of predominance
† (Simoneit & Lonsdale 1982)

surface crust and as various accumulations on mounds and vent spires. Many of the mineral assemblages are cemented by the oily condensate/precipitate while at depth. These accretions become soft and brittle when brought to the surface, apparently as a result of temperature and pressure changes.

The GC patterns obtained from samples with significant total extracts can be separated into three major categories of approximate equal occurrence (Table 1). There are those samples whose extracts are dominated by the *n*-alkanes with an occasional naphthenic component. In direct contrast, the second group is dominated by a naphthenic hump of unresolved branched and cyclic alkanes with minor resolved components and is indicative of biodegradation effects prevalent in exposed samples (Simoneit, 1985). The third category is exemplified by patterns dominated by both *n*-alkanes and branched or unsaturated hydrocarbons. Examples of these three patterns are presented in Fig. 3. The GC traces of Figures 3a and 3b were obtained from subsamples of the interior and exterior, respectively (about 5 cm apart), of a mound-shaped accretion. The surficial sample is clearly biodegraded while the interior sample shows a broad distribution of *n*-alkanes ranging from C_{11} to C_{34} with a dominance of C_{26}. The apparent rapidity with which the exposed sample is biodegraded may reflect the significance of this hydrothermal organic exudate as a food source for microbes and higher forms of life at the vent areas. The smooth *n*-alkane pattern for the interior sample has no odd-carbon number preference and a minimal naphthenic hump. This relatively smooth distribution is one indication of a hydrothermal pyrolysate origin for the bitumen. Figures 3c and 3d, on the other hand, are examples of extracts containing significant contributions of branched/unsaturated hydrocarbons. The maximum extent of the resolved *n*-alkanes in both samples is C_{18}. The lower range differs between the two samples with the oily crust of 1177-3 (Fig. 3c) exhibiting significant numbers of resolved components below C_{12} and the rock fragment of 1172-1 (Fig. 3d) containing minimal components below C_{12}. Another significant difference between these two is that the *n*-alkanes of the former are dominant over the branched/unsaturated hydrocarbons, while they are in lesser abundance in the latter. Such a contrast may reflect differential thermal regimes and catalytic effects of the mineral matrix.

The presence of alkenes within the oily residue is atypical of mature petroleums (Hoering 1977; Tissot & Welte 1978; Hunt 1979) and is a further indication that the petroliferous effluent is a hydrothermal pyrolysate rather than a seep of mature petroleum. The previous analysis of dredge haul sample 7D-4A, B from the Southern Rift of Guaymas Basin revealed the presence of in-chain and methyl branched mono- and di-alkenes and the absence of terminal alkenes (Simoneit 1982b). Alk-1-enes were reported in thermally altered sediments near sill intrusions at depth in the sediments of Guaymas Basin—DSDP Sites 481A and 477 (Simoneit & Philp 1982). The higher reactivity of terminal alkenes relative to in-chain alkenes (Hoering 1977) apparently removes (reduces) them during their ascent through the sediments. The observed distribution of alkenes at the sediment surface not only depends on the thermal regime at depth during the cracking of saturated hydrocarbons and kerogen, but also on the mutual reactivities of the pyrolysate and transport medium and on the speed of transport away from the source.

The character of the pyrolysates, with *n*-alkanes dominant, can be further subdivided into subgroups depending on their molecular weight range and dominant hydrocarbon (Table 1). A few additional examples are given in Fig. 4. The red wax of sample 1172-2A was observed as a crystalline substance within vugs of spires through which hydrothermal fluids had migrated, and it became liquified when brought to surface pressures and temperatures. The sample has a smooth range of *n*-alkanes from C_{10} to C_{34} with C_{24} dominant (Fig. 4a). The rock fragments of 1172-3 (Fig. 4b), on the other hand, exhibit a narrower range beginning at *n*-C_{12} and ending very abruptly at *n*-C_{24} with *n*-C_{20} dominant. Assuming that the character of the organic matter undergoing hydrothermal pyrolysis at depth is uniform throughout most of the Trough, such an asymmetric and truncated distribution, relative to the red wax, could be the result of selective fractionation during the vertical migration, due to differential condensation/distillation or precipitation, with variable pyrolytic temperatures imparting their own effect. The other GC traces in Fig. 4 further support the likelihood of such a process. The *n*-alkanes of 1172-4 rock fragments (Fig. 4c) are dominated by C_{19} and decrease smoothly in concentration to C_{30}, and homologues less than C_{19} decrease stepwise down to C_{11}. The *n*-alkanes of sample 1173-2 from a crusty vent spire (Fig. 4d) range from C_9 to C_{21} with a maximum at C_{12}. The isoprenoids pristane and phytane are the dominant hydrocarbons in the range C_{15} to C_{21} region.

All of the *n*-alkane patterns in Fig. 4 can be differentiated on the basis of the molecular weight range. Fractionation by carbon chain length or molecular weight can occur by way of differences

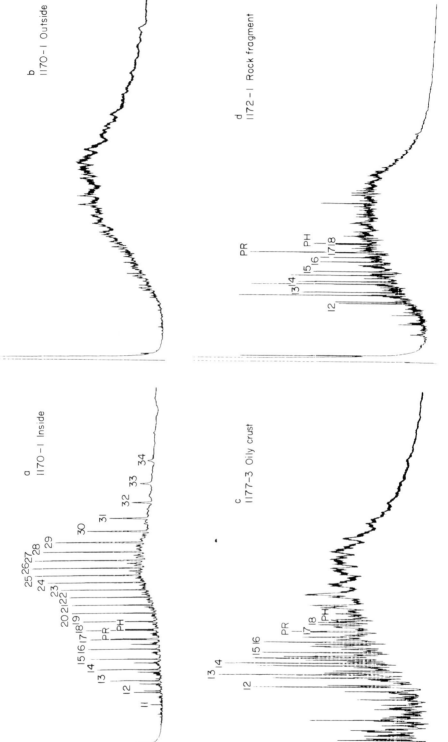

FIG. 3. Capillary gas chromatograms of the total extracts for samples: a) 1170–1 inside; b) 1170–1 outside; c) 1177–3 oily crust; d) 1172–1 rock fragment. (Carbon chain length of the *n*-alkanes identified by the arabic numerals; Pr = Pristane, Ph = Phytane. GC conditions as given in text).

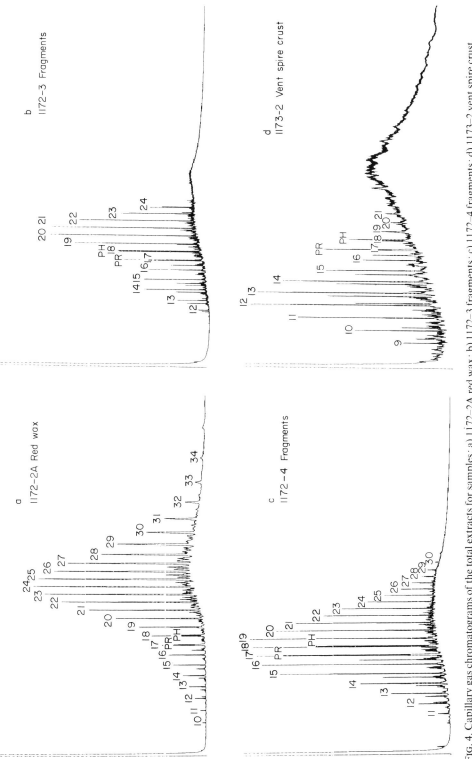

FIG. 4. Capillary gas chromatograms of the total extracts for samples: a) 1172–2A red wax; b) 1172–3 fragments; c) 1172–4 fragments; d) 1173–2 vent spire crust.

in two properties: melting point (viscosity) and solubility in the transport medium. The thermal regime of the transport path and pyrolytic origin can affect both the phase and solubility of a hydrocarbon. Laboratory studies have determined some of the solubility characteristics of hydrocarbons in water at various temperatures at elevated system pressures (Price 1976). The solubilities of hydrocarbons increase gradually with increasing temperature, with the most rapid increase above 100°C. The relative increase in solubility is reported to be greatest for the least soluble (high molecular weight compounds). Salinity of the aqueous phase will also affect hydrocarbon solubility with great decreases in solubility at salinities above 150‰. These reported results support solubility variation as an important factor in the control of fractionation during and/or after transport along vertical thermal gradients. In addition, regional or local lateral gradients resulting from structural deformations of sediments and changes in porosity may, in part, be reflected in the fractionation patterns observed.

Significant amounts of hydrothermally derived hydrocarbon gases have been identified at depth within Guaymas Basin sediments (Galimov & Simoneit 1982; Simoneit & Galimov 1984). Methane with water at elevated temperatures and pressures can act as an excellent solvent of crude oil (Price, L. C., personal communication) and be a significant means by which hydrothermal pyrolysate may be transported to the sediment surface. In addition, the suggested differential solubilities of hydrocarbons in such gaseous mixtures may impart a selective fractionation of their own.

The observed fractionation patterns can also reflect differential condensation and crystallization of the hydrocarbon components during ascent along the thermal gradient and upon mixing with relatively cold seawater.

Selective fractionation of pyrolysates is not limited to inter-sample differentiation by molecular weight ranges of the hydrocarbons. The GC trace for the total extract of 1170–20–1, ruby wax (Fig. 5a) presents a hydrocarbon pattern whose origin is more difficult to conceptualize. For the n-alkane range between C_{20} and C_{30}, the dominant n-alkane is C_{23} with a gradual decrease in relative concentrations for longer chained hydrocarbons. The short-chain limit of the n-alkanes is reached at C_{20} below which only branched alkanes are present. Pristane and phytane are the dominant isoprenoids in this region. A mechanism for the condensation of such a mixture is difficult to envisage. It may reflect a multistep process in which a secondary emplacement or dissolution of a more volatile fraction into a waxy condensate could occur as a result of fluctuations in hydrothermal fluid temperatures. *In situ* biodegradation of the samples may also affect the observed pattern.

The gasoline range (C_5 to C_{10}) hydrocarbons are low in concentration in all of the samples except for the 1177-3 (Fig. 3c) in which a minor amount of the low molecular weight n-alkanes are present. A chromatogram of the Bradford Crude Oil (Fig. 5b) exemplifies the usual presence of gasoline range hydrocarbons in more mature petroleums. The general absence of such light hydrocarbons, even after careful sampling to control loss of volatiles, is indicative of preferential loss due to solubilization and removal by bottom waters and/or leaching (non-condensation) of the volatiles during the expulsion of the relatively hot hydrothermal fluid. The vent water temperatures ranged from 100°C to 315°C (Von Damm, K., personal communication).

Although pristane/phytane (Pr/Ph) ratios may change with the concentration of dissolved oxygen in bottom sediments at the time of deposition (Didyk *et al.* 1978), Simoneit *et al.* (1981) have observed that this value increases as a function of maturity in sediments near sills. This has been rationalized as evidence of preferential production of pristane relative to phytane during the thermal degradation of immature organic matter. Thus, where depositional conditions are similar, Pr/Ph ratios may be used to assess the degree of thermal alteration. Pr/Ph ratio calculations for the samples (Table 1) range from a low of 0.30 for the claystone of sample 1175-1 to a high of 2.49 for the oily crust of 1177-3 (Fig. 4c) which has a definite character attributable to hydrothermal alteration. The hydrocarbon pattern of the claystone appears immature and very unlike the others, which may reflect the least amount of hydrothermal alteration. A preferential removal of the hydrocarbons below C_{18} may be due to solubility differences or biodegradation. Pr/Ph ratios derived from the downcore data at Site 477 within the Southern Trough (Figs. 1 and 2) range from 0.28 to 0.86 with an average of 0.61 (Galimov *et al.* 1982) and represent reducing depositional conditions. Transformation ratios, $S_1/(S_1+S_2)$ (Tissot & Welte 1978) obtained from Rock-Eval pyrolysis of thermally immature sediments from the Guaymas Basin Slope, Sites 479 and 480 (Fig. 1) are approximately zero (Peters & Simoneit 1982). This signifies that the total yield of hydrocarbons, (S_1+S_2), is much higher than the concentration of the free hydrocarbons, S_1, in these sediments containing primarily protokerogen. Therefore, bitumen derived by pyrolytic cracking of the

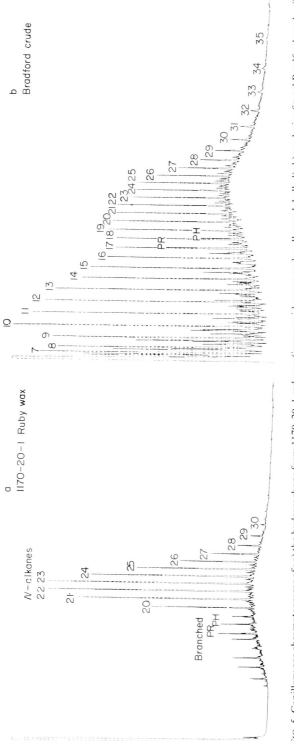

FIG. 5. Capillary gas chromatograms of: a) the hydrocarbons from 1170–20–1 red wax (isoprenoid group and *n*-alkanes labelled); b) analysis of total Bradford crude oil.

proto-kerogen at depth within the Southern Trough (Site 477) would tend to overwhelm the bitumen component from biologic input. The subsequent transport of the pyrolysate to the sediment surface by the hydrothermal flux would result in seabed deposits with a character similar to that derived by thermal cracking. Most of the seabed samples have Pr/Ph ratios greater than one and therefore appear to contain at least some thermally derived isoprenoids. The observed fluctuations in the ratio could arise from variable mixing of diagenetically derived products with hydrothermally altered effluent. The C_{17}/pristane ratios calculated for the samples (Table 1) exhibit a large amount of variation which precludes interpretation. Both C_{17} and the thermally-derived isoprenoids, mainly pristane, would increase during hydrothermal pyrolysis. The observed ratios may then reflect either differential temperature dependence of the rates of formation or post-pyrolysis effects such as fractionation and/or biodegradation.

The major molecular markers of sample 7D-2B have been previously identified and compared with thermally unaltered surface sediments from Guaymas Basin (Simoneit & Lonsdale 1982). The triterpenoids of the hydrothermal exudate are, for the most part, in their thermodynamically more stable form and have apparently undergone thermal isomerization at depth. The steroidal markers indicate a marine autochthonous origin with a large 5α(H)-sterane concentration probably resulting from steroid interconversion also during hydrothermal pyrolysis at depth. Extended tricyclic terpanes ranging from C_{20} to C_{29}, commonly found in mature petroleums (Simoneit & Kaplan 1980), are present in sample 7D-2B but absent in the unaltered sediments.

The aromatic hydrocarbons of dredge samples 7D-2B and 7D-4A, B (Simoneit & Lonsdale 1982) and the biodegraded sample 7D-3B have been characterized. Polynuclear aromatic hydrocarbons (PAH) constitute a significant portion of these fractions. Derived during high temperature pyrolysis, these PAH (Blumer 1975) are not very common in petroleums and are thus indicative of hydrothermal alteration of sediments. The peri-condensed aromatic series (pyrene, benzopyrene, perylene, benzoperylene, and coronene) and the five-membered acyclic rings (acenaphthene, fluorene, and fluoranthene) are found in all three samples. Furthermore, the amount of the highly toxic benzo(a)pyrene is quite significant in the samples. Although perylene is normally found in thermally unaltered sediments (Simoneit & Philp 1982), its high concentration in these samples may have a thermogenic component in addition to the normal diagenetic input.

The significant accumulations of petroliferous exudate at the Guaymas Basin rift area are apparently derived from the high-temperature alteration of immature organic matter at depth within the sediments. The hydrothermal discharge of fluids, which aids in the transport of the pyrolysate to the surface, is a manifestation of this high heat flow at depth resulting from the formation of new oceanic crust at the spreading ridge. The magnitude of the accumulations suggest that high-temperature alteration or hydrothermal pyrolysis may be a viable mechanism for petroleum formation. Provided a structural cap is present, a thick sedimentary sequence undergoing thermal alteration at depth by high-temperature intrusive events or high heat flow, from a magmatic source, could become a significant petroleum source. The presence of water, as in hydrothermal systems, would aid in the transport of the pyrolysate and the advection of the thermal energy. The actual effect of water on the pyrolysis products still needs to be resolved, and future research should provide insights into such processes.

Conclusions

The petroliferous material at the sediment surface of Guaymas Basin has many characteristics common to petroleums:
(1) presence of gasoline range hydrocarbons,
(2) broad distribution of *n*-alkanes with no carbon number preference,
(3) presence of the naphthenic hump,
(4) thermodynamically isomerized and thus stabilized molecular markers (e.g., 17α(H)-hopanes),
(5) pristane and phytane at significant concentrations.

Unlike normal petroleums, though, these samples also contain significant concentrations of alkenes and PAH. This fact along with the unusual structure of the Basin, which precludes petroleum formation by conventional theory, leads us to conclude that the exudate is of a hydrothermal pyrolytic origin rather than a natural seepage of mature petroleum.

Various controls on the observed bitumen patterns are suggested. Different temperatures of pyrolysis and water content at the various locations within the Southern Trough may affect the character of the organic exudate. In addition, selective fractionation of the hydrothermal pyrolysate during the rapid transport to the sediment surface is indicated. Variable lateral thermal regimes and vertical gradients result in differential condensation and precipitation/crystallization of the generated hydrocarbons. Enhanced solubilization of the pyrolysate in a water/methane solution by high temperatures and pressures may impart its own fractionation effect due to differing solubilities. Post-depositional effects such as biodegradation and removal by water solubilization of the low molecular weight hydrocarbons (gasoline range) are also indicated.

ACKNOWLEDGEMENTS: We thank the National Science Foundation for access to the various samples and for financial support (Division of Ocean Sciences, Grant OCE81-18897). We thank A. S. Mackenzie and J. Gray for the review of this manuscript and acknowledge their useful suggestions for improvement.

References

AUBRY, M. P., MATOBA, Y., MOLINA-CRUZ, A. & SCHRADER, H. 1982. Synthesis of Leg 64 biostratigraphy. *In*: CURRAY, J. R., MOORE, D. G., *et al., Initial Rep. Deep Sea drill. Proj.,* **64**, Part II. U.S. Government Printing Office, Washington, DC. 1057–1064.

BALLARD, R. D., FRANCHETEAU, J., JUTEAU, T., RANGAN, C. & NORMARK, N. 1981. East Pacific Rise at 21°N: The volcanic, tectonic and hydrothermal processes of the central axis. *Earth planet. Sci. Lett.* **55**, 1–10.

BLUMER, M. 1975. Curtisite, idrialite and pendletonite, polycyclic aromatic hydrocarbon minerals: their composition and origin. *Chem. Geology,* **16**, 245–256.

COCHRAN, J. R. 1981. The Gulf of Aden: Structure and evolution of a young ocean basin and continental margin. *J. geophys. Res.,* **86**, 263–287.

CORLISS, J. B., DYMOND, J. *et al.* 1979. Submarine thermal springs on the Galapagos Rift. *Science,* **203**, 1073–1083.

CURRAY, J. R. *et al.* 1982. Guaymas Basin: Sites 477, 478 and 481. *In*: CURRAY, J. R., MOORE, D. G., *et al., Initial Rep. Deep Sea drill. Proj.,* **64**, Part I. U.S. Government Printing Office, Washington, D.C. 211–415.

DIDYK, B. M., SIMONEIT, B. R. T., BRASSELL, S. C. & EGLINTON, G. 1978. Organic geochemical indicators of paleoenvironmental conditions of sedimentation. *Nature,* **272**, 216–222.

EDMOND, J. M., MEASURES, C. *et al.* 1979. Ridge crest hydrothermal activity and the balances of the major and minor elements in the ocean: the Galapagos data. *Earth planet. Sci. Lett.,* **46**, 1–18.

EDMOND, J. M. & VON DAMM, K. 1983. Hot springs on the ocean floor. *Scientific American,* **248**, 78–93.

EINSELE, G. 1982. Mass physical properties of Pliocene to Quaternary sediments in the Gulf of California: DSDP Leg 64. *In*: CURRAY, J. R., MOORE, D. G., *et al., Initial Rep. Deep Sea drill. Proj.,* **64**, Part II. U.S. Government Printing Office, Washington, DC. 529–542.

GALIMOV, E. M., KODINA, L. A., BOGACHEVA, M. P. & SHIRINSKY, V. G. 1982. Organic geochemical studies of samples from Deep Sea Drilling Project Leg 64, Gulf of California. Sites 474, 477, 478, 479, and 481. *In*: CURRAY, J. R., MOORE, D. G., *et al., Initial Rep. Deep Sea drill. Proj.,* **64**, Part II. U.S. Government Printing Office, Washington, D.C. 819–836.

—— & SIMONEIT, B. R. T. 1982. Geochemistry of interstitial gases in sedimentary deposits of the Gulf of California, DSDP leg 64. *In*: CURRAY, J. R., MOORE, D. G., *et al., Initial Rep. Deep Sea drill. Proj. 64 Part II.* U.S. Govt. Print. Off., Washington, D.C. 781–787.

GIESKES, J. M., KASTNER, M., EINSELE, G., KELTS, K. & NIEMITZ, J. 1982. Hydrothermal activity in the Guaymas Basin, Gulf of California: a synthesis. *In*: CURRAY, J. R., MOORE, D. G. *et al., Initial Rep. Deep Sea drill. Proj. 64 Part II.* U.S. Govt. Print. Off. Washington, D.C. 1159–1167.

HOERING, T.C. 1977. Olefinic hydrocarbons from Bradford, Pennsylvania crude oil. *Chem. Geology* **20**, 1–8.

HONNOREZ, J., VON HERZEN, R. P. *et al.* 1981 Hydrothermal mounds and young ocean crust of the Galapagos: Preliminary Deep Sea Drilling Results, Leg 70. *Bull. geol. Soc. Am.* **92**, 457–472.

HUNT, J. M. 1979. *Petroleum Geochemistry and Geology*. W. H. Freeman, San Francisco. 617 pp.

KASTNER, M. 1982. Evidence for two distinct hydrothermal systems in the Guaymas Basin. *In*: CURRAY, J. R., MOORE, D. G. *et al. Initial Rep. Deep Sea drill. Proj. 64 Part II.* U.S. Govt. Print. Off. Washington, D.C. 1143–1157.

LONSDALE, P. 1978. Submersible exploration of Guaymas Basin: a preliminary report of the Gulf of California 1977 operations of DSV-4 'Seacliff'. *Scripps Institute of Oceanography Ref.* 78-1.

—— & LAWVER, L. A. 1980. Immature plate boundary zones studies with a submersible in the Gulf of California. *Bull. geol. Soc. Am.* **91**, 555–569.

——, BISCHOFF, J. L., BURNS, V. M., KASTNER, M. & SWEENEY, R. E. 1980. A high-temperature hydrothermal deposit on the seabed at a Gulf of California spreading center. *Earth planet. Sci. Lett.* **49**, 8–20.

MINSTER, J. B. & JORDAN, T. H. 1978. Present-day plate motions. *J. geophys. Res.* **83**, 5331–5354.

MOORE, D. G. & CURRAY, J. R. 1982a. Geologic and tectonic history of the Gulf of California. *In*: CURRAY, J. R., MOORE, D. G. *et al. Initial Rep. Deep Sea drill. Proj. 64 Part II.* U.S. Govt. Print. Off. Washington, D.C. 1279–1294.

—— & CURRAY, J. R. 1982b. Objectives of drilling on young passive margins: applications to the Gulf of California. *In*: CURRAY, J. R., MOORE, D. G. *et al., Initial Rep. Deep Sea drill. Proj. 64, Part I.* U.S. Govt. Print. Off. Washington, D.C. 27–33.

PETERS, K. E. & SIMONEIT, B. R. T. 1982. Rock-Eval pyrolysis of Quaternary sediments from Leg 64,

Sites 479 and 480, Gulf of California. *In*: CURRAY,
J. R., MOORE, D. G. *et al. Initial Rep. Deep Sea drill.
proj. 64, Part II.* U.S. Govt. Print. Off. Washington,
D.C. 925–931.

PRICE, L. C. 1976. Aqueous solubility of petroleum
applied to its origin and primary migration. *Bull.
Am. Assoc. Petrol. Geol.* **60**, 213–244.

SIMONEIT, B. R. T. 1982a. Shipboard organic geochem-
istry and safety monitoring Leg 64, Gulf of
California. *In*: CURRAY, J. R., MOORE, D. G. *et al.
Initial Rep. Deep Sea drill. Proj. 64, Part II.* U.S.
Govt. Print. Off. Washington, D.C. 723–727.

——— 1982b. Hydrothermal effects on Recent diatomaceous sediments in Guaymas Basin, Gulf of California: a genesis of petroleum and degradation of
protokerogen. *Spectra,* **8**, 52–57.

——— 1982c. Organic Geochemistry, Leg 64: Introduc-
tion and summary. *In*: CURRAY, J. R., MOORE, D.
G. *et al. Initial Rep. Deep Sea drill. Proj. 64, Part II.*
U.S. Govt. Print. Off. Washington, D.C. 717–721.

——— 1985. Hydrothermal petroleum: composition and
utility as a biogenic carbon source. *In*: Symp.
Hydrothermal Vents of the Eastern Pacific, *Biol.
Soc. Wash. Bull.,* **6**, 49–56.

——— & GALIMOV, E. M. 1984. Geochemistry of
interstitial gases in Quaternary sediments of the
Gulf of California. *Chem. Geol.* **43**, 151–166.

——— & KAPLAN, I. R. 1980. Triterpenoids as molecular
indicators of paleoseepage in recent sediments of
the Southern California Bight. *Marine Environmental Research,* **3**, 113–128.

——— & LONSDALE, P. F. 1982. Hydrothermal petroleum
in mineralized mounds at the seabed of Guaymas
Basin. *Nature,* **295**, 198–202.

——— & PHILP, R. P. 1982. Organic geochemistry of
lipids and kerogen and the effects of basalt intrusions
on unconsolidated oceanic sediments: Sites 477, 478
and 481, Guaymas Basin, Gulf of California. *In*:
CURRAY, J. R., MOORE, D. G. *et al. Initial Rep. Deep
Sea drill. Proj. 64, Part II.* U.S. Govt. Print. Off.
Washington, D.C. 883–904.

———, MAZUREK, M. A., BRENNER, S., CRISP, P. T. &
KAPLAN, I. R. 1979. Organic geochemistry of Recent
sediments from Guaymas Basin, Gulf of California.
Deep-Sea Research, **26A**, 879–891.

———, BRENNER, S., PETERS, K. E. & KAPLAN, I. R.
1981. Thermal alteration of Cretaceous black shale
by diabase intrusions in the Eastern Atlantic—II.
Effects of bitumen and kerogen. *Geochim. Cosmochim. Acta,* **45**, 1581–1602.

SPIES, F. N., MACDONALD, K. C., ATWATER, T. *et al.*
1980. East Pacific Rise: hot springs and geophysical
experiments. *Science,* **207**, 1421–1433.

SPIKER, E. C. & SIMONEIT, B. R. T. 1982. Radiocarbon
dating of Recent sediments from Leg 64, Gulf of
California. *In*: CURRAY, J. R., MOORE, D. G. *et al.
Initial Rep. Deep Sea drill. Proj. 64, Part II.* U.S.
Govt. Print. Off. Washington, D.C. 757–758.

TISSOT, B. P. & WELTE, D. H. 1978. *Petroleum Formation
and Occurrence, a New Approach to Oil and Gas
Exploration.* Springer-Verlag, Berlin. 538 pp.

WILLIAMS, D. L., BECKER, K., LAWVER, L. A. & VON
HERZEN, R. P. 1979. Heat flow at the spreading
centers of the Guaymas Basin, Gulf of California.
J. geophys. Res. **84**, 6757–6796.

B. R. T. SIMONEIT and O. E. KAWKA, School of Oceanography, Oregon State University,
Corvallis, Oregon 97331 U.S.A.

Part III
The Stratigraphic Record

Stratigraphic distribution and palaeo-oceanographic significance of European early Palaeozoic organic-rich sediments

A. Thickpenny & J. K. Leggett

SUMMARY: Marine, organic-rich sediments of early Palaeozoic age are thicker, and were deposited over longer time-periods, than those of other Phanerozoic intervals. They occur widely throughout North and West Europe. Their palaeogeographic setting is less certain than those of their Mesozoic and Caenozoic counterparts, making genetic models difficult to construct. The stratigraphic distribution of organic-rich sediments in the area from the Ural Mountains to Portugal is briefly reviewed for the Cambrian, Ordovician and Silurian Systems. The occurrence of organic-rich sediments in different palaeoenvironments (shelf, slope, basin) is compared for the three palaeocontinents Gondwanaland, Baltica and Laurentia, using the reconstructions of Cocks and Fortey (1982). Organic-rich sediments are shown to be more widely distributed at certain times: the middle and late Cambrian, the Caradoc and the Llandovery–Wenlock intervals. Two areas are selected for more detailed discussion: the Middle and Upper Cambrian Alum Shales of Scandinavia, illustrative of shelf organic-rich sedimentation and Caradoc–Llandovery sediments of the British Isles, which include common black shales deposited in varying abyssal to shelf environments. Possible controls on black shale deposition include variations in sea level stand, degree of geographical restriction, climatic variation, oxygen levels in the atmosphere and hydrosphere, variations in organic productivity and sedimentation rates. Our ability to recognize the relative effects of these controls in the past is variable. Where information is sufficient, it suggests that high sea-level stands associated with warm climatic conditions, and low hydrospheric oxygen contents are important in the development of early Palaeozoic organic-rich sediments.

The widespread development of organic-rich sediments during the early Palaeozoic has been documented by several authors (e.g. Berry & Wilde 1978; Leggett 1980). Leggett (1980), in a review of the stratigraphic and palaeoenvironmental distribution of black shales in the British Isles, emphasized that most examples fall in three time bands: late Cambrian (Merioneth Epoch), mid-late Ordovician (Caradoc Epoch) and earliest Silurian (early Llandovery times). In this paper we extend that review to include organic-rich deposits in north and west Europe.

Figure 1 shows the occurrence of Lower Palaeozoic rocks in north and west Europe and includes place names referred to in the text. It also shows probable ancient plate boundaries relevant to our subsequent discussion of early Palaeozoic palaeogeography and the relative importance of the likely controls on widespread black shale accumulation in early Palaeozoic seas.

latitude continent (Gondwanaland), a mid-latitude continent (Baltica) and an equatorial continent (Laurentia), separated by several palaeo-oceans. From the point of view of NW Europe the reconstructions of Cocks and Fortey (1982) seem to us the most plausible because they are based on detailed biogeographic data. We use their maps as a basis for viewing European stratigraphic successions in their 'global' palaeogeographic context. Perhaps the most contentious aspect of the reconstructions is the presence of Törnquist's sea (Fig. 2) separating Baltica from Gondwanaland until the late Caradoc. Palaeontological evidence for this ocean is cited in Cocks and Fortey (1982) and support for its presence comes from Polish workers (e.g. Tomczykowa & Tomczyk 1979). Bearing in mind the uncertainties in early Palaeozoic palaeogeography we present possible distributions of organic-rich sediments for each palaeocontinental block for the Cambrian, Ordovician and Silurian systems.

Early Palaeozoic palaeogeography

Recent global reconstructions of the early Palaeozoic (e.g. Smith *et al.* 1981; Cocks & Fortey 1982; Scotese *et al.* 1979) differ in detail. However, all authors recognize three palaeocontinental blocks in the area of NW Europe (e.g. Fig. 2): a high

Stratigraphic summary

The stratigraphic compilations presented in the following figures are, for the most part, a result of literature surveys and thus subject to uncertainties in the terminology of various authors. 'Organic-rich deposits' in the diagrams include lithotypes

From: BROOKS, J. & FLEET, A. J. (eds) 1987, *Marine Petroleum Source Rocks* Geological Society Special Publication No. 26 pp. 231–247.

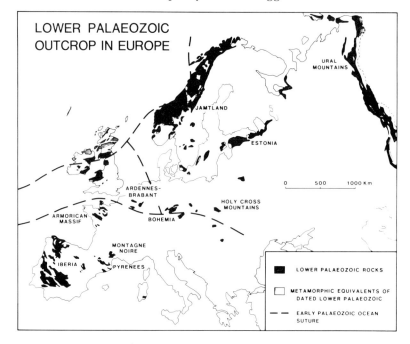

FIG. 1. Outcrop of Lower Palaeozoic rocks in Europe.

referred to as black, dark, dark grey, Alum, or, in some cases, merely graptolitic where other descriptive terms are lacking. They essentially fall into the umbrella term 'black shale', including not only sapropels but also organic-rich marine mudstones not necessarily deposited under totally anoxic conditions. However, all the lithotypes preserve significant amounts of organic carbon (in our experience of analysing described lithologies c. $> 1\%$).

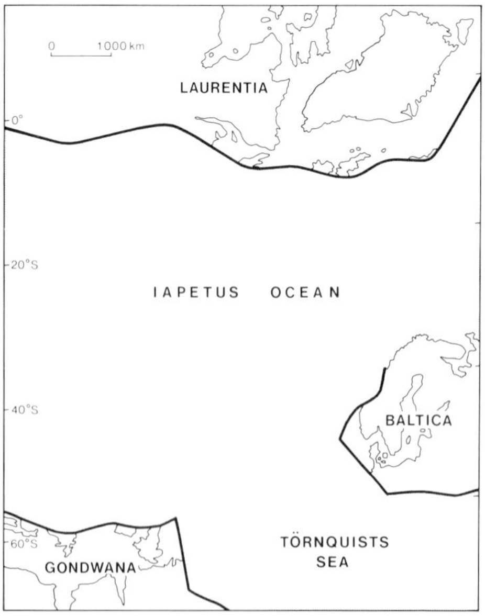

Cambrian

A palaeogeographic reconstruction for late Cambrian–early Ordovician times is shown in Fig. 2, indicating three palaeocontinents: Laurentia,

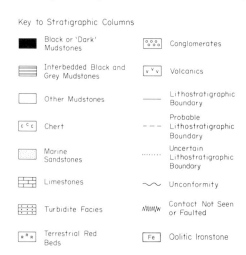

FIG. 2. Arenig Palaeogeographic reconstruction (after Cocks & Fortey 1982).

FIG. 3. Key to stratigraphic columns.

Baltica and Gondwanaland, with southern Britain and southern Ireland part of Gondwanaland and the Iberian peninsula attached to Africa. In the following account the stratigraphic distribution of organic-rich deposits is discussed for each palaeocontinent in turn.

Laurentia

The southern margin of Laurentia was subequatorial during the Cambrian period and no organic-rich deposits were formed in the European segment.

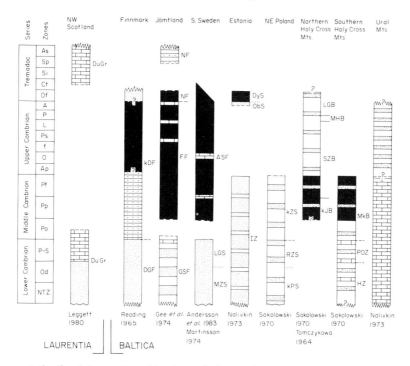

FIG. 4. Representative Cambrian stratigraphic columns for Laurentia and Baltica.

Cambrian Baltica/Laurentia

Stratigraphic units:

ASF	Alum Shale Formation	kZS	Kostrzyn Beds
DGF	Duolbasgaissa Formation	LGB	Lysogory Beds
DuGr	Durness Group	LGS	Lingulid Sandstone
DyS	Dictyonema Shales	MHB	Machocice Beds
FF	Fjällbränna Formation	MkB	Marinkowice Beds
GSF	Gårdsjon Formation	MZS	Mickwitzia Sandstone
HZ	'Holmia Zone'	NF	Norråker Formation
IZ	Izhorian Beds	ObS	Obolus Sandstone
kDF	Kistedal Formation	POZ	'Protolenus Zone'
kJB	Krajno Beds	RZS	Radzyn Series
kPS	Kaplonosy Series	SZB	Swietokrzyskie Beds

Zones:

A	Acerocare	Od	Olenellid
Ap	Agnostus pisiformis	P	Peltura
As	Angelina sedgwickii	Pf	Paradoxides forchhammeri
Ct	Clonograptus tenellus	Po	Paradoxides oelandicus
Df	Dictyonema flabelliforme	Pp	Paradoxides paradoxissimus
f	'fossilfrit' interzone	Ps	Parabolina spinulosa
L	Leptoplastus	P-S	Protolenid-Strenuellid
NTZ	Non-trilobite zone	Si	Symphysurus incipiens
O	Olenus	Sp	Shumardia pusilla

Baltica

Middle and Upper Cambrian organic-rich mud-stones occur mainly in shelf environments over large areas of the Scandinavian shield, (Reading 1965; Thorslund 1960; Gee *et al.* 1974; Martinsson 1974; Andersson *et al.* 1983; Nalivkin 1973, Fig. 4) and adjacent areas in Poland (Sokolowski 1970 and references therein). They comprise condensed shallow marine deposits which accumulated over long periods of time in stable conditions. In shallowest water environments, coarser clastic sedimentation occurred (e.g. The Holy Cross Mountains).

Gondwanaland

The Gondwanan palaeo-continent was situated at medial-to high latitudes (Fig. 2) during the Cambrian period and supported a distinctive fauna (Cocks & Fortey 1982). Leggett (1980) has documented the abundance of black shales in the early late Cambrian of southern Ireland, Wales and the shelf areas of England and the Welsh borders (Fig. 5). Similar organic-rich sediments occur throughout the Middle and Upper Cambrian of the Brabant and Ardennes massifs (Walter 1980) testifying to a continuation of shallow waters prone to oxygen depletion south-

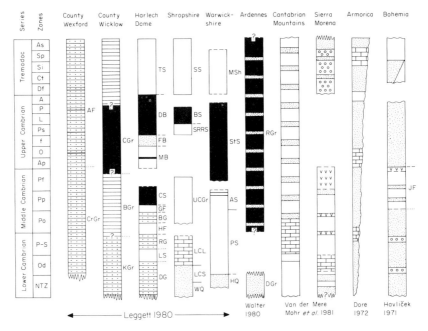

FIG. 5. Representative Cambrian stratigraphic columns for Gondwanaland

Cambrian Gondwanaland

Stratigraphic units:

AF	Askingarran Formation	JF	Jnice Formation
AS	Abbey Shales	KGr	Knockrath Group
BG	Barmouth Grits	LCL	Lower Comley Limestone
BGr	Bray Group	LCS	Lower Comley Sandstone
BS	Bentleyford Shales	LS	Llanbedr Shales
CGr	Clara Group	MB	Maentwrog Beds
CrGr	Cahore Group	MSh	Merevale Shales
CS	Clogau Shale	PS	Purley Shales
DB	Dolgelly Beds	RG	Rhinog Grits
DG	Dolwen Grits	RGr	Revin Group
DGr	Deville Group	SRRS	Shoot Rough Road Shales
DuGr	Durness Group	SS	Shineton Shales
FB	Festiniog Beds	StS	Stockingford Shales
GF	Gamlan Formation	TS	Tremadoc Shales
HF	Hafotty Formation	UCGr	Upper Comley Group
HQ	Hartshill Quartzite	WQ	Wrekin Quartzite

eastwards. Deeper water sediments are turbiditic (e.g. County Wexford), while on the shallow inner shelf coarse clastics and limestones were deposited in Spain (Van der Meer Mohr *et al.* 1981 and references therein) and Armorica (Doré 1972).

Ordovician

Figure 6 shows the early Silurian palaeogeographic reconstruction of Cocks and Fortey (1982). Three important events pertinent to black shale formation occurred during the Ordovician: the Iapetus Ocean narrowed considerably, Törnquist's Sea closed (probably in the Caradoc) and the Rheic Ocean began to open (again, probably in the Caradoc). A by-product of these relatively

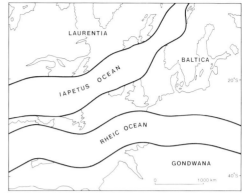

FIG. 6. Llandovery Palaeogeographic reconstruction (after Cocks & Fortey 1982)

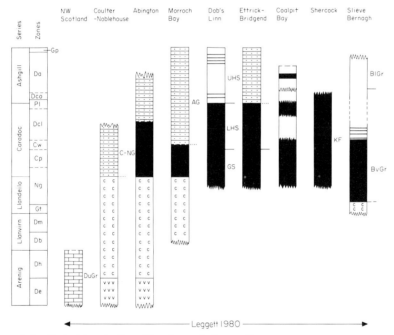

FIG. 7. Representative Ordovician stratigraphic columns for Laurentia

Ordovician Laurentia

Stratigraphic units

AG	Afton Greywackes	GS	Glenkiln Shales
BlGr	Ballyvorgal Group	KF	Keghernaghkilly Formation
BvGr	Belvoir Group	LHS	Lower Hartfell Shales
C-NG	Coulter-Noblehouse Greywackes	UHS	Upper Hartfell Shales
DuGr	Durness Group		

Zones:

Cp	C. peltifer	Dh	D. hirundo
Cw	C. wilsoni	Dm	D. murchisoni
Da	D. anceps	Gt	G. teretiusculus
Db	D. bifidus	Gp	G. persculptus
Dcl	D. clingani	Ng	N. gracilis
Dco	D. complanatus	Pl	P. linearis
De	D. extensus		

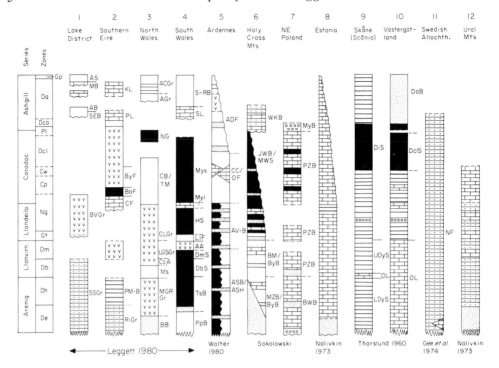

FIG. 8. Representative Ordovician stratigraphic columns for Baltica. N.B. The assignment of columns 1–5 to either Baltica or Gondwanaland is problematical since the timing of closure of Törnquist's Sea and the opening of the Rheic Ocean is uncertain.

Ordovician Baltica

Stratigraphic units:

AA	Asaphus Ash
AB	Applethwaite Beds
ACGr	Aber-Corris Group
ADF	Assise de Fosse
AGr	Abercwmeiddaw Group
AS	Ashgill Shales
ASB/ASH	Assise de Sart-Berbard/Assise de Huy
AV-B	Assise de Vitrival-Bruyère
BaF	Ballinatray Formation
BB	Basement Beds
BM/ByB	Bukowka Mojcza ssts & Lsts/Upper part of Brzeziny Beds
BVGr	Borrowdale Volcanic Group
BWB	Bialowieza Beds
ByF	Ballymoney Formation
CB/TM	Ceiswyn Beds/Tallyllyn Mudstones
Cca	Cwm-Clwyd Ash
CC/OF	Concriamont conglomerate/Ombrette Flysch
CF	Courtown Formation
CLGr	Craig-y-Llam Group
DaB	Dalmanitina Beds
DbS	D. bifidus Shales
DclS	Dicranograptus clingani Shales
DiS	Dicellograptus Shales
DmS	D. murchisoni Shales
HS	Hendre Shales

JWB/ MWS	Jeleniow Beds/Morawica Shales
KL	Kildare Limestone
LDyS	Lower Didymograptus Shales
LGSGr	Llyn-y-Gafr spilitic Group
LlF	Llandeilo Flags
MB	'Mucronatus Beds'
MGRGr	Mynydd-y-Gdder Rhyolitic Group
Ms	Maesgwm Shales
MyB	Mazury Beds
Myl	Mydrim Limestone
Mys	Mydrim Shale
MZB/ByB	Miedzygotz Beds/Lower part of Brzeziny Beds
NF	Norråker Formation
NG	Nod Glas
OL	Orthoceratite Limestone
PL	Portrane Limestone
PM-B	Prioryland Mudstone and Breccia
PpB	Peltura punctata Beds
PZB	Pomorze Beds
RiGr	Ribband Group
SEB	Stile End Beds
SL	Sholeshook Limestone
S-RB	Slade and Redhill Beds
SSGr	Skiddaw Slate Group
TsB	Tetragraptus Beds
UDyS	Upper Didymograptus Beds
WKB	Wolka Beds

narrow seaways may have been reduced oceanic circulation and a concomitant increase in stratification within the water column.

Laurentia

Stratigraphic compilations for Laurentia are presented in Fig. 7, based on Leggett (1980) and references therein. Widespread development of a highly condensed, deep-water Caradocian black shale facies is recorded in sections of 'eugeosynclinal' character in southern Scotland and Northern Ireland (the lower part of the Moffat shales). These deposits are discussed in more detail in a later section.

Baltica

Several palaeoenvironments can be recognized within the Ordovician of Baltica. Early Ordovician black shales were developed locally in south Wales (Fig. 8) and in the Ardennes and Brabant massifs (Walter 1980) in possible restricted basinal environments. From Llanvirn to Caradoc times, black shales accumulated locally in island arc environments of SE Ireland and the Lake District in times of volcanic quiescence (e.g. the Ballinatray Formation). Black shales are more common in the Llandeilo and Caradoc deposits of Poland and the Baltic area (Thorslund 1960; Nalivkin 1973; Tomczyk 1964a, b, 1963; Tomczyk & Tomczykowa 1976, Tomczykowa 1964;

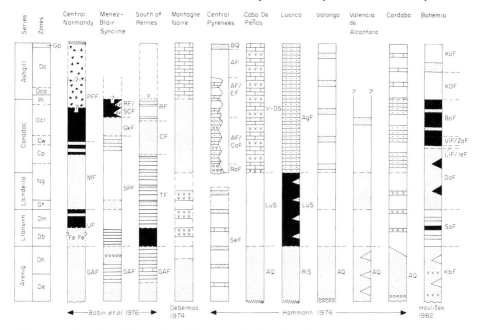

FIG. 9. Representative Ordovician stratigraphic columns for Gondwanaland

Ordovician Gondwanaland

Stratigraphic units:

AF	Ansobell Formation	LuS	Luarca Shales
AF/CaF	Ansobell Formation/Cava Formation	MF	May Formation
AF/EF	Ansobell Formation/Estana Formation	PFF	Pélites a Fragments Formation
AgF	Agueira Formation	RaF	Rabassa Formation
AQ	Armorican Quartzite	RF	Riadan Formation
BoF	Bohdalec Formation	RF/SCF	Rosan Formation/Schistes de Cosquer Formation
BQ	Bar Quartzite		
CF	Chatellier Formation	RiS	Ria Series (Quartzite member)
DoF	Dobrotiva Formation	SaF	Sarka Formation
GAF	Grès Armoricain Formation	SeF	Seo Formation
GkF	Grès de kermeur Formation	SPF	Schistes de Postolonnec Formation
KbF	Klabava Formation	TF	Traveusot Formation
KDF	Kraluv Dvur Formation	UF	Urville Formation
KoF	Kosov Formation	V-Ds	'Volcano-detritic' Series
LiF/leF	Liben Formation/Letna Formation	ViF/ZaF	Vinice Formation/Zahorany Formation

238   *A. Thickpenny & J. K. Leggett*

Sokolowski 1970; Bednarczyk 1971; Modlinski 1973; Modlinski & Szymanski 1980) and may be the result of restriction arising from the closing phases of Törnquist's Sea. Nappes within the Swedish Caledonides preserve essentially turbiditic successions (Gee *et al.* 1974), likely to have been associated with trench sedimentation. Deformed sequences in the Urals, marking the eastern margin of Baltica, suggest varied turbiditic-limestone sedimentation and lack organic-rich sediments (Nalivkin 1973).

Gondwanaland

Simplified stratigraphic columns for Gondwanaland are shown in Fig. 9. Black shales are limited to the Llanvirn–Caradoc interval. Local developments occur in the Armorican Massif (Babin *et al.* 1976 and references therein), in central Spain (Hammann 1976 and references therein) and in Bohemia (Havlíček 1982) during the Llanvirn and Llandeilo, while Caradocian black shales are present in Normandy (Babin *et al.* 1976) and Bohemia (Havlíček 1982). The dominant sediments, however, are shallow marine arenacous deposits (Normandy) and turbidites and volcano-detrital successions (Spain), indicating environments generally unsuited to black shale deposition. Basinal and abyssal deposits are rare, most sediments having been deposited on shelves.

Silurian

Fig. 10 shows a late Silurian palaeogeographic reconstruction of north and west Europe, with a widening Rheic Ocean and only remnants of the closing Iapetus Ocean.

Laurentia

In the European portion of the Laurentian plate, black shales are again widespread during early to

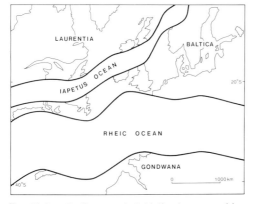

Fig. 10. Late Ludlow—early Pridoli palaegeographic reconstruction (after Cocks & Fortey 1982)

mid-Llandovery times in the accretionary fore-arc zone of southern Scotland–Northern Ireland (e.g. South Ards to Talla–Tweedsmuir, Fig. 11). In many places in this belt they are in abrupt contact with the grey mudstones of the Ashgill. They were deposited in abyssal depths, ocean-ward of the palaeotrench, where turbiditic sedimentation could not dilute the highly condensed succession. Shelf sequences are not preserved in the European part of Laurentia. Fore-arc basin successions contain Llandovery organic-rich mudstones, deposited in variable but much shallower environments than those to the south (e.g. Midland Valley inliers, Pomeroy, Fig. 11).

Baltica

Organic-rich deposits were also developed on the SE margin of Iapetus during the Llandovery (Fig. 12), in the Lake District, North Wales and SE Ireland (Leggett 1980). They are mostly of early Llandovery age, becoming less common upwards. Similar intermittent occurrences are found in the Ardennes (Walter 1980), Poland (Sokolowski 1970, and references therein; Tomczyk 1963, 1964a, b, 1968; Tomczyk & Tomczykowa 1976; Tomczykowa & Tomczyk 1979) and in southern Sweden and Estonia (Thorslund 1960; Nalivkin 1973). Black shales are rarer in the Wenlock, occurring in the Lake District and the Ardennes and occur only in NE Poland during the Přidoli. On the eastern side of Baltica, black shales are found as one lateral facies change in the Ural Mountains during the Llandovery (Nalivkin 1973).

Gondwanaland

A less systematic concentration of organic-rich sediments occurs in Gondwana (Fig. 13), the greatest occurrence being in northern Spain (Julivert *et al.* 1971) where a fairly uniform development occurs from Early Llandovery to Přidoli times. Llandovery and lower Wenlock black shales also occur in southern Spain (Saupé 1971) as lateral equivalents of a volcanic formation. In Armorica sapropels are confined to the Ludlovian part of the Formation de la Lande-Murée (Paris 1977), while in Bohemia, black shale intercalations are concentrated in the lower Llandovery (Horný 1962).

Summary

It is evident from the brief account given that organic-rich sediments were deposited over broad geographical areas on all early Palaeozoic continental blocks in Europe over long periods of time, and at various palaeo-depths. To illustrate the sedimentological and palaeo-oceanographic conditions that may have prevailed, two examples

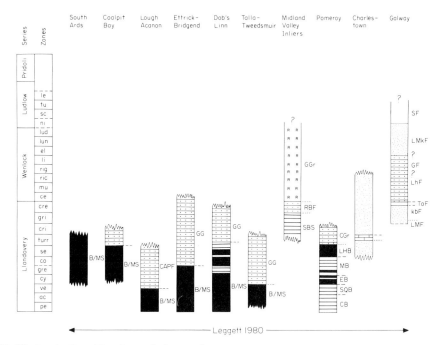

FIG. 11. Silurian stratigraphic columns for Laurentia

Silurian Laurentia

Stratigraphic units:

B/MS	Birkhill Shales (Upper Division of Moffat Shales)	LHB	Lime Hill Beds
		LhF	Lettergesh Formation
CAPF	Carrickallen Psammitic Formation	LMF	Lough Mask Formation
CB	Crocknagargan Beds	LMkF	Lough Muck Formation
CGr	Corrycroar Group	MB	Mullaghnabuoyah Beds
EB	Edenvale Beds	RBF	Ree Burn Formation
GF	Glencraff Formation	SBS	Smithy Burn Siltstone
GG	Gala Greywackes	SF	Salrock Formation
GGr	Glenback Group	SQB	Slate Quarry Beds
KbF	Kilbride Formation	ToF	Tonalee Formation

Zones:

ac	acuminatus	lun	lundgreni
ce	centrifugus	mu	murchisoni
co	convolutus	ni	nilssoni
cre	crenulatus	pe	persculptus
cri	crispus	ric	riccartonensis
cy	cyphus	rig	rigidus
el	ellesae	sc	scanicus
gre	gregarius	se	sedgwickii
gri	griestoniensis	tu	tumescens
le	leintwardinensis	turr	turriculatus
li	linnarssoni	ve	vesiculosus
lud	ludensis		

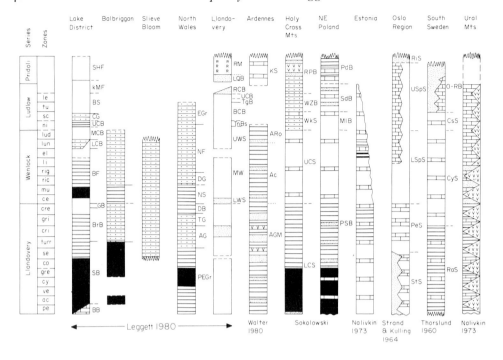

FIG. 12. Representative Silurian stratigraphic columns for Baltica

Silurian Baltica

Stratigraphic units:

Ac	Assise de Corroy	NF	Nantglyn Flags
AG	Aberystwyth Grits	NS	Nant-ysgollen Shales
AGM	Assise de Grand Manil	O-RB	Öved-Ramsåsa Beds
ARo	Assise de Rouquière	PdB	Podlasie Beds
BB	Basal Beds	PEGr	Pont Erwyd Group
BCB	Black Cock Beds	PeS	Pentamerus Series
BF	Brathay Flags	PSB	Pastek Beds
BrB	Browgill Beds	RaS	Rastrites Shale
BS	Bannisdale Slates	RCB	Roman Camp Beds
CG	Coniston Grits	RiS	Ringerike Sandstone
CsS	Colonus Shale	RM	Red Marls
CyS	Cyrtograptus Shale	RPB	Rzepin Beds
DB	Dolgau Beds	SB	Skelgill Beds
DG	Denbigh Grits	SdB	Siedlice Beds
EGr	Elwy Group	SHF	Scout Hill Flags
GB	Grey Beds	StS	Stricklandia Series
kMF	Kirkby Moor Flags	TG	Tallerddig Grits
KS	Koebbinghäuser Schichten	TgB	Trichrûg Beds
LCB	Lower Coldwell Beds	TnBs	Tresglen Beds
LCS	Lower Ciekoty Shales	UCB	Upper Coldwell Beds
LQB	Long Quarry Beds	UCB	Upper Cwm Clŷd Beds
LSpS	Lower Spiriferid Series	UCS	Upper Ciekoty Shale
LWS	Lower Wenlock Sandstones	USpS	Upper Spiriferid Series
MCB	Middle Coldwell Beds	UWS	'Upper Wenlock' Siltstones
MlB	Mielnik Beds	WkS	Wilkow Shales
MW	'Middle Wenlock'	WZB	Wydryszow Beds

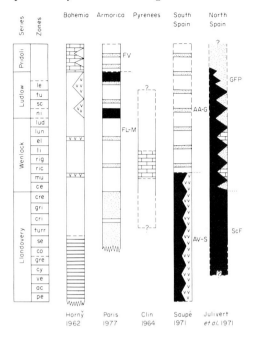

FIG. 13. Silurian stratigraphic columns for Gondwanaland

Silurian Gondwanaland

Stratigraphic units:

AA-G	'Alternances Argilito-gréseuses'	FV	Formation du Val
AV-S	'Alternances volcano-sédimentaires'	GFP	Grés de Furada—San Pedro
FL-M	Formation de la Lande-Murée	ScF	Schistes de Formigoso

will be discussed in more detail: the Middle and Upper Cambrian Alum Shale of Sweden and its lateral equivalents, and the Caradoc–Llandovery black shale developments in the British Isles.

Alum shale deposition

The Alum Shale Formation (Andersson *et al.* 1983, 1985) and its lateral equivalents were deposited during all or part of the middle and late Cambrian and early Tremadoc over much of Scandinavia. The present Cambrian outcrop is shown in Fig. 14 and for the most part it was deposited on stable continental basement. Hence, the present outcrop roughly represents the original depositional area. However, in the Caledonides probable Alum shale equivalents have been thrust eastwards (Gee 1975) suggesting an original basin extent well west of the present Norwegian coast. The area of deposition was thus very large, yet sediment thickness variations are small (12–80 m, Fig. 15) and no plausible marginal deposits crop out.

Organic-rich mudstones with up to ~20% organic carbon are the dominant lithotype with subordinate concretionary limestones, grey mudstones and rare siltstones with overall sedimentation rates of $3–15$ mm/10^3 years (Thickpenny, 1984) similar to modern pelagic oozes. The formation is underlain by shallow shelf clastics and overlain by shallow shelf limestones, strongly suggesting a shallow shelf origin for the shales themselves. The environment of deposition indicated is that of a broad epicontinental sea, prone to stagnation similar to Hallam's (1981) model (Fig. 16).

Intermittent less toxic periods allowed fossiliferous limestone formation, possibly due to fluctuations in the level of the oxic/anoxic boundary within the water column. Local depressions may have allowed black shale formation over longer periods, with ponding of sediment and a consequent decrease in limestone content. The Alum shale thus appears to represent a typical shelf organic-rich sequence; such deposits were common during the Phanerozoic but have no exact modern analogues.

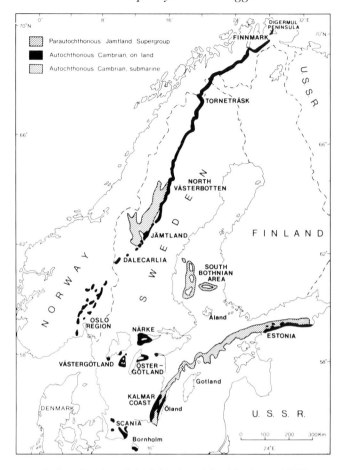

FIG. 14. Cambrian outcrop in Scandinavia and the Baltic Area (after Martinsson 1974.)

Caradoc–Llandovery sedimentation in the British Isles

Leggett (1980) in his review of British Lower Palaeozoic black shale distribution commented on the widespread development of organic-rich mudstones in Caradocian and Llandoverian times and their relative paucity during the Ashgill. The palaeogeography of Britain in Lower Silurian times is relatively well known (Fig. 10, Cocks *et al.* 1979). The width of the ocean which traversed the British Isles is unknown, but possibly attained as much as several thousand kilometres. Various palaeoenvironments are recognizable along its margins. In Laurentia, condensed organic-rich mudstones were deposited extremely slowly (~ 1.7–4.1 mm/10^3 years), oceanward of the palaeotrench (Leggett 1978). These are, for the most part, very finely laminated implying anoxic conditions at abyssal depths (e.g.

Fig. 7, Abington–Slieve Bernagh, Fig. 11, South Ards–Talla–Tweedsmuir). Aligned graptolites (Williams & Rickards 1984) suggest the presence of winnowing currents and the sparse indications of benthic activity indicate that even these may have been anoxic in nature. Trenchward (i.e. in northern sequences of the accretionary belt), turbidites become dominant, swamping all pelagic sedimentation by the Upper Llandovery. Shallower black shale intercalations in fore-arc basin sequences, e.g. near Girvan, Scotland (Leggett 1980) testify to intermittent oxygen-deficiency higher in the water column. On the south-east margin of Iapetus, Caradocian black mudstones are common deposits in the 'marginal' (*sensu lato*) Welsh basin, and blanket almost the entire region in latest Caradoc times. In addition black mudstones are locally developed in association with limestones and volcanic sequences indicative of shallow marine environments in the belt of calc-alkaline volcanism related to south-

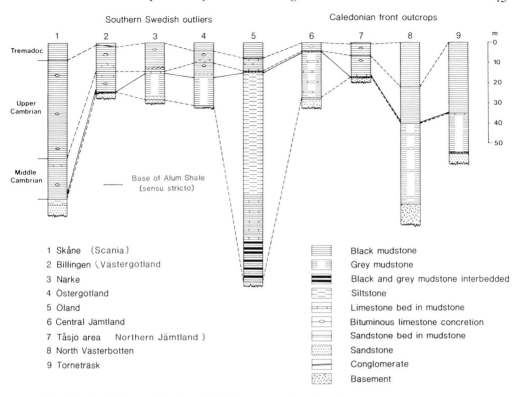

FIG. 15. Variation in thickness of the Alum Shale Formation in Scandinavia

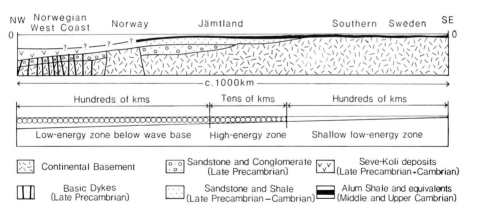

FIG. 16. Comparison of Hallam's epicontinental sea model (Hallam 1981), with a cross-section through the Central Scandinavian Caledonides (Gee 1975)

ward subduction, running through SE Ireland and the Lake District. Llandovery black mudstones are less widespread. They occur in the Lake District, parts of SE Ireland and North Wales, which are all deep shelf to continental margin environments, but are not present in shelf areas.

The development of black shales suggests that anoxic, or oxygen-deficient waters, occurred over a broad depth-range during much of Caradoc and early Llandovery times. The abundant shelly benthos and lack of carbonaceous strata in sequences deposited in the intervening Ashgillian Epoch indicate that they are virtually absent.

A. Thickpenny & J. K. Leggett

Several of the Caradoc and Llandovery black shale deposits were laid down very slowly (Leggett 1978) and yet still appreciable organic matter was preserved (e.g. ~2–4% organic carbon for the Moffat Shales). This need not imply that overall productivity was high (relative to known rates in modern upwelling zones, for example) rather that prevailing oceanographic conditions were extremely favourable to the development of oxygen-deficient waters. Productivity variations, nonetheless, are an attractive explanation for small-scale variations in the dominantly black mudstones.

Controls on Lower Palaeozoic black shale formation

The fundamental controls on organic-rich sediment development at the present day are those of organic production and biochemical degradation. However, evidence from the geological record indicates that these primary controls are strongly affected by second order controls such as global climate variation, sea-level stand, basin restriction and palaeogeography, upwelling zones, sedimentation rates and depositional depths. We shall consider each of these controls in turn in an attempt to assess their relative contributions to the formation of early Palaeozoic black shales.

Organic production

Obviously the amount of organic matter (predominantly marine algae in the early Palaeozoic) produced within the photic zone is of great importance to organic matter preservation. However, estimates of ancient ocean productivity are extremely difficult to make, due to the presence of many unquantifiable variables. Locally, in zones of upwelling, high primary productivity may cause high preservation of organic matter due purely to supply rate. By analogy with modern and more recent deposits, however, high organic productivity does not appear to be the best explanation for black shale development in the early Palaeozoic. Arthur (this volume) suggests that the rate of organic carbon burial was in fact lower during the early Palaeozoic than at subsequent intervals in the Phanerozoic.

Climate

Long term global climatic variations may have important oceanographic consequences affecting organic carbon preservation. High global temperatures associated with a decreased pole–equator temperature gradient are almost certainly associated with decreased global ocean current circulation, such that deeper waters are less oxygenated. In addition, warmer waters contain less dissolved oxygen. These two factors might aid the production of stratification and anoxic conditions. Periods of overall colder climate with higher pole–equator temperature gradients (possibly culminating in major glaciations) would have the reverse effect. These two 'modes' have been referred to as polytaxic and oligotaxic states respectively (Fischer & Arthur 1977).

Leggett (1980) has suggested that climatic changes associated with major eustatic sea-level changes could have been a contributing influence in the genesis of British Lower Palaeozoic black shales. Evidence presented here suggests that a high proportion of northern European organic-rich deposits were also formed in the same time bands as those in Britain, suggesting that ambient oceanographic conditions during such polytaxic modes favoured black shale deposition on a very large scale. Shorter term fluctuations in climate and/or productivity might best be invoked as causes for mm-scale sedimentological variations in many of the sequences.

Sea-level stand

Leggett (1980) and Leggett et al. (1981) have described the evidence for relative sea-level changes during the early Palaeozoic. Sea-level variations relate in large part to large-scale climatic variation. In the case of the early Palaeozoic, eustatic regression is associated with a major glaciation on Gondwanaland during Ashgillian times. However, geotectonic processes which change the volume of mid-ocean ridges are apparently more important in controlling long-term sea-level changes (e.g. Vail et al. 1977), and the importance of such processes is difficult to assess in the early Palaeozoic.

The concentration of Caradoc and Llandovery black shales in northern Europe is closely associated with contemporaneous transgressions and flooding of shelves (Leggett 1980; Leggett et al. 1981). In addition, stratigraphic evidence (Leggett et al. 1981) supports a major middle and late Cambrian transgression which adds weight to the idea of a broad flooded epicontinental area across Baltica during this period, allowing accumulation of the Alum Shales.

Palaeogeography

The palaeogeographic position of continents and the size and shape of oceans and marginal basins are important factors determining possible sites of anoxic conditions. Three important palaeogeographic controls can be recognized: the geographical orientation of major continental masses, the degree of circulatory restriction of narrow oceans and the possibility of silled or otherwise restricted basins. Parrish and Curtis (1982) have produced models for upwelling zones for Mesozoic and Caenozoic palaeocontinental reconstructions. However, uncertainties in the exact orientations of early Palaeozoic continents make prediction of upwelling zones difficult. The presence of phosphorite deposits in association with black shales may be a useful criterion (e.g. the Caradocian black shales of North Wales). A similar model might be put forward for some of the phosphate-rich black shales of the Upper Cambrian (e.g. Bentleyford Shales).

The possibility of ocean circulation restriction due to palaeogeography is perhaps underestimated during the early Palaeozoic. Leggett (1980) has suggested that Arenig–Llandeilo black shales in south Wales may have developed in restricted basins. We further suggest here that a major factor concentrating black shales in the Caradoc may have been oceanic restriction due to the closing of Törnquist's Sea, the narrowing of the Iapetus Ocean and the initial opening of the Rheic Ocean—similar to the situation during the opening of the South Atlantic (McCoy *et al.* this volume). We do not feel that circulation patterns can be reconstructed with much confidence. Silled basins, as opposed to merely restricted circulation, are almost impossible to recognize in the early Palaeozoic.

Sedimentation rates

Differing views exist as to the relationship between rates of sedimentation and organic carbon preservation (e.g. Calvert, this volume; Pelet, this volume). Evidence presented here and elsewhere (e.g. Thickpenny 1984; Leggett 1978; Churkin *et al.* 1977) suggests that many early Palaeozoic organic-rich sediments were deposited extremely slowly, and that not only bulk sedimentation, but also organic carbon production may have been low. In contrast, where sedimentation rates are higher, organic carbon contents generally appear to drop. This apparent contrast with recent results may be a result of the overall greater oxygen impoverishment of early Palaeozoic seas, (Wilde & Berry 1982; Berry & Wilde 1978) a factor which may have allowed the establishment of broader, longer-lived oxygen minima than was possible later.

Depth of deposition

Those littoral sequences in Gondwanan shelf sequences showing wave and current structures lack black shales. In addition, deposits formed at depth (e.g. turbiditic sequences in Eire and Sweden) generally lack black shales except during the most intense parts of the 'polytaxic' phases described. This is because the more rapid sedimentation rates effectively swamp black shale accumulation and because, for much of the period, even an expanded oxygen minimum zone would have been unlikely to reach abyssal depths.

Conclusions

We have shown in this brief review that Lower Palaeozoic black shales developed throughout much of northern Europe and are particularly common (though not confined) to three main periods: the middle and late Cambrian, the Caradoc and the Llandovery. Assuming the validity of Arthur's suggestion (this volume) that the rate of organic carbon burial was low during the early Palaeozoic, then the major controls on black shale accumulation were: eustatic sea-level changes, global climate variation and palaeographic restriction. Where the three factors coincide favourably (e.g. Caradocian times) the potential for oil source rock generation is highest.

We have also shown that organic-rich sediments were developed in a variety of palaeodepths. In the Caradoc and Llandovery, abyssal sediments were dominantly anoxic in the Iapetus Ocean, implying a greater expanded oxygen minimum zone, and anoxic water column. Elsewhere in the Caradoc and Llandovery the detailed palaeogeography is less clear so that it is difficult to estimate the palaeodepths of black shales in the Törnquist's Sea–Rheic Ocean area. Most late Cambrian organic-rich deposits were deposited in shelf environments, perhaps indicating a less expanded oxygen minimum zone.

Overall it is apparent that several genetic models of black shale formation can be postulated for the early Palaeozoic, all with the potential of forming oil source rocks. That these conditions have not produced significant accumulations is due to the complex post-Caledonian structural history of NW Europe. However, the widespread and varied development of early Palaeozoic organic-rich sediments merits their continued study as an aid to predictive modelling of formational environments for more recent oil source rocks.

References

ANDERSSON, A., DAHLMAN, B. & GEE, D. G. 1983. Kerogen and Uranium resources in the Cambrian alum shales of the Billingen-Falbygden and Närke areas, Sweden. *Geol. För. Stockh. Förh.* **104**, 197–209.

——, ——, —— & SNÄLL, S. 1985. *The Scandinavian Alum Shales.* Sveriges geol. unders. Sev. Ca, **56**, 50 pp.

ARTHUR, M. A. 1987. Secular variations in amounts of and environments of organic carbon burial during the Phanerozoic. *This volume.*

BABIN, C., ARNAUD, A. *et al.* 1976. The Ordovician of the Armorican Massif (France). *In*: BASSETT, M. G. (ed.), *The Ordovician System.* Univ. Wales Press and National Museum of Wales, Cardiff.

BEDNARCZYK, W. 1971. Stratigraphy and palaeogeography of the Ordovician in The Holy Cross Mountains. *Acta geol. pol.* **21**, 573–616.

BERRY, W. B. N. & WILDE, P. 1978. Progressive ventilation of the oceans—an explanation for the distribution of the Lower Palaezoic black shales. *Am. J. Sci.* **278**, 257–75.

CALVERT, S. E. 1987. Oceanographic controls on the accumulation of organic matter in the ocean. *This volume*, pp. 137–152.

CHURKIN, M., CARTER, C. & JOHNSON, B. R. 1977. Subdivision of Ordovician and Silurian time scale using accumulation rates of graptolitic shale. *Geology*, **5**, 452–56.

CLIN, M. 1964. Étude géologique de la haute chaine des Pyrénées centrales. *Mem. Bureau. Rech. geol. mineres*, **27**.

COCKS, L. R. M. & FORTEY, R. A. 1982. Faunal evidence for oceanic separation in the Palaeozoic of Britain. *J. Geol. Soc. London*, **139**, 465–78.

——, McKERROW, W. S. & LEGGETT, J. K. 1979. Silurian palaeogeography on the margins of the Iapetus Ocean in the British Isles. *In*: WONES, D. R. (ed.), *The Caledonides in the USA.* Virginia Polytechnic Institute & State Univ. Memoir, **2**, 49–55.

DEBELMAS, J. 1974. *Géologie de la France. Volume 1: Vieux Massifs et grands bassins Sedimentaires.* Doin, Paris.

DORÉ, F. 1972. La transgression majeure du Paleozoique inferieur dans le nord-est due Massif Armoricain. *Bull. Soc. geol. Fr. (7)*, **9**, 79–93.

FISCHER, A. G. & ARTHUR, M. A. 1977. Secular variations in the pelagic realm. *In*: COOK, H. E. & ENOS, P. (eds), *Deep Water carbonate environments. Spec. Publ. Soc. Econ. Palaeont. Mineral.* **25**, 19–50.

GEE, D. G. 1975. A tectonic model for the central part of the Scandinavian Caledonides. *Am. J. Sci.* **275**, 468–515.

GEE, D. G., KARIS, L., KIMPULAINEN, R. & THELANDER, T. 1974. A summary of Caledonian front stratigraphy, northern Jämtland/southern Västerbotten central Swedish Caledonides. *Geol. För. Stockh. Förh.* **96**, 389–97.

HALLAM, A. 1981. *Facies interpretation and the stratigraphic record.* Freeman, Oxford.

HAMMANN, W. 1976. The Ordovician of the Iberian peninsula—a review. *In*: BASSETT, M. G. (ed), *The Ordovician System.* Univ. Wales Press and Nat. Mus. of Wales, Cardiff.

HAVLICEK, V. 1971. Stratigraphy of the Cambrian of central Bohemia. *Sb. Geol. Ved. Geol.* **20**, 7–52.

HAVLICEK, V. 1982. Ordovician in Bohemia: development of the Prague Basin and its benthic communities. *Sb. Geol. Ved. Geol.* **37**, 103–36.

HORNY, R. 1962. Das Mittelböhmische Silur. *Geologie*, **11**, 873–916.

JULIVERT, M., MARCOS, A. & TRUYOLS, J. 1971. L'évolution palaeogéographique du nord-ouest de l'Espagne pendant l'Ordovicien-Silurien. *Bull. Soc. Geol. Miner. Bretagne C*, **4**, 1–7.

LEGGETT, J. K. 1978. Eustacy and pelagic regimes in the Iapetus Ocean during the Ordovician and Silurian. *Earth Planet. Sci. Lett.*, **41**, 163–9.

—— 1979. Oceanic sediments from the Ordovician of the southern Uplands. *In*: HARRIS, A. L., HOLLAND, C. H. & LEAKE, B. E. (eds), *The Caledonides of the British Isles—reviewed.* Spec. Publ. Geol. Soc., London, **8**, 495–98.

—— 1980. British Lower Palaeozoic black shales and their palaeo-oceanographic significance. *J. Geol. Soc., London*, **137**, 139–56.

——, McKerrow, W. S., Cocks, L. R. M. & RICKARDS, R. B. 1981. Periodicity in the early Palaeozoic marine realm. *J. Geol. Soc., London*, **138**, 167–76.

MARTINSSON, A. 1974. The Cambrian of Norden. *In*: HOLLAND, C. H. (ed.), *Cambrian of the British Isles, Norden and Spitsbergen.* Wiley, London.

McCOY, F. W., BOERSMA, A. & ZIMMERMAN, H. B. 1987. South Atlantic sapropels. *This volume*, pp. 271–286.

MODLINSKI, Z. 1973. Stratigraphy and development of the Ordovician in north-eastern Poland. *Pr. Inst. Geol.*, **72**, 1–74.

—— & SZYMANSKI, B. 1980. *The Ordovician in Poland. Kwart. Geol.* **24**, 123–28.

NALIVKIN, D. V. 1973. *Geology of the USSR.* Oliver and Boyd, Edinburgh.

PARIS, F. 1977. Les Formations Siluriennes du synclinorium du Menez-Belair; comparaisons avec d'autre formations Siluriennes du Massif Armoricain. *Bull. Bur. Rech. Geol. Minieres (deuxieme serie), section 1*, 75–87.

PARRISH, J. T. & CURTIS, R. L. 1982. Atmospheric circulation, upwelling and organic-rich rocks in the Mesozoic and Cenozoic. *Palaeogeogr. Palaeoclimatal. Palaeocol.* **40**, 67–102.

PELET, R. 1987. A model of organic sedimentation on present day continental margins. *This volume*, pp. 167–180

READING, H. G. 1965. Eocambrian and Lower Palaeozoic geology of the Digermul Peninsula, Tanafjord, Finnmark. *Norg. geol. Unders.* **234**, 167–91.

SAUPÉ, F. 1971. La serie ordovicienne et silurienne d'Almaden (Province de Ciudad Real, Espagne); point des connaissances actuelles. *Mem. Bur. Rech. geol. Minières*, **73**, 355–66.

SCOTESE, C. R., BAMBACH, R. K., BARTON, C. VAN DER VOO, R. & ZIEGLER, A. M. 1979. Palaeozoic Base Maps. *J. Geol.* **87**, 217–78.

SMITH, A. G., HURLEY, A. M. & BRIDEN, J. C. 1981. *Phanerozoic palaeocontinental world maps.* Cambridge Univ. Press, Cambridge.

SOKOLOWSKI, S. (ed.) 1970. *Geology of Poland. Volume 1, Stratigraphy. Part 1: Pre-Cambrian and Palaeozoic.* Publishing House Wydawnictwa Geologiczene, Warsaw.

STRAND, T. & KULLING, O. 1972. *Scandinavian Caledonides.* Wiley-Interscience, London.

THICKPENNY, A. 1984. The sedimentology of the Swedish Alum shales. *In:* STOW, D. A. V. & PIPER, D. J. P. (eds), *Fine-grained sediments: deep water processes and environments.* Spec. Publ. Geol. Soc. 15, Blackwell Scientific Publications, Oxford. pp. 511–26.

THORSLUND, P. 1960. The Cambro-Silurian. *In:* MAGNUSSON, N. H., THORSLUND, P., BROTZEN, F., ASKLUND, B. & KULLING, O. Description to accompany the map of the Pre-Quaternary rocks of Sweden. *Sver. Geol. Unders. Ba* **16**, 69–110.

TOMCZYK, H. 1963. Ordovician and Silurian in the basement of the Fore-Carpathian depression. *Roczn. pol. Tow. geol.* **33**, 289–320.

—— 1964a. Silurian stratigraphy in north-eastern Poland. *Kwart. geol.* **8**, 506–23.

—— 1964b. The Ordovician and Silurian sedimentation cycles in Poland and phenomena of Caledonian Orogeny. *Bull. Acad. pol. Sci. Ser. geol., geogr.* **12**, 119–31.

—— 1968. Silurian stratigraphy in the Peri-Baltic area of Poland, based on drilling data. *Kwart. geol.* **12**, 15–36.

—— & TOMCZYKOWA, E. 1976. Development of Ashgill and Llandovery sediments in Poland. *In:* BASSETT, M. G. (ed.), *The Ordovician System.* Univ. of Wales Press and Nat. Mus. of Wales, Cardiff.

TOMCZYKOWA, E. 1964. Ordovician of the eastern European Platform in the area of Poland. *Kwart. geol.* **8**, 491–505.

—— & TOMCZYK, H. 1979. Stratigraphy of the Polish Silurian and Lower Devonian and development of the Proto-Tethys. *Acta Palaeontol. Pol,* **24**, 165–81.

VAN DER MEER MOHR, C. G., KUIJPER, R. P., VAN CALSTEREN, P. W. C. & DEN TEX, E. 1981. The Hesperian Massif: from Iapetus aulacogen to ensialic orogen. A model for its development. *Geol. Rdsch.,* **70**, 459–72.

VAIL, P. R., MITCHUM, R. M., Jr., & THOMPSON, S. III, 1977. Seismic stratigraphy and global changes of sea level, part 4: Global cycles of relative changes of sea level. *In:* PAYTON, C. E. (ed), *Seismic stratigraphy—applications to hydrocarbon exploration. Mem. Am. Assoc. Petrol. Geol.* **26**, 83–97.

WALTER, R. 1980. Lower Palaeozoic palaeogeography of the Brabant Massif and its southern adjoining areas. *Meded. Rijks. geol. Dienst.,* **32**, 14–25.

WILDE, P. & BERRY, W. B. N. 1982. Progressive ventilation of the Oceans—potential for return to anoxic conditions in the post-Palaeozoic. *In:* SCHLANGER, S. O. & CITA, M. B. (eds) *Nature and Origin of Cretaceous Carbon-rich Facies.* Academic Press, London.

WILLIAMS, S. H. & RICKARDS, R. B. 1982. Palaeoecology of graptolitic black shales. *Palaeontological contribs., Univ. Oslo, 280.*

A. THICKPENNY and J. K. LEGGETT, Department of Geology, Royal School of Mines, Imperial College, London, SW7 2PB. England.

The depositional environment and petroleum geochemistry of the Marl Slate-Kupferschiefer

M. J. Gibbons

SUMMARY: The Marl Slate is the basal unit of the Upper Permian (Zechstein) in northeast England. A finely laminated, organic-rich, silty dolomite/dolomitic siltstone, it is equivalent to the Kupferschiefer of the Southern North Sea basin and northern Germany and Poland. Several lines of evidence indicate the Marl Slate/Kupferschiefer accumulated in the anoxic bottom waters of a shallow (<200 m), stratified, epicontinental sea. The vertical succession of the first Zechstein cycle is explicable in terms of the effect on sedimentation of a stratified water column undergoing progressive evaporitic concentration.

Total organic contents of the Marl Slate generally fall in the range 5–15%, decreasing upwards. The kerogen is largely amorphous and oil-prone. Original pyrolysis yields approach 100 kg hydrocarbon/tonne rock. It is immature in northeast England but even where mature in the Southern North Sea basin and Northern Europe the unit is unlikely to have sourced commercially significant amounts of oil because of its limited thickness (generally <2 m).

Only a summary is available for this paper.

M. J. GIBBONS, Exploration & Production Division, B.P. Research Centre, Chertsey Road, Sunbury-on-Thames, Middlesex, UK.

From: BROOKS, J. & FLEET, A. J. (eds) 1987, *Marine Petroleum Source Rocks*
Geological Society Special Publication No. 26 p. 249.

Mesozoic marine organic-rich shales

A. Hallam

SUMMARY: A survey of Mesozoic organic-rich shales in space and time indicates that they are widely distributed through much of the era but are concentrated especially at two levels: Upper Jurassic (Kimmeridgian–Volgian/Tithonian) and Middle Cretaceous (Aptian–Turonian). Stable carbon isotope studies prove to be a particularly useful tool in both palaeoenvironmental and diagenetic analysis. Anoxic events in the ocean may be characterized by high concentrations of δ^{13} carbonate carbon. The carbon isotope values obtained may, however, reflect diagenesis in the sulphate reduction zone rather than conditions in the original sea water. Calcite concretions formed at successive stages in diagenesis may record a change from strongly negative to strongly positive values of $\delta^{13}C$, indicating a switch from the sulphate-reduction to the fermentation zone.

Analysis of benthic palaeoecology leads to a classification of marine mudrocks into barren laminite, shelly laminite, shelly shale and shelly mudstone, of which the last lacks any significant quantity of kerogen. By analogy with Recent sediments an attempt is made at a tentative estimate of the oxygen content at the sediment/water interface during the original deposition. Environments of deposition are considered in general terms and the respective merits of several facies models for the Mesozoic deposits are briefly discussed.

Introduction

Besides posing intriguing problems concerning their mode of origin, Mesozoic (more particularly late Mesozoic) marine organic-rich shales are by far the most important source of petroleum. Thus Irving et al. (1974) estimate that more than 70% of all known pooled oil is Tithonian to Danian in age, with 60% of this being Albian–Coniacian. Tissot (1979) estimates an even higher figure of ~85% of world resources for Jurassic and Cretaceous oil.

The rocks in question have traditionally been known as black shales or, more recently, bituminous shales. Because, however, only a minor proportion of the organic matter present is in the form of soluble bitumen, the bulk being insoluble kerogen, the term organic-rich shales is currently the most favoured. Characteristically the shales are finely laminated and weather to paper shales, with organic carbon content usually ranging from ~1 to 20% by weight, but most commonly in the 4 to 10% range.

They have been deposited in more or less anoxic bottom waters, hence the preservation of organic matter in the form of laminae. Because anaerobic bacterial degradation is less efficient than aerobic, the resulting organic residue is relatively lipid-rich and reduced (i.e. hydrogen-rich, oxygen-poor), which is critical for petroleum genesis. The kerogen is mainly either type I or type II, in the terminology of Tissot and Welte (1978), which is derived principally from phytoplankton. There is a variable, but usually insubstantial, admixture of terrestrially-derived organic matter, which gives rise to gas-prone type III kerogen, which is oxygen-rich and hydrogen-poor. In the considerable experience of Demaison and Moore (1980), the vast bulk of shales with more than a small percentage of organic matter have a predominance of type I or type II kerogen.

Distribution in space and time

The following survey makes no claim to be exhaustive, but is thought to include at least the majority of the more significant deposits, particularly those thought to include the source beds of major oilfields. The data are presented in summary form in Table 1, in terms of Mesozoic stages and major regions. It should not be assumed that organic-rich shales are wholly absent in those boxes left blank, because such rocks were probably deposited wherever the environment was appropriate, throughout the Mesozoic in some regime or other.

Triassic

There are few reported beds of organic-rich shales for this period, which is no doubt mainly the result of the restriction of epicontinental seas compared with the later Mesozoic and the lack of preservation of deep-sea deposits. An important unit, up to several tens of metres thick, occurs in the Southern Alps of Ticino, Switzerland at the Anisian–Ladinian boundary. The shales have a high content of organic matter, up to about 50%, and consist of finely laminated claystones together with subordinate bituminous dolomites and thin argillaceous tuffites (Rieber 1974, 1982).

From: BROOKS, J. & FLEET, A. J. (eds) 1987, Marine Petroleum Source Rocks
Geological Society Special Publication No. 26 pp. 251–261.

TABLE 1. *General distribution in space and time of Mesozoic organic-rich shales*

	Europe	West Asia	Africa	East Asia	West Australia	North America	South America	Atlantic	Pacific
Maastrichtian		xPxP		xPxP					
Campanian		xPxP							
Santonian			xxxx	xxxx			xxxx	xxxx	
Coniacian	xxxx		xxxx		xxxx		xxxx	xxxx	
Turonian	xxxx		XXXX		xxxx	xxxx	XXXX	xxxx	xxxx
Cenomanian	xxxx		XXXX		xxxx	xxxx	XXXX	XXXX	xxxx
Albian	XXXX	XXXX		?	xxxx	XXXX	XXXX	XXXX	xxxx
Aptian	XXXX	XXXX				xxxx		XXXX	xxxx
Barremian	xxxx						xxxx	xxxx	xxxx
Hauterivian								xxxx	
Valanginian								xxxx	
Berriasian							xxxx	xxxx	
Tithonian/Volgian	XXXX	XXXX				x?x?	xxxx	xxxx	
Kimmeridgian	xxxx	xxxx				xxxx		xxxx	
Oxfordian		xxxx							
Callovian	XXXX	xxxx						xxxx	
Bathonian									
Bajocian									
Aalenian									
Toarcian	XXXX			xxxx		xxxx	xxxx		
Pliensbachian	xxxx			xxxx					
Sinemurian	xxxx					XXXX	XPXP		
Hettangian	xxxx					xxxx			
Norian	xxxx								
Carnian									
Ladinian	xxxx								
Anisian						xxxx			
Scythian									

X = major deposits, x = minor deposits, P = phosphorites. The absence of an x symbol should not be held to signify a total absence.

Of greater economic significance, however, are widespread Lower Anisian deposits in Arctic North America; the North Alaskan deposits are most probably the source rock for the Prudhoe Bay oilfield (A. F. Embry, personal communication).

The topmost Triassic stage has usually been taken as the Rhaetian but following Tozer (1980), this is here relegated to the Upper Norian. Within the Upper Norian of north west Europe there is a widespread thin unit of organic-rich shales finely laminated in part, termed Contortaschichten in Germany and forming the lower part of the Westbury Formation (Penarth Group) in England and Wales. Thin horizons within the contemporary Kössen Formation of the Northern Limestone Alps of Austria and Bavaria exhibit a similar facies (Hallam 1981b).

Jurassic

The lower part of the basal, Hettangian, stage in north west Europe contains extensive but thin laminated organic-rich alternating bands of shale, marl and limestone (basal Blue Lias in England; Hallam 1960) and a similar facies occurs in northern Canada (Hallam 1981c). A more important unit, with greater source-rock potential, occurs in the lower part of the succeeding, Sinemurian, stage. This is known in Dorset as the Shales-with-Beef Formation and in southern Germany as the Ölschiefer. A stratigraphically equivalent unit in the Paris Basin is thought to be a source rock. There is an exactly contemporary (Semicostatum and Turneri Zones) and much thicker unit in the Peruvian Andes known as the Aramachay Formation. This consists of organic-rich shales passing up into phosphatic siltstones. Determination of the H/C and O/C atomic ratios in the kerogen fraction of the shales indicates that temperatures in excess of 300°C have been attained and that the kerogen has passed through the oil formation zone (Loughman & Hallam 1982). In consequence what could originally have been a major source rock can no longer be counted as such, as a consequence of Andean tectonism. It is very likely that contemporary shales in east central Mexico contain significant organic-rich components (Schmidt-Effing 1980) and the same is true of Nevada, where the only exposures are highly weathered outcrops that have so far ruled out conclusive confirmation (Hallam 1981c).

By far the best known organic-rich shale deposits in the Lower Jurassic are of Lower Toarcian (Falciferum Zone) age, forming an extensive unit in north-west Europe known in Germany as the Posidonienschiefer, in the Paris Basin as the Schistes Cartons and in north east England as the Jet Rock and Bituminous Shales formations (Hallam 1967b; Morris 1980). The Schistes Cartons are thought to be the petroleum source rock for the Paris Basin (Tissot & Welte 1978) and are also thought to be a possible source rock in the southern North Sea (Bodenhausen & Ott 1981). Organic-rich shale horizons of exactly the same age are known from Japan and western North America (Hallam 1981c). The only other Lower Jurassic deposits worthy of note are thin horizons in the Pliensbachian (Davoei and Margaritatus Zones) of parts of central and south west Europe (Hallam 1981c).

The next European deposit, in stratigraphic order, is the Lower Oxford Clay of southern England, which consists of organic-rich shale through the Middle Callovian and into the basal Upper Callovian. Unlike the earlier-cited horizons only the topmost few metres and parts of the base are well laminated, and these are the ones with the highest organic carbon content of up to 10% (I. Fisher, *personal communication*). Whereas the Lower Jurassic horizons can frequently be traced across extensive parts of Europe this is not the case for these Callovian deposits, though organic-rich horizons might well occur in the partly correlative Terre Noire shales of France. However, a recent DSDP hole penetrated Lower and Middle Callovian deposits, consisting of alternating horizons of organic- and phosphate-rich and more oxidized sediments, on the Blake-Bahama Outer Ridge (Sheridan *et al.* 1983).

The most important petroleum source deposits are of late Jurassic, Kimmeridgian to Tithonian/Volgian age. The use of three different terms for the youngest Jurassic stage, and the different European and British use of the term Kimmeridgian, is a source of potential confusion to non-specialists. Though the Kimmeridgian Clay of Dorset is the type section of the Kimmeridgian stage, its upper part, traditionally included within the Kimmeridgian by British geologists, corresponds with the lower part of both the Volgian stage of the Boreal, and Tithonian stage of the Tethyan ammonite realm. In England the term Portlandian has normally been used for that part of the Jurassic between the Kimmeridgian *sensu*

anglico and Cretaceous, and hence had a shorter duration than the Volgian and Tithonian (Hallam 1975).

The Kimmeridge Clay is generally accepted as the source rock of North Sea oil. The most important organic-rich shale horizons in the classic Dorset coast section occur in the topmost Kimmeridgian *sensu gallico* and Lower Volgian (Tyson *et al.* 1979; Morris 1980). Whereas, unlike the Lower Toarcian unit, these cannot readily be traced across western Europe, there is a very widespread correlative unit in the West Siberian basin which is evidently the source of most of the enormous oil reserves of that province (Kontorovich 1971). In the North Sea organic-rich shales continue upwards to the top of the Jurassic and into the basal Cretaceous (Ryazanian) (Rawson & Riley 1982). The Kimmeridgian (and topmost Oxfordian) Hanifa Formation of the Lurestan Basin consists of laminated organic-rich shales and limestones which have acted as a prolific oil source for the Upper Jurassic Arab limestone reservoirs of the Middle East (Murris 1980). There are also some Callovian and Lower Oxfordian horizons in Saudi Arabian basinal settings, of subordinate importance.

Kimmeridgian and Tithonian laminated organic-rich shales also occur in the Magallanes Basin of the southern Andes and in West Antarctica (Farquharson 1982) and thin horizons of this age and facies have been located in DSDP drilling site 534 in the western North Atlantic (Sheridan *et al.* 1983). Tithonian–Berriasian organic-rich shales are an important oil source rock in the Neuquen Basin of Argentina (Mitchum & Uliana 1985). Sapropelic claystones ranging in age from Oxfordian to Aptian have been recorded from the Falkland Plateau (Baker *et al.* 1977). Upper Oxfordian to Lower Volgian mudstones in East Greenland contain abundant ammonites and the bivalve *Buchia* and contain laminated, presumably organic-rich horizons (Surlyk 1977). Extensive Upper Jurassic shales also rich in *Buchia* occur in western North America. Many of these shales have been mildly metamorphosed, for instance in California, so that it is difficult to determine to what extent the original rocks were organic-rich. The faunal facies suggests that a fair proportion were. The same applies to correlative deposits elsewhere in the circum-Pacific region.

Cretaceous

For this period there is an extensive record of organic-rich deposits both on the continents and under the oceans. As regards source rocks for major oilfields the most important are the very widespread Aptian–Albian shale-limestone sequences of the Khuzestan and Lurestan basins of the Middle East, notably the Nahr Umr Shale (Morris 1980). Secondly there are important, predominantly mid-Cretaceous organic-rich shale-limestone sequences in Central and South America, such as the thick Napo Formation of the Andean foothills of Colombia, Equador and Peru and the approximately correlative La Luna Formation of Venezuela and Agua Nueva Formation of Mexico. The most organic-rich horizons occur within the range Aptian to Coniacian. A number of occurrences in western Europe, mainly in the circum-Mediterranean Alpine fold zone, are also concentrated in this age range (Jenkyns 1980).

Other notable occurrences of organic-rich shales are in the Upper Cretaceous Mowry Shale and Pierre Shale of the United States Western Interior (Byers & Larsen 1979; Schultz *et al.* 1980), the Upper Cenomanian-Lower Santonian Eze-Aku and Awgu Formations of the Benue Trough, Nigeria (Petters & Ekweozor 1982) and in the Albian–Coniacian sequence of the Carnarvon Basin, Western Australia (Jenkyns 1980). Organic-rich shales are comparatively sparse in the youngest Cretaceous stages but Campanian and Maastrichtian deposits occur in association with phosphorites in Morocco, Israel and Turkey.

The extensive literature on deep Atlantic and Pacific occurrences is reviewed by Arthur and Schlanger (1979), Jenkyns (1980), Tissot *et al.* (1980) and Cool (1982). In the Pacific deposits have been found on four plateaus. Thus there are Barremian–Aptian deposits on the Manihiki Plateau and Cenomanian–Turonian deposits on the Hess Rise. Aptian to Turonian anoxic deposits are recorded from both the North and South Atlantic. According to Cool's (1982) detailed study of North Atlantic occurrences, the increasing frequency of laminated organic-rich deposits suggests that bottom conditions became increasingly anoxic from the early to the mid Cretaceous, with the greatest intensity of anoxia being attained in Aptian–Cenomanian times. Thereafter there was a progressive restoration of more oxidizing conditions. A striking feature of the early and mid Cretaceous North Atlantic deposits is the unexpected richness in terrestrial plant material, but it is clear that there is also a substantial component of phytoplankton-derived organic matter in this region, as elsewhere.

In summary (Fig. 1) organic-rich deposits are widely distributed through Mesozoic strata but tend to be concentrated especially at two levels: Upper Jurassic (Kimmeridgian–Volgian/Tithonian) and middle Cretaceous (Aptian to Turonian), with Sinemurian, Toarcian and Callovian levels seemingly next in importance.

Aspects of petrology, isotope geochemistry and diagenesis

The only petrological feature common to all the deposits under consideration is the presence of significant quantities of kerogen, normally concentrated in regularly spaced laminae no more than a few tens of microns thick. There is usually in addition a small percentage of diagenetic pyrite in the form of scattered euhedral crystals, framboidal clusters and micronodules. The framboids form early in diagenesis but some of the larger nodules post-date sediment compaction. Evidently pyrite can form over a long time span and throughout the sediment (Hudson 1982).

Clay mineralogy shows no correlation with the presence of kerogen. There may be a variable admixture of detrital silt-grade quartz and subordinate feldspar but more commonly non silty organic-rich shales grade into organic-rich marls and fine-grained limestones. Even the most calcareous sequences, however, tend to consist of shale- or marl-limestone alternations.

Interesting results relevant to both palaeoenvironmental and diagenetic interpretations have recently been obtained from the study of stable carbon isotopes. Scholle and Arthur (1980) undertook a comprehensive study of the isotope ratio in Cretaceous carbonates. They found that what have been widely interpreted as anoxic events, in the Aptian and Albian and more particularly at the Cenomanian–Turonian boundary, correlated with high concentrations of $\delta^{13}C$ carbonate carbon. Scholle and Arthur tentatively attributed this to the increased preservation by burial of light $\delta^{12}C$ organic carbon during anoxic episodes, so that the dissolved carbon remaining in the oceanic reservoir became progressively heavier isotopically. Similar results have been obtained for Lower Toarcian organic-rich shales in Europe and an early Toarcian anoxic event is inferred (Jenkyns 1985; Jenkyns & Clayton 1986).

Quite different results were obtained by Küspert (1982) in his isotopic study of the Toarcian Posidonienschiefer and its lateral equivalents in France and England. He found that the $\delta^{13}C$ values of the kerogen and carbonate fluctuated in sympathy, notably at a horizon at the base of the Falciferum Zone which has unusually low values. This horizon is considered on other grounds, notably fossil content (or rather its absence) to represent the most anoxic episode of deposition. To account for the low $\delta^{13}C$ values of the included carbonate as well as the kerogen, Küspert postulates that during episodes of very strong stagnation, bottom water enriched in isotopically light carbon as a result of oxidation of organic matter, escaped to the photic zone by convection and diffusion, and was in due course taken up by plankton for calcification and photosynthesis. Because of equilibration with atmospheric CO_2 only extraordinarily intensive stagnation-induced carbon recycling could lower the $\delta^{13}C$ more than 3–4%.

Küspert notes elsewhere in his paper that calcareous concretions within the Posidonien-schiefer are depleted in $\delta^{13}C$ to varying degrees with respect to the adjacent oil shale. Since the concretions have been produced in early diagenesis it is vital to have an understanding of how diagenetic reactions can affect carbon isotope composition.

The biochemical degradation of organic matter proceeds by several stages, which may correspond to a depth zonation in the sediment (Irwin *et al.* 1977; Demaison & Moore 1980). Initially bacterial oxidation may take place in oxidizing conditions, leading to the production of CO_2 and H_2O. In normal sediments this will take place only in the top few cm of sediment, in free contact with sea water, but is unlikely to be relevant to the sediments under consideration, for which anoxic conditions would appear to have extended at least up to the sediment-water interface (see below).

In normal sediments the oxygen supply becomes exhausted eventually, and certainly below more than a few cm below the sediment-water interface, and anaerobic bacteria take over from aerobic bacteria; in organic-rich shales they will operate *ab initio*. Nitrates may initially be a source of oxygen until they are exhausted, but there will invariably be a phase of sulphate reduction leading ultimately to the production of CO_2, H_2O and H_2S. The hydrogen sulphide reacts with the available iron to form iron sulphide, which eventually crystallizes as pyrite; the ^{13}C content of organic matter becomes strongly depleted. When the sulphate is exhausted, bacterial fermentation will commence, with the production of methane. It is common to find a fermentation zone below the sulphate-reduction zone in Recent sediments. Since the methane carbon is isotopically very light, that carbon which is retained in the sediment as diagenetic carbonate carbon will be strongly enriched in ^{13}C.

It follows that, for continued precipitation of $CaCO_3$, there should be a dramatic change in $\delta^{13}C$ from strongly negative values in the sulphate-reduction zone to strongly positive values in the fermentation zone (Irwin *et al.* 1977).

Strong support for this postulation comes from a study of limestone concretions in the Yorkshire

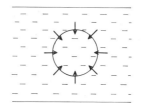

EARLY STAGE
Lower sediment compaction, higher porosity.
Concretion calcite and pyrite content higher.
Zone of sulphate reduction.
(negative $\delta^{13}C$)

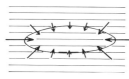

LATE STAGE
Higher sediment compaction, lower porosity.
Concretion calcite and pyrite content lower.
Zone of fermentation (positive $\delta^{13}C$)

FIG. 1. Early- and late-stage formation of calcite concretions during diagenesis of organic-rich mudrocks. Length of arrows proportional to freedom of migration of calcite-precipitating fluids.

Jet Rock, the stratigraphic equivalent of the extremely similar lower part of the Posidonien-schiefer (Campos & Hallam 1979). Two phases of concretionary growth can be distinguished (Fig. 1). The early phase is characterized by relatively high $CaCO_3$ content and either irregular (e.g. 'pseudovertebrae' concretions) or spheroidal shape (e.g. 'cannon ball' concretions); also by a high pyrite content (Raiswell 1976). The later phase is characterized by relatively low $CaCO_3$ content, ellipsoidal shape, with long axes parallel to the bedding (e.g. 'whalestones' and 'millstones' concretions) and negligible pyrite content. At one horizon the age relations are clearly established, because the 'pseudovertebrae' are enveloped by the 'whalestones'. The early phase concretions are characterized as predicted by strongly negative, the later phase concretions by strongly positive $\delta^{13}C$.

The high $CaCO_3$ content of both types of concretion indicates that they formed in early diagenesis no more than a few metres below the sediment/water interface, because at greater burial depths compaction would have reduced porosity by too much. In the early stages, when organic degradation took place by sulphate reduction, the mud porosity was sufficiently high that migration of carbonate-precipitating fluids could proceed freely in all directions. Pyrite was produced after H_2S reacted with the small amount of iron in the sediment. Subsequently, anisotropy was imposed by compaction, and migration of fluids parallel to the bedding became easier than migration normal to the bedding. Hence the shape of the concretions tended to change from spheroidal to ellipsoidal, with growth being easier in the plane of the bedding. Carbonate content is lower because of the reduced porosity and permeability during this later growth phase, and pyrite is very subordinate because the H_2S and perhaps the Fe supply had become exhausted.

The promise of carbon isotope studies as a tool in understanding the diagenesis of petroleum source rocks, taken in conjunction with other data, should be evident from this example. With regard to Küspert's (1982) interpretation of the basal Posidonienschiefer horizons, one can suggest that the shale carbonate analysed was formed during diagenesis in the sulphate-reduction zone, and that consequently the carbon isotope values do not reflect those of the original surface waters.

Palaeoecology

The maximum saturation of oxygen dissolved in sea water is about 6–8.5 ml/l, and benthic metazoans are unaffected by oxygen concentrations down to ~ 1 ml/l. There is a sharp decrease in fauna between 0.7 and 0.3 ml/l. Below 0.3 ml/l deposit feeders are rare and below 0.1 ml/l suspension feeders disappear. Waters with concentrations of less than 0.5 ml/l dissolved oxygen can be regarded as effectively anoxic (Demaison & Moore 1980).

It has long been recognized that, whereas organic-rich shales may contain well preserved nekton such as fish and reptiles, and less well preserved but abundant nekton such as ammonites, the benthic fauna is restricted. Either it is absent entirely, sparse or, if present in large quantities, of very low diversity, monospecific assemblages being quite characteristic. It consists virtually entirely of epifauna, and indeed the presence of significant endofauna would have led to the rapid destruction of the fine organic lamination. Finally, individuals tend to be small in size, signifying either stunting of adults or high rates of juvenile mortality (Hallam 1965).

Frequently if not generally the most common macrobenthos are pterioid bivalves which are believed from their facies associations to have occupied relatively deep-water, offshore habitats. They include, in the Triassic; *Daonella, Halobia, Monotis*: in the Jurassic; *Bositra* (='*Posidonia*'), *Pectinula, Pseudomytiloides, Buchia*: in the Cretaceous; *Inoceramus*. Such forms characteristically occur crowding bedding planes as high density, low diversity (usually monospecific)

assemblages in the midst of more barren strata. This mode of occurrence is characteristic of opportunistic species transiently occupying high stress environments. The intervention of barren strata of greater thickness suggests that temporary alleviation of the bottom water anoxia allowed short-term colonization of the sea bed. (The scattered specimens of *Pseudomytiloides* (= *Inoceramus* auct.) in the Toarcian Jet Rock of Yorkshire probably attached themselves in life to drifting logs, because pieces of driftwood are known from the correlative Posidonia Shales of southern Germany crowded with such specimens).

With a slightly greater concentration of oxygen at the sediment-water interface there may be a greater diversity of epifauna, and perhaps also shallow-burrowing endofauna, such as deposit-feeding nuculids in the Lower Oxford Clay (Duff 1975) and suspension-feeding lucinids and *Protocardia* in the Kimmeridge Clay (Aigner 1980). Lamination tends to disappear with increasing burrowing activity, and there is a slight reduction in kerogen content as organic matter is destroyed by oxidation. With an even higher oxygen content, over 1 ml/l, benthos are little inhibited. Diversity increases and abundant bioturbation, by both shallow and deep burrowers, completely destroys any lamination originally present; organic carbon is almost or entirely absent.

Figure 2 presents a four-fold classification of rocks occurring in alternation in organic-rich shale sequences, which expresses the points just outlined, and gives approximate estimates of the oxygen content at the sediment-water interface, based on data from Recent sediments. The term *barren* related only to benthos, of course. Several examples from the European Jurassic will be discussed.

With regard to the Toarcian Posidonienschiefer or Posidonia Shales of southern Germany, Kauffman (1981) challenged the conventional interpretation of total bottom water anoxia and proposed from his palaeocommunity analysis a regime of fluctuating weak to moderately oxygenated benthic environments interrupted episodically by short-term anoxic events. Among his most important supporting evidence was the occurrence of epifauna on large ammonite shells.

Seilacher (1982) has argued that, on the contrary, anoxic bottom conditions were normal, with brief interruptions of improved oxygenation allowing short-lived episodes of low-diversity benthos colonization. There is strong evidence that encrusting and byssally attached bivalves were associated with living ammonites, living on both sides of their shells, and did not attach themselves only to the upper surface of the empty

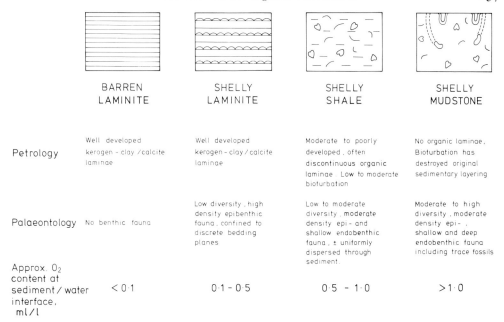

	BARREN LAMINITE	SHELLY LAMINITE	SHELLY SHALE	SHELLY MUDSTONE
Petrology	Well developed kerogen - clay /calcite laminae	Well developed kerogen - clay /calcite laminae	Moderate to poorly developed , often discontinuous organic laminae . Low to moderate bioturbation	No organic laminae , Bioturbation has destroyed original sedimentary layering
Palaeontology	No benthic fauna	Low diversity , high density epibenthic fauna , confined to discrete bedding planes	Low to moderate diversity , moderate density epi- and shallow endobenthic fauna , ± uniformly dispersed through sediment.	Moderate to high diversity , moderate density epi- , shallow and deep endobenthic fauna including trace fossils
Approx. O_2 content at sediment / water interface, ml / l	< 0·1	0·1 - 0·5	0·5 - 1·0	> 1·0

FIG. 2. Classification of mudrocks in terms of degree of lamination or bioturbation and character of benthic macrofauna, with inferred oxygen content of bottom sea water.

shells lying on the sea bed. Furthermore, there is evidence that the crinoid *Seirocrinus* was suspended from floating driftwood. Perhaps most convincing is the evidence of endoskeletons in the form of belemnites and reptile bones. Unlike normal shales these are never encrusted or bored in the Posidonia Shales and, unlike the ammonites, only became available for colonization after death of the organism and decay of the soft parts on the sea bed. A final point supporting a condition of total bottom anoxia in at least the basal part of the formation is the virtual absence of benthic forams and ostracods. Likewise, the dinoflagellate flora is very restricted (Küspert 1982).

The higher part of the Posidonia Shales is the one with layers of undoubtedly epibenthic *Bositra*, *Variamussium* and echinoids, their articulated shells or tests indicating very little water disturbance. Thin horizons are bioturbated with *Chondrites* (e.g. Seegrasschiefer). The latter are clearly thin horizons signifying highest oxygen concentrations. In terms of the classification of Fig. 2, the basal part of the Posidonia Shales represents barren laminites, which pass up into shelly laminites with thin intervals of shelly shale or mudstone. A parallel change up the succession can be seen at equivalent stratigraphic horizons in Yorkshire, from the Jet Rock to the Bituminous Shale Formation (Morris 1980).

The English Lower Oxford Clay consists mostly of shelly shale, with shelly laminite at the top, indicating slightly more oxygen at the sediment-water interface for most of the period of deposition, though still broadly within the anoxic zone (Morris 1980). The Kimmeridge Clay of Dorset contains many small cycles of barren laminite ('oil shales'), shelly laminite ('bituminous shales') and shelly shale ('clay', 'mudstone'), indicating frequent oscillations in bottom-water oxygen concentration (Tyson *et al.* 1979; Morris 1980; Aigner 1980).

An important question that remains to be considered, if not resolved, concerns the height in the water column to which anoxic water reached. The regular alternation in many organic-rich shale sequences of laminites with shelly shales and mudstones is most economically explained in terms of slight vertical fluctuations of the O_2/H_2S interface around the sediment/water interface. This would imply that, for many laminites, anoxic waters extended up from the sediment/water interface by only a short distance, perhaps only a few centimetres. In support of this is the frequent occurrence of nektonic elements such as ammonites and fish in what were often quite shallow epicontinental seas. Occasional bedding planes crowded with such nekton suggest episodes of mass mortality provoked by a short-term rise of the O_2/H_2S interface, or a storm-induced overturn of water. Within the upper part of the Kimmeridge Clay, horizons of coccolith limestone are interpreted by Tyson *et al.* (1979) as signifying the maximum development of anoxic bottom water. It is argued that the top of the H_2S zone moved upwards to provide nutrients to the euphotic zone and hence to stimulate coccolith production. One could argue that on the contrary such an event would be more likely to induce mass mortality. Furthermore it must be borne in mind that the limestones in question record intervals of time over tens of thousands of years, signifying 'blooms' of exceptionally long duration.

Environments of deposition

There is a striking correlation between organic-rich shale units and marine transgressions, especially in the early stages. The Anisian deposits of Arctic North America are associated with a major transgression, the Southern Alps occurrence corresponds in time with the upper Muschelkalk transgression, and the Westbury Beds and Contortaschichten occur close to the base of the late Norian transgressive sequence (Hallam 1981b). Besides the Jurassic examples discussed in these terms by Hallam and Bradshaw (1979) it should be noted that the widespread early Tithonian horizon corresponds with a major episode of transgression in the Andes. Cretaceous examples have been reviewed by Jenkyns (1980) and a correlation noted with postulated deep-ocean anoxic events. Compared with the Cretaceous, the Jurassic deep-ocean record is negligible and does not extend back in time beyond the Callovian. As indicated earlier, however, organic-rich shale horizons have been located in the North Atlantic for both Callovian and Kimmeridgian–Tithonian deposits, (i.e. for times when there were important epicontinental transgressions and widespread bottom-water anoxia). A possible exception to the general relationship outlined above occurs in the North Sea, where organic-rich shales occur in a Middle to Upper Volgian sequence interpreted by Rawson and Riley (1982) as comparatively regressive.

The correlation of marine transgressions with continent-to-ocean anoxic events is explained in terms of the promotion of plankton productivity within epicontinental seas and consequent expansion of the oxygen minimum layer (Schlanger & Jenkyns 1976). The brief residence time of dead plankton descending through the shallow water column in epicontinental seas acts in favour of preservation of organic matter (Arthur & Jenkyns 1981).

The high content of terrestrial plant matter in early to mid Cretaceous deposits in the North Atlantic is probably due to a combination of factors. The ocean was narrow, not especially deep, and was flanked by continents which experienced a humid climate, as signified by the presence of bauxites, coals, rich plant-bearing and abundant fluvial deposits; runoff was consequently high. In contrast, the early South Atlantic opened in an arid regime, as indicated by thick evaporite sequences. In the later Cretaceous, marine transgression would have driven back the bordering lands and the ocean would have been wider.

An additional possible factor concerns the rapid spread of the early angiosperms at this time, quickly replacing the gymnosperms as the dominant land flora. It has been argued that the earliest angiosperms had an opportunistic ecology, like weeds (Doyle 1977). This implies high reproductive potential and hence enormous productivity in humid regimes. A high runoff of plant debris to the adjacent ocean would be an obvious consequence of this. Subsequently a more mature vegetation with lower reproductive potential would have evolved. Thus the unexpected occurrence of so much terrestrially-derived plant matter in the North Atlantic may reflect, at least to a limited account, an evolutionary phenomenon.

Actualistic comparisons suggest rather strongly that the kerogen-clay/calcite microlamination is annual in origin, related in most cases to seasonal blooms of plankton (Hallam 1967a, b). On this assumption, the larger scale decimetre-to-metre-scale cyclicity, involving alternations of more and less oxidizing bottom conditions, implies major environmental changes of the order of tens of thousands of years. Such cyclicity has been recorded from the Blue Lias (Hallam 1960), Kimmeridge Clay (Tyson *et al.* 1979), Mowry Shale (Byers & Larsen 1979) and North Atlantic Cretaceous (Cool 1982).

For both epicontinental and oceanic deposits it seems necessary to invoke a stratified water column, more probably maintained by a thermocline than a halocline, in a world of equable climate (Tyson *et al.* 1979; Jenkyns 1980). The origin of the environmental changes is unresolved but amenable to speculation. Sea-level changes could act in two different ways. Within a given epicontinental basin, a rise in sea level would lead to water-column deepening which might be sufficient to create an anoxic layer at the bottom; this would be lost during a subsequent sea-level fall. Alternatively, or in addition, sea-level rise would cause transgression, which could promote organic productivity and a consequent upward and downward expansion of the oxygen minimum zone. Thus this process could affect epicontinental sea and ocean basin alike. The prime weakness of a eustatic hypothesis is the frequency of the cyclicity, which is well beyond the biostratigraphic resolution attainable even with ammonites, but sea-level changes cannot be excluded for at least some of the more important events.

The obvious alternative hypothesis involves changes in climate, especially as the duration of the alternating depositional episodes is similar to Milankovich cycles. The mediation between atmospheric temperature change and bottom-water anoxicity remains uncertain, however. One possible explanation is that episodes of cooler climate provoke increased latitudinal energy transfer and hence increased ocean current activity. This could have had an effect on the delicate balance involved in establishing a stratified water column.

Facies models

No single facies model will account for all occurrences of Mesozoic organic-rich shales but the range of possibilities is limited. Demaison and Moore (1980) put forward three models based on Recent marine environments, to which an extra one is added here (Fig. 3).

The silled basin model (Fig. 3A) is based primarily on the Black Sea, though there are plenty of other modern examples, but the extent to which it is apposite for Mesozoic epicontinental shales remains questionable. It was argued by Hallam (1967a, b, 1975), on grounds of facies associations, that Jurassic shales were deposited in quite shallow water, no more than a few tens of metres deep. This has been supported more recently on two other grounds: the evidence of occasional storm action (shell orientation by currents, scours, graded laminae) and ammonites embedded at high angles to the bedding (Aigner 1980; Morris 1980; Seilacher 1982). Aigner's (1980) estimate of 30 m (for the Kimmeridge Clay), based on ammonite orientations, seems excessively shallow, and one is bound to question the reliability of the technique. If an epicontinental sea is extensive and shallow enough, the hydrodynamic regime will tend towards restriction of circulation without the presence of one or more sills being required. Even slight topographic variations will have a disproportionately large effect in restricting water circulation, especially during the early stages of a marine transgression. Subsequently, as irregularities are progressively smoothed out by sedimentation, freer circulation should ensue (Hallam 1981a). Stratigraphic and facies relationships suggest that, within this

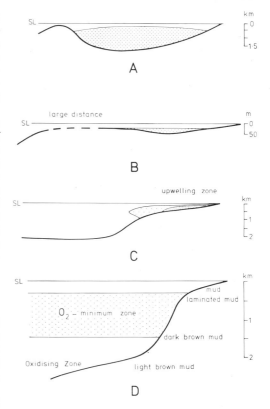

FIG. 3. Facies models to account for Mesozoic anoxic deposits. A, C and D based on Demaison and Moore (1980). A, silled deep basin; B, shallow epicontinental sea; C, oceanic upwelling zone; D, anoxic open ocean. Density of stippling corresponds to degree of anoxia.

shallow setting, the organic-rich shales tend to be relatively deep-water deposits which are concentrated in basinal environments (Fig. 3B).

The silled deep-basin model may indeed apply best to the late Jurassic and Cretaceous of the young, narrow and therefore probably restricted North Atlantic basin. Fig. 1 indicates that, although there is a mid Cretaceous concentration, organic-rich deposits are present almost continuously through this time.

Demaison and Moore's second marine model concerns anoxic layers caused by upwelling, as off Namibia and Peru (Fig. 3C). The sea-floor deposits in these regions are enriched in phosphorites. With regard to Mesozoic examples, the likeliest appear to be the Sinemurian shales and phosphorites of Peru (Loughman 1984; Loughman & Hallam 1982) and similar deposits of late Cretaceous to early Tertiary age laid down on the southern margins of Tethys, stretching from North Africa into the Middle East (Arthur & Jenkyns 1981).

Finally, Demaison and Moore refer to the anoxic open ocean, as exemplified today by the equatorial East Pacific and northern Indian Ocean, where large volumes of anoxic water occur at intermediate oceanic depths. This is bound up with the Coriolis Force causing a tendency to stagnation on the eastern side of oceans. Where the anoxic layer impinges on the sea bed, organic-rich sediments are deposited (Fig. 3D). The possible Mesozoic examples are the mid Cretaceous deposits on Pacific plateaus, which, because of subsequent sea-floor spreading, would have been located further to the east at the time they were laid down.

ACKNOWLEDGEMENTS: I wish to express my thanks to Drs S. Brown, I. Fisher and J. D. Hudson for their critical reading of the manuscript.

References

AIGNER, T. 1980. Biofacies and stratinomy of the Lower Kimmeridge Clay (U. Jurassic, Dorset, England). *N. Jb. Geol. Palaont. Abh.* **159**, 324–38.

ARTHUR, M. A. & SCHLANGER, S. O. 1979. Cretaceous 'oceanic anoxic events' as causal factors in development of reef-reservoired giant oilfields. *Bull. Am. Ass. Petrol. Geol.* **63**, 870–85.

—— & JENKYNS, H. C. 1981. Phosphorites and paleoceanography. *Oceanologica Acta*, Proc. 26th Int. geol. Congr., Geology of oceans sympos., Paris 1980, 83–96.

BARKER, P. F., DALZIEL, I. W. D. *et al.* 1977. Initial Reports of the Deep Sea Drilling Project, vol. 36, U.S. Govt. Printing Office, Washington, D.C.

BODENHAUSEN, J. W. A. & OTT, W. F. 1981. Habitat of the Rijswijk Oil Province, onshore, The Netherlands. *In*: ILLING, L. V. and HOBSON, G. D. (eds), *Petroleum Geology of the Continental Shelf of North-West Europe*. Inst. Petrol. Lond., 301–309.

BYERS, C. W. & LARSEN, D. W. 1979. Paleoenvironments of Mowry Shale (Lower Cretaceous), Western and Central Wyoming. *Bull. Am. Ass. Petrol. Geol.* **63**, 359–61.

CAMPOS, H. S. & HALLAM, A. 1979. Diagenesis of English Lower Jurassic limestones as inferred from oxygen and carbon isotope analysis. *Earth Planet. Sci. Lett.* **45**, 23–31.

COOL, T. E. 1982. Sedimentological evidence concerning the paleoceanography of the Cretaceous western North Atlantic Ocean. *Palaeogeog., Palaeoclimatol., Palaeocol.* **39**, 1–36.

DEMAISON, G. J. & MOORE, G. T. 1980. Anoxic environments and oil source bed genesis. *Bull. Am. Ass. Petrol. Geol.* **64**, 1179–1209.

DOYLE, J. A. 1977. Patterns of evolution in early angiosperms. *In*: HALLAM, A. (ed.), *Patterns of Evolution as Illustrated by the Fossil Record*. Elsevier, Amsterdam, 501–546.

DUFF, K. L. 1975. Palaeoecology of bituminous shale—the Lower Oxford Clay of Central England. *Palaeontology*, **18**, 433–82.

FARQUHARSON, G. W. 1982. Late Mesozoic sedimentation in the northern Antarctic Peninsula and its relationship to the southern Andes. *J. geol. Soc.* **139**, 721–28.

HALLAM, A. 1960. A sedimentary and faunal study of the Blue Lias of Dorset and Glamorgan. *Phil. Trans. roy. Soc.* **243B**, 1–44.

—— 1965. Environmental causes of stunting in living and fossil marine benthonic invertebrates. *Palaeontology*, **8**, 132–55.

—— 1967a. The depth significance of shales with bituminous laminae. *Marine Geology*, **5**, 481–93.

—— 1967b. An environmental study of the Upper Domerian and Lower Toarcian in Great Britain. *Phil. Trans. roy. Soc.* **252B**, 393–445.

—— 1975. *Jurassic Environments*. Cambridge Univ. Press. 269 pp.

—— 1981a. *Facies Interpretation and the Stratigraphic Record*. Freeman, Oxford and San Francisco. 291 pp.

—— 1981b. The end-Triassic bivalve extinction event. *Palaeogeog., Palaeoclimatol., Palaeoecol.* **35**, 1–44.

—— 1981c. A revised sea level curve for the early Jurassic. *J. geol. Soc.* **138**, 735–43.

—— & BRADSHAW, M. J. 1979. Bituminous shales and oolitic ironstones as indicators of transgressions and regressions. *J. geol. Soc.* **136**, 157–64.

HUDSON, J. D. 1982. Pyrite in ammonite-bearing shales from the Jurassic of England and Germany. *Sedimentology*, **29**, 639–67.

IRVING, E., NORTH, F. K. & COVILLARD, R. 1974. Oil, climate and tectonics. *Can. J. Earth Sci.* **11**, 1–25.

IRWIN, H., CURTIS, C. D. & COLEMAN, M. L. 1977. Isotopic evidence for source of diagenetic carbonates formed during burial of organic-rich sediments. *Nature*, **269**, 209–13.

JENKYNS, H. C. 1980. Cretaceous anoxic events: from continents to oceans. *J. geol. Soc.* **137**, 171–188.

—— 1985. The early Toarcian and Cenomanian–Twonian anoxic events in Europe: comparisons and contrasts. *Geol. Rundschau*, **74**, 505–18.

—— & CLAYTON, C. J. 1986. Black shales and carbon isotopes in pelagic sediments from the Tethyan lower Jurassic. *Sedimentology*, **33**, 87–106.

KAUFFMAN, E. G. 1981. Ecological reappraisal of the German Posidonienschiefer (Toarcian) and the stagnant basin model. *In*: GRAY, J., BOUCOT, A. J. & BERRY, W. B. N. (eds), *Communities of the past*. Hutchinson Ross, Stroudsburg, Penns., 311–81.

KONTOROVICH, A. E. (ed.) 1971. Geochemistry of petroleum-bearing Mesozoic formations in the Siberian basins. *USSR Ministry of Geology Publ. SN11G—IMS Bull.* **118**, 1–85 (in Russian).

KÜSPERT, W. 1982. Environmental changes during oil shale deposition as deduced from stable isotope ratios. *In*: EINSELE, G. & SEILACHER, A. (eds), *Cyclic and Event Stratification*. Springer Verlag, Berlin, Heidelberg, New York, 482–501.

LOUGHMAN, D. L. 1984. Phosphate authigenesis in the Aramachay Formation (Lower Jurassic) of Peru. *J. sedim. Petrol.* **54**, 1147–56.

LOUGHMAN, D. L. & HALLAM, A. 1982. A facies analysis of the Pucará Group (Norian-Toarcian carbonates, organic-rich shales and phosphate) of Central and North Peru. *Sedim. Geol.* **32**, 161–94.

MITCHUM, R. M. & ULIANA, M. A. 1985. Seismic stratigraphy of carbonate depositional sequences, Upper Jurassic–Lower Cretaceous, Neuquen Basin, Argentina. *Mem. Am. Ass. Petrol. Geol.*, **39**.

MORRIS, K. A. 1980. Comparison of major sequences of organic-rich mud deposition in the British Jurassic. *J. geol. Soc.* **137**, 157–70.

MURRIS, R. J. 1980. Middle East: stratigraphic evolution and oil habitat. *Bull. Am. Ass. Petrol. Geol.* **64**, 595–618.

PETTERS, S. W. & EKWEOZOR, C. M. 1982. Origin of mid-Cretaceous black shales in the Benue Trough, Nigeria. *Palaeogeog., Palaeoclimatol., Palaeoecol.* **40**, 311–20.

RAISWELL, R. 1976. The microbiological formation of carbonate concretions in the Upper Lias of N.E. England. *Chem. Geol.* **18**, 227–44.

RAWSON, P. F. & RILEY, L. A. 1982. Latest Jurassic-Early Cretaceous events and the 'Late Cimmerian Unconformity' in North Sea area. *Bull. Am. Ass. Petrol. Geol.* **66**, 2628–48.

RIEBER, H. 1974. Ammoniten und Stratigraphie der Grenzbitumenzone (Mittlere Trias) der Tessiner Kalkalpen. *In*: ZAPFE, H. (ed.), *Die Stratigraphie der Alpin-mediterranen Trias*. Springer Verlag, Vienna, New York, 167–76.

—— 1982. The formation of the bituminous layers of the Middle Triassic of Ticino (Switzerland). *In*: EINSELE, G. & SEILACHER, A. (eds.), *Cyclic and event stratification*. Springer Verlag, Berlin, Heidelberg, New York, 527.

SCHLANGER, S. O. & JENKYNS, H. C. 1976. Cretaceous anoxic events: causes and consequences. *Geol. Mijnb.* **55**, 179–84.

SCHMIDT-EFFING, K. 1980. The Huayacocotla aulacogen in Mexico (Lower Jurassic) and the origin of the Gulf of Mexico. *In*: PILGER, R. H. (ed.), *The Origin of the Gulf of Mexico and the early Opening of the Atlantic Ocean*. Louisiana State Univ., 79–86.

SCHOLLE, P. A. & ARTHUR, M. A. 1980. Carbon isotope fluctuations in Cretaceous pelagic limestones: potential stratigraphic and petroleum exploration tool. *Bull. Am. Ass. Petrol. Geol.* **64**, 67–87.

SCHULTZ, L. G., TOURTELOT, H. A., GILL, J. R. & BOERNGEN, J. G. 1980. Composition and properties of the Pierre Shale and equivalent rocks, northern Great Plains region. *U.S. Geol. Surv. Profess. Paper* **1064-B**, 1–114.

SEILACHER, A. 1982. Posidonia Shales (Toarcian, S. Germany)—stagnant basin model revalidated. *In*: MONTANARO GALLITELLI, E. (ed.), *Palaeontology, Essential of Historical Geology* (Proc. of internat. meeting, Venice). STEM Mucchi Modena Press, 25–55.

SHERIDAN, R. E., GRADSTEIN, F. M. *et al.* 1983. Initial Reports of the Deep Sea Drilling Project, vol. LXXVI, Washington (U.S. Govt. Printing Office).

SURLYK, F. 1977. Stratigraphy, tectonics and palaeogeography of the Jurassic sediments of the areas north of Kong Oscars Fjord, East Greenland. *Gronl. Geol. Undersog. Bull.* **123**, 1–56.

TISSOT, B. P. 1979. Effects on prolific petroleum source rocks and major coal deposits caused by sea-level changes. *Nature*, **277**, 463–5.

—— & WELTE, D. H. 1978. *Petroleum formation and occurrence*. Springer Verlag, Berlin.

——, DEMAISON, G., MASSON, P., DELTEK, J. R. & COMBAZ, A. 1980. Paleoenvironment and petroleum potential of middle Cretaceous black shales in Atlantic basins. *Bull. Am. Ass. Petrol. Geol.* **64**, 2051–63.

TOZER, E. T. 1980. Latest Triassic (Upper Norian) ammonoid and *Monotis* faunas and correlations. *Riv. Ital. Paleont.* **85**, 843–76.

TYSON, R. V., WILSON, R. C. L. & DOWNIE, C. 1979. A stratified water column environmental model for the type Kimmeridge Clay. *Nature*, **277**, 377–80.

A. HALLAM, Department of Geological Sciences, Univerisity of Birmingham, U.K.

A review of petroleum source rocks in parts of the Middle East

R. Stoneley

SUMMARY: The oils in the Mesozoic and Tertiary reservoirs of the region surrounding the inner Persian/Arabian Gulf were derived from Jurassic and Cretaceous argillaceous and carbonate source rocks, which accumulated at various times in more or less restricted intra-shelf basins and depressions, and were preserved under anoxic conditions. Maturation, migration and accumulation took place from the late Cretaceous onwards, at different times in different parts of the region; however, Upper Cretaceous and Tertiary sediments are, for the most part, still immature. This sourcing history is one of a number of favourable circumstances contributing to the richness of the region.

One of the factors contributing to the petroleum abundance of the Middle East is the richness and efficiency of the source rocks. This paper is a brief review of the available information concerning their development in a restricted region around the inner Persian/Arabian Gulf (hereafter referred to as the Gulf) (Fig. 1). It is based essentially on the very limited amount of published data and inferences that can be made from them. It is hoped that it will stimulate the release of additional, presently confidential, studies.

Little information is available on the source rocks of the Palaeozoic oil in the Oman and, beyond speculation, of the gas that is widespread

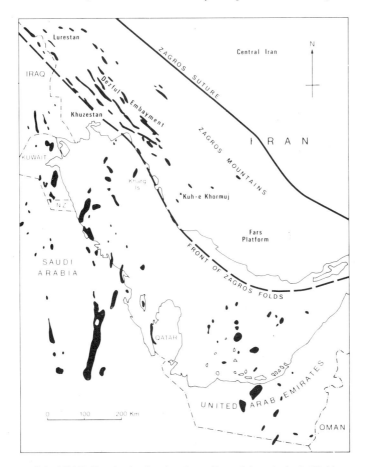

FIG. 1. Locality map of the Middle East basin, showing the outlines of the principal oilfields.

From: BROOKS, J. & FLEET, A. J. (eds) 1987, *Marine Petroleum Source Rocks*
Geological Society Special Publication No. 26 pp. 263–269.

in the Permian: it may have been derived from the underlying Palaeozoic, although an indigenous source in the Permian is still not excluded. This review, therefore, is confined to the Mesozoic source rocks, which are considered in their stratigraphical context.

Regional setting

Our study begins in the Permian with a marine transgression that was widespread over much of the Middle East region. It may have been centered on and related to incipient rifting associated with the Zagros suture, through a continent that then included the present central Iran. This rifting led eventually in the late Triassic to the separation of central Iran from the Afro-Arabian continent and the formation of a new ocean, the Southern Tethys, between them (Stöcklin 1974; Stoneley 1974; Koop & Stoneley 1982). Thereafter, the entire region of eastern Arabia, the Gulf and southwest Iran evolved as an extensive shelf at an inactive continental margin on the southwestern side of the Southern Tethys, until its closure again through collision of the shelf with central Iran early in the Miocene. The only event to disturb this tranquility was the emplacement of ophiolites on the outer edge of the shelf in the late Cretaceous, which there is reason to believe may have resulted from further incipient rifting along the continental margin (Stoneley 1975, 1981; Hall, in press).

The Mesozoic–Palaeogene continental shelf covered an area 2000 to 3000 km wide by at least twice as long (Murris 1980), and included a number of sub-basins separated by more stable elements subject to the effects of sea-level changes. The basins range in scale from the rather persistent Sargelu (middle–late Jurassic) and Garau (early–middle Cretaceous) basin; through temporary and deep depressions such as the Albian Kazhdumi basin; to generally more localized, short-lived, relatively shallow water depressions in which shifting sedimentary environments are reflected. The latter are exemplified in the Tuwaiq Mountain and Hanifa Formations of Saudi Arabia, and the Shuaiba and Shilaif Formations of the southern Gulf. The distribution of these basins is believed, to a large extent, to have been governed by gentle vertical movements of ancient structural features in the crystalline basement (Aramco 1975; Ayres *et al.* 1982). The location of the basins in turn governs the distribution of source rocks, as well as of many of the reservoirs, in which primary porosity is often preserved, in the surrounding shallow-water areas. It is this shifting interplay of sea-floor highs and lows, within an essentially carbonate shelf, that provides the first control on the distribution of petroleum.

The second important factor is the organic richness of the shelf. This is reflected both by the enormous volumes of carbonate which accumulated, and by the organic content of the deeper water sediments which were preserved under anoxic conditions. It has been suggested (Irving *et al.* 1974) that marine organic material may have been driven north-westwards by winds from the more open waters of the Indian Ocean into the restricted Southern Tethys. However, it is also possible that the shelf margin was in a position to satisfy the conditions required for oceanic upwelling (e.g. Parrish 1982) during the Jurassic and Cretaceous.

A third factor is the extent and efficiency of seals in the sequence. Argillaceous and carbonate seals have generally not been disturbed sufficiently to lose their integrity; and evaporites, principally in the uppermost Jurassic (Hith–Gotnia) and in the Miocene (Gach Saran) but also locally in other parts of the succession, are effective. It is one of the unexplained paradoxes that, whilst particularly the Hith is very effective as a seal, it has apparently been breached locally to feed higher reservoirs (Wilson 1982).

A fourth factor was the progressive development of a number of the potential trap-forming structures, ensuring that sealed traps were available by the time that the source rocks reached maturity. Basement related structures were certainly being developed by the Late Cretaceous, and possibly considerably earlier. And more localized features, due to movements of the underlying infra-Cambrian Hormuz salt, date from at least the beginning of the Cretaceous (Kent 1979); a few of them may have been growing as early as the Triassic.

This regime came to an end in the early Miocene with the closure of Southern Tethys and the subsequent compression of the outer parts of the shelf. The style of the Zagros folds permitted by detachment above the Hormuz salt (e.g. Coleman-Sadd 1978) was such that, where the integrity of the evaporite seal above reservoirs as high as the Oligo–Miocene has been preserved, they form perfect traps for Mesozoic oil that otherwise would have been lost (e.g. Ala *et al.* 1980).

It is the exceptionally favourable conjunction of a large number of independent factors that is responsible for the richness of the region. We are concerned, however, with the source rocks, and enough information is available for us to review them from the point of view of their stratigraphical development.

Stratigraphical distribution of source rocks (Fig. 2)

Following the generally arid conditions of the Triassic, a major marine transgression spread across the shelf late in the early Jurassic; within it the deep-water Sargelu basin soon became differentiated over the area of south-eastern Iraq and the Lurestan and north-west Khuzestan provinces of Iran (Murris 1980; Koop & Stoneley 1982). Stable conditions prevailed through the middle Jurassic. Over the shelf, high energy carbonates are interspersed with pelletoidal mud packstones (Dhruma, Araej) which have generated oil that has accumulated locally in the oolitic grainstones on the southern side of the Gulf (Murris 1980; Ayres *et al.* 1982). In the Sargelu basin, deep water shales and argillaceous limestones of middle Jurassic age (Setudehnia 1978) form an extensive and prolific source rock with organic contents that can exceed 5%.

The Sargelu basin persisted through the late Jurassic, although it became more restricted as a result of flank progradation. It became the site of anhydrite deposition (Gotnia), which gradually spread south-eastwards and covered almost the entire shelf (Hith) towards the close of the period. Within the more stable shelf itself, two broad depressions developed sequentially. The first, in the late Callovian–Oxfordian, covered the main oilfield area of eastern Saudi Arabia (Ayres *et al.* 1982). In the centre of the basin some 100 m of laminated peloidal carbonates (Tuwaiq Mountain) contain an average of 3–5% of Type II amorphous organic matter, although interleaved with thin beds of oxygenated sediment: they are the source of most of the oil in Saudi Arabia. Further east, in the Qatar-southern Gulf region, a rather similar depression developed in the Late Oxfordian–Early Kimmeridgian following renewed transgression (Murris 1980): the argillaceous limestones of the Hanifa–Dukhan Formation gave rise to much of the oil in this region. In contrast, at this time, a shallow-water sill separated the shelf from an open-marine basin still further to the east, where marls and occasional limestones apparently have a low source potential (Murris 1980).

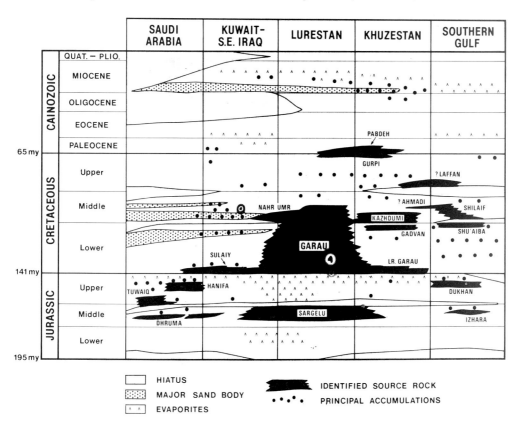

FIG. 2. The stratigraphical positions of the identified source rocks in the Middle East basin.

Following the 'salinity crisis' of the latest Jurassic, the early Cretaceous saw a further transgression and a return to shelf conditions over most of the region. The Sargelu basin persisted as the deep water Garau basin, becoming gradually displaced to the north-east in the Lurestan area of Iran: deep water shales and limestones accumulated throughout the early and middle Cretaceous reaching a total thickness in excess of 2,000 m. The initial transgression briefly carried the Garau euxinic facies over much of the Dezful Embayment of Khuzestan: it constitutes one of the source rocks of the region and total organic contents up to about 4% have been reported. The equivalent transgressive beds at the base of the Cretaceous (Sulaiy) may have acted locally as a source in the northernmost part of the Gulf and in south-east Iraq (Ayres et al. 1982; Ibrahim 1983).

Further shallow transgression in the Aptian, contemporaneous with the first flood of sand from the Arabian shield into the northern Gulf region (Zubair), gave rise to varied carbonate shelf facies. Restricted shales in the Gadvan Formation of Iran and the Shu'aiba of the southern Gulf (Murris 1980) provide localized sources with organic carbon contents up to about 2%, and have intertonguing relationships with the surrounding carbonates.

In the Albian a restricted, initially deep water, basin suddenly developed in Khuzestan and the northernmost Gulf. The Kazhdumi Formation and the equivalent argillaceous distal parts of the Nahr Umr Formation constitute the most important source of this part of the region. In the centre of the basin, shales and cherts lead up into up to 600 m of black euxinic shales with Type II kerogen and organic carbon contents up to some 10% (Ala et al. 1980): these pass laterally into oxygenated grey shales with thin limestones and then into neritic carbonates. Towards the west, the black shales interfinger with sands of the second siliciclastic wedge (Burgan–Nahr Umr), whilst northwestwards they grade into the Garau Formation. In the southern Gulf a probably separated shelf depression (Murris 1980) contains source rocks in shales of the Shilaif Formation, and may have persisted for longer than the Kazhdumi as the Cenomanian Ahmadi shale.

The Lower Senonian Laffan shale could have acted as a source locally in the southern Gulf region. However, the main feature of the late Cretaceous was a change in the outer part of the shelf (Iran) from the earlier basement controlled shelf conditions to the development of a north-west–south-east trough parallel to the continental margin (Koop & Stoneley 1982). Although of more open marine marl-pelagic limestone facies,

the uppermost Cretaceous Gurpi and Lower Tertiary Pabdeh Formations contain up to 6% of organic carbon (Ala et al. 1980) and locally act as source rocks.

Maturation and migration (Fig. 3)

The kerogens of the Gulf region seem to be almost exclusively Type II and oil-prone. Although we are reminded by Wilson (1982) of the possibilities of early generation in evaporite-associated source rocks, it is assumed here that the Middle East source rocks are subject to the normally accepted temperature/time constraints on maturation: certainly the bulk of the evidence is consistent with this.

Our conclusions concerning maturation levels and generation/migration times are based on (a) published geochemical data and (b) theoretical estimations of TTI values (Waples 1980). What follows is largely based on these, much of the thickness information for the latter being derived from Koop and Stoneley (1982). The only actual proof that oil was migrating in the Cretaceous, that the writer is aware of, comes from Kuh-e Khormuj, adjacent to the south-eastern edge of the Dezful Embayment in Iran: the Cenomanian/Turonian Sarvak Formation thins and becomes dolomitic towards a salt plug, and at one locality contains a bed in which dolomite crystals are held apart by pitch. This is interpreted as a fossil seepage (Kent 1979). Other considerations all involve the use of TTI calculations and assumptions of past heat-flow, which are constrained by present values and by observed maturation levels.

The earliest time at which any of the Mesozoic source rocks are believed to have reached the oil generation threshold is the Turonian, when the middle Jurassic Sargelu Formation may locally have been sufficiently buried. This is consistent with the evidence from Kuh-e Khormuj. During the late Cretaceous, strong north–south troughs were developing in southern Khuzestan (Setudehnia 1978; Koop & Stoneley 1982), and in these the basal Cretaceous Garau source rocks could have reached maturity by the close of the period. The Upper Jurassic and Lower Cretaceous oils, found for example at Kharg Island and Gach Saran, which are compositionally different from the higher Cretaceous oils (Ala et al. 1980), may have started to accumulate at this stage. Ibrahim et al. (1981) suggest that, in Saudi Arabia, the deeper Jurassic sources may have been mature by the latest Cretaceous; the middle Jurassic reservoirs may have been fed at this

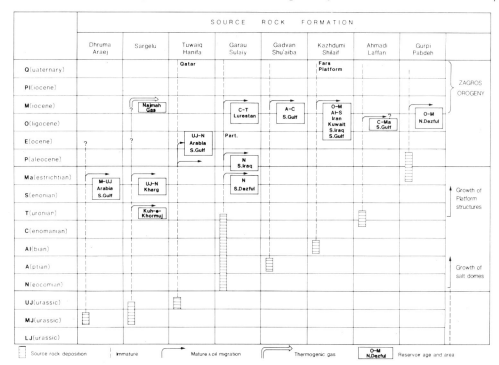

FIG. 3. Diagram showing tentatively the timing of source rock maturation and oil migration in the Middle East Basin.

time, and the same could apply locally in the southern Gulf area.

Lastly, to the east of our area, and although the source rock is not specified, Burruss *et al.* (1983) have indicated that, on the evidence of hydrocarbon inclusions in the calcite cement of fractures in Upper Cretaceous rocks of the Oman foredeep, oil was migrating within the period from late Turonian to early Campanian. Further west, in the shallower part of the foredeep, they mention that migration occurred later, in the early Tertiary.

It should be noted that the basement-controlled structures of Arabia were developing from about the Turonian onwards (Steineke *et al.* 1958; Ibrahim *et al.* 1981), whilst salt structures were active earlier: in Kuwait, structural growth is documented from the beginning of the Cretaceous (Al-Refai 1967), and some of the Iranian domes may have been growing as early as the Triassic. Early Cretaceous faulting controlled development of the Kharg Island structure. There is little doubt, therefore, that traps were available by the time that oil started migrating.

The main Upper Jurassic source rocks of Arabia reached maturity locally in off-structure positions in the Paleocene (Ibrahim *et al.* 1981), and widely in the early Eocene. Although still

immature over the north–south Qatar Arch (Murris 1980), they reached peak generation in the early Eocene in Saudi Arabia (Ibrahim *et al.* 1981; Ayres *et al.* 1982) and also in the southern Gulf area. The lowest Cretaceous of southern Iraq (Sulaiy) may also have attained maturity by the Eocene (Ibrahim 1983). Again, traps were available at this stage to receive the oil, and it seems unnecessary to postulate long-distance migration.

The prolific Albian source-rocks of the Kazhdumi Formation have been shown beyond doubt to have supplied most of the oil found in the Upper Cretaceous and Tertiary reservoirs of Iran (e.g. Ala *et al.* 1980), and to have fed the middle Cretaceous reservoirs of Kuwait, southern Iraq (Ibrahim 1983) and probably some of the Arabian offshore fields in the northern Gulf (Ayres *et al.* 1982). The Kazhdumi may locally have reached the oil generation threshold in the late Eocene (Ala 1982) but it was not widely mature until the Miocene: it is believed to be still immature over the Fars Platform of southern Iran. Peak generation and migration in the Dezful Embayment were more or less coincident with the beginning of the Zagros orogeny, and indeed volumetric considerations suggest that, in general, the oil found in the Zagros anticlines of Iran could have been supplied from within their present structural drainage areas. Migration to the Tertiary reservoirs is attributed to fractures, possibly temporary, caused by the folding and a similar origin is likely for the oil in higher reservoirs on the Arabian side of the Gulf, such as that in the Tertiary of the Neutral Zone. The Shu'aiba Formation of the southern Gulf also probably reached maturity in the Miocene.

The post-Albian rocks are still immature over most of Gulf region. In localized basins of the southern Gulf area, the Shilaif is believed to have reached a sufficient depth to provide oil to Upper Cretaceous reservoirs (Mishrif), and the Ahmadi and Laffan shales could have contributed in a few places. In Iran, the uppermost Cretaceous Gurpi and Lower Tertiary Pabdeh Formations are generally immature (e.g. Ala *et al.* 1980), but there is evidence that they have supplemented the Asmari oils in the northern recesses of the Dezful Embayment. Fossil seepages in the Upper Miocene–Pliocene Agha Jari Formation further attest the migration of oils during the Zagros orogeny.

Finally, it should be noted that the deeper parts at least of the Sargelu basin could have reached the gas generation zone by about the Miocene. This conclusion, reached from depth of burial considerations, may be supported by the presence of gas in the Upper Jurassic (Najmah) at a few fields in the area of the former basin.

Conclusions

Astonishing juxtapositions of unusually favourable circumstances appear to have been responsible for the oil richness of the Middle East. Moreover, these juxtapositions were repeated in different ways in different places and at different times.

Rich source rocks, both shales and limestones, accumulated in restricted intra-shelf depressions and, either singly or in combination, are present at one level or another over much of the region except for the Fars Platform of southern Iran. They reached maturity at times when traps were available nearby to receive the oil: this applies both to the Cretaceous–early Tertiary structures on the Arabian side of the Gulf, and to the Neogene folds in Iran.

Reservoirs with good porosity and effective seals lay in reasonably close proximity to the source rocks. This again applies to the Jurassic and Cretaceous reservoirs of the Arabian side, where the Aptian to Cenomanian sheet sands of the northern Gulf complement the grainstones of the Middle and Upper Jurassic and the Lower Cretaceous to the south; it also applies to the Upper Cretaceous and Tertiary of Iran. In some fields, we are forced to suppose that temporary fractures or faults, together with localized absence of sealing formations, have permitted migration to higher levels, and we cannot yet always account for the present vertical distribution of oils and gas. However, the evidence that this has happened seems overwhelming.

It has been argued (e.g. Wilson 1982) that differences of cementation between the oil and water legs of certain reservoirs point to migration considerably earlier than geochemical and TTI considerations suggest. This need not, however, apply if we can establish that primary porosity was preserved for up to 100 million years. Evidence has been produced from elsewhere that primary porosity can be preserved in oolitic grainstones for considerable periods of time (e.g. Evamy & Shearman 1965), and two considerations from the Middle East may be relevant. Holocene hard-grounds in the Gulf overlie and intervene between locally uncemented carbonate sands (D. J. Shearman, *pers. comm.*) and, in the absence of extensive water circulation, there would be little to disturb this situation (suggestion of R. C. Selley). Secondly, Upper Cretaceous grainstone turbidites found near the outer edge of the Middle East shelf contain isolated and unbroken grains of shelf debris including cleanly separated Upper Jurassic and Lower Cretaceous benthonic foraminifera (e.g. Glennie *et al.* 1973; Stoneley 1981): these suggest that earlier shelf carbonates were partly uncemented in the late Cretaceous. There should therefore be little difficulty in imagining the preservation of primary porosity, in both carbonate and siliciclastic reservoirs, until the migration of oil or contemporaneous earth-movements initiated the circulation of formation waters.

Indeed fortune has smiled upon the Middle East!

ACKNOWLEDGEMENTS: The writer is grateful to Dr Jim Brooks for suggesting this paper, and to numerous past and present colleagues for useful discussions at various times. Mr A. R. Brown, Imperial College, London, drafted the diagrams.

References

ALA, M. A. 1982. Chronology of trap formation and migration of hydrocarbons in the Zagros sector of Southwest Iran. *Bull. Am. Assoc. Petrol. Geol.* **66**, 1535–41.

ALA, M. A., KINGHORN, R. R. F. & RAHMAN, M. 1980. Organic geochemistry and source rock characteristics of the Zagros petroleum province, Southwest Iran. *J. Petrol. Geol.* **3**, 61–89.

AL-REFAI, B. H. 1967. The stratigraphy and sedimentation of Jurassic and Lower Cretaceous of Kuwait. *6th Arab Petrol. Congr.* **47** (B-3), Baghdad.

ARAMCO 1975. Eastern Arabia and adjacent areas—geological sketch. *In: Schlumberger Well Evaluation Conference: Arabia.* 9–25.

AYRES, M. G., BILAL, M., JONES, R. W., SLENTZ, L. W., TARTIR, M. & WILSON, A. O. 1982. Hydrocarbon habitat in main producing areas, Saudi Arabia. *Bull. Am. Assoc. Petrol. Geol.* **66**, 1–9.

BURRUSS, R. C., CERCONE, K. R. & HARRIS, P. M. 1983. Regional distribution of hydrocarbon fluid inclusions in carbonate fracture filling cements: geohistory analysis and timing of oil migration, Oman Foredeep (abstract). *Bull. Am. Assoc. Petrol. Geol.* **67**, 434.

COLEMAN-SADD, S. P. 1978. Fold development in Zagros simply folded belt. *Bull. Am. Assoc. Petrol. Geol.* **62**, 984–1003.

EVAMY, B. D. & SHEARMAN, D. J. 1965. The development of overgrowths from echinoderm fragments. *Sedimentology*, **5**, 211–33.

GLENNIE, K. W., BOEUF, M. G. A. *et al.* 1973. Late Cretaceous nappes in Oman Mountains and their geologic evolution. *Bull. Am. Assoc. Petrol. Geol.* **57**, 5–27.

HALL, R. 1982. Ophiolites and passive continental margins. *Ofioliti*, **2/3**, 279–98.

IBRAHIM, M. W. 1983. Petroleum geology of Southern Iraq. *Bull. Am. Assoc. Petrol. Geol.* **67**, 97–130.

IBRAHIM, M. W., KHAN, M. S. & KHATIB, H. 1981. Structural evolution of Harmaliyah oil field, Saudi Arabia. *Bull. Am. Assoc. Petrol. Geol.* **65**, 2403–16.

IRVING, E., NORTH, F. K. & COUILLARD, R. 1974. Oil, climate and tectonics. *Can. J. Earth Sci.* **11**, 1–17.

KENT, P. E. 1979. The emergent Hormuz salt plugs of Southern Iran. *J. Petrol. Geol.* **2**, 117–44.

KOOP, W. J. & STONELEY, R. 1982. Subsidence history of the Middle East Zagros Basin, Permian to Recent. *Phil. Trans. R. Soc. Lond. A.*, **305**, 149–68.

MURRIS, R. J. 1980. Middle East: stratigraphic evolution and oil habitat. *Bull. Am. Assoc. Petrol. Geol.* **64**, 597–618.

PARRISH, J. T. 1982. Upwelling and petroleum source beds, with reference to Paleozoic. *Bull. Am. Assoc. Petrol. Geol.* **66**, 750–74.

SETUDEHNIA, A. 1978. The Mesozoic sequence in southwest Iran and adjacent areas. *J. Petrol. Geol.* **1**, 3–42.

STEINEKE, M., BRANKAMP, R. A. and SANDER, N. J. 1958. Stratigraphic relations of Arabian Jurassic oil. *In:* WEEKS, L. G. (ed.) *Habitat of Oil*, Am. Assoc. Petrol. Geol., pp. 1294–1329.

STÖCKLIN, J. 1974. Possible ancient continental margins in Iran. *In:* Burk, C. A. & Drake, C. L. (eds) *The Geology of Continental Margins*, Springer-Verlag, New York, pp. 873–88.

STONELEY, R. 1974. Evolution of the continental margins bounding a former Southern Tethys. *In:* BURK, C. A. & DRAKE, C. L. (eds) *The Geology of Continental Margins*, Springer-Verlag, New York, pp. 889–903.

—— 1975. On the origin of ophiolite complexes in the Southern Tethys region. *Tectonophysics*, **25**, 303–22.

—— 1981. The geology of the Kuh-e Dalneshin area of southern Iran, and its bearing on the evolution of Southern Tethys. *J. Geol. Soc. Lond.*, **138**, 509–26.

WAPLES, D. W. 1980. Time and temperature in petroleum formation: application of Lopatin's method to petroleum exploration. *Bull. Am. Assoc. Petrol. Geol.*, **64**, 916–26.

WILSON, H. H. 1982. Hydrocarbon habitat in main producing areas, Saudi Arabia: discussion. *Bull. Am. Assoc. Petrol. Geol.*, **66**, 2688–91.

Carbonaceous sediments and palaeoenvironment of the Cretaceous South Atlantic Ocean

H. B. Zimmerman, A. Boersma and F. W. McCoy

SUMMARY: The distribution of sapropelic sediments in the early South Atlantic Ocean is used to test palaeocirculation models related to oxygen-deficient conditions. The data presented here demonstrate that preservation of organic matter was widespread and occurred in many phsyiographic settings. Given the silled-basin physiography of the relatively isolated South Atlantic and the benign Cretaceous climate, a preservational model of sapropel accumulation and its corollary of restricted bottom circulation successfully satisfy the constraints of the geological record. Under the environmental conditions outlined for the early and mid-Cretaceous, a generally dysoxic condition for the warm saline bottom-water is appropriate. The prevailing dysoxia, however, was punctuated by episodic bottom anoxia, which often expanded into the upper reaches of the water column. In the Cretaceous South Atlantic, the only excursion from the dysoxic condition occurred during a Cenomanian 'ventilation event' (represented by a widespread hiatus in the stratigraphic record) which is tied to an interval of climatic cooling and the establishment of effective circulation between the North and South Atlantic Oceans. The geological record for epicontinental regions, although modified by local physiography and other environmental parameters, suggests a relationship between sea-level positions and sapropel accumulation. No relationship, however, can be established between sea-level and sapropel preservation in the oceanic basins of the South Atlantic.

Through reconstruction of the physiographic and environmental boundary conditions associated with organic-rich sediments in the South Atlantic Ocean, we have demonstrated that an oxygen deficient (dysoxic) condition was the normal state of the early and mid-Cretaceous Ocean. Due to the multi-silled physiography and overall isolation of this ocean basin, it is difficult to reconcile its history completely with global oceanic anoxic events (OAE) proposed for the Jurassic through mid-Cretaceous (Schlanger & Jenkyns 1976; Jenkyns 1980).

The cause of the widespread preservation of organic-rich sediment in the Cretaceous ocean has been one of the key problems of palaeoceanography. There are two fundamental models which address the problem. The *preservational* model is based on the reduction of dissolved oxygen flux to the site of deposition, thereby allowing the incorporation of organic-rich material into the sediment. The ocean dynamic corollary to this model is a much diminished vertical circulation by which the oxygen flux is limited. The result is a basin-wide oxygen deficiency in which the most intense dysoxia/anoxia occurs in the deepest areas of the basin; the potential for deposition of sapropelic sediments is thus based on an absence or restriction of ventilation. Tectonically isolated basins, such as the modern Black Sea and Cretaceous Atlantic (e.g. McCoy & Zimmerman 1977; Natland 1978; Arthur & Natland 1979; de Graciansky *et al.*

1984), are often cited as examples of basins where restricted circulation and oxygen depletion contributed to the deposition of organic-rich sediments.

The *productivity* model is based on a greatly increased surface productivity which overwhelms the oxygen content of the water column; the excess, unoxidized organic matter being incorporated into the sediment. The ocean dynamic corollary of this model is an enhanced vertical circulation which quickly recycles biolimiting nutrients into the ocean's productive zones. The model of Southam, *et al.* (1982) suggests that mid-water oxygen minimum zones are the most likely result of this scenario. In this case, sapropel deposition occurs only where an oxygen minimum zone impinges on the continental margin or other elevated portions of the sea floor; the deepest area of the basins may retain an oxygenated condition. For this model, the northwest Indian Ocean and the Cretaceous Pacific Ocean have been cited (e.g. Schlanger & Jenkyns 1976; Thiede & van Andel 1977).

For the South Atlantic, we have addressed this problem by mapping the changing distribution of organic-rich sediment on a series of palinspastic reconstructions of the Cretaceous South Atlantic. Preparation of these synoptic maps required the summation of a large literature on South Atlantic open ocean and marginal basin sediments (McCoy & Zimmerman 1977). Events have been updated to the revised stratigraphic

From: BROOKS, J. & FLEET, A. J. (eds) 1987, *Marine Petroleum Source Rocks*
Geological Society Special Publication No. 26 pp. 271–286.

correlation and planktonic foraminiferal bio-stratigraphy of Robaszynski, *et al.* (1979) and the Cretaceous timescale of Kent, *et al.* (1985).

In this paper, sediments are considered 'sapropels' if they contain significant amounts of organic carbon. Where quantitative data was available, we have termed sediment sapropelic if it has an organic content $>0.5\%$ (wt. %). Where only descriptive criteria were available, we have included as sapropelic such terms as: 'petroliferous', 'bluish black', 'black muds' and 'organic-rich'. Oxic waters have been defined as containing >1 ml/l dissolved oxygen, dysoxic waters contain $1\text{--}0.1$ ml/l O_2, and anoxic waters contain <0.1 ml/l O_2 (Funnell, this volume).

In the marine record sapropels occur as thin layers within more extensive intervals of dark grey or green muds which *in toto* represent dysoxic conditions. In the Angola Basin, as one example, black shales form less than 10% of the mid-Cretaceous section and are mixed with numerous

green and red claystones (Hay & Sibuet (1982). These sequences represent extended periods of dysoxia with intermittent anoxia, although red claystones may indicate deposition under oxygenated conditions. Marginal basin facies are composed of considerably thicker sequences of black shales usually intercalated within dysoxic sediments which occasionally form important petroleum source rocks.

Evolution of South Atlantic physiography, dysoxia and palaeocirculation

In this section, we describe the boundary conditions under which dysoxic and anoxic sedimentation occurred in the early South Atlantic (Figs 1, 2 and 3). Such conditions include the physiographic evolution of the South Atlantic basins

FIG. 1. Index map of continental marginal basins and major sea-floor physiographic features mentioned in the text. These are shown on an early Turonian reconstruction of the South Atlantic Ocean with palaeobathymetry in kilometres, palaeocoastlines in solid hachured lines, and modern coastlines in dotted lines.

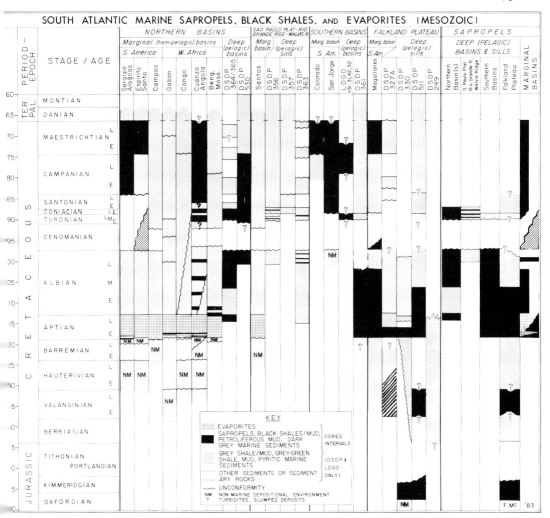

FIG. 2. Chart illustrating stratigraphic position and duration of Mesozoic sapropels, black shales, evaporites and hiatuses in the South Atlantic area as determined from drilled cores by DSDP and LDGO piston cores (pelagic sections), and from mapping and subsurface information (hemipelagic sections) in marginal basins. Locations of coring sites are given in Figs 4–7. Biostratigraphic zonation and age correlations follow Robaszynski, Caron *et al.* 1979 and Kent & Gradstein 1985.

and the transgression/regression cycles of sea level. The combination of physiography and relative location of sapropelic sediments are the key factors constraining models of palaeocirculation.

Late Jurassic–early Cretaceous

During the Oxfordian–Kimmeridgian, the nascent South Atlantic consisted of a small basin wedged between the continental masses of Africa, Antarctica and southern South America (Fig. 4).

Oceanic black shales of this age have been cored at DSDP Sites 330 and 511 (Fig. 2) on the topographic high south of the African continent—the basin province of the modern Falkland Plateau (Barker *et al.* 1976). In this basin, black shales occur as a massive sequence of sapropelic clays and mudstones which are separated from overlying sedimentary sequences by a Kimmeridgian–Barremian unconformity. In the marginal basins, marine black shales are present in the Agulhas–Angola Basin of South Africa as outcrops of the Colchester member of the Kirkwood Formation (SOEKOR 1976).

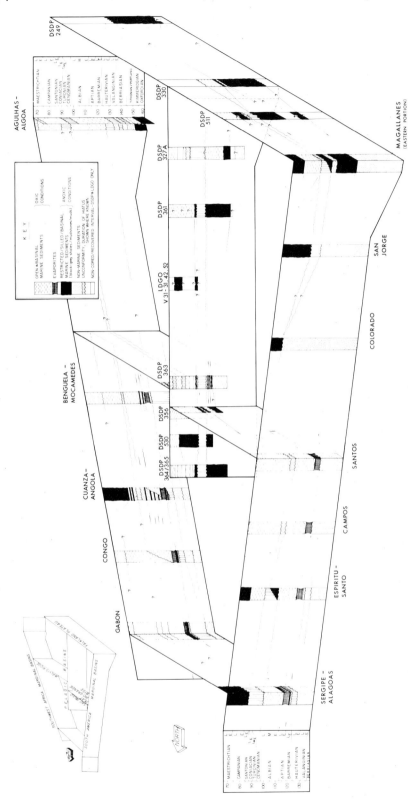

FIG. 3. Fence diagram of the Cretaceous South Atlantic Ocean schematically illustrates the general stratigraphic relationships between sedimentary facies in pelagic basins and in surrounding marginal basins. The diagram is based upon an Aptian palinspastic reconstruction of the ocean (Fig. 6). Stratigraphic information from Fig. 2. Correlations are made between sapropel/black shale sequences and unconformities. Note particularly the extent and duration of the Neocomian and Cenomanian unconformities, and correlations of anoxic sedimentary facies between marginal basins and the pelagic basins.

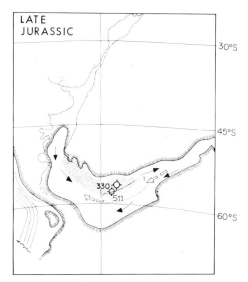

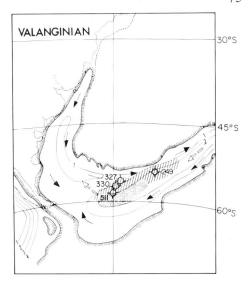

FIG. 4. Palinspastic reconstruction of the South Atlantic Ocean during the late Jurassic illustrating the distribution of Kimmeridgian stage sapropels of open-ocean origin (marginal basin deposits not shown), oceanic palaeocirculation, and deep-sea sampling sites. Palaeobathymetry is in kilometres. Palaeocoastlines are outlined by a solid line with hachures on the continental margin; modern coastlines shown by dotted lines for reference. Reconstructions are from McCoy and Zimmerman (in prep). Distribution of sapropels, including black muds/shales, petroliferous muds and other dark grey marine sediments, is approximated by the solid tone; distribution of grey muds/shales, grey-green muds/shales and pyritic marine sediments is outlined by the hachured pattern. Solid arrows depict surface currents and open arrows suggest deep-water current flow; no implication of current velocities is intended.

FIG. 5. Palinspastic reconstruction of the South Atlantic Ocean during the Valanginian stage (Neocomian) of the early Cretaceous illustrating the distribution of sapropels of open-ocean origin, palaeobathymetry (km), oceanic palaeocirculation, and deep-sea sampling sites. Symbols, patterns, etc. are explained in caption of Fig. 4.

By the Valanginian stage of the early Cretaceous, the South Atlantic (Fig. 5) extended on oceanic crust northward between Africa and South America probably as far as the major tectonic lineament of the Rio Grande Fracture Zone (Gamboa & Rabinowitz 1981; Larson & Ladd 1973). Marine sediments of this age have been recovered at sites drilled on the Falkland Plateau (Barker *et al.* 1976; Ludwig *et al.* 1983), and further to the east on the Mozambique Plateau within the Africa-Antarctic seaway (Simpson *et al.* 1974). Black shales were recovered at Site 511 and grey and grey-green shales and sapropelic clays were recovered at Sites 327A and 330 on the Falkland Plateau (Figs 2 and 3) and at Site 249 on the Mozambique Plateau. Sediments of the Magallenes Basin at the western end of the Falkland Plateau do not indicate anoxic conditions. Sediments from the Falkland barrier demonstrate that anoxia was common in the Indian Ocean–Weddell Sea of the early Creta-

ceous. Data, however, are restricted to relatively shallow water environments.

Models for the circulation system in the South Atlantic north of the Falkland barrier during the late Jurassic and early Cretaceous are highly conjectural. During this time the deep waters in the Argentine–Cape Basin were almost totally isolated from communication with the world ocean by the Falkland barrier. Circulation within such a basin is dependent on the regional evaporation-precipitation balance and may be represented by the estuarine model (see Fig. 8). In this model precipitation is prompted by saturated westerly winds from the Pacific; the excess precipitation producing a relatively fresh-water cap inhibiting thermohaline circulation. Flow at the basin's entrance is thus dependent on the basin's water budget, degree of seawater entrainment, and sill depth across the Falkland barrier. Because of basin geometry and sediment distribution, and in the absence of extensive evaporite deposits on the margins, the estuarine model best explains circulation in the late Jurassic and early Cretaceous South Atlantic.

A similar mechanism has been proposed for the Mediterranean Sea by Rossignol-Strick *et al.* (1982). In Neogene sediments of the eastern Mediterranean, periodic occurrence of black, pelagic muds are attributed to a low salinity surface water layer which limits bottom water renewal.

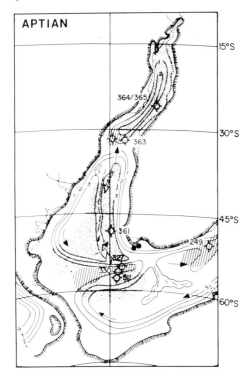

FIG. 6. Palinspastic reconstruction of the South
Atlantic Ocean during the Aptian illustrating the
distribution of Aptian–Albian sapropels of open-
ocean origin, palaeobathymetry (km), oceanic
palaeocirculation, and deep-sea sampling sites.
Symbols, patterns, etc. are explained in caption of Fig.
4.

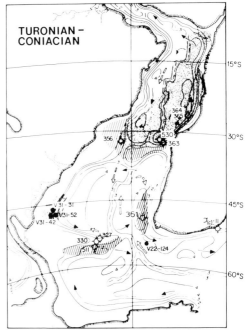

FIG. 7. Palinspastic reconstruction of the South
Atlantic Ocean during the Turonian–Coniacian stages
of the mid-Cretaceous illustrating the distribution of
sapropels of open-ocean origin palaeobathymetry
(km), oceanic palaeocirculation, and deep-sea
sampling sites. Symbols, patterns, etc. are explained in
caption of Fig. 4.

Early Aptian

By the early Aptian the southern South Atlantic
had been divided by a medial spreading ridge
into two abyssal basins, the proto-Cape and
Argentine Basins which extended as far north as
the Rio Grande–Walvis sill at about 30° South
palaeo-latitude (Fig. 6). Thick sapropel sequences
were deposited throughout the southern area: at
Sites 330, 327A and 511 on the Falkland Plateau,
and in the marginal Magellenes Basin to the west
of the Falkland Plateau. At deep water Site 361
in proto-Cape Basin, the carbonaceous material
consisted of both terrigenous plant debris and
marine plankton (Bolli *et al*. 1978).

At this time, the South Atlantic rift extended
to the north of the Sao Paulo–Walvis sill where
some 2 km of evaporites were deposited during
seawater transgression into the subsiding proto-
Brazil–Angola Basin (Pautot *et al*. 1973; Leyden
et al. 1976). The mediterranean circulation
depicted in Fig. 8 is a more probable circulation
model for the northern basin as the rift extended
northward into lower latitudes of the continental

interior where precipitation was less extensive.
The haline-driven bottom circulation of the
mediterranean model requires an excess of
evaporation in the northern reaches of the South
Atlantic, forcing an influx of surface water across
the Sao Paulo–Walvis barrier. Having its origin
in the southern areas of the Argentine Basin,
surface water flowing into the northern basin
may have been of relatively low salinity. Maintenance of its low salinity through latitude,
however, is questionable due to the increasing
potential for evaporation along its flow path.

Surface water of relatively low salinity may
have episodically reached the Cape Basin in
Aptian–Albian time. At Site 361, Noel and
Melguen (1978) noted laminae of unispecific
Nannoconus flora indicating a very stable upper
water column in contradiction to the vigorous
circulation required by the surface-productivity
model. The fact that *Nannoconus* is characteristic
of near shore environments also suggests the
possibility of low salinity surface water.

Although haline-driven bottom flow into the
Argentine and Cape Basins may have occurred;
the development of extensive sapropels in the

proto-Cape Basin (Site 361) suggests that ventilation of bottom waters in the Cape and Argentine Basins was negligible.

Late Aptian

During the late Aptian, the proto-Brazil–Angola Basin extended as far north as palaeolatitude 15° south. Within the limits of the biostratigraphy several events occurring in the late Aptian appear to be related. Sea level curves of both the South Atlantic and the world ocean (Fig. 9) indicate a late Aptian regression with gradually rising sea level by the Aptian–Albian boundary. Tectonic studies indicate an eastward spreading centre jump and emplacement of the Frio Ridge segment of the Sao Paulo–Walvis Ridge in late Aptian–Albian (Cande & Rabinowitz 1978; Boli *et al*. 1978). Sediment accumulation at Site 363 on Frio Ridge also constrains the age of basement to late Aptian. A result of this spreading centre jump was the formation of the Rio Grande Gap, the first deep water passage in the western South Atlantic (note: we follow the nomenclature of LePichon *et al*. 1971; the Rio Grande Gap is the large passage between the Brazil and Argentine Basins, the Vema Channel was incised into the floor of the Rio Grande Gap at a later date).

Pautot *et al*. (1973) placed the termination of evaporite deposition at about the close of Aptian time; this is shown dramatically in the marginal basin record (Fig. 2). Sequences consisting of lagoonal evaporites and dark gypsiferous clays, however, still occurred in the late Aptian–Albian of the African marginal basins (Siesser 1978). Evaporite accumulation in the eastern Angola

Basin itself had ended by at least the late Aptian, as evidenced by the initiation of sapropel deposition in late Aptian time at Site 364. By creating the deep water conduit between the basins of the western South Atlantic and thereby integrating the basins' circulation, the spreading centre jump may have been indirectly responsible for the termination of evaporite deposition.

Sapropel deposition in the late Aptian was much less extensive than in the early Aptian. In the Brazil–Angola Basin dark clays and grey limestone were recovered within the basin at Site 364 and from the north-western marginal basins. A few sapropel layers, intercalated with clays, were deposited in the north-eastern marginal basins. With uplift of the Frio Ridge, shelf-depth limestones were formed at Site 363 (Bolli *et al*. 1978). Sapropels, however, continued to be deposited at Site 511 on the Falkland Plateau, whereas at the somewhat shallower Site 327, clays were deposited. Sapropels occur also in the marginal Magallenes Basin. In the Cape Basin, Site 361, sapropelic sediments are found interbedded with black shales containing terrestrial organic matter.

In both South Atlantic basins the level of anoxia was depressed in the late Aptian. On the Angola Basin margin, sapropels were deposited only up to the palaeodepth of Site 364, but not to the depth of Site 363 on the Frio Ridge. In the basinal province of the Falkland Plateau, sapropels were deposited up to the depths of Site 511, but not Site 327. Since both pairs of sites are separated by only 200 m of water depth, a distinct boundary between anoxic intermediate and oxic surface waters of this time can be located near the 300 to 400 m palaeodepth level.

In the late Aptian, the South Atlantic remained isolated by physiographic barriers (Fig. 6) made all the more effective by the sea level fall. The only connection to the world ocean was a shallow flow of 200–400 metres over the Falkland Plateau. Despite the deep water conduit between the Argentine and Brazil Basins, a mediterranean model remains the most likely description of the northern South Atlantic circulation. Evaporation in the northern subtropical areas of the Brazil–Angola Basin and in marginal basins provided the drive for circulation of deep water. Sapropel preservation around the southern end of the basin, however, attests to the inefficient advection of oxygenated water into this region from the north. Oxygen deficient conditions in the deep Cape Basin, and probably in the Argentine Basin as well, indicate the continued lack of deep water renewal.

In the Cape–Argentine Basin, an anticyclonic pattern of surface circulation is likely to have

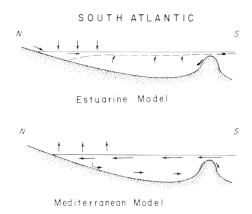

SOUTH ATLANTIC

Estuarine Model

Mediterranean Model

FIG. 8. Estuarine (A) and mediterranean (B) circulation models in silled basins (after Dietrich *et al*. 1980). Estuarine circulation requires a positive water balance in humid climates; the mediterranean circulation requires an excess of evaporation.

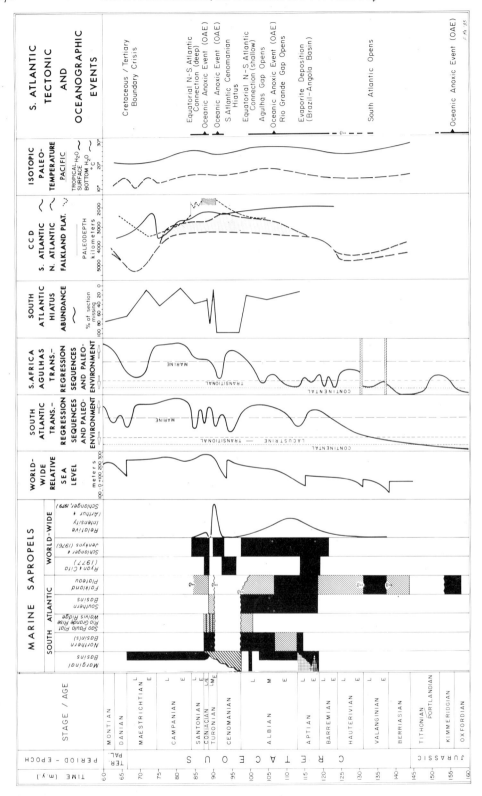

developed as a rudimentary subtropical oceanic gyre reflecting the widening basin size and the westerly winds sweeping the southern region. For similar reasons a primitive cyclonic gyre may have developed by this time in the Weddell Basin.

Albian

Throughout the Albian, sea level gradually rose over the changing physiographic framework of the South Atlantic. Continued spreading during Albian time led to the creation of the Agulhas Gap, a deep water passage which formed as the westward spreading Falkland Plateau cleared the southern tip of Africa. This finally connected the deep South Atlantic to the global ocean and initiated ventilation of the Cape Basin in mid-to late Albian time.

Sapropelic sediments occur in a variety of locations during this time, but appear diachronously through depth in both the southern and northern areas of the South Atlantic. In the late Albian Angola Basin, sapropelic sediments were deposited at Site 364; by latest Albian, sapropelic sediments occurred throughout the depth range from deep water Site 530 to Site 363 on the crest of the Walvis Ridge, where they occur as thin layers intercalated with oxic shallow water limestones. By contrast, on the Sao Paulo Ridge on the western margin of the Brazil Basin, sediments are blue-grey limestones with abundant shallow water detritus; sequences in the adjacent marginal basins consist primarily of clays.

Throughout the Albian, dysoxic sediments were deposited on the crest of the Falkland barrier. However, at Site 511 sapropel deposition occurred during the early Albian, whereas dysoxic clays were deposited from mid to late Albian time. This sequence represents the gradual ventilation of the basinal province of the Falkland Plateau (Deroo *et al.* 1983; Von der Dick *et al.* 1983).

Ventilation of the Cape Basin began in mid to late Albian time with the initiation of deep circulation through the Agulhas Gap. This is indicated by the termination of marine pelagic preservation in the basin, although degraded terrestrial organic matter continued to be deposited (Bolli 1978).

Under the constraints described above, a mediterranean circulation model for the northern basins is likely to have persisted through the Albian, although modified by a deep water passage between the basins of the western South Atlantic. Evaporation in the northern reaches of the Brazil–Angola Basin continued to force an influx of surface water northward, whereas the haline-driven deep flow could pass southward into the Argentine Basin. Continued sapropel deposition in the deep Angola Basins, however, indicates that the bottom circulation of the northeastern South Atlantic remained restricted.

Anoxic sediments of this age occur occasionally in the marginal basins of Albian time as discrete sapropelic layers. In the Magallanes and Cuanza–Angola marginal basins, sapropel layers result from flooding during the Albian sea level transgression coupled with the basin subsidence (Siesser 1978).

The Cenomanian–early Turonian hiatus

The Albian-Cenomanian boundary is marked by a profound unconformity throughout most of the South Atlantic (Figs 2 and 3). The open ocean record of the Cenomanian–early Turonian is lost; sedimentation resumes in the early-mid Turonian (*P. helvetica* Zone) except at DSDP Site 327A on the Falkland Plateau where sediments are not preserved until the Santonian. A coeval mid-Cretaceous hiatus is present through much of the North Atlantic and western Tethyan Seaway (de Graciansky *et al.* 1984).

We interpret this widespread hiatus in the open ocean sediment record of the South Atlantic to represent an erosional event associated with an abrupt circulation change related to the establishment of the deep connection between

---

FIG. 9. Summary chart of South Atlantic marine sapropel occurrences during the late Jurassic and Cretaceous (from Fig. 2) in comparison to world-wide sapropel depositional events and the relative intensity of these global events. World-wide relative sea-level variations are from Vail *et al.* (1977). South Atlantic transgression–regression variations are summarized from marginal basin data (McCoy & Zimmerman 1977), with palaeoenvironmental conditions of regional sedimentation indicated from continental through open marine conditions. Transgression–regression sequences from the Agulhas Basin in South Africa are shown, with the paleosedimentation environment suggested by these sequences; stratigraphy at the earliest and latest Valanginian is unclear (SOEKOR 1976). For both transgression–regression curves, the median line through the open-marine palaeoenvironment indicates modern sea-level; duration of continental and transitional paleoenvironments are emphasized by shading for ease in distinguishing these episodes. South Atlantic hiatus abundances are from Premoli-Silva and Boersma (1977). South Atlantic calcite compensation depth (CCD) variations are from Thierstein (1979); North Atlantic CCD curve is from Tucholke and Vogt (1979). Isotopic paleotemperature curve for Pacific Ocean is from Douglas and Woodruff (1981).

the North and South Atlantic. Although surface water exchange between these oceans had certainly been initiated by the late Albian (Reyment & Tait 1972; Kennedy & Cooper 1975; Premoli-Silva & Boersma 1977), deeper, more significant exchange developed through the Cenomanian. This interval of energetic circulation marks the only major interruption in the record of mid-Cretaceous dysoxia of the South Atlantic. Because the opening of the Equatorial Seaway resulted in the removal of the sedimentary record, we cannot determine the extent of dysoxia during the Cenomanian prior to the event.

The hiatus coincides in part with a sea level regression, an event particularly significant for marginal basins, where erosion removed sediments deposited earlier in the Cenomanian. Exception to this occurs in the Espirito Santo, Magallanes, Gabon and Congo Basins. The depositional record of the African basins indicate sedimentation under oxygenated conditions, whereas sedimentary sequences in the two South American basins preserve sapropelic sediments of the earliest Cenomanian.

Mid-Turonian–Coniacian

Following the Cenomanian–early Turonian Hiatus, the final episode of sapropel deposition in the South Atlantic during the Mid-Turonian through Coniacian was limited to the northern deep basins (Figs 2, 3). In the Angola Basin (Site 364), sapropelic sediments continue to be deposited in the Turonian and Coniacian and in the southern Angola Basin (Site 530) deposition of sapropelic sediments persists through the Campanian, although turbidite sequences are interbedded (Hay *et al.* 1982). Sapropelic sediments also occur in the Brazil Basin, but only as thin layers in the turbiditic sequence (Site 356; Supko *et al.* 1977).

During the mid-Cretaceous (Fig. 7) a large seaway had opened in the equatorial Atlantic and the Brazil and Angola Basins became distinctly separate abyssal basins divided by the mid-Atlantic Ridge. As a result of the Aptian–Albian spreading-centre jump, the deep waters of the western basins were joined at the Rio Grande Gap. Despite these deep water connections, the influence of dysoxic conditions at intermediate depths is clearly seen in the distribution of limited sapropelic layers on the Sao Paulo Plateau and grey shales over the Rio Grande Rise (Figs 2, 3, 7).

By the Turonian, the Agulhas Gap between the eastern end of the Falkland Plateau and the continental margin of Africa had widened to allow deep water exchange and an increasing

degree of ventilation of the deep Cape Basin. In both the Cape Basin and the Falkland Plateau, grey shales apparently represent the transitional phase to a ventilated ocean. The continued deposition of dysoxic sediments in the deep Cape Basin, (Site 361), however, suggests that the new flow system was not very vigorous in the Turonian and that the newly introduced bottom water may itself have been oxygen-deficient.

In the mid-Cretaceous, reasonably good surface water exchange had commenced between the North and South Atlantic, although the trade wind system probably forced most of the surface flow through the equatorial seaway to the north. These prevailing winds may also have generated an 'Ekman transport' to the west with concomitant strong upwelling along the eastern and southern margins of the Angola Basin. The increased biological productivity, indicated by the progressive increase in marine organic matter through the Turonian sequence at Site 530 (Meyers 1984), corroborates this circulation model. Preservation in the still isolated basin accounts for the maximum black shale interval of the early Turonian. Sapropel deposition continued through the Turonian in the southern and eastern Angola Basin where dysoxic conditions may have lingered on into the Coniacian. By Coniacian times the waters of the Brazil Basin were more fully integrated within the developing Atlantic circulation and the basin became sufficiently ventilated to bring dysoxic conditions to an end.

Late Cretaceous

The late Cretaceous South Atlantic is characterized by its increasing size and the equatorial seaway which becomes increasingly effective as a conduit for water exchange. Except for local marginal basinal occurrences, widespread dysoxic conditions have ended in the South Atlantic and the ocean was sufficiently ventilated to prevent widespread sapropelic deposition.

Discussion

Models of oxygen deficiency

Within the context of the South Atlantic basins, the distribution and sequence of sediments provide constraints to the early physical development of the ocean. Sapropelic sediments, in particular, point to a reducing, oxygen-deficient depositional environment. Conditions favourable to the preservation of sapropelic sediments may be explained in two ways: the *preservational* or *basinal* model, where stratified waters limit the oxygen flux to the basin's deepest regions; and the *productivity* or *oxygen-minimum* model where enhanced vertical circulation increases organic productivity in the surface zone. The two models are not mutually exclusive; anoxic conditions may be attributed to either or both of the models and examples of both exist in the modern ocean. The two models do, however, point to very different dynamic conditions in the water column. The basinal model implies a relatively restricted bottom, whereas the productivity model implies a ventilated bottom and enhanced vertical circulation (upwelling) in the near surface.

In the preceding presentation of sediment distribution and palaeocirculation, we have implied the preservational/basinal model of anoxia for the Cretaceous South Atlantic. This seemed to us to have been dictated by the distribution of sapropelic sediments. The following summary outlines the evidence in corroboration of the preservation/basinal model of anoxia.

1 Organic-rich sediments were deposited in the deep areas of the early South Atlantic basins. Sapropel deposition is thus consistent with the model of a highly stratified water column in a poorly ventilated basin. The ubiquity of sapropelic sediments through depth and latitude is in opposition to the oxygen-minimum model.

In a similar analysis for the North Atlantic, de Graciansky *et al.* (1984) noted that the wide geographical extent and palaeodepths of the Cenomanian–Turonian black shales argue against the model of upwelling (productivity) as the only factor in the deposition of carbonaceous shales.

2 The physiographic framework consisting of a series of linked shallow-silled basins, largely isolated from the world ocean, tends to restrain bottom circulation and promotes oxygen-deficiency. Separation of the Cretaceous South Atlantic from the North Atlantic is confirmed by the austral affinities of nearly every fossil group studied to date and by the palinspastic reconstructions presented here (Figures 4–7). The palaeontologic evidence corroborates the physiographic reconstructions which indicate that the only connection with the world ocean was to the south over the shallow sill of the Falkland barrier.

3 If the preservation/basinal circulation model is operative in the physiographic context of the early Cretaceous South Atlantic, then a predictable sequence of depositional environments should occur. The sequence of depositional environments—saline/non-marine, anoxic, oxic— is a logical consequence of the transition from a series of isolated basins to increasing integration with the global ocean.

4 Unusually saline bottom waters in the north-ern South Atlantic of the early Cretaceous are indicated by the authigenic mineral assemblages (Natland 1978). Oxygen isotope analysis of mid-Cretaceous sediments suggests warm bottom water with palaeotemperature near 15°C (Savin 1977), and for late Cretaceous sediments in the Angola Basin, Saltzman and Barron (1982) suggest even higher palaeotemperatures. The production of dysoxic/anoxic bottom water appears to follow the scenario of Brass, *et al.* (1982). Confined areas of excess evaporation in the arid northern and marginal regions of the South Atlantic were likely sources of warm saline bottom water. Oxygen solubility is considerably reduced in warm seawater, thus an initially reduced oxygen content would promote bottom dysoxia. Anoxia would occur when organic matter was sufficiently available to consume the remaining dissolved oxygen. Excess organic matter is then incorporated and preserved as sapropelic sediments.

5 Laminae of unispecific *Nannoconus* in the deep Cape Basin are indicative of episodically restricted growth conditions and a stratified water column in the near surface (Noel & Melguen, 1978). Such stratified surface water, even when not a permanent condition, is in contradiction to the high productivity and vigorous upwelling required by the oxygen-minimum model of Southam, *et al.* (1982).

6 There is little evidence from sedimentary structures suggesting vigorous current activity during the deposition of sapropelic sediments. The finely laminated nature of these sediments (about 80% of the sapropel black beds are laminated) indicate a quiet water environment for the deposition of most organic-rich sediment.

Although organic matter in most sapropels is dominated by autochthonous pelagic-marine material, a variable proportion of the beds are allochthonous, of terrestrial origin (Arthur *et al.* 1984; Tissot *et al.* 1980). Occurrence of anoxic bottom water does not exclude down-slope processes of redeposition, such as turbidity current or debris flow activity. Episodic redepositional processes and quiescent bottom conditions are not mutually exclusive; preservation of moderately degraded terrestrial organic matter as black shales and sapropels provide additional evidence for the dysoxic/anoxic character of bottom waters.

The presence in some sapropelic sediments of evidence of 'contour current' activity also does not indicate a flow of oxygenated water. Warm saline bottom water of a dysoxic/anoxic nature may certainly have moved for long distances within and through the South Atlantic basins especially after the formation of the deep gaps.

Based on early work in the South Atlantic (through DSDP Leg 40), an often cited argument for the oxygen-minimum model was made by Thiede and van Andel (1977, Figure 4). Their analysis is based on a plot of the percentage of organic carbon in a sediment sample plotted against the palaeodepth of that sample for the Aptian–Albian and Cenomanian–Campanian— the plot does not, however, indicate the relationship between palaeodepth of the sample and its physiographic position within the basin. In addition, we note that percentage of organic carbon cannot be a true indicator of anoxic intensity without some indication of the rate of sediment accumulation (Stein in press). This plot, therefore may actually indicate only the rate of organic carbon dilution or rapid burial by other sediments.

Sea level

Sea level rises affect silled basins by the breaching of barriers and flooding of otherwise low-lying and restricted areas. In the case of the South Atlantic marginal basins, widespread epicontinental anoxia is often associated with sea level transgression. Sapropelic sediments occur in marginal basins when sea level rises to flood large epicontinental areas thus trapping nutrients and fostering organic productivity. Some marginal basins, however, never or rarely preserve sapropelic sediments (Fig. 2). Sapropel development is a complex process promoted by sea level rise, basin subsidence, low to moderate rates of terrigenous sediment supply, and a restrictive basin physiography. Given the complexity of the factors, it is not surprising that the depositional history of marginal basins is so varied and independent of one another. The single overriding factor, however, that promotes widespread epicontinental sapropel deposition is a global sea level rise.

Deposition of sapropelic sediments in the deep ocean has been linked by some authors to sea level position (Schlanger & Jenkyns 1976; Jenkyns 1980; Arthur *et al.* this volume). While sea level rises may affect large, silled oceanic basins by altering the precipitation/evaporation balance at the closed ends of the basin and thus ventilating the bottom (for example: the Red Sea during interglacials), sea level changes do not *per se* cause or alleviate anoxia within oceanic basins. In the South Atlantic the isolation of each basin gradually decreases through the course of the early and middle Cretaceous. Sea level fluctuations through this time occurred within very different basinal configurations. For example, the sea level rise of the early Aptian South Atlantic occurred in a framework of silled basins with

very little surface exchange, no bottom-water influx, and large potential for evaporation at its subtropical northern end. The transgression resulted in evaporite deposition in the northern basins. To the south, however, widespread anoxic conditions were more prevalent due to the combination of basin physiography and oceanographic factors. The Albian transgression, by contrast, occurred within the varied South Atlantic framework of a Brazil Basin with a deep and surface connection to the South, and the Angola Basin with surface influx from the South and later possibly some influx from the North; a Cape Basin connected to the world ocean by deep and shallow passages; and the Argentine Basin to which only shallow surface flow penetrates from the south. The pattern of sapropel deposition was similarly diverse. The Angola Basin demonstrated a progressively expanding anoxia. Dysoxic conditions persisted in the Cape Basin even with an open Agulhas Gap, while in the Brazil Basin with a deep gap to the south, the Sao Paulo Plateau did not experience anoxia in the late Albian. There is no clear relationship between transgressions and sapropel deposition in the deep oceanic basins of the South Atlantic.

It is tempting to suggest that sea level *regression* may promote deposition of sapropelic sediment in deep oceanic basins. Regression should encourage sapropelic deposition, especially in small basins, by supplying nutrients of terrestrial origin directly to the surface waters of the basin margin and by supplying moderately degraded and residual terrestrial organic debris through erosion of previously-deposited epicontinental sapropelic sediments. In deep ocean basins, a generally high rate of sediment supply by regression might also enhance the rate of organic carbon accumulation through rapid burial. Although the early to mid-Cenomanian sea level fall should provide the best evidence for this effect, the South Atlantic Cenomanian is represented by widespread hiatus. The sedimentary record of the Aptian regression is also unclear, being complicated by tectonic events associated with the initial opening of South Atlantic basins.

Prior to open connection with the world ocean, the South Atlantic patterns of sedimentation and anoxia differed between transgressive and regressive phases. Beginning in the mid-Turonian, and including the Coniacian, however, the pattern of sediment distribution and the more limited deposition of anoxic sediment (mainly in the deeper areas of the Angola Basin) were the same during transgressive and regressive episodes. Apparently, in all but the Angola Basin, as long as there was deep inflow, dysoxic sediments with only occasional anoxic layers were deposited.

For the deep basins of the early South Atlantic, we have no evidence for sea level control of the deposition of organic-rich sediments. If the input of terrestrial/degraded organic matter is controlled by regression, the sediment record of the deep South Atlantic basins does not clearly confirm it. There is good evidence for sea level rise promoting sapropel deposition in marginal and epicontinental basins, but little evidence that sea level rise enhances sapropel deposition in the deep oceanic basins.

Relationship with 'global OAE'

Dean *et al.* (1984) noted that it is '... highly unlikely that a coincidence of local conditions of morphometry and circulation in the Angola Basin would have permitted the accumulation of organic carbon at precisely the same time (Cenomanian/Turonian boundary) that high concentrations of organic carbon were accumulating at many different places in the world ocean in a variety of paleobathymetric settings ...'

In the South Atlantic, however, the pattern of sapropel deposition appears to reflect and is easily explained by the tectonic and oceanographic history of the region—rather than a global Oceanic Anoxic Event (OAE). We note that organic-rich sediment had been accumulating in the South Atlantic since the late Jurassic and their re-occurrence at the early-mid-Turonian boundary was, rather than an unusual event, a return to normal dysoxic/anoxic conditions of the pre-Cenomanian.

The development of the early South Atlantic occurred within the context of generally rising sea level and benign global climate of the mid-Cretaceous which affected the entire world ocean. In many respects, therefore, the sediment sequences of both the South Atlantic and world ocean may be roughly similar.

It was the coincidence of three environmental parameters that created the Turonian sapropel of the South Atlantic and probably the widespread OAE near the Cenomanian–Turonian boundary (Bonarelli time). The first two parameters are global in nature, the very high late Cenomanian–Turonian sea level which encouraged sapropel deposition in widespread epicontinental settings and the Turonian climatic warming (Savin 1977). For the South Atlantic, the third parameter was the still restricted circulation in the deep basins which encouraged preservation of organic carbon. The result of these occurrences was the deposition of sapropelic sediments in both deep restricted basins and global epicontinental settings. A similar analysis applies to the deeply-silled basins of the North Atlantic and Mediter-ranean Tethys, where sources of ventilating bottom water and vigorous circulation are not immediately obvious.

Yet another set of coincidences occurred just prior to deposition of the Turonian sapropel, when the mid-Cenomanian global sea level fall (Fig. 9) and the first cooling of the Cretaceous Ocean (Savin 1977) coincided with the deep opening of the Equatorial Atlantic Seaway. The eustatic regression resulted in widespread erosion of the epicontinental record (Fig. 2; de Graciansky *et al.* 1984), while the oceanic record of this regression in the South Atlantic was apparently also lost in the widespread erosion associated with a more vigorous deep ocean circulation during Cenomanian and early Turonian.

The restricted circulation of the early Cretaceous, thus gave way for a limited time to a more energetic flow in the Cenomanian. Although no record exists in the South Atlantic, it is probable that this circulation oxygenated the South Atlantic in the Cenomanian. The hiatus in the sediment record is itself a good indicator of such a 'ventilation event'.

We suspect that the primary cause of this interval of vigorous circulation was the climatic cooling of the Cenomanian. This cool interval may have established a sufficient meridional surface temperature gradient to allow the production of cool bottom water in the Weddell Basin and force its penetration into the South Atlantic through the Agulhas Gap. In the deep South Atlantic, this 'ventilation event' may be represented as a conflict between salty, oxygen-depleted water from the north and relatively cool, oxygenated water entering from the south. This may have occurred as episodic flow-reversal events, controlled by variations in the intensity of high latitude cooling or by the intensity of evaporation in the north. The Cenomanian, therefore, represents an excursion from mid-Cretaceous dysoxia.

We expect this 'ventilation event' to have stimulated vertical mixing and diffusion. To some degree, the mid-Turonian sapropelic sediments may be linked to the greater surface productivity thus engendered. However, the limited occurrence of Turonian sapropelic sediments in the northeastern South Atlantic, suggests that restricted bottom conditions are still a necessary condition to organic carbon preservation in oceanic basins.

Conclusions

Our purpose here was to review the extensive data set of sapropelic sediments from the early and mid-Cretaceous South Atlantic and place it within the framework of the area's reconstructed palaeogeography. The temporal and spatial distribution of these sediments is demonstrated to have been ubiquitous throughout the early development of the South Atlantic. Within the context of deep, silled basins this requires application of the preservational/basinal model of anoxia. Given the likely evaporative origin for warm saline bottom waters, the water column is inferred to have been highly stratified and generally dysoxic. Complete anoxia occurs in the deepest basinal areas with lowest flow rates.

A number of authors (e.g. Hay *et al.* 1982) have noted the association of black sapropelic sediments with red and green mudstones. In agreement with these authors, we suggest that these result from a fluctuating balance between dysoxic and completely anoxic conditions at the site of deposition.

Dissolved oxygen content at any oceanic location varies inversely to the rate of organic carbon supply and is directly proportional to the rate of water renewal. Given the benign Cretaceous climate, which tends to reduce upwelling, and the generally high Cretaceous sea level, which tends to trap nutrients in peripheral basins, it is unlikely that open ocean surface productivity of the Cretaceous would have been enhanced to any significant extent. It appears likely that the preservation of organic matter in the deep South Atlantic occurred primarily as a result of limited

oxygen flux caused by restricted bottom circulation.

Note added in proof

In a recent paper, Bralower and Thierstein (1984) reached conclusions concerning the Cretaceous world ocean circulation which are similar to those presented here for the South Atlantic. Based on Holocene surface productivity and rates of sediment accumulation, they present an elegant model for a palaeoproductivity estimate of the mid-Cretaceous. They conclude that Cretaceous productivity was an order of magnitude lower than the present and the world ocean was in a generally dysoxic state. This argues strongly against the productivity/oxygen-minimum model and is further confirmation of the benign mid-Cretaceous climate.

ACKNOWLEDGEMENTS: Preparation of this synthesis was made possible through the Deep Sea Drilling Project and the information assembled by the shipboard scientific parties aboard D/V *Glomar Challenger*. We are indebted to our many colleagues with whom we had free exchange of ideas concerning oceanic anoxia and thank the Geological Society of London and British Petroleum, Ltd. for the opportunity to participate in the symposium on Marine Petroleum Source Rocks. Special thanks to Andrew Fleet for his constant encouragement and John La Brecque for his aid with reconstructions. H.B.Z. thanks the National Science Foundation for providing support under Grant #OCE 82–07164.

References

ARTHUR, M. A., DEAN, W. E & STOW, D. A. V. 1984. Models for the deposition of Mesozoic-Cenozoic fine-grained organic-carbon-rich sediments in the deep sea. *In:* STOW, D. A. V. & PIPER, D. J. W. (eds) *Fine-Grained Sediments: Deep Water Processes and Facies.* Blackwell Scientific Publications, Oxford. pp. 527–60.

—— & NATLAND, J. H. 1979. Carbonaceous sediments in the North and South Atlantic: the role of salinity in stable stratification of early Cretaceous basins. *In:* TALWANI, M., HAY, W. W. & RYAN, W. B. F. *Deep Drilling Results in the Atlantic Ocean. Continental Margins and Paleoenvironment,* Ewing Series 3, Am. Geophys. Union, Washington, D.C. pp. 375–401.

—— & SCHLANGER, S. U. 1979. Cretaceous 'Oceanic Anoxic Events' as causal factors in development of reef-reservoired giant oil fields. *Amer. Assoc. Petrol. Geo. Bull.* **63**, 870–885.

——, —— & JENKYNS, H. C. 1986. The Cenomanian-Turonian oceanic anoxic event, II, this volume.

BARKER, P. F., DALZIEL, I. W. D. 1976. Initial Reports of the Deep Sea Drilling Project, **36**, Washington (U.S. Government Printing Office), 1080 pp.

BOLLI, H. M., RYAN, W. B. F. 1978. Initial Reports of the Deep Sea Drilling Project, **40**, Washington (U.S. Govt. Printing Office), 1079 pp.

BRALOWER, T. J. & THIERSTEIN, H. R. 1984. Low productivity and slow deep-water circulation in mid-Cretaceous oceans. *Geology,* **12**, 614–618.

BRASS, G. W., SOUTHAM, J. R. & PETERSON, W. H. 1982. Warm saline bottom water in the ancient ocean. *Nature,* **296**, 620–623.

CANDE, S. & RABINOWITZ, P. D. 1978. Mesozoic seafloor spreading bordering conjugate continental margins of Angola and Brazil. *Proc. Offshore Tech. Cont., Rep. OTC 3268,* Houston, Tex. 1869–1876.

DE GRACIANSKY, P. C., DEROO, G., HERBIN, J. P., MONTADERT, L., MULLER, C., SCHAAF, A. & SIGAL, J. 1984. Ocean-wide stagnation episode in the Late Cretaceous. *Nature,* **308**, 346–349.

DEAN, W. E., HAY, W. W. & SIBUET, J-C. 1984. Geologic evolution, sedimentation, and paleoenvironments of the Angola Basin and adjacent Walvis Ridge: synthesis of results of Deep Sea Drilling Project Leg 75. *In:* HAY, W. W., SIBUET, J-C. (eds), *Init. Repts. DSDP,* **75**. Washington (U.S. Govt. Printing Office), 509.

DEROO, G., HERBIN, J. P. & ROUCACHE, J. 1983. Organic geochemistry of Upper Jurassic-Cretaceous sediments from Site 511, Leg 71, Western South Atlantic. *In:* LUDWIG, W. J. & KRASHENINNIKOV, V. A. (eds), *Init. Repts. DSDP,* **71.** Washington (U.S. Govt. Printing Office), 1001–1013.

DIETRICH, G., KALLE, K., KRAUSS, W. & SIEDLER, G. 1980. *General Oceanography,* 2nd Ed., John Wiley and Sons, New York, 626 pp.

DOUGLAS, R. & WOODRUFF, F. 1981. Deep-sea benthic foraminifera. *In:* EMILIANI, C. (ed), *The Oceanic Lithosphere,* **7,** John Wiley and Sons, New York, 1233–1327.

GAMBOA, L. A. P. & RABINOWITZ, P. D. 1981. The Rio Grande Fracture Zone in the western South Atlantic and its tectonic implications. *Earth and Planet. Sci. Letts.* **52,** 410–418.

HAY, W. W. & SIBUET, J-C. 1982. Sedimentation and accumulation of organic carbon in the Angola Basin and on Walvis Ridge: preliminary results of Deep Sea Drilling Project Leg 75. *Geol. Soc. Amer. Bull.* **93,** 1038–1050.

JENKYNS, H. C. 1980. Cretaceous anoxic events: from continents to oceans. *Journ. Geol. Soc. London,* **137,** 171–188.

KENNEDY, W. J. & COOPER, M. 1975. Cretaceous ammonite distributions and the opening of the South Atlantic. *Journ. Geol. Soc. London,* **131,** 283–288.

KENT, D. V. & GRADSTEIN, F. M. 1985. A Cretaceous and Jurassic geochronology. *Geol. Soc. Am. Bull.* **96,** 1419–27.

LARSON, R. L. & LADD, J. W. 1973. Evidence for the opening of the South Atlantic in the Early Cretaceous. *Nature,* **246,** 209–212.

LE PICHON, X., EWING, M. & TRUCHAN, M. 1971. Sediment transport and distribution in the Argentine Basin. 2. Antarctic bottom current passage into the Brazil Basin. *In:* AHRENS, L. H. *et al.* (eds), *Physics and Chemistry of the Earth,* **8** Pergamon. Press, New York. 31–48.

LEYDEN, R., ASMUS, H., ZEMBRUSCKI, S. & BRYAN, G. 1976. South Atlantic diapiric structures. *Bull. Amer. Assoc. Petrol. Geol.* **60,** p. 196.

LUDWIG, W. J. & KRASHENINNIKOV, V. 1983. *Init. Repts. DSDP,* **73,** Washington (U.S. Govt. Printing Office), 1187 pp.

McCOY, F. W. & ZIMMERMAN, H. B. 1977. A history of sediment lithofacies in the South Atlantic Ocean. *In:* PERCH-NIELSEN, K. & SUPKO, P. *Init. Repts. DSDP,* **39.** Washington (U.S. Govt. Printing Office), 1047–1079.

MEYERS, P. A. 1984. Organic geochemistry of sediments from the Angola Basin and the Walvis Ridge: a synthesis of studies from Deep Sea Drilling Project Leg 75. *In:* HAY, W. W. & SIBUET, J. C. *Init. Repts. DSDP,* **75.** Washington (U.S. Govt. Printing Office), 459–467.

NATLAND, J. H. 1978. Composition, provenance, and diagenesis of Cretaceous clastic sediments drilled on the Atlantic continental rise off southern Africa, DSDP Site 361. *In:* BOLLI, H. M. & RYAN, W. B. F. *Init. Repts. DSDP,* **40.** Washington (U.S. Govt. Printing Office), 1025–1061.

NOEL, D. & MELGUEN, M. 1978. Nannofacies of Cape Basin and Walvis Ridge Sediments, Lower Cretaceous to Pliocene (Leg 40). *In:* BOLLI, H. M. & RYAN, W.B. F. *Init. Repts. DSDP,* **40.** Washington (U.S. Govt. Printing Office), 487–524.

PAUTOT, G., RENARD, V., DANIEL, J. & DUPONT, J. 1973. Morphology, limits, origin, and age of salt layer along South Atlantic African margin. *Bull. Amer. Assoc. Petrol. Geol.* **57** 1658–1671.

PREMOLI-SILVA, I. & BOERSMA, A. 1977. Cretaceous planktonic foraminifers—DSDP Leg 39 (South Atlantic). *In:* PERCH-NIELSEN, K. & SUPKO, P. *Init. Rept. DSDP,* **39.** Washington (U.S. Govt. Printing Office), 615–642.

REYMENT, R. A. & TAIT, E. A. 1972. Biostratigraphical dating of the early history of the South Atlantic Ocean. *Phil. Trans. Roy. Soc. London, Ser. B.* **264,** 55–95.

ROBASZYNSKI, F., CARON, M. *et al.* 1979. Atlas de Foraminiferes planctoniques du Cretace moyen (mer boreale et tethys). *In: Cahiers de Micropaleontologie,* **2,** 159 pp.

ROSSIGNOL-STRICK, M., NESTEROFF, W., OLIVE, P. & VERGNAUD-GRAZZINA, C. 1982. After the deluge: Mediterranean stagnation and sapropel formation. *Nature,* **295,** 1105–10.

SALTSMAN, E. S. & BARRON, E. J. 1982. Deep circulation in the Late Cretaceous: oxygen istotope paleotemperatures from Inoceramus remains in DSDP coves. *Paleo., Palea. Paleo.* **40,** 167–181.

SAVIN, S. M. 1977. The history of the Earth's surface temperature during the past 100 million years. *In: Ann. Rev. Earth. Planet. Sci.* **5,** 319–355.

SCHLANGER, S. O. & JENKYNS, H. C. 1976. Cretaceous oceanic anoxic events: causes and consequences. *Geol. Mijnbow,* **55,** 179–184.

SIBUET, J-C, HAY, W. W., PRUNIER, A., MONTADERT, L., HINZ, K. & FRITSCH, J. 1984. The eastern Walvis Ridge and adjacent basins (South Atlantic): morphology, stratigraphy, and structural evolution in light of the results of Legs 40 and 75. *In:* HAY, W. W. & SIBUET, J-C. *Init. Repts. DSDP,* **75.** Washington (U.S. Govt. Printing Office), 483–508.

SEISSER, W. G. 1978. Leg 40 results in relation to continental shelf and onshore geology. *In:* BOLLI, H. M. & RYAN, W. B. F. *Init. Repts. DSDP,* **40.** Washington (U.S. Govt. Printing Office), 965–979.

SIMPSON, E. S. W. & SCHLICH, R. 1974. *Initial Reports of the Deep Sea Drilling Project,* **25.** Washington (U.S. Govt. Printing Office), 884 pp.

SOEKOR. 1976. Structure of the Mesozoic succession of the Agulhas Bank, South. *Oil Expl. Corp.*

SOUTHAM, J. R., PETERSON, W. H. & BRASS, G. W. 1982. Dynamics of anoxia. *Paleogeogr., Paleoclimatol., Paleoecol.* **40,** 183–198.

STEIN, R. in press. Organic carbon and sedimentation rate—further evidence for anoxic deep-water conditions in the Cenomanian/Turonian Atlantic Ocean. *Marine Geology.*

SUPKO, P. R. & PERCH-NIELSEN, K. 1977. *Initial Reports of the Deep Sea Drilling Project,* **39.** Washington (U.S. Govt. Printing Office), 1139 pp.

THIEDE, J. & VAN ANDEL, Tj.H. 1977. The palaeoenvironment of anaerobic sediments in the late Mesozoic South Atlantic Ocean. *Earth and Planet. Sci. Letts.* **33**, 301–309.

THIERSTEIN, H. R. 1979. Paleoceanographic implications of organic carbon and carbonate distribution in Mesozoic deep sea sediments. *In:* TALWANI, M., HAY, W. & RYAN, W. B. F. (eds), *Deep Drilling Results in the Atlantic Ocean* (Maurice Ewing Series), **3**, 249–274.

TISSOT, B., DEMAISON, G., MASSON. P., DELTEIL, J. R. & COMBAZ, A. 1980. Paleoenvironment and petoleum potential of middle Cretaceons black shales in Atlantic basins. *Bull. Am. Assoc. Petrol. Geol.* **64**, 2051–2063.

TUCHOLKE, B. E. & VOGT, P. R. 1979. Western North Atlantic; sedimentary evolution and aspects of tectonic history. *In:* TUCHOLKE, B. E. & VOGT, P. R., *et al. Init. Rep. DSDP Proj.* **43**. Washington (U.S. Govt. Printing Office), 791–825.

VAIL, P. R., MITCHUM, R. M. & THOMPSON, S. 1977. Seismic stratigraphy and global changes of sea level, part 4: Global cycles of relative changes of sea level. *Amer. Assoc. Petrol. Geol.* **26**, 83–97.

VON DER DICK, H., RULLKOTTER, J. & WELTE, D. H. 1983. Content, type, and thermal evolution of organic matter in sediments from the eastern Falkland Plateau. Deep Sea Drilling Project, Leg 71. *In:* LUDWIG, W. J. & KRASHENINNIKOV, V. A. *Init. Repts. DSDP* **71**. Washington (U.S. Govt. Printing Office), 1015–1031.

H. B. ZIMMERMAN, Union College, Schenectady, N.Y. USA. (Present address: Division of Polar Programs, National Science Foundation, Washington, D.C. 20550, USA.)

A. BOERSMA, 404 Gate Hill Road, Stony Point, N.Y. USA.

F. W. McCOY, Lamont-Doherty Geological Observatory, Palisades, N.Y. USA.

South Atlantic organic-rich sediments: facies, processes and environments of deposition

D. A. V. Stow

SUMMARY: Organic-rich sediments (black shales) occur in parts of the South Atlantic ocean within Jurassic, Cretaceous and Neogene sections. These black shales are represented by various lithologies, including mudstones, marlstones, limestones, sandstones, pebbly mudstones and diatomites. They range from thin to very thick bedded, laminated, fissile or structureless, and show varying degrees and types of bioturbation. Texturally and compositionally they are equally varied. Organic carbon may be of principally marine or terrigenous source and forms from 1% to over 20% of the sediment. In many cases, the black shales are interbedded with organic-poor lithologies in cycles with irregular periodicities that average 20,000 to 140,000 years. The range of depositional processes of these black shales includes sliding, debris flows, high- and low-concentration turbidity currents, pelagic/hemipelagic sedimentation, and winnowing by shelf bottom currents. They occur in various palaeogeographical settings from nearshore shelf to ocean basin, and have been differently influenced by variations in bottom water oxygenation, organic matter supply and rates of sedimentation.

Introduction

Sediments containing more than about 2% organic carbon are common at certain stratigraphic intervals in the South Atlantic. Such sediments are often loosely described as 'black shales' and occur commonly throughout the world, although black-shale sections usually comprise interbedded dark- and light-coloured intervals that show variations in both organic-carbon and carbonate content. The lithologies are most often mudstones and shales, but may include coarser terrigenous sediments, limestones and dolomites. The term 'black shale' is used interchangeably with organic-rich sediments in this paper.

Previous work on South Atlantic organic-rich sediments includes overview of the Mesozoic occurrences (Arthur & Natland 1979), documentation of the present day upwelling system off Namibia (Calvert & Price 1971), and more detailed studies of sediment facies (Stow & Dean 1984), inorganic geochemistry (Dean et al. 1984; Calvert & Price 1983), and organic geochemistry (Meyers et al. 1984). Arthur et al. (1984) have recently synthesized much of the current thinking concerning models for the deposition of fine-grained organic-rich sediments in the deep sea. Studies of North Atlantic, Pacific, Mediterranean and onshore examples of black shales have been equal or more numerous (see reviews by Demaison & Moore 1980; Weissert 1981; Arthur et al. 1984).

Against this background of interest in and knowledge of black shales worldwide, this paper focuses more specifically on the detailed sedimentology of selected examples of South Atlantic black shales with a view to its bearing on their processes and environments of deposition. We first present a brief updated overview of South Atlantic black shale occurrences set in the context of regional development.

Stratigraphy and occurrence

Mesozoic black shales

The oldest black shales recovered during DSDP drilling in the South Atlantic are the Callovian–Oxfordian dark-coloured mudstones at Sites 330 and 511 on the Falkland Plateau (Fig. 1) with up to 8.5%, mainly marine and part terrestrial, organic carbon (type II of Tissot et al. 1974). This black shale sequence extends throughout the early and mid Cretaceous period, whereas that at Site 361 in the Cape Basin is mainly Aptian in age, with up to 6% organic carbon of dominantly terrestrial origin (type III of Tissot et al. 1974). In the Angola Basin and on the Walvis/Rio Grande Ridge (Fig. 1) the main interval of black shale accumulation was during the mid to late Cretaceous (Albian to Santonian). Organic carbon contents are up to 23% and, particularly in the Cenomanian-Turonian sediments, are mainly of amorphous marine material (types I and II of Tissot et al. 1974). At many of the sites, marked hiatuses are present through at least part of this upper black shale section.

From: BROOKS, J. & FLEET, A. J. (eds) 1987, *Marine Petroleum Source Rocks*
Geological Society Special Publication No. 26 pp. 287–299.

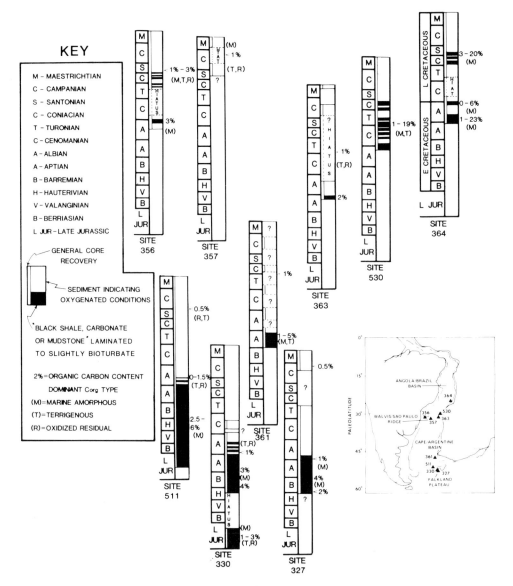

FIG. 1. Summary stratigraphic columns for the Mesozoic sections of DSDP holes in the South Atlantic that have recovered organic-carbon-rich sediments. Inset map shows DSDP Site locations on a mid-Cretaceous palaeoreconstruction. From Arthur, Dean & Stow (1984).

Cenozoic black shales

The Palaeogene sediments recovered at DSDP sites throughout the South Atlantic do not show any appreciable enrichment in organic carbon. However, the development of the Benguela Current upwelling system off south-western Africa during the Neogene led to the accumulation of organic-rich sediments over a broad belt in the southeast Atlantic (Sites 362, 364, 365, 530 and 532) (Fig. 2). Organic-carbon contents reach up

to 8% in the early Pliocene to late Pleistocene sediments and are dominantly of marine origin. The direct influence of the upwelling system extends to depths of at least 1330 m and decreases generally offshore. However, the late Miocene to Recent section at Site 530, in 4650 m water depth, comprises similar organic-rich sediments that have been redeposited downslope from the Walvis Ridge (see later).

The organic-rich sediments appear to be limited to this eastern belt. The cluster of DSDP

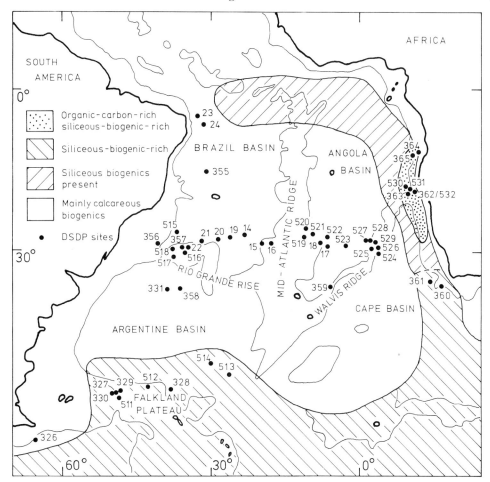

FIG. 2. South Atlantic ocean showing location of all DSDP sites drilled to date, and generalized areas of Pleistocene and/or Recent sediments rich in organic carbon and siliceous biogenic material.

sites (14–22, 355–359, 515–529) (Fig. 2) across the central South Atlantic are nearly all dominated by calcareous oozes, with muds and some siliceous biogenics at the deepest sites. There is a high latitude belt of siliceous biogenic-rich sediment of late Miocene to Recent age, recovered at Sites 327–330 and 511–514 (Fig. 2). This is commonly darker coloured than the calcareous oozes, rarely laminated, but does not seem to be rich in organic carbon.

Sedimentary characteristics

Falkland Plateau

The Callovian–Oxfordian to Aptian–Albian sections recovered on the Falkland Plateau at Sites 327, 330 and 511 contain a dominant black shale facies throughout the 130 to 220 m cored interval. These dark-coloured, organic-rich mudstones and calcareous mudstones are interbedded with only rare lighter-coloured calcareous mudstones, zeolitic mudstones and limestones (Fig. 3), although these interbedded lithologies become more common through the Aptian and Albian sections (Barker, Dalziel *et al.* 1977; Thompson 1976; Ludwig, Krasheninnikov *et al.* 1983), in which an irregular cyclicity or carbon and carbonate content on the order of 100,000 years has been noted (Parker *et al.* 1983).

Organic geochemical results indicate an average content of about 3.5% organic carbon (maximum 8.5%), decreasing upwards through a transition zone in the Aptian–Albian section, in which the average is about 0.3% and the maximum about 3.5%. The carbon is dominantly

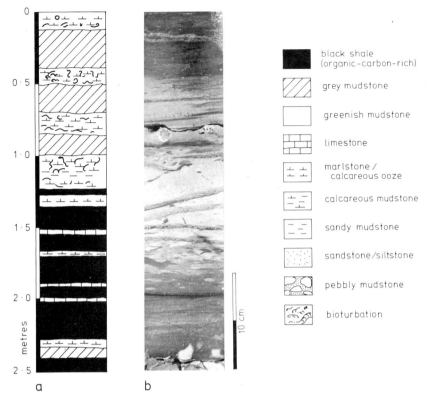

black shale
(organic-carbon-rich)

grey mudstone

greenish mudstone

limestone

marlstone /
calcareous ooze

calcareous mudstone

sandy mudstone

sandstone/siltstone

pebbly mudstone

bioturbation

FIG. 3. Sedimentary characteristics of Jurassic-Cretaceous black shale sections from Falkland Plateau Sites 327, 330 and 511. (a) typical vertical sequence showing interbedded black shales, grey mudstones, marlstones and limestones; (b) photograph from DSDP Site 511–56–5.

of marine origin, with some increase in terrestrial material in the lowermost (Callovian–Oxfordian) sediments and towards the top (Aptian–Albian), in which residual (oxidized) marine kerogen is also present (Comer & Littlejohn 1976; Deroo *et al.* 1983; von der Dick *et al.* 1983; Parker *et al.* 1983).

The black shales show a range of sedimentary structures from essentially structureless through faintly laminated and well-laminated to highly fissile. They show some degree of bioturbation in parts, with burrows being more evident in black shales associated with the interbedded lithologies (Parker *et al.* 1983). There is little evidence of resedimentation, apart from the sharp bases to some black shale beds and isolated examples of (?) slump folds and inclined laminae. Sedimentation rates are extremely low throughout (0.1 to 1 cm/1000 years) and favour dominantly pelagic-hemipelagic sedimentation.

Inorganic geochemical analyses of the organic-rich sediments at Site 511 (Varentsov 1983) reveal concentrations of trace metals (Zn, Cu, Cr, Rb and Ba) associated with the late Jurassic section,

and relatively lower concentrations of V, Zn, Cu and Cr in the early Cretaceous black shales. In this latter section, diagenetic concentrations of Zn, Ni, La and perhaps Mo are associated with the carbonate phase.

Cape Basin

The Aptian section at Site 361 in the southern Cape Basin comprises thin to thick sandstones, pebbly sandstones and contorted slump units, interbedded with grey, green and black mudstones and minor marlstones and limestones (Natland 1978) (Fig. 4). The organic-rich sediments make up an average of 10–20% of the total section (maximum about 50% in parts) and occur in over 100 distinct beds, each from 1 cm–40 cm in thickness. Organic-carbon contents are from 1.5–6% in the black shales and <0.5% in the interbedded lithologies; land-derived organic-carbon is dominant with various admixtures of marine-derived material.

Two types of sequence are common: (a) an alternation of thick sandstones, mostly rich in

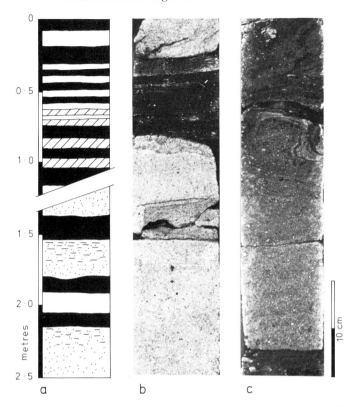

Fig. 4. Sedimentary characteristics of mid Cretaceous black shale sections from Cape Basin Site 361. (a) two typical vertical sequences showing interbedded green, grey and black mudstones (upper), and mudstones with organic-rich sandstones and muddy sandstones (lower); (b) photograph from DSDP Site 361–35–2; (c) photograph from DSDP Site 361–36–2. For legend see Fig. 3.

terrestrial organic debris, and thin laminated dark grey or black mudstones containing both terrestrial and marine organic matter; and (b) an alternation of green and dark grey or black mudstones, with rare interbedded limestone and marlstone intervals.

The first sequence is clearly turbiditic in origin, the couplets showing positive grading over a sharp scoured base and internal lamination and cross-lamination. At least the upper parts of the black mudstones overlying the sandstones may be of pelagic origin, whereas the lower parts are more probably turbiditic. The sediments of the second sequence are more typical of fine-grained facies associated with coarse turbiditic intervals and may be part turbidite, part hemipelagite-palagite in origin. Structures within the black shales include horizontal- and micro-cross-lamination and micro-bioturbation.

The average sedimentation rate for the Aptian black shale section was between 5 and 10 cm/1000 years, yielding a periodicity for the occurrence of black shale horizons of 20,000 to 60,000 years. However, with such clear evidence of significant contribution from turbidites, giving very high instantaneous rates of sedimentation, these figures provide only an order of magnitude.

Angola Basin

The late Albian to early Santonian section at Site 530A in the southeastern Angola Basin comprises red, green, grey and black mudstones and calcareous mudstones with thin siltstones and rare limestones (Stow & Dean 1984) (Fig. 5). The organic-rich sediments make up just less than 10% of the complete 170 m thick section, and up to 50–60% in parts of the late Cenomanian–Turonian interval. They occur in some 260 separate beds ranging from less than 1 cm to over 60 cm in thickness, with organic-carbon contents from about 1% to 19%, mainly marine sapropelic but with small variable admixtures of terrigenous material.

Two types of sequence are most common: (a) an alternation of dark grey or black organic-rich

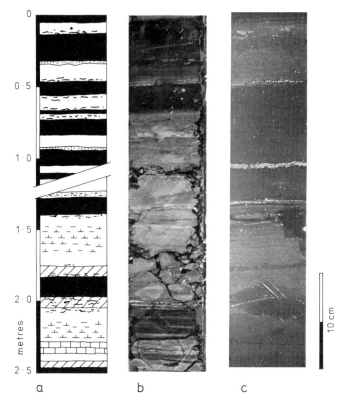

FIG. 5. Sedimentary characteristics of mid-Cretaceous black shale sections from Angola Basin DSDP Sites 364, 365 and 530. (a) two typical vertical sequences showing interbedded green and black mudstones (upper), and green, grey and black mudstones, marlstones and limestones (lower); (b) photograph from DSDP Site 530A–87–4; (c) photograph from DSDP Site 530A–98–3. For legend see Fig 3.

mudstone and green organic-poor mudstone; and (b) a rather thicker sequence from pale-coloured limestones, through pale greenish marlstone and grey ($\pm$ calcareous) mudstone to black organic-rich mudstone, and back through grey to green mudstone.

Silt laminae and thin beds may occur at any part of either sequence; they commonly show micro-structures such as scoured bases, positive grading and micro-climbing-ripples that suggest a probable turbiditic origin, and tend to be pyritiferous when associated with the black shale beds. Bioturbation is most evident in the limestones, marlstones and green mudstones, and tends to diminish in both intensity and in burrow size towards the black shales. Black shale beds may be finely laminated, structureless or with microbioturbation in parts.

The average sedimentation rate for the Albian to Santonian interval is of the order of 1 cm/1000 years; certain minor hiatuses may be present in the Turonian. The periodicity of occurrence of black shale beds is very variable, from about 10,000 to 350,000 years (most commonly between 20,000 and 80,000 years). It has been estimated (Stow & Dean 1984) that some 5–20% of the section is of basinal turbiditic aspect, the remainder being hemipelagic and pelagic in origin, but that these depositional processes have varied for the most part independently of the black shale cycles.

Results of inorganic geochemical analyses through the Cretaceous section (Dean & Parduhn 1984; Dean et al. 1984) reveal significant enrichment of a wide range of trace metals, notably Cd, Co, Cr, Cu, Mo, Ni, Pb, V and Zn, in the black shales relative to the interbedded organic-poor lithologies. These elements show markedly different concentration gradients within the section, suggesting differential mobility has occurred during diagenesis. Concentrations of Cd, Zn, V, Cu and Mo are highest in parts of the section where black shales are most abundant, which suggests that they have not migrated far. However, Pb, Ni, Co and Cr, together with the major elements Ba and Mn appear to be more mobile, and may have migrated up to tens of metres from their original organic-rich source (Dean *et al.* 1984).

At Site 364 further north on the Angola continental slope, the period during which black shales accumulated intermittently was somewhat more prolonged, from late Aptian through to early Santonian, although for much of the Albian only limestones and marly limestones were deposited and there was an important hiatus in sedimentation through much of the Cenomanian and early Turonian. Both the Aptian and, more particularly, the younger sections are very similar to that drilled at Site 530A. The sediments are generally richer in carbonate, including dolomite, limestone and marly limestones, and the black shale beds are less numerous but equally varied in their thickness, carbon content (dominantly marine) and in their periodicity of occurrence. Bioturbation is common throughout the limestone, marlstone and mudstone facies and microbioturbation is present in many of the black shale beds. Many of these also show fine horizontal lamination. Sedimentation rates were very low and hemipelagic-pelagic processes apparently dominated.

Other DSDP sites in the Angola Basin did not penetrate mid-Cretaceous sections, although Site 365 on the continental slope off Angola recovered a thick displaced unit of Albian–Turonian sediments within a Tertiary sequence. These organic-rich Cretaceous sediments are generally similar to those at Site 364, but not so rich in organic carbon, and probably represent a large slide block that caved from a now partly buried canyon wall during the Miocene (Bolli *et al.* 1978).

Namibian shelf and Walvis ridge

The Recent sediments on the Namibian continental shelf were sampled with short gravity corers and described by Senin (1968), Avilov & Gershanovich (1970) and Calvert & Price (1971). Organic-rich diatom ooze, containing fish debris and phosphorite, occurs in a 600 km long coastal belt up to 70km wide off Walvis Bay in water depths less than 140 m. There are smaller areas of terrigenous gravelly sands and muddy sands within this belt. Much of the middle and outer shelf is covered by calcareous oozes and muds, rich in foraminifera and mollusc debris.

The siliceous oozes contain up to a maximum of 22% organic carbon and have accumulated at rates between 30 and 120 cm/1000 years. The calcareous shelf facies contain rather less organic carbon, from 1–15%, and have accumulated more slowly, with sedimentation rates on the order of

5 cm/1000 years on the outer shelf. The organic carbon in both cases is entirely marine planktonic in origin. Pelagic sedimentation and a certain amount of redistribution and winnowing across the shelf have been the main processes operating.

Inorganic geochemical analyses of the Namibian Shelf sediments have shown relative enrichment in trace metals (Cu, Mo, Ni, Pb, Zn and U) of the diatomaceous oozes compared with the outer shelf calcareous muds. The distribution of these elements closely mirrors that of organic carbon, apart from uranium which also appears to reflect phosphorite concentration (Calvert & Price 1970, 1983; Calvert & Morris 1977).

DSDP Sites 532 and 362 were drilled at more or less the same location on the eastern end of the Walvis Ridge in a water depth of 1330 m some 600 km NW of Walvis Bay. There are 300 m of late Miocene to Recent oozes, muddy oozes and biogenic muds, which were particularly well recovered by hydraulic piston coring at Site 532 (Hay *et al.* 1984). These sediments occur as a regular alternation of lighter coloured beds, richer in $CaCO_3$, and darker coloured beds, richer in terrigenous clays and organic carbon (Fig. 6). The dark coloured beds make up 30–60% of the section, occurring as over 100 separate beds from 10–100 cm in thickness and with an average content of 3–8% organic carbon. This carbon is entirely of marine planktonic origin. The periodicity of the light-dark cycles ranges from 10,000 to 80,000 years (average 41,000 years), whereas the organic-carbon-rich to organic-carbon-poor cycles are not entirely coincident with the colour changes, averaging 24,000 years over the last 2.5 million years (Gardner *et al.* 1984). The average sedimentation rate was on the order of 4–6 cm/1000 years.

The sedimentary characteristics of the organic-rich beds at Site 532 are significantly different from those of the Mesozoic black shales described above, and much more similar to those of the present day organic-rich sediments on the Namibian shelf. They are dark olive greens and greys, biogenic rich with a dominance of diatoms in the more organic-rich intervals, and completely devoid of primary sedimentary structures. Bioturbation is intense throughout and has resulted in relatively thick intermixed zones between the light and dark layers. There is little evidence for anything other than pelagic-hemipelagic depositional processes, although sedimentation rates are almost an order of magnitude higher than those of many open-ocean pelagic sediments.

Geochemically there is only very slight enrichment of trace metals in the darker beds relative to the lighter beds, particularly of Cr, Cu, Ni, V and Zn (Dean & Parduhn 1984).

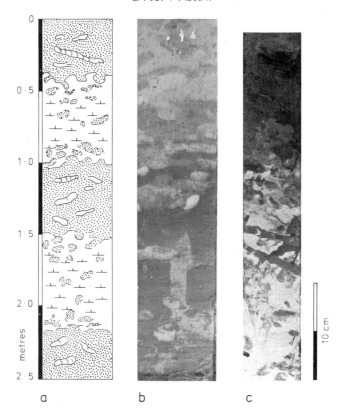

FIG. 6. Sedimentary characteristics of Pliocene-Recent organic-rich biogenic oozes and muddy oozes from Walvis Ridge Sites 362, 363, 531 and 532. (a) typical vertical sequence showing interbedded and bioturbated dark greenish grey siliceous oozes (organic-rich) and light greyish-white calcareous oozes and muds; (b) photograph from DSDP Site 532–42–2; (c) photograph from DSDP Site 532–5–3. For legend see Fig. 3.

At the present day the Benguela Current upwelling system off Namibia results in high primary productivity in the surface waters and the accumulation of diatomaceous, organic-rich sediments on the Namibian shelf. The records of diatom abundance and organic-carbon content in the sediments at Site 532 suggest that upwelling began in the late Miocene (about 5 my ago), and increased to a maximum in the late Pliocene to early Pleistocene. On the Walvis Ridge, upwelling activity then declined to the present day, most likely due to a southward migration of the system (Hay *et al.* 1982, 1984). It is interesting to note that the rise and decline of upwelling intensity at Site 532 did not apparently disturb the cyclicities of carbonate and organic-carbon that remain relatively constant throughout (Dean & Parduhn 1984).

Immediately adjacent to the Walvis Ridge at the foot of its northern flank (4.6 km water depth), Site 530B penetrated 270 m of late Miocene to Recent calcareous and siliceous oozes, muds and pebbly muds (Hay *et al.* 1984). The lithologies are very similar to those on the crest of the Ridge described above (Sites 532, 363), with organic-rich sediments making up 20–40% of the section, occurring in over 100 beds from 5 cm to >10 m thick (Fig. 7). The total organic carbon content of these beds ranges from 1–6% and is of dominantly marine origin. The darker beds are rich in diatoms and/or terrigenous clays and are interbedded with nannofossil foraminifera oozes and muds.

However, the dark organic-rich beds nearly all show very clear structures indicative of resedimentation, including sharp scoured bases, minor parallel lamination near the base, marked positive grading, and bioturbation increasing towards the gradational upper boundary. Some of the thicker beds contain reworked clasts of semi-lithified muds and oozes in either a dark organic-rich or light carbonate-rich matrix. The whole sequence has been interpreted as part of a small, ridge-flank, deep-sea fan system, con-

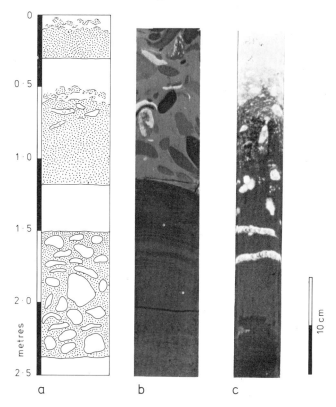

FIG. 7. Sedimentary characteristics of Pliocene-Recent organic-rich resedimented biogenic oozes and muddy oozes from Angola Basin Sites 530A and 530B (a) typical vertical sequence showing interbedded dark greenish-grey siliceous ooze turbidites (organic-rich), light greyish-white calcareous oozes and muds, and pebbly mud debrites (organic-rich); (b) photograph from DSDP Site 530B–8–2; (c) photograph from DSDP Site 530B–5–3. For legend see Fig. 3.

structed by resedimentation of mainly organic-rich sediments from the adjacent Walvis Ridge into the mainly carbonate-rich pelagic-hemipelagic facies of the Angola Basin (Stow 1984a, b).

Discussion

Processes of deposition

It is clear from this brief survey of the sedimentary characteristics of organic-rich sediments in the South Atlantic ocean, that black shales may be deposited or affected by one of a number of different processes:

(a) resedimentation by large-scale sliding (e.g. Angola Basin Sites 365 and 530B);

(b) resedimentation by large-scale debris flows (e.g. Angola Basin Site 530B);

(c) high-concentration sandy and muddy turbidity currents (e.g. Cape Basin Site 361 and Angola Basin Site 530B, respectively);

(d) low-concentration turbidity currents (e.g. Angola Basin and Cape Basin Sites);

(e) normal pelagic (biogenic) and hemipelagic (part terrigenous silt) sedimentation (e.g. parts of all areas and Sites discussed); and

(f) winnowing and reworking by shelf bottom currents (e.g. Namibian Shelf).

These different processes result in black shales having a wide range of structural, textural and compositional characteristics. The coarser grained sandstone turbidites and mud-clast debrites, commonly structureless or indistinctly stratified, are clearly recognizable. The finer grained silty and muddy black shales show more subtle micro-structural and micro-fabric differences (Fig. 8). A sub-horizontal lensoid fissility appears to be characteristic of many hemipelagic

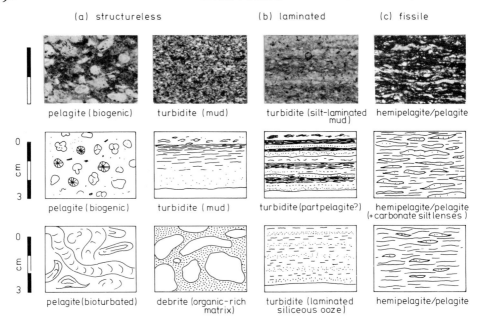

FIG. 8. Characteristic microstructure and fabric of various organic-rich sediments from the South Atlantic. Upper row = photographs of thin sections; lower two rows = sketches from polished core slabs. (a) structureless sediment with more or less random fabric may result from pelagic, hemipelagic, turbiditic or debris flow processes; (b) laminated sediment resulting from part turbiditic and part pelagic processes; (c) fissile sediment probably resulting from hemipelagic/pelagic processes. For legend see Fig. 3.

and pelagic black shales. The lenses of lighter-coloured terrigenous, biogenic or diagenetic material are on a millimetre to micrometre scale and form from 10–60% of the rock. They are draped with darker-coloured, finer-grained, organic-rich material. A more regular horizontal lamination or thin bedding characterizes turbiditic black shales. The laminae may be from less than 1 mm to 1 cm in thickness and show grading, sharp contacts, internal lamination, etc. They tend to be composed of lighter-coloured, terrigenous silty material separated by thin to thick layers of darker, muddy, more organic-rich material that is largely structureless. A more structureless aspect with more or less random internal fabric can occur in some biogenic pelagic black shales (either siliceous or calcareous), in some hemipelagic black shales that have been homogenized by extensive bioturbation, as well as in the thick-bedded, massive, organic-rich turbidites and debrites.

The composition of and type and amount of organic carbon in black shales are equally variable and partly related to the depositional process but also, of course, to the original source of sediment and organic matter. The turbiditic and other resedimented black shales tend to have a more marked terrigenous signature, in terms of both mineral and organic composition. However, this does not apply to, for example, the resedimented siliceous organic-rich sediments in the Angola Basin at the foot of the Walvis Ridge flank, which are thoroughly marine. Open ocean pelagic black shales are the most fully marine, whereas continental margin and shelf hemipelagites are commonly mixed with some terrigenous material.

Environments of deposition

The paleogeographical settings in which the black shales of the South Atlantic accumulated are equally as varied as their processes of deposition. They include:

(a) nearshore and shelf environments (e.g. Namibian Shelf);

(b) outer shelf and oceanic plateau or ridge (e.g. the Falklands Plateau and Walvis Ridge sites);

(c) continental slope and rise or submarine fan settings (e.g. the Cape Basin and Angola Basin margin sites); and

(d) deep ocean basin environments (e.g. Angola Basin Site 530).

What is clearly more important for the preservation of organic matter in sediments, than either depositional process or geographical setting are the following three main variables (Demaison & Moore 1980; Arthur *et al.* 1984; Stow & Dean 1984):

(a) the degree of bottom-water oxygenation within an oxygen minimum zone, throughout the water column or throughout the bottom waters within a basin;

(b) the volume of supply of marine and terrigenous organic matter from primary productivity at the surface, from fluvial discharge and from downslope resedimentation processes; and

(c) the rate of sedimentation and hence the rate of burial/dilution of organic matter.

That these factors were variable in both time and space during the accumulation of black shales is well illustrated by the range of interbedded organic-rich and organic-poor lithologies that occur at different ages in the South Atlantic. The percentage of organic carbon preserved and the percentage of the total section that is black shale both increase with the degree of anoxicity and the volume of organic matter supply. The rate of sedimentation is a balancing variable.

The Jurassic-lower Cretaceous black shales of the Falkland Plateau sites were, most probably, principally the result of low bottom-water oxygenation in the narrow, restricted, southern Atlantic ocean of that period. Similarly, the middle Cretaceous black shales of the Cape and Angola Basins were influenced by restricted basin circulation, a warm equable climate and a high sea-level, that all contributed to the ancient South Atlantic ocean being poised at relatively low oxygen levels. Only small changes in the flux of organic matter, ocean circulation, climate, or other variables would then have been sufficient to cause anoxia or near-anoxia in the bottom waters and sediments. Variable periodicity of such changes led to the cyclic interbedding of black shales with organic-poor sediments. At site 361 in the Cape Basin, terrigenous input of organic matter and high sedimentation rates were also a factor in the formation of black shales. This complex interplay of variables is illustrated in Fig. 9.

The oceanographic and climatic conditions under which the Miocene–Recent organic-rich sediments accumulated on the shelf and margin off Namibia are markedly different from those of the Cretaceous. The principal factors for organic-carbon preservation on the Namibian shelf are high organic-matter influx from primary productivity in surface waters over an upwelling system, together with the consequent high rates of

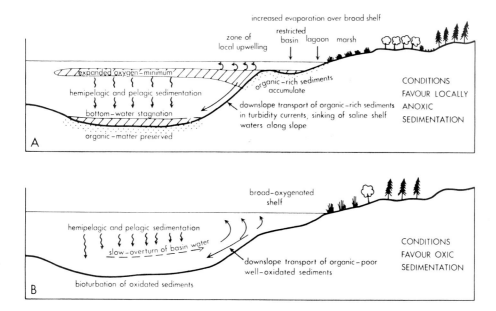

FIG. 9. Schematic model for accumulation and preservation of interbedded organic-carbon-rich (upper) and organic-carbon-poor sediments (lower). Note multiple interacting variables, each of which may have been relatively more or less important for any particular black shale section. After Stow & Dean (1984).

sedimentation. Only in the central part of this system are the bottom waters over the shelf also anoxic. The high preservation of organic-carbon in the fully-oxygenated Angola Basin (Site 530B) is due primarily to high organic-matter influx and high rates of sedimentation caused by downslope resedimentation processes.

ACKNOWLEDGEMENTS: Financial support has been from the Natural Environment Research Council and the Royal Society of Edinburgh. Secretarial, drafting and technical support was from staff at the Geology Department, Nottingham University. Simon Kay, Peter Kahn and Andy Fleet are thanked for their reviews of an earlier version of this manuscript.

References

ARTHUR, M. A., DEAN, W. E. & STOW, D. A. V. 1984. Models for the deposition of Mezozoic–Cenozoic fine-grained organic-carbon-rich sediment in the deep sea. *In:* STOW, D. A. V. & PIPER, D. J. W. (eds), *Fine-Grained Sediments: Deep-Water Processes and Facies.* Geol. Soc. Spec. Publ. 15. Blackwell Scientific Publications, Oxford. 527–60.

—— & NATLAND, J. H. 1979. Carbonaceous sediments in North and South Atlantic: the role of salinity in stable stratification of early Cretaceous basins. *In:* TALWANI, M., HAY, W. W. & RYAN, W. B. F. (eds), *Deep Drilling Results in the Atlantic Ocean: Continental Margins and Paleoenvironment.* Maurice Ewing Series 3, Am. Geophys. Union, Washington, D.C. 375–401.

AVILOV, I. K. & GERSHANOVICH, D. Y. 1970. Investigation of the relief and bottom deposits of the southwest Africa shelf. *Oceanology.* **10**, 229–323.

BARKER, P. F., DALZIEL, I. W. D. *et al.* 1977. *Init. Repts. DSDP*, **36**. US Govt. Print. Off., Washington, D.C. 1079 pp.

BOLLI, H. M., RYAN, W. B. F. *et al.* 1978. *Init. Repts. DSDP*, **40**. US Govt. Print. Off., Washington, D.C. 1079 pp.

CALVERT, S. E. & MORRIS, R. J. 1977. Geochemical studies of organic-rich sediments from the Namibian Shelf. II. Metal-organic associations. *In:* ANGEL, M. (ed.). *A Voyage of Discovery*, Pergamon Press, London, 580–667.

—— & PRICE, N. B. 1970. Minor metal contents of recent organic-rich sediments off Southwest Africa. *Nature,* **227**, 593–595.

—— & PRICE, N. B. 1971. Upwelling and nutrient regeneration in the Benguela Current, October 1968. *Deep Sea Res.* **18**, 505–23.

—— & PRICE, N. B. 1983. Geochemistry of Namibian shelf sediments. *In:* SUESS, E. & THIEDE, J. (eds), *Coastal Upwelling, Part A.* Plenum, New York. 337–75.

COMER, J. B. & LITTLEJOHN, R. 1976. Content, composition and thermal history of organic matter in Mesozoic sediments, Falkland Plateau. *In:* BARKER, P. F., DALZIEL, I. W. D. *et al. Init Repts. DSDP*, **36**, US Govt. Print. Off., Washington, D.C. 941–944.

DEAN, W. E. & PARDUHN, N. L. 1984. Inorganic geochemistry of sediments and rocks recovered from the southern Angola Basin and adjacent Walvis Ridge Sites 530 and 532. *In:* HAY, W. W., SIBUET, J. C. *et al. Init. Repts. DSDP*, **75**. US Govt. Print. Off., Washington, D.C. 923–58.

——, ARTHUR, M. A. & STOW, D. A. V. 1984. Origin and geochemistry of Cretaceous deep-sea black shales and multicolored claystones, with emphasis on DSDP Site 530, southern Angola Basin. *In:* HAY, W. W., SIBUET, J. C. *et al. Init. Repts. DSDP*, **75**, US Govt. Print. Off., Washington, D.C. 819–44.

——, HAY, W. W. & SIBUET, J. C. 1984. Geologic evolution, sedimentation and palaeoenvironments of the Angola Basin and adjacent Walvis Ridge: Synthesis of results of DSDP Leg 75. *In:* HAY, W. W., SIBUET, J. C. *et al. Initial Repts. DSDP*, **75**. US Govt. Print Office, Washington, D.C., 509–544.

DEMAISON, G. J. & MOORE, G. T. 1980. Anoxic environments and oil source bed genesis. *Bull. Am. Assoc. Petrol. Geol.* **64**, 1179–209.

DEROO, G., HERBIN, J. B. & ROUCACHE, J. 1983. Organic geochemistry of Upper Jurassic-Cretaceous sediments from Site 511, Leg 71, western South Atlantic. *In:* LUDWIG, W. J. & KRASHENINNIKOV, V. A. *et al. Init. Rept. DSDP*, **71**. US Govt. Print. Off., Washington, D.C. 1001–1014.

GARDNER, J. V., DEAN, W. E. & WILSON, C. 1984. Carbonate and organic-carbon cycles and the history of upwelling DSDP Site 532, Walvis Ridge, South Atlantic Ocean. *In:* HAY, W. W., SIBUET, J.-C., *et al. Init. Repts. DSDP*, **75**. US Govt. Print. Off., Washington, D.C. 905–22.

HAY, W. W., SIBUET, J.-C. *et al.* 1982. Sedimentation and accumulation of organic carbon in the Angola Basin and on Walvis Ridge: Preliminary results of Deep Sea Drilling Project Leg 75. *Bull. Geol. Soc. Am.* **93**, 1038–50.

——, SIBUET, J.-C. *et al.* 1984. *Init. Repts. DSDP* 75. US Govt. Print. Off., Washington, DC.

LE PICHON, X., SIBUET, J. C. & FRANCHATEAU, J. 1978. A schematic model of the evolution of the South Atlantic. *In:* CHARNOCK, H. & DEACON, G. (eds), *Advances in Oceanography*, 1–48.

LUDWIG, W. J., KRASHENINNIKOV, V. A. *et al.* 1983. *Init. Repts. DSDP*, **71**. US. Govt. Print. Off., Washington, D.C. 1187 pp.

MEYERS, P. A., BRASSELL, S. C. & HUC, A. Y. 1984. Geochemistry of organic carbon in South Atlantic sediments from Deep Sea Drilling Project Leg 75. *In:* HAY, W. W., SIBUET, J. C. *et al.* Init. Repts. DSDP, **75**. US Govt. Print. Off., Washington, D.C. 967–82.

NATLAND, J. H. 1978. Composition, provenance, and diagenesis of Cretaceous clastic sediments drilled on the Atlantic continental rise off southern Africa. DSDP Site 361. *In:* BOLLI, H., RYAN, W. B. F. *et al.*

Init. Repts. DSDP, **40**. US Govt. Print. Off., Washington, D.C. 1025–62.

PARKER, M. E., ARTHUR, M. A., WISE, S. W. & WENKAM, C. P. 1983. Carbonate and organic carbon cycles in Aptian-Albian black shales at DSDP Site 511, Falkland Plateau. *In:* LUDWIG, W. J., KRASHENINNIKOV, V. A. *et al. Init. Rept. DSDP*, **71**. US Govt. Print. Off., Washington, D.C. 1051–1072.

SENIN, Y. M. 1968. Characteristics of sedimentation on the shelf of southwestern Africa. *Litologiya: Poleznye Iskopaeme.* **4**, 108–111.

SIBUET, J. C. *et al.* 1984a. Early evolution of the South Atlantic Ocean: Role of the rifting episode. *In:* HAY, W. W., SIBUET, J. C. *et al. Initl. Repts. DSDP.* **75**, US Govt. Print. Office, Washington, D.C. 469–481.

—— *et al.* 1984b. The eastern Walvis Ridge and adjacent basins (South Atlantic): morphology, stratigraphy and structural evolution in light of the results of Legs 40 and 75. *In:* HAY, W. W., SIBUET, J. C. *et al. Initial Repts. DSDP*, **75**. US Govt. Print. Office, Washington, D.C. 483–508.

STOW, D. A. V. 1984a. Turbidite facies, associations and sequences in the Angola Basin. *In:* HAY, W. W., SIBUET, J.-C. *et al. Init. Repts. DSDP.* **75**. US Govt. Print. Off., Washington, D.C. 785–800.

—— 1984b. Cretaceous to Recent submarine fans in the southeast Angola Basin. *In:* HAY, W. W., SIBUET, J. C. *et al. Init. Repts. DSDP.* **75**. US Govt. Print. Off., Washington, D.C. 771–84.

—— & DEAN, W. E. 1984. Middle Cretaceous Black Shales at Site 530 in the southeastern Angola Basin. *In:* HAY, W. W., SIBUET, J.-C. *et al. Init. Repts. DSDP*, **75**. US Govt. Print. Off., Washington, D.C. 809–18.

THOMPSON, R. W. 1976. Mesozoic sedimentation on the eastern Falkland Plateau. *In:* BARKER, P. F., DALZIEL, I. W. D. *et al. Init. Repts. DSDP*, **36**. US Govt. Print. Off., Washington, D.C. 877–892.

TISSOT, B., DURRAND, B., ESPITALIE & COMBAZ, A. 1974. Influence of nature and diagenesis of organic matter information of petroleum. *Bull. Am. Assoc. Petrol. Geol.* **58**, 499–506.

VARENTSOV, I. M. 1983. Trace element geochemical history of late Mesozoic sedimentation in the southwest Atlantic, Falkland Plateau, Site 511. *In:* LUDWIG, W. J., KRASHENINNIKOV, V. A. *et al. Init. Rept. DSDP*, **71**. US Govt. Print. Off., Washington, D.C. 391–408.

VON DER DICK, H., RULLKÖTTER & WELTE, D. H. 1983. Content, type and thermal evolution of organic matter in sediments from the eastern Falkland Plateau, DSDP, Leg 71. *In:* LUDWIG, W. J., KRASHENINNIKOV, V. A. *et al. Init. Rept. DSDP*, **71**. US Govt. Print. Off., Washington, D.C., 1015–1032.

WEISSERT, H. 1981. The environment of deposition of black shales in the Early Cretaceous: an ongoing controversy. *In:* WARME, J. E., DOUGLAS, R. C. & WINTERER, E. L. (eds). The Deep Sea Drilling Project: a decade of progress. *Soc. Econ. Paleo. Min. Spec. Publ.* **32**, 547–60.

D. A. V. STOW, Grant Institute of Geology, Department of Geology, University of Nottingham, Nottingham NG7 2RD, UK.

Organic-rich Cretaceous sediments from the North Atlantic

C. P. Summerhayes

S U M M A R Y : Organic-rich sediments are abundant in the early and middle Cretaceous of the deep North Atlantic, in the calcareous Blake–Bahama Formation (Valanginian–Barremian), in the siliceous Hatteras Formation (Aptian–Cenomanian), and, in some places, in the Plantagenet Formation (Turonian–Santonian).

The regional patterns of organic facies and organic enrichment reflect:
(1) the rate of supply of marine versus terrestrial organic matter,
(2) the rate of burial of organic matter,
(3) the oxygenation of the bottom water, and
(4) the oceanographic history of the North Atlantic basin.

Rates of supply of marine organic matter (most now present as amorphous matter) seem to have been similar in the eastern and western North Atlantic, though they became higher in the east in Cenomanian and younger times, when coastal upwelling intensified there. Rates of supply of terrestrial organic matter were higher in the west, and off Iberia and in Biscay (except in the Cenomanian–Turonian). Organic matter is most abundant where rates of sedimentation were highest, presumably because organic matter was rapidly removed from the zone of intensive recycling near the sediment water interface. Some of the organic rich deposits were introduced by downslope displacement from the oxygen minimum zone on the continental margins.

The evidence suggests that bottom waters were intermittently suboxic (0.5–0.2 ml/l O_2) or anoxic (<0.2 ml/l O_2), encouraging preservation of organic matter on the deep sea floor. A more or less permanently anoxic expanded oxygen minimum zone is also implied.

While the global Cretaceous ocean seems to have been generally poorly oxygenated, local events within the North Atlantic give it a somewhat different history of accumulation of organic matter from other ocean basins. Nevertheless, the global organic enrichment event at the Cenomanian–Turonian boundary is clearly visible in the North Atlantic.

Introduction

Deep-sea drilling in the deep North Atlantic shows that black, dark green, or dark grey sediments with 1% or more of total organic carbon (TOC) are widespread in middle Cretaceous sediments and, to a lesser extent, in the early Cretaceous. They are commonly referred to as black shales, and are considered to be possible source rocks for petroleum where buried sufficiently to have become mature (Tissot *et al.* 1979, 1980). They were first discovered in piston cores off Florida (Windisch *et al.* 1968) and have since been recorded at many Deep Sea Drilling Project (DSDP) sites in the North Atlantic, beginning with DSDP Leg 1 (Ewing *et al.* 1969) (Fig. 1).

It is somewhat surprising, given the extensive scrutiny to which these deposits have been subjected, that there should be conflicting views on their origin. In large part the controversy stems from the scarcity of the sort of integrated, multidisciplinary studies recommended by Arthur (1979) and Tyson (1984), involving sedimentology, micropalaeontology, palynology, kerogen studies, and organic and inorganic geochemistry. All too often, the specialist or reductionist, rather than the holistic approach has been the only one employed. Weissert (1981), Arthur & Dean (1984) and Arthur *et al.* (1984a) provide elegant reviews of the problem and show how the controversial points may be resolved.

This paper is an attempt to resolve some of the controversy by asking some basic questions about the organic matter in these sediments:
(1) What is its source: marine or terrestrial?
(2) How was it deposited: by turbidity currents, or through pelagic processes?
(3) How was it preserved: by rapid burial, or by deposition in anoxic bottom waters?
(4) What palaeoenvironmental factors are detectable from the interplay of source, deposition, and preservation, that might tell us something about the palaeoceanographic history of the North Atlantic?

This is a follow up to, and an expansion of, my previous studies on these sediments (see Summerhayes 1981; Summerhayes & Masran 1983).

Stratigraphy

The black shales occur in three formations (Jansa *et al.* 1979; Arthur & Dean 1984):
(1) *Plantagenet Formation:* Turonian–Santonian: red-brown variegated clays which are locally black (e.g. at Site 367, Fig. 1).

From: BROOKS, J. & FLEET, A. J. (eds) 1987, *Marine Petroleum Source Rocks*
Geological Society Special Publication No. 26 pp. 301–316.

301

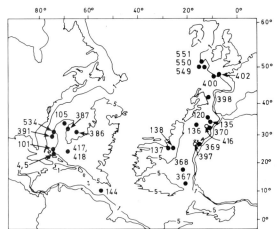

FIG. 1. Locations of DSDP sites discussed here, with 1000 m and 5000 m isobaths.

(2) *Hatteras Formation:* Aptian–Cenomanian: black and green siliceous clays.
(3) *Blake–Bahama Formation:* Berriasian–Barremian: white limestone—grey marl couplets.

The stratigraphic age of these deposits has recently been redefined by de Graciansky *et al.* (1982), and Cool (1982). Further stratigraphic details are given by Arthur (1979), Tucholke & Vogt (1979), and Arthur & Dean (1984).

The black shale section is not uniform in colour nor in organic content (Cool 1982; Tucholke & Vogt 1979). Usually, black or dark green layers rich in organic matter alternate with lighter green layers poor in organic matter in the Hatteras Formation. In the Blake–Bahama Formation white limestones poor in organic matter alternate with dark grey marls rich in organic matter (e.g. Robertson & Bliefnick 1983). These different couplets recur with a periodicity of 20,000–50,000 years (McCave 1979; Robertson & Bliefnick 1983; Arthur & Dean 1984).

Many of the black shale and grey marl layers of the mid and Early Cretaceous are finely laminated (Cool 1982; Arthur 1979; Tucholke & Vogt 1979; Robertson & Bliefnick 1983). These structures could be taken to indicate deposition under anoxic conditions hostile to benthic macrofauna (Demaison & Moore 1980). Furthermore, the lighter coloured interbeds that are poor in organic matter commonly are bioturbated, indicating deposition under well oxygenated conditions (Demaison & Moore 1980). Simplistic assumptions like these have to be examined cautiously, however. Many of the light coloured and organic-poor limestones of the Blake–Bahama Formation are also laminated, not bioturbated, while some of the dark coloured organic rich layers in this Formation and the Hatteras Formation are homogeneous rather than laminated (e.g. Robertson & Bliefnick 1983; De Graciansky *et al.* 1982). Furthermore, some of the dark organic rich beds clearly are graded turbidites (Dean & Gardner 1982; Robertson & Bliefnick 1983; Arthur *et al.* 1984a). It has been argued recently that the black shale beds may have been deposited in rather well oxygenated bottom waters (Habib 1983; Robertson & Bliefnick 1983). These differing points and observations are discussed below.

Distribution of organic matter

In examining the distribution of organic matter in the Cretaceous section it seemed important to me to treat the darker, more organic-rich, and the lighter, more organic-poor sediments as two separate facies probably representing quite different depositional conditions. To discriminate between the two, their TOC values were used. Fig. 2 (right) shows that the TOC of light and dark Cretaceous sediments together follows a log normal distribution, which, at low TOC values (Fig. 2, left), seems to be a mixture of two populations—one with more than 0.5% TOC, the other with less. These two populations were treated as 'peak' and 'background'; erring on the side of caution 1% TOC was used as the cutoff between them. The average TOCs of samples with peak TOC values are given for different Ages in Table 1. The peak TOC samples are termed black shales in this report.

From Table 1 we see that peak TOCs tend to

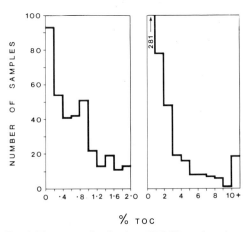

FIG. 2. Frequency distribution of TOC in early and middle Cretaceous (data sources as in Table 1). Diagram at left is detail from same data population used on right (note different scales).

TABLE 1. *Peak TOC averages. Calculated using the stratigraphy of de Graciansky* et al. *(1982) and TOC data from (1) Summerhayes (1981)*, (2) DSDP tables from Leg 76 (Site 534), (3) Herbin* et al. *(1983: Site 534), (4) Summerhayes & Masran (1983: Site 534), (5) DSDP Vol. 51, 52, 53 (Sites 417, 418), and (6) Deroo* et al. *(1980: Sites 417, 418), for samples with > 1% TOC.*

		West							East							
		105	386	387	391	417	418	534	135 136	137 138	367	368	369	370	398	144
CO	L															
	M										15.9					
	E											3.7				7.1
TU	L										26.3					
	M									6.6		3.8				
	E										6.9					
CE	L	8.7	13.7													
	M		8.5							1.8	8.4				4.6	
	E	4.9	1.4										1.2			
AL	L			2.5							9.5					
	M	2.6	2.0		1.5		3.0	1.5					3.8	2.2		
	E		3.5	2.8		5.0					5.7				1.7	
AP	L									1.6						
	M			11.7	3.3	3.7		2.2	1.0	1.8	1.6					
	E	3.3													2.5	
BA		1.9		5.1				1.9			2.1			1.6	2.3	
HA					1.1			1.9			2.7			1.0		
VA		1.8		2.0	1.2			2.0								

CO—Coniacian, TU—Turonian, CE—Cenomanian; AL—Albian; AP—Aptian; BA—Barremian; HA—Hauterivian; VA—Valanginian; (L.M.E. = late, middle, early; where there was no differentiation between late and early, I plotted samples as middle).

* the original TOC and Kerogen data used by Summerhayes (1981) are available from DSDP archives; or from the author.

be low (range of averages is 1–3%) in the black shales from the earlier Cretaceous (Valanginian through Barremian), except locally (5.1% average at Site 387). Peak TOCs increase in the Aptian/Albian black shales (range of averages is 1–5.7%), with local highs (9.5% at Site 367; 11.7% at Site 387), and are highest in the Cenomanian, Turonian and Coniacian black shales (range of averages is 1.2–13.7%), especially at Site 367 (26.3%). Erosion in the west removed much of the post Cenomanian section.

This pattern of TOC enrichment in the middle Cretaceous has been used to support the idea that this was a time when the global ocean was disposed towards anoxia (the global oceanic anoxic event idea of Schlanger & Jenkyns 1976; Jenkyns 1980).

Actually, the accumulation of organic matter was rather different from the picture seen in Table 1, because for much of the early Cretaceous the organic matter was diluted by carbonate (Summerhayes & Masran 1983; Thierstein 1983; Arthur & Dean 1984). As shown in Fig. 3, on a carbonate-free basis the peak TOCs for the Valanginian–Barremian interval are as high, if not higher, than those of the Aptian–Albian. There is little difference between the TOC and the carbonate-free TOC in the Aptian and younger section in these deep water sediments, because the carbonate compensation depth (CCD) rose sharply near the Barremian–Aptian boundary, so eliminating the diluting carbonate material in these younger sediments (Thierstein 1979; Arthur & Dean 1984).

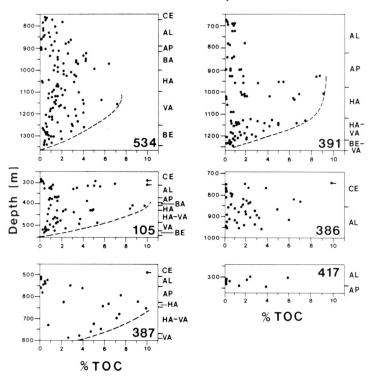

FIG. 3. Distribution of TOC on carbonate-free basis, western North Atlantic. Modified from Summerhayes & Masran (1983) by adding stratigraphy of de Graciansky *et al.* (1982) and Cool (1982). Sub-bottom depths are in metres.

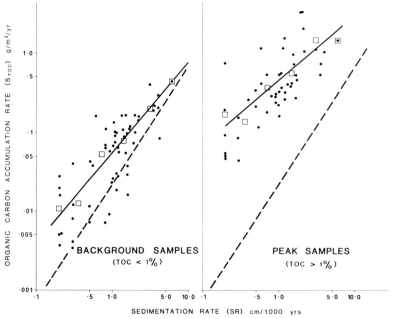

FIG. 4. Relation of S_{TOC} to SR. Squares are group mean averages. Dashed line is from Müller and Suess (1979). $S_{TOC} = SR. P_s (1-\theta)$. $TOC.10^{-4}$ mg/cm^2/yr where SR = sedimentation rate (cm/yr), from de Graciansky *et al.* (1982), corrected to time scale of Harland *et al.* (1982); P_s = sediment density (I used 2000 mg/cm^3, an arbitrary value between averages of 2160 mg/cm^3 and 1520 mg/cm^3 reported by Tucholke & Vogt (1979) for carbonates and black clays respectively); θ = porosity (I used 30%, or 0.3: Summerhayes & Masran 1983); and TOC = %, from data sources in Table 1.

Rate of accumulation of organic matter

In recent years our understanding of what controls the distribution of organic matter has been improved by considering its rate of accumulation rather than its abundance (Müller & Suess 1979).

In early and middle Cretaceous sediments from the North Atlantic the rate of accumulation of organic matter (S_{TOC}) in samples with background TOC values is proportional to sedimentation rate (SR) in much the same way as it is in modern sediments (Fig. 4, left). The slight displacement between the Cretaceous and modern data sets (Fig. 4, left) could reflect the use of a 1% rather than a 0.5% TOC cutoff between peak and background TOC populations. It might also be influenced by the effect of time span on SR, short time spans (thousands of years) having been used to calculate the modern SRs and long ones (millions of years) having been used to calculate the Cretaceous SRs (see Sadler 1981; for further discussion of this problem).

The S_{TOC} for black shales is also proportional to SR (Fig 4, right). After preparation of this diagram it was discovered that much the same observation had been made independantly by Arthur & Dean (1984). The difference between the peak S_{TOC} values and those of modern sediments is quite striking (Fig. 4, right) and requires some explanation. One possible explanation is that at the time these organic rich sediments were deposited the bottom waters were anoxic (< 0.2 ml/l O_2) or suboxic ($0.2–0.5$ ml/ l O_2) allowing larger than normal amounts of organic matter to be preserved. This idea is favoured by some geologists (e.g. Arthur & Dean 1984; Arthur et al. 1984a) but not by others. A key question here is—to what extent does the S_{TOC}–SR relationship observed by Müller & Suess

(1979) apply to anoxic depositional environments? In contrast with Calvert (1983, 1987), Glen & Arthur (1984) suggest that the deposition of organic matter in anoxic environments may differ from that in oxygenated environments.

Another possible explanation for the displacement is that the black shales were deposited rapidly as turbidites and, therefore, the SR of the section cannot be used to calculate the S_{TOC} for these sediments. There is little evidence to support this idea, although some of the black shales may indeed be turbidites (Dean & Gardner 1982; Robertson & Bliefnick 1983).

Both background samples and black shales show an increase in S_{TOC} with increasing SR that is assumed to reflect a decrease in the amount of degradation by the benthic biomass at faster burial rates (cf. Müller & Suess 1979).

Given the relationship in Fig. 4, we may expect variations in SR through time to be accompanied by variations in S_{TOC}. Figure 5 shows the variation in SR through time in the eastern North Atlantic, western North Atlantic, and off Iberia (Site 398) and, for comparison, the curve of global eustatic change in relative sealevel (Vail et al. 1977). Although comparison between the two sides of the North Atlantic is made difficult by the greater abundance of time-slice data for the west (De Graciansky et al. 1982), there are obvious basic similarities between east and west (Fig. 5): for example, high SRs in the early Cenomanian, mid to early Albian, early Aptian, and Hauterivian–late Valanginian, and low SRs in the late Cenomanian, late Albian, mid to late Aptian, late Hauterivian to Barremian, and Berriasian–early Valanginian. These patterns can be represented effectively by placing all the data points from east and west on one curve (SR_{MEAN}) (Fig. 5). The similarities of pattern suggest that the SR is controlled by tectonostratigraphic events and/ or eustatic changes that are Atlantic-wide in their

SEDIMENTATION RATE (SR) m /MY

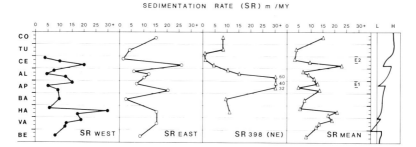

FIG. 5. Changes in SR through time. Derived by averaging SRs given by de Graciansky *et al.* (1982), and correcting to time scale of Harland *et al.* (1982). Coastal onlap, or sea level curve at right is from Vail *et al.* (1977), showing low (L) and high (H) sea level. E1 and E2 represent prominent hiatuses (de Graciansky *et al.* 1982). Note the vertical axis is not a time scale: for convenience each age is subdivided into 3, representing early, middle and late parts of each age. Ages are Berriasian (BE), Valanginian (VA), Hauterivian (HA), Barremian (BA), Aptian (AP), Albian (AL), Cenomanian (CE), Turonian (TU), and Coniacian (CO).

effects. Although there is no precise relationship between the SR_{MEAN} curve and the eustatic curve, peaks in SR are associated with the late Aptian and early Cenomanian sea-level drops, and are followed by declines in SR as sea level rises.

The SR picture for the Aptian and younger sediments represents mostly the deposition of clastics. The SR picture for the Berriasian through Hauterivian is obscured by the addition of carbonates to the section, so cannot be compared directly with that for younger Ages. In fact clastic SRs for the Berriasian through Barremian are almost the same as those for the Aptian–Albian (Summerhayes & Masran 1983; Tucholke & Vogt 1979).

The very low SRs of the late Cenomanian and Mid Aptian represent widespread events labelled E2 and E1 by de Graciansky et al. (1982). Each is in places a hiatus. E1 is associated with red brown muds, E2 with black shales.

Site 398 shows a different SR profile through time, because a large part of its Aptian–Albian section is a proximal deep sea fan (Fig. 5) (Arthur 1979). That excepted, its SR profile is similar to SR_{EAST} in showing a drop from the early into the late Cenomanian and a rise in the Turonian–Coniacian. Deep sea fans with high SRs were

also drilled at Sites 397 (Hauterivian) and 416 (Valanginian–Hauterivian) (Fig. 1). They did not contain any black shales (i.e. TOCs were <1%) (Cornford 1979, 1980; Arthur et al. 1979), so were not considered further.

As expected from Fig. 4, the S_{TOC} curves through time do tend to follow SR. The S_{TOC} (background) curve (Fig. 6) shows a close match to SR (compare with Fig. 5), apart from minor discrepancies in the Aptian that are probably due to TOC data not being available for all time slices for which SR data were available. Similarly, the slight discrepancies between the S_{TOC} east and west curves reflect most probably the differences in time slices used. Thus the combined curve (S_{TOC} mean) is considered a reasonable representation of organic accumulation in the pelagic section of the North Atlantic at times when black shales were not accumulating. Again, Site 398 diverges from the other patterns, although even here there is a dip in S_{TOC} in the late Aptian (see values on profile), as in the east and west (Fig. 6).

The S_{TOC} curve for black shales (Fig. 7) also shows a fair match with that of SR (compare with Fig. 5), except that:

(1) the Aptian peak in SR_{EAST} is not matched by S_{TOC},

BACKGROUND ORGANIC CARBON ACCUMULATION RATE mg/cm²/yr (× 100)

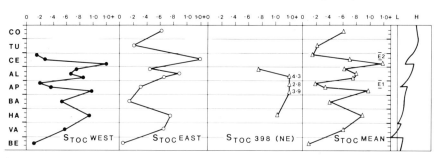

FIG. 6. Variation in background S_{TOC} through time (for samples with TOC <1%). See caption to Fig. 5 for details.

PEAK ORGANIC CARBON ACCUMULATION RATE mg/cm²/yr (× 100)

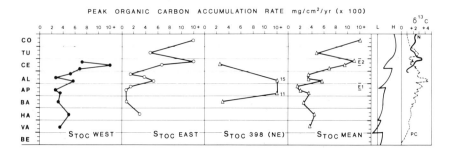

FIG. 7. Variation in peak S_{TOC} through time for black shales (TOC >1%). $\delta^{13}C$ isotope curve is from Scholle and Arthur (1980): N = Norfolk, PC = Peregrina Canyon sections. See caption to Fig. 5 for sea level curve and other details.

(2) the S_{TOC} peaks are offset after the SR peaks in the Cenomanian in both the east and west, and,

(3) the high SRs of the Hauterivian–Valanginian are not reflected to the same extent in the S_{TOC}.

The effect of combining the SR_{TOC} east and west curves is to produce a composite $SR_{TOC\ MEAN}$ curve. Its S_{TOC} peaks in the early Albian and late Cenomanian are associated with:

(1) transgressions (compare $S_{TOC\ MEAN}$ with Vail's sea level curve in Fig. 7) and,

(2) positive excursions on the $\delta^{13}C$ stable isotope curve (compare $S_{TOC\ MEAN}$ with Scholle and Arthur's isotope curve in Fig. 7).

The various S_{TOC} curves of both Figs 6 and 7 show that there was, on average just as much accumulation of organic matter in the Valanginian, Hauterivian, and Barremian, as in the Aptian and Albian, confirming the impression given in Fig. 3, rather than that given by Table 1. Background and peak S_{TOC} curves follow one another quite well (compare Figs 6 and 7), except in the Cenomanian, where the black shale S_{TOC} peaks later than the background one.

Sources of organic matter

As shown in Fig. 8, and in other reports on this subject (Summerhayes 1981; Summerhayes & Masran 1983), the organic matter in the samples with the highest TOCs is dominated by amorphous organic matter. The relationship between TOC and amorphous organic matter changes from one area to another (Fig. 8). It can be explained in terms of:

(1) the preservation, and

(2) the supply, of different types of organic matter.

The preservation factor works as follows: generally, where bottom waters and sediments are well oxygenated, and where rates of sedimentation are moderate to slow, easily decomposable structured marine and amorphous organic matter is destroyed by benthic macrofauna, leaving refractory material (especially the structured remains of land plants, and carbonized material often referred to as fusain, charcoal, or inertinite) to be preserved; TOCs are correspondingly low. In contrast, where this destruction is inhibited by rapid burial and/or by low oxygen in bottom waters, much of the easily degradable amorphous and structured marine material is preserved, TOCs are correspondingly high.

The supply factor affects the original ratio of amorphous and structured marine material on the one hand to structured land plant remains and fusain on the other. This ratio is low nearshore where the climate of the hinterland is humid and the supply of structured terrestrial material by rivers is high, as off Iberia (Site 398) (Fig. 8). It is higher further offshore from this type of coast, as off eastern N. America (Sites 101, 105, 391, 534) (Fig. 8), and highest furthest from those coasts

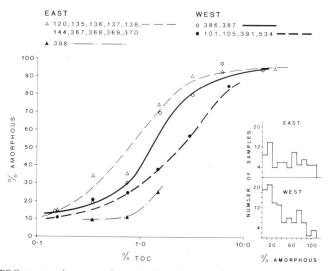

FIG. 8. Relation of TOC to amorphous organic matter (actually sum of amorphous and minor structured marine material). Data from Summerhayes (1981). Points are group mean averages. Samples with <1% TOC (inset) have bimodal TOC distribution usually reflecting lithology: carbonate = high amorphous, clay = low amorphous. Low TOC carbonates with >50% amorphous were ignored to make data sets compatible, because richer samples are usually clay or marl.

(Sites 386, 387) (Fig. 8). Off dry coasts where the supply of terrestrial material is limited, the ratio is high even nearshore, as off north west Africa (Sites 120, 135, 136, 137, 138, 367, 368, 369, 370) and Guyana (Site 144) (Fig. 8).

More information about regional variations in organic facies comes from the ratio of structured terrestrial organic matter to fusain (Fig. 9). This ratio is highest in nearshore deep-sea fan complexes, in areas of humid climate (e.g. at Site 398 off Iberia) (Fig. 9), and decreases with increasing distance from shore, as off eastern North America (Fig. 9). Unlike the ratio of amorphous and structured marine material to structured terrestrial material and fusain (Fig. 8), it is lowest off northwest Africa (Fig. 9): this excludes the nearshore African deep sea fan sites 397 & 416, where the content of terrestrial material can be high (Cornford 1979, 1980). These organic facies variations can be interpreted in terms of control by climate and transport. As mentioned above, the high amorphous contents and the low ratio of structured terrestrial material to fusain off west Africa probably reflect drier climates there than in Iberia and eastern North America, in agreement with the climatic models of Parrish et al. (1982). The decrease in the ratio of structured terrestrial material to fusain with increasing distance from shore off North America probably reflects fractionation during transport, with the fine grained carbonized material moving furthest seaward. The seaward increase in amorphous material off eastern North America may also be due to fractionation during transport of an

originally homogeneous organic facies, but, if the amorphous material is marine (as much seems to be—see next section), it could merely reflect the progressive waning in seaward transport of terrigenous organic matter.

Unfortunately, it is difficult to compare these findings and interpretations with those of Habib (1979a, 1979b, 1982, 1983), because he oxidizes his palynological preparations with nitric acid, so destroying much of the fine grained amorphous organic matter recorded in these sediments by Summerhayes (1981) and Summerhayes and Masran (1983). Nevertheless within the nitric-acid resistant terrigenous fraction, Habib (op. cit.) also recognizes fractionation of structured terrestrial material and 'fusain' during transport.

Evidence from silt sized quartz and clay minerals suggests that much of the fine-grained component of these sediments is aeolian and was blown offshore from both West Africa and North America (Lever & McCave 1983). There is a strong possibility, therefore, that at least some of the organic matter is aeolian. Most probably the fine grained fusain rich component dominates aeolian organic matter. The greater abundance of this component off west Africa compared with North America (Fig. 9) may reflect the larger aeolian input off west Africa (as detected from mineralogical studies by Lever & McCave 1983).

Origin of amorphous organic matter

Is the amorphous organic matter derived from marine or terrestrial precursors? In some samples relics of the original cell structure can be seen within the amorphous material, allowing its parentage to be determined (Masran & Pocock 1981). Only 30 of the many black shale samples examined by Masran (in Summerhayes 1981) contained amorphous material with structural relics; in all but one of these samples the parentage was marine. Originally 6 of the 30 were thought to have terrestrial parentage (Summerhayes 1981), but re-examination of the slides by Masran (personal communication) showed ample signs of marine rather than terrestrial origin. One third of these 30 samples were from the western North Atlantic, the rest being from the eastern North Atlantic (excluding Site 398 and the Biscay sites).

Chemical analysis may help to assign a marine or terrestrial source to the amorphous fraction. The bulk of the available chemical data was obtained by pyrolysis—mostly using the Rock-Eval method (Tissot et al. 1979, 1980; Herbin &

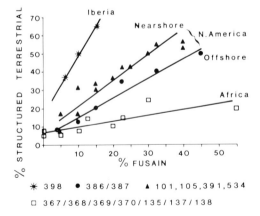

FIG. 9. Relation of structured terrestrial organic matter to fusain (equivalent to the charcoal, coaly material, inertinite, or carbonized debris of other investigators). Points are group mean averages of data from Summerhayes (1981) and Summerhayes & Masran (1983).

Deroo 1982). These data show that the TOC (and, by inference from Fig. 8, the amorphous content) is proportional to the hydrogen index (Fig. 10; and see Waples & Cunningham 1983, for a similar plot for the mid Cretaceous samples from Sites 549, 550, 551—located on Fig. 1). The poorest black shale samples (TOCs 1–2%) generally have hydrogen indices of less than 200, and belong to the Kerogen Type III category of Tissot *et al.* (1980). The richest samples have hydrogen indices that are either near 600 (Sites 367, 368— eastern North Atlantic), corresponding to Type II of Tissot *et al.* (1980), or between 250 and 550 (western North Atlantic, and Site 398), corresponding to mixtures of Types II and III (Fig. 10). Most of the very low hydrogen indices in samples with $> 1\%$ TOC (Fig. 10) are from sites 400 and 402, which are anomalous with respect to the rest of the North Atlantic. A compilation of pyrolysis data by Herbin & Deroo (1982) confirms the regional pattern, showing the highest hydrogen indices in the south east (Sites 367, 368, 369), especially in the Cenomanian–Coniacian. Samples of these Ages at those sites have the highest TOCs and contents of amorphous organic matter (Fig. 8, Table 1; also Summerhayes, 1981).

In the past, the hydrogen index has been rather simplistically interpreted, with Type II taken to represent lipid rich marine organic matter (struc-

tured or amorphous), and Type III taken to represent terrestrial organic matter (structured or amorphous) (e.g. Tissot *et al.* 1980). Recently Tissot & Pelet (1981) have shown that this is an oversimplification. Degradation of marine organic matter changes it chemically from Type II to a mixture of Types II and III. Furthermore, the TOC and mineral matrix have a considerable effect on the hydrogen index—increasing the unreliability of pyrolysis data for evaluating organic facies in any simplistic way (Katz 1983).

It seems likely that where amorphous material is abundant, with very few terrestrial plant remains, and where the hydrogen index is Type II, or a mixture of Types II & III, the amorphous material is mostly marine and in various states of degradation. In contrast, where the kerogen fraction contains abundant remains of land plants (which would lower the hydrogen index), and where the hydrogen index is a mixture of Types II and III, the amorphous fraction may be either marine, or terrestrial, or mixed. Other chemical data, along with observations of relics of structure in amorphous fragments, suggest that the amorphous material of these last samples is marine or mixed, rather than exclusively terrestrial (Summerhayes 1981; Simoneit & Stuermer 1982).

Interpretation of the available organic geochemical data is not easy. Many geochemists have analysed sections of DSDP cores in black shale that were frozen especially for organic geochemical purposes. As pointed out by Simoneit *et al.* (1982), i), these sections may not be fully representative of the cores from which they were taken; ii) different investigators received samples from different depths within each frozen section, without regard for lithological differences; iii) each investigator may have chosen to analyse different sets of frozen sections; iv) the different investigators usually used different analytical methods; v) where the same methods were used there was no interlaboratory calibration. As an example of the sort of confusion that may result, Herbin and Deroo (1982) show that the Cenomanian of Site 367 is dominated by Type II organic matter which is assumed to be more or less entirely marine, while Simoneit and Stuermer (1982) show that an organic rich Cenomanian sample from this site contains *abundant* fatty acids and n-alkanes of terrigenous origin. The preponderance of *n*-alkanes of terrigenous origin in lipid extracts from these organic-rich muds may be due to the *absence* of *n*-alkanes in the predominantly marine organic matter, i.e. the terrestrial contribution may be over-represented in the lipid fraction, as noted elsewhere by Cornford (1979) & Simoneit *et al.* (1982, page 946).

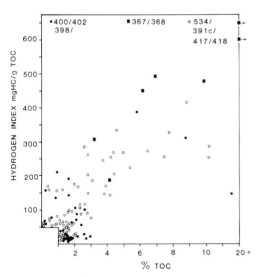

FIG. 10. Relation of hydrogen index to TOC in Cretaceous samples from North Atlantic. Data from Herbin *et al.* 1983 (Sites 534, 391C); Deroo *et al.* 1978 (Sites 367, 368); Deroo *et al.* 1979a (Site 398), 1979b (Sites 400, 402), and 1980 (Sites 417, 418). Note—only 8 samples from Sites 400, 402 have hydrogen indices > 50, of which none are > 150.

Rate of accumulation of amorphous organic matter

Because the S_{TOC} is a composite of marine and terrestrial components some attempt must be made to differentiate between the effects of marine and terrestrial accumulation. This can be done by considering solely the rate of accumulation of the amorphous (i.e. probably marine) + structured marine material in black shale samples ($S_{TOC(AM)}$) (Fig. 11). As in Figures 6 and 7, there is rough parallelism on both sides of the Atlantic; much of the slight difference is due to the nature of the stratigraphic data set used for SR determinations. Again, the composite ($S_{TOC(AM)\ MEAN}$) curve is probably a good overall representation of the pattern of accumulation. Now that the largely terrigenous material from Site 398 has been removed, we see a similar pattern to that in the east and west (Fig. 11).

There are three pronounced peaks in the accumulation of amorphous organic matter; one associated with the early Albian transgression, one with the transgression at the Cenomanian–Turonian boundary, and one in the Coniacian. All three are associated with positive excursions on the stable carbon isotope curve of Scholle and Arthur (1980) (Fig. 11).

Discussion

(1) Source of organic matter and depositional mechanisms: west

The most likely explanation for the abundance of land plant debris in the western North Atlantic and off Spain (also off the southern UK at Sites 400, 402) is that humid climates there (Parrish et al. 1982) led to high runoff and a high rate of supply of terrigenous organic matter.

As today, terrestrial organic matter most probably sank nearshore and was transported to the deep sea in turbidity currents (Robertson & Bliefnick 1983), and in slow-moving downslope turbid flows (Summerhayes 1981). Some, particularly fine grained material (and perhaps especially the fusain fraction, which may be (at least in part) the residue of forest fires), was probably blown into the basin from these same areas, along with quartz and clay minerals.

Turbidity currents most probably reached the basin through the deep sea fans that lined the Atlantic continental margin at this time (e.g. see Mountain & Tucholke 1984; Tucholke & Mountain 1979).

Once the organic matter reached the deep ocean basin it was most probably moved across it, along with clay, in a near bottom turbid layer (the nepheloid layer) (Summerhayes 1981). As it moved, whether in deep ocean waters or in the air, its components were fractionated—presumably by differences in shape and density (see also Habib 1982, 1983). The seaward transport of terrestrial material decreased with increasing distance from shore. Offshore increases in the amorphous (probably marine) content were probably caused not by fractionation, nor by a seaward increase in productivity, but by decreasing dilution by terrigenous material.

The abundance of terrestrial organic material in the western North Atlantic has led some geologists to postulate that unusually large amounts of terrestrial plant remains were supplied to the middle Cretaceous North Atlantic (Jenkyns 1980; Cool 1982; Habib 1982; Robertson & Bliefnick 1983). This concept has been found wanting on mass balance grounds by Waples (1983). Moreover, as Figs 8 and 10 illustrate, organic enrichment in the western North Atlantic is clearly associated with amorphous (i.e. marine) organic matter, and this material dominates accumulation in black shales in the

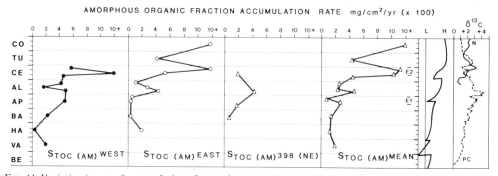

AMORPHOUS ORGANIC FRACTION ACCUMULATION RATE   mg/cm²/yr (× 100)

FIG. 11. Variation in rate of accumulation of amorphous organic matter $S_{TOC(AM)}$ through time in black shales (>1% TOC).

mid Cretaceous section (Fig. 11). There are substantial amounts of 'low grade' black shales (i.e. with TOCs near 1%) in the western North Atlantic, and these do tend to contain more terrestrial than marine organic matter (Fig. 8). In composition they are very much like modern muds from the Mississippi Fan, so one does not need to call upon unusual terrestrial productivity to explain their occurrence.

(2) Source of organic matter and depositional mechanisms: east

The most likely explanation for the abundance of amorphous (marine) organic matter in the east, and of the highly fusain rich terrestrial fraction of the organic residue there, is that the African hinterland had a dry climate (cf. Parrish *et al.* 1982). The abundance of marine organic matter off this coast could be taken as indicating upwelling and associated high productivity (Summerhayes 1981). However, Parrish and Curtis (1982) show that there may also have been upwelling along the eastern margin of North America at this time. Furthermore, the rates of accumulation of amorphous (probably marine) material are rather similar on both sides of the Atlantic (Fig. 11). Thus the difference between east and west (Fig. 8) may be mainly in the terrigenous supply. Nevertheless, as the rates of accumulation of organic matter at the Cenomanian–Turonian boundary are higher in the east than in the west (Fig. 11), as are the TOCs (Table 1), it seems likely that upwelling may have been more intense off north West Africa than off eastern North America at that time. Continuation of organic enrichment into the Coniacian suggests persistence of upwelling off northwest Africa (Fig. 11). Well-developed upwelling in the mid Cretaceous is called upon to explain not only microfossil assemblages in this area (Roth 1983; Roth & Bowdler 1981), but also molluscan assemblages in coastal basins (Einsele & Wiedmann 1982), and differentiates the eastern from the western basins in the North Atlantic.

Transport of organic matter to the deep ocean probably occurred, as in the west, in turbidity currents (Dean & Gardner 1982), and in slow-moving turbid downslope flows (Summerhayes 1981). Lateral movement of marine organic matter by such means is needed to connect the productive waters of the continental margin (sources) with deep ocean depocentres (sinks). To explain why organic matter is abundant in the centre of the basin (e.g. Sites 417, 418) we may call upon a mid ocean divergence, like that of today's Pacific Ocean, with its attendant high productivity (see Hochuli & Kelts 1980).

As in the western basin, much of the terrestrial component of the deep ocean organic matter (especially the fusain) may have been brought in, like the fine grained quartz and clay, by the wind (see Lever & McCave 1983).

(3) Anoxia, circulation models, and the Cenomanian–Turonian boundary event

To restate the controversy, some geologists argue that bottom waters were poorly oxygenated during deposition of the black shales (e.g. Arthur 1979; McCave 1979; Theirstein 1979; Tucholke & Vogt 1979; Summerhayes 1981), while others argue that the organic-rich facies in the deep sea were originally deposited under poorly oxygenated conditions on the slope and rise and subsequently moved downslope by some means to their present location where they were deposited under well oxygenated conditions (e.g. Dean & Gardner 1982; Habib 1982; Robertson & Bliefnick 1983). Yet another group use the multiple working hypothesis, and invoke different models for different black shale deposits in the basin (e.g. de Graciansky *et al.* 1982; Arthur & Dean 1984; Arthur *et al.* 1984a). This last approach is the preferable one.

There is general agreement that there was a well developed and very poorly oxygenated oxygen minimum zone throughout the North Atlantic. At intermediate water depths it affected deposition on the Demerara Rise (Site 144), on the Goban Spur (Sites 549, 550, 551—Waples & Cunningham 1984), at Site 397 (giving rise to laminated sediments: Arthur *et al.* 1979), and in West African coastal basins (Einsele & Wiedmann 1982). It is also believed to have been the upslope source of organic matter off eastern North America at Site 603 (Van Hinte *et al.* 1984) and Site 534 (Robertson & Bliefnick 1983). Arthur & Dean (1984) and Arthur *et al.* (1984a) note, further, that organic enrichment on the flanks of the Cretaceous mid ocean ridge in the North Atlantic (e.g. Sites 417, 418) implies the impingement of an anoxic/suboxic oxygen minimum zone there.

As Calvert (1983, 1987) points out, it is difficult to find concrete evidence that deep waters were anoxic (although recently Glen and Arthur, 1984, suggest how this could be tested in future). Although the presence of laminations in the black shales can be taken as evidence that bottom waters were anoxic, it is not evidence that the entire deep water column was anoxic. Decomposition of organic matter on the bottom may have made near bottom waters anoxic, thereby allowing laminae to be preserved—as in parts of the modern ocean (Summerhayes 1983; Calvert 1983,

1987). However, in the North Atlantic, laminations may characterize not only black shales, but also intervening white limestones in the Blake Bahama Formation (Robertson & Bliefnick 1983). This widespread evidence for the lack of significant benthic macrofaunal activity suggests to me that bottom waters were more or less persistently anoxic or suboxic and that they were predisposed to preserve laminae in organic-rich and organic-poor deposits alike. The organic rich beds, deposited in 20,000–50,000 year cycles may represent, then, not anoxicity but, instead, productivity (this may not apply where the organic-rich beds are turbidites).

High productivity is generally agreed to be an important precursor of organic enrichment, and is undoubtedly the major factor in controlling organic enrichment in regions of upwelling currents on continental margins today (Summerhayes 1983; Calvert 1983, 1987).

An important argument against purely local mechanisms for organic enrichment (such as periodic bursts of terrestrial productivity, to explain organic enrichment in the western North Atlantic) is that the organic rich deposits occupy a broad time envelope of organic enrichment and occur in widely different environments. Thus, as proposed by Schlanger & Jenkyns (1976), Arthur & Dean (1984), & Arthur *et al.* (1984a), it seems that the deposits occur because the ocean was predisposed to allow their accumulation through a combination of high productivity along the margins and low oxygen on the margins and on the deep sea floor. Oxygen depletion was not confined to the North Atlantic in this time envelope, but characterized the world ocean, mostly at intermediate water depths (Schlanger & Jenkyns 1976; Arthur *et al.* 1984a).

Following Thierstein & Berger (1978), I think it likely that the North Atlantic was estuarine with respect to the Pacific. The influx into the Atlantic of Pacific intermediate water rich in nutrients and poor in oxygen (Fig. 12), would have made the North Atlantic an oxygen-poor nutrient trap. Productivity along the margins would have tended to enhance oxygen depletion in intermediate bottom waters there, reinforcing the already strong oxygen minimum 'imported' from the Pacific.

The oxygen deficiency of subsurface North Atlantic water would have been maintained and strengthened in the absence of any vigorous vertical circulation. The North Atlantic was far removed from any source of cold deep water, so vertical circulation was probably haline and driven by saline water sinking either from Atlantic margins (e.g. Brass *et al.* 1982) or from the open central Atlantic (e.g. Wilde & Berry 1982).

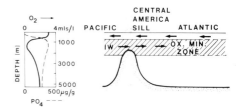

FIG. 12. Estuarine circulation model involving nutrient rich and oxygen poor intermediate water (IW) moving east from the Pacific into the Atlantic in an equatorial undercurrent, so strengthening the Atlantic oxygen minimum zone. The oxygen (O_2) and nutrient (PO_4) profiles at left are modern analogues from GEOSECS station 214 in the Pacific.

Fig. 13 presents a simplistic model based on a combination of the estuarine circulation concept of Theirstein & Berger (1978) (Fig. 12), and the vertical circulation concept of Wilde & Berry (1982). It shows how, given differences in the rates of supply of sinking surface water, North Atlantic bottom waters may have fluctuated from oxygenated to anoxic, perhaps at 20,000–50,000 year intervals. This cyclicity of black shale formation seems to relate to the earth's orbital parameters and associated climatic changes (McCave 1979; De Boer 1982, 1983; Robertson & Bliefnick 1983; Arthur & Dean 1984), as implied in Fig. 13. De Boer (1982, 1983) argues

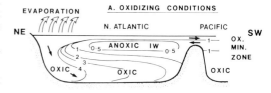

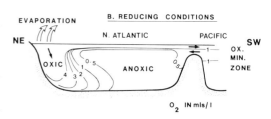

FIG. 13. Highly simplified vertical circulation model involving the control of stratification and anoxia by circulation dynamics (e.g. less evaporation, less production of oxygenated deep water). A = circulation during well oxygenated periods; B = circulation when bottom waters severely oxygen depleted. Oxygen contents are hypothetical. Note link to Fig. 12 (estuarine model).

that the black shales represent times of increased preservation (as depicted in Fig. 13), rather than production.

The widespread Aptian red clay unit may represent a period when the oxidizing model of Fig. 13 (top) predominated. Alternatively it may represent a period when the influx of poorly oxygenated Pacific intermediate water (Figs. 12, 13) was cut off by a lowering of sea level (Summerhayes & Masran 1983).

(4) Cenomanian–Turonian boundary event

The divergence of S_{TOC} and SR patterns at the Cenomanian–Turonian boundary is interpreted as a productivity signal (compare Figs 5 and 7). This is a widespread (indeed global) event, described in detail for other regions by Arthur & Premoli-Silva (1982), Schlanger *et al.* (1987), Arthur *et al.* (1987), and De Graciansky *et al.* (1984), and recognized by a massive short term accumulation of organic matter.

Tucholke & Vogt (1979) and Summerhayes (1981) have suggested that the productivity signal was the response to a massive injection of nutrients into surface waters, caused by a change in circulation as Africa separated from South America (Fig. 14). The separation eventually led to the influx into the North Atlantic of large amounts of highly saline, old, nutrient-rich and oxygen-deficient water from the northern South Atlantic. These waters displaced surfacewards the nutrient-rich North Atlantic deep water (Fig. 15). Transfer of these nutrients to the food chain probably occurred where upwelling took place (e.g. in open ocean divergences, along continental margins, etc.). If the resulting productivity was concentrated along continental margins, as is oceanographically most plausible, the signal could have been distributed basin-wide via turbid downslope flows.

Interestingly, the rich black shale beds of this boundary zone seem to span more time in Atlantic DSDP holes than in nearby continental margins and epicontinental seas (where the boundary black shales span only about 500,000 years— Arthur & Premoli-Silva 1982). This suggests that the shallow water deposits are the transgressive 'feather edge' of what is essentially a continental margin/deep sea deposit of greater time extent.

As mentioned earlier, the Cenomanian–Turonian boundary event is accompanied by a prominent stable carbon isotope signal (see Fig. 7, and Arthur *et al.* 1987). The signal is interpreted to result from entrapment of organic matter in oceanic sediments. It may or may not represent bottom water anoxia: it certainly does represent excessive productivity. The amount of organic

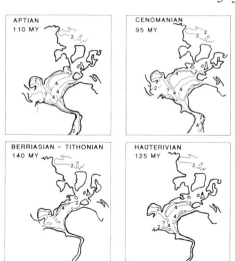

FIG. 14. Palaeogeographic evolution of N. Atlantic in the Mesozoic (from Thiede 1979) showing probable 2000 m and 4000 m isobaths.

matter trapped during this productivity event in the North Atlantic must be very considerable (cf. Figs. 6 & 7). Clearly organic entrapment in this ocean basin must, by exchange of surface water with adjacent oceans, have influenced the carbon signature of the global ocean.

During the Cenomanian there is a significant change in the facies of N. Atlantic sediments, which become red brown with some black intervals off eastern N. America, and remain black or green off northwest Africa (e.g. De Graciansky *et al.* 1982). This development may be explained by the model presented in Fig. 15, showing the S. Atlantic deep water influx affecting the eastern but not the western basins.

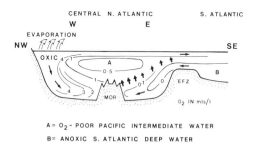

FIG. 15. Highly simplified model for influence of S. Atlantic deep water on N. Atlantic nutrient distribution in Cenomanian–Turonian. MOR = Mid-ocean ridge; EFZ = equatorial fracture zone; IW = intermediate water from Pacific (see Fig. 12); SDW = saline deep water from Brazil Basin. Arrows depict upward displacement of old, nutrient-rich North Atlantic bottom water. Oxygen contents are hypothetical.

Conclusions

What is the organic matter; how did it get there; what made the sediments organic rich; and what does this tell us about circulation? These questions, posed in the Introduction, can now be answered rather more definitively than before.

The organic matter in black shales (TOC > 1%) is predominantly amorphous and probably marine. Terrestrial organic matter is abundant in organic-poor black shales (1–2% TOC), especially off what were humid coasts with high terrestrial productivity (North America, Iberia). Fractionation during transport changed the organic facies. In both black shales and their organic-poor interbeds, the accumulation of organic matter increased with increasing burial rate.

Both the black shales and the interbeds may have been deposited under oxidizing conditions, in which case they are not laminated, or under anoxic conditions, in which case they are laminated. The black shales may be original pelagic/hemipelagic deposits in some places, and redeposited sediments (turbidites) in others. Recurrence of black shales at 20,000–50,000 year intervals suggests a climatic control forced by the earth's orbital variations.

Organic matter enrichment began early in the Valanginian and continued into the Coniacian. Its presence over such a time span in many different depositional settings suggests that the enrichment reflects an ocean-wide palaeoenvironment favourable to organic accumulation. Productivity was favourable for supplying organic matter, burial rates were suitable for its preservation, and anoxia (in intermediate and possibly also in deep waters) enhanced the potential for its preservation. A major change in deep ocean circulation in the Cenomanian caused a massive productivity event by bringing nutrient rich Atlantic deep water towards the ocean surface. This change in circulation had a global effect for a short period at the Cenomanian–Turonian boundary, until the newly available nutrient reservoir was exhausted.

ACKNOWLEDGEMENTS: BP gave permission for the publication of this paper. During preparation of the manuscript I benefited from extensive discussions with Sy Schlanger, Mike Arthur, Andy Fleet, Steve Calvert, and Richard Tyson.

References

ARTHUR, M. A. 1979. North Atlantic Cretaceous black shales: the record at Site 398 and a brief comparison with other occurrences. *Init. Repts. Deep Sea Drilling Project*, **47**, pt. 2, 719–751.

—— & DEAN, W. E. 1984. Cretaceous palaeoceanography. *In:* TUCHOLKE, B. & VOGT, P. (eds) *Decade of North American Geology, Western North Atlantic Synthesis*. Geol. Soc. America (in press).

—— & PREMOLI-SILVA, I. 1982. Development of widespread organic-carbon-rich strata in the Mediterranean Tethys. *In:* SCHLANGER, S. O. & CITA, M. B. (eds) *Nature & Origin of Cretaceous Carbon-Rich Facies*. Academic Press, London. 7–54.

——, DEAN, W. E. & STOW, D. A. V. 1984a. Models for the deposition of Mesozoic–Cenozoic fine-grained organic-carbon-rich sediment in the deep sea. *In:* STOW, D. & PIPER, D. (eds) *Fine-grained Sediments*, Special Publ. Geol. Soc. No. 14, Blackwell Scientific Publications, Oxford.

——, SCHLANGER, S. O. & JENKYNS, H. C. 1987. The Cenomanian–Turonian anoxic event II. Palaeoceanographic controls on organic matter production and preservation. *This volume*, pp. 401–420.

——, VON RAD, U., CORNFORD, C., McCOY, F. W. & SARNTHEIN, M. 1979. Evolution & sedimentary history of the Cape Bojador continental margin, northwestern Africa. *Init. Repts. Deep Sea Drilling Project 47* pt. 1, 773–816.

BRASS, G. W., SOUTHAM, J. R. & PETERSON, W. H. 1982. Warm saline bottom water in the ancient ocean. *Nature*. **296**, 620–623.

CALVERT, S. E. 1983. Geochemistry of Pleistocene sapropels and associated sediments from the eastern Mediterranean. *Oceanolog. Acta*, **6** (3), 255–267.

—— 1987. Oceanographic controls on the accumulation of organic matter in marine sediments. *This volume*, pp. 137–52.

COOL, T. E. 1982. Sedimentological evidence concerning the paleoceanography of the Cretaceous western North Atlantic Ocean. *Palaeo., Palaeo., Palaeo.* **39**, 1–35.

CORNFORD, C. 1979. Organic deposition at a continental rise; organic geochemical interpretations and synthesis at DSDP Site 397, eastern North Atlantic. *Init. Repts. Deep Sea Drilling Projects*. **47**, pt. 1, 503–510.

—— 1980. Petrology of organic matter, Deep Sea Drilling Project Site 415 and 416, Moroccan Basin, Eastern North Atlantic. *Init. Repts. Deep Sea Drilling Project*. **50**, 609–614.

DEAN, W. A. & GARDNER, J. V. 1982. Origin and geochemistry of redox cycles of Jurassic to Eocene age, Cape Verde Basin (DSDP Site 367), continental margin of north-west Africa. *In:* SCHLANGER, S. O. & CITA, M. B. (eds), *Nature and Origin of Cretaceous Carbon-rich Facies*. Academic Press, London. 55–78.

DE BOER, P. L. 1982. Cyclicity and the storage of organic matter in Middle Cretaceous pelagic sediments. *In:* EINSELE, G. & SEILACHER, A. (eds), *Cyclic & Event Stratification*. Springer-Verlag, Berlin. 456–473.

—— 1983. Aspects of middle Cretaceous pelagic sedimentation in southern Europe. *Geologica Ultraiectina*, **31**, University of Utrecht, 112 pp.

DEMAISON, G. J. & MOORE, G. T. 1980. Anoxic environments and oil source bed genesis. *A.A.P.G. Bull.* **64**, 1179–1209.

DEROO, G. *et al.* 1978. Organic geochemistry of some Cretaceous black shales from Sites 367 & 368, Leg 41, eastern North Atlantic. *Init. Repts. Deep Sea Drilling Project.* **41**, 865–873.

—— *et al.* 1979a. Organic geochemistry of Cretaceous shales from DSDP Site 398, Leg 47B, eastern North Atlantic. *Init. Repts. Deep Sea Drilling Project*, **47**, *pt. 2*, U.S. Govt. Print. Off., Washington, D.C. 513–522.

—— *et al.* 1979b. Organic geochemistry of Cretaceous mudstones and marly limestones from DSDP Sites 400 & 402, Leg 48, eastern North Atlantic. *Init. Repts. Deep Sea Drilling Project*, **48**, U.S Govt. Print. Off., Washington, D.C. 921–930.

——, HERBIN, J.-P., ROUCACHE, J. & TISSOT, B. 1980. Organic geochemistry of Cretaceous sediments at DSDP holes 417D (Leg 51), 418A (Leg 52), and 418B (Leg 53) in the western North Atlantic. *Int. Repts. Deep Sea Drilling Project.* **51, 52, 53**, *pt. 2*, U.S. Govt. Print. Off., Washington, D.C. 737–746.

EINSELE, G. & WIEDMANN, J. 1982. Turonian black shales in the Moroccan coastal basins: first upwelling in the Atlantic Ocean? *In:* VON RAD, U., HINZ, K., SARNTHEIN, M. & SEIBOLD, E. (eds), *Geology of the northwest African continental margin.* Springer-Verlag, Berlin. 396–414.

EWING, M., WORZEL *et al.* 1969. *Initial Reports of the Deep Sea Drilling Project*, **1**, U.S. Govt. Print. Office, Washington, D.C.

GLEN, C. R. & ARTHUR, M. A. 1984. Sedimentary and geochemical indicators of productivity and oxygen contents in modern and ancient basins: the Holocene Black Sea as the 'type' anoxic basin. *Chem. Geol.* (in press).

DE GRACIANSKY, P. C., BROSSE, E. *et al.* 1982. Les formations d'age Cretace de l'Atlantique Nord et leur matiere organique: palaeogeographie et milieux de depot. *Rev. Inst. Franc. Petr.* **37** (3), 275–336.

——, DEROO, G., HERBIN, J. P., MONTADERT, L., MÜLLER, C., SCHAAF, A. & SIGAL, J. 1984. Ocean-wide stagnation episode in the Late Cretaceous. *Nature.* **308**. 346–349.

HABIB, D. 1979a. Sedimentology of palynomorphs and palynodebris in Cretaceous carbonaceous facies south of Vigo Seamount. *Init. Repts. Deep Sea Drilling Project.* **47**, *pt. 2*, 451–460.

—— 1979b. Sedimentation of North Atlantic Cretaceous palynofacies. *In:* TALWANI, M., HAY, W. & RYAN, W. B. F. (eds) *Deep Drilling Results in the Atlantic Ocean: Continental Margins & Palaeoenvironment. Maurice Ewing Srs.* **3**, 420–437.

—— 1982. Sedimentary supply origin of Cretaceous black shales. *In:* SCHLANGER, S. O. & CITA, M. B. (eds), *Nature and Origin of Cretaceous Carbon-rich Facies.* Academic Press, London. 113–128.

—— 1983. Sedimentation-rate-dependent distribution of organic matter in the North Atlantic Jurassic-Cretaceous, *Init. Repts. Deep Sea Drilling Project.* **76**, 781–794.

HARLAND, W. B., COX, A. V., LLEWELLYN, P. G., PICKTON, C. A. G., SMITH, A. G. & WALTERS, R. 1982. *A Geologic Time Scale.* Cambridge Univ. Press. 131 pp.

HERBIN, J.-P. & DEROO, G. 1982. Sedimentologie de la matière organique dans les formations du Mésozoique de l'Atlantique Nord. *Bull. Soc. Geol. France.* **24** (3), 497–510.

——, DEROO, G. & ROUCACHE, J. 1983. Organic geochemistry in the Mesozoic and Cenozoic formations of Site 534 in Blake–Bahama Basin, and comparison with Site 391, Leg 44. *Init. Repts. Deep Sea Drilling Project.* **76**, 481–493.

HOCHULI, D. & KELTS, K. 1980. Palynology of middle Cretaceous black clay facies from Deep Sea Drilling Project Sites 417 & 418 of the western North Atlantic. *Init. Repts. Deep Sea Drilling Project.* **51, 52, 53**, *pt. 2*, 897–936.

JANSA, L. F., ENOS, P., TUCHOLKE, B. E., GRADSTEIN, F. M. & SHERIDAN, R. E. 1979. Mesozoic–Cenozoic sedimentary formations of the North American Basin: western North Atlantic. *In:* TALWANI, M., HAY, W. & RYAN, W. B. F. (eds), *Deep Drilling Results in the Atlantic Ocean: Continental margins and palaeoenvironments. Maurice Ewing Srs.* **3**, 1–56.

JENKYNS, H. C. 1980. Cretaceous anoxic events: from continents to oceans. *J. Geol. Soc. Lond.* **137**, 171–188.

KATZ, B. J. 1983. Limitations of Rock-Eval pyrolysis for typing organic matter. *Org. Geochem.* **4**, 195–199.

LEVER, A. & MCCAVE, I. N. 1983. Eolian components in Cretaceous and Tertiary North Atlantic sediments. *Jour. Sed. Pet.* **53**, 811–832.

MASRAN, TH. C. & POCOCK, S. A. J. 1981. The classification of plant-derived particulate organic matter in sedimentary rocks. *In:* BROOKS, J. (ed.), *Organic Maturation Studies and Fossil Fuel Exploration.* Academic Press, New York. 145–159.

MCCAVE, I. N. 1979. Depositional features of organic carbon-rich black and green mudstones at DSDP Sites 386 & 387, western North Atlantic. *Init. Repts. Deep Sea Drilling Project* **43**, 411–416.

MOUNTAIN, G. S. & TUCHOLKE, B. E. 1984. Mesozoic and Cenozoic geology of the U.S. Atlantic continental slope and rise. *In:* POAG, C. W. (ed.) *Geological evolution of the United States Atlantic Margin.* Van Nostrand Reinhold, Stroudsberg, P-A. (in press).

MÜLLER, P. J. & SUESS, E. 1979. Productivity, sedimentation rate, and sedimentary organic matter in the oceans—1. Organic carbon preservation. *Deep Sea Res.* **26A**, 1347–1362.

PARRISH, J. T. & CURTIS, R. L. 1982. Atmospheric circulation, upwelling, and organic-rich rocks in the Mesozoic & Cenozoic Eras. *Palaeo., Palaeo., Palaeo.* **40**. 31–66.

——, ZIEGLER, A. M. & SCOTESE, C. R. 1982. Rainfall patterns and the distribution of coals and evaporites in the Mesozoic and Cenozoic. *Palaeo., Palaeo., Palaeo.* **40**. 67–101.

ROBERTSON, A. H. F. & BLIEFNICK, D. M. 1983. Sedimentology & origin of lower Cretaceous pelagic carbonates & redeposited clastics, Blake–Bahama Formation, Deep Sea Drilling Project Site 534, western equatorial Atlantic. *Init. Repts. Deep Sea Drilling Project.* **76**. 795–828.

ROTH, P. H. 1983. Cretaceous palaeoceanography: calcareous nannofossil evidence. *Abstract 1st Int. Conf. Palaeoceanography*, Zurich. p. 50.

—— & BOWDLER, J. L. 1981. Middle Cretaceous calcareous nannoplankton biogeography and oceanography of the Atlantic Ocean. *SEPM. Spec. Pub.* **32**, 517–546.

SADLER, P. M. 1981. Sediment accumulation rates and the completeness of stratigraphic sections. *J. Geol.* **89**, 569–584.

SCHLANGER, S. O. & JENKYNS, H. C. 1976. Cretaceous oceanic anoxic events: causes and consequences. *Geologie Mijnbouw.* **55**, 179–184.

——, ARTHUR, M. A., JENKYNS, H. C. & SCHOLLE, P. A. 1987. The Cenomanian–Turonian oceanic anoxic event, I. stratigraphy and distribution of organic carbon-rich beds and the marine $\delta^{13}C$ excursion. *This volume*, pp. 399–417.

SCHOLLE, P. A. & ARTHUR, M. A. 1980. Carbon isotope fluctuations in Cretaceous pelagic limestones: potential stratigraphic and petroleum exploration tool. *A.A.P.G. Bull:* **64** (1), 67–87.

SIMONEIT, B. R. T. & STUERMER, D. H. 1982. Organic geochemical indicators for sources for organic matter and palaeoenvironmental conditions of Cretaceous oceans. *In:* SCHLANGER, S. O. & CITA, M. B. (eds), *Nature & Origin of Cretaceous Carbon-rich Facies.* Academic Press, London. 145–164.

——, SUMMERHAYES, C. P. & MEYERS, P. A. 1982. Sources preservation, and maturation of organic matter in Pliocene and Quaternary sediments of the Gulf of California: a synthesis of organic geochemical studies from Deep Sea Drilling Project Leg 64. *Init. Repts. Deep Sea Drilling Project.* **64**, 939–951.

SUMMERHAYES, C. P. 1981. Organic facies of middle Cretaceous black shales in deep North Atlantic. *A.A.P.G. Bull.* **65** (*11*), 2364–2380.

—— 1983. Sedimentation of organic matter in upwelling regimes. *In:* THIEDE, J. & SUESS, E. (eds) *Coastal Upwelling, Part B.* Plenum, London. 29–72.

—— & MASRAN, TH. C. 1983. Organic facies of Cretaceous and Jurassic sediments from DSDP Site 534 in the Blake–Bahama Basin, western North Atlantic. *Init., Repts. Deep Sea Drilling Project.* **76**, 469–480.

THIEDE, J. 1979. History of the North Atlantic Ocean: evolution of an asymmetric zonal palaeoenvironment in a latitudinal ocean basin. *In:* TALWANI, M., HAY, W. & RYAN, W. B. F. (eds) *Deep Drilling Results in the Atlantic Ocean: Continental Margins & Palaeoenvironment. Maurice Ewing Srs.* **3**, 275–296.

THIERSTEIN, H. 1979. Palaeoceanographic implications of organic carbon and carbonate distribution in Mesozoic deep sea sediments. *In:* TALWANI, M., HAY, W. & RYAN, W. B. F. (eds), *Deep Drilling Results in the Atlantic Ocean: Continental Margins and Palaeoenvironment, Maurice Ewing Srs.* **3**, 249–274.

—— 1983. Trends and events in Mesozoic oceans. *In:* *Proc. Joint Oceanogr. Assembly, Halifax, Nova Scotia, 1982,* 127–130.

—— & BERGER, W. H. 1978. Injection events in ocean history. *Nature,* **276**, 461–466.

TISSOT, B. & PELET, R. 1981. Sources and fate of organic matter in ocean sediments. *Oceanol. Acta, Actes 26 Int. Congr. Geol., Paris,* 97–103.

——, DEROO, G. & HERBIN, J. P. 1979. Organic matter in Cretaceous sediments of the North Atlantic: contribution to sedimentology and palaeogeography. *In:* TALWANI, M., HAY, W. & RYAN, W. B. F. (eds), *Deep Drilling Results in the Atlantic Ocean: continental margins and palaeoenvironment. Maurice Ewing Srs.* **3**, 362–374.

——, DEMAISON, G., MASSON, P., DELTEIL, J. R. & COMBAZ, A. 1980. Palaeoenvironment and petroleum potential of middle Cretaceous black shales in Atlantic basins. *A.A.P.G. Bull.* **64** (11), 2051–2063.

TUCHOLKE, B. E. & MOUNTAIN, G. S. 1979. Seismic stratigraphy, lithostratigraphy, and palaeosedimentation patterns in the North American Basin. *In:* TALWANI, M., HAY, W. & RYAN, W. B. F. (eds), *Deep Drilling Results in the Atlantic Ocean: Continental Margins and Palaeoenvironment. Maurice Ewing series.* **3**, 58–86.

—— & VOGT, P. R. 1979. Western North Atlantic: sedimentary evolution and aspects of tectonic history. *Init. Repts. Deep Sea Drilling Project.* **43**, 791–826.

TYSON, R. V. 1984. Palynofacies investigation of Callovian (Middle-Jurassic) sediments from DSDP Site 534, Blake–Bahama Basin, western central Atlantic. *Marine Petrol. Geol.* **1**, 3–13.

VAIL, P. R., MITCHUM, R. M. & THOMPSON, S. 1977. Global cycles of relative changes of sea level. *A.A.P.G. Mem.* **26**, 83–98.

VAN HINTE, J. E., WISE, S. W. & SHIPBOARD PARTY, 1984. Summary of Deep Sea Drilling Project Leg 93. *Init. Repts. Deep Sea Drilling Project,* **93** (preliminary report). 694 pp.

WAPLES, D. W. 1983. A reappraisal of anoxia and organic richness, with emphasis on Cretaceous of North Atlantic. *A.A.P.G. Bull.* **67**, 963–978.

—— & CUNNINGHAM, R. 1983. Shipboard organic geochemistry, Leg 80, Deep Sea Drilling Project. *Init. Repts. Deep Sea Drilling Project* **80**, (in press).

WEISSERT, H. 1981. The environment of deposition of black shales in the Early Cretaceous: an ongoing controversy. *SEPM Spec. publ.* **32**, 547–560.

WILDE, P. & BERRY, W. B. N. 1982. Progressive ventilation of the oceans: potential for return to anoxic conditions in the post-Palaeozoic. *In:* SCHLANGER, S. O. & CITA, M. B. (eds) *Nature & Origin of Cretaceous Carbon-rich Facies.* Academic Press, London; 209–224.

WINDISCH, C. C., LEYDEN, R. J., WORZEL, J. L., SAITO, T. & EWING, J. 1968. Investigations of Horizon Beta. *Science.* **162**, 1473–1479.

C. P. SUMMERHAYES, B.P. Research Centre, Chertsey Road, Sunbury-on-Thames, Middlesex TW16 7LN, England.

Organic-rich sediments and palaeoenvironmental reconstructions of the Cretaceous North Atlantic

P. C. de Graciansky, E. Brosse, G. Deroo, J.-P. Herbin, L. Montadert, C. Müller, J. Sigal & A. Schaaf

SUMMARY: A survey of DSDP black shales from the North Atlantic has been carried out in order to study the evolution of Cretaceous palaeoenvironments in the region. The study involved a reappraisal of the biostratigraphy of the Cretaceous formations and considered accumulation rate, mineralogical and organic geochemical data. Special attention was paid to distinguishing between redeposited and autochthonous sediments. Three main phases of deposition are recognized which are separated by two unconformities:

The Blake–Bahama phase (Valanginian–early Aptian (Bedoulian)) corresponds to relatively uniform depositional conditions over the whole of the North Atlantic with periods of anoxia. The clay mineral assemblages reflect different sedimentary influxes from the continents into the eastern and western parts of the basin which were separated by the mid-ocean ridge.

The transition to the Hatteras phase (Event E1) is marked by a drastic fall in sediment accumulation rate and by a rapid rise in the CCD but not by any appreciable change in clay mineral fluxes.

The Hatteras phase (late Aptian–late Cenomanian) is characterized by distinctly diverse depositional conditions. In the southeastern part of the basin anoxic conditions were persistent, while in the northeast along the European margin there is no, or only very rare, evidence of anoxia. In the west, periods of oxia and anoxia alternated. Over the mid-ocean ridge conditions were oxic. A 'barrier' in the region of the present-day Bermuda Rise separated two areas of distinct clay mineral deposition.

The transition to the Plantagenet phase (Event E2) corresponds to low sedimentation rates. It was immediately preceded by, or was coincident with, deposition of a black shale rich in marine organic matter.

The Plantagenet phase (Turonian–Senonian) was a period of uniform sedimentation under oxic conditions.

Possible causes of these changes in sedimentation are outlined.

Introduction

During the last decade deep-sea drilling operations (DSDP) in the North Atlantic have provided a score of more or less continuously cored Mesozoic sequences (Fig. 1). These important data were collected during DSDP legs 11, (Hollister *et al.* 1972), 14 (Hayes *et al.* 1972), 41 (Lancelot & Siebold 1977), 43 (Tucholke *et al.* 1979), 44 (Benson *et al.* 1978), 47 (Sebuet *et al.* 1979), 48 (Montadert *et al.* 1979), 50 (Lancelot *et al.* 1980), 51–52–53 (Donelly *et al.* 1979), 76 (Sheridan *et al.* 1983) and 80 (Graciansky *et al.* 1984) of the R.V. Glomar Challenger highlighted the stratigraphic similarities of the North Atlantic and Tethyan realms during Mesozoic times (Bernoulli & Jenkyns 1974). They also allowed comparison of deep-sea deposits which are still below in the ocean floor and those which outcrop widely on-shore. Such comparisons involved field studies of onshore regions, some of which were specially carried out to study the Cretaceous in the Atlantic (Graciansky *et al.* 1980). Among the

results of deep-sea drilling, the discovery of the so-called black shales in the deep Atlantic provided a very abundant literature; (see Arthur & Schlanger (1979), Arthur (1979), Fischer & Arthur (1977), Jenkyns (1980), Schlanger & Jenkyns (1976), Bralower & Thierstein (1982), Dean *et al.* (1981), Habib (1982), Summerhayes (1980), Tissot *et al.* (1979), Schlanger & Cita (1982) and Waples (1984) among others) which provided interesting discussions of the preservation and accumulation of organic matter, though some of these authors were influenced by the realistic but somewhat pessimistic point of view of Ryan and Cita (1977) concerning our ignorance on such subjects.

The DSDP studies considered here were undertaken over more than ten years from 1970 (leg 11) to 1981 (leg 80). A concise programme of sampling and new data collection by a team of scientists, who would adopt a uniform approach to interpretation was considered essential for re-evaluation of our understanding of North Atlantic palaeoenvironments. This time-consuming,

From: BROOKS, J. & FLEET, A. J. (eds) 1987, *Marine Petroleum Source Rocks*
Geological Society Special Publication No. 26 pp. 317–344.

317

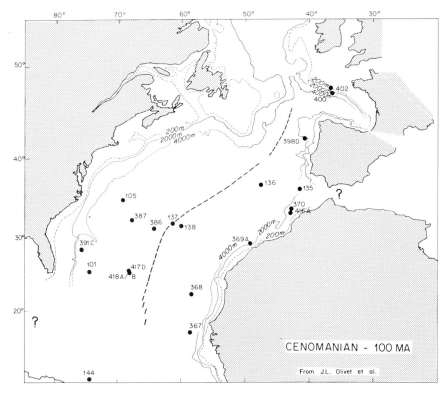

FIG. 1. Location of DSDP sites in the North Atlantic at 100 Myrs (from Olivet *et al.*, 1982).

but fruitful, method of investigation offered the best guarantees for obtaining results which would be both of homogenous quality and beneficial.

These efforts mainly concentrated on:

(a) Establishing a revised stratigraphy of the North-Atlantic Cretaceous based on radiolarians, foraminiferans and nannofossil scales. Our use of common chronostratigraphical scales ensured uniform dating (Müller *et al.* 1983–1984).

(b) Characterizing the main lithofacies. We were especially careful to distinguish between redeposited and non-redeposited, autochthonous sediments.

(c) Determining the type and the origin of the organic matter (OM) (Fig. 2) and the Total Organic Carbon (TOC) contents of the sediments by pyrolysis (Espitalie *et al.* 1977) and relating these to lithology. We believe that these data are comparable with those involving direct microscopic examination (Summerhayes 1980).

These studies led to:

(a) The extension to the whole North Atlantic and greater knowledge of three main formations: Blake–Bahama, Hatteras and Planta-

genet, previously defined in the North-American margins.

(b) Dating of two main ocean-wide unconformities: i.e. the so-called *Event E1* of late Aptian (= Gargasian) age and the *Event E2* of late Cenomanian to earliest Turonian age.

(c) The characterization of the periods of organic matter accumulation and the depositional conditions which gave rise to them.

Underlying principles

Two main types of cycle have been identified in the North Atlantic deposits. One type resulted from rhythmic redeposition of sediments. These deposits can be either poorly sorted, such as mud flows and debris flows or well sorted Bouma-type, turbiditic cycles. The other type of cycle is most probably related to changes in the chemical composition of bottom waters. These changes led to mineralogical and colour variations in sediments, the latter ranging from black to red (for discussion, see Gardner *et al.* 1975; Dean & Gardner 1982).

We considered several techniques and lines of evidence concerning these cycles: organic geochemistry, mineralogy and sedimentology.

A knowledge of the organic geochemistry of sediments is essential when attempting to distinguish whether oxic or anoxic environments occurred in bottom waters at the time of deposition (Fig. 2). Marine organic matter is more susceptible to oxidation in sea water than is terrestrial matter (Tissot *et al.* 1979). Phytoplankton remains have higher surface-to-volume ratios than terrestrial organic detritus and will be degraded more rapidly (Waples 1984). Therefore the presence of marine OM in sediments can be considered as indicative of anoxic conditions on the sea floor. In contrast, high TOC contents which chiefly result from terrestrial organic matter are not necessarily characteristic of anoxic environments. For example abundant plant debris is often preserved in alluvial (fluvial) sedi-

ments due to rapid transportation and burial and similarly in deep-water turbiditic layers. The same is true of residual OM of uncertain origin which results from the sub-aerial alteration of OM contemporaneously with, or prior to, deposition. Marine sediments with TOC contents of more than 1%, which are due to terrestrial or residual OM, therefore, cannot be taken as indicative of anoxia on the sea floor, though it must be remembered that anoxic conditions will favour the preservation of terrigenous or residual OM.

Sedimentary features such as bioturbation or lamination, are also highly relevant. Sediments deposited under bottom waters containing more than 0.2 ml/l of oxygen are bioturbated (Douglas 1981). Under more oxygen-deficient contents most benthic species cannot survive (Waples 1984). So that primary sedimentary features such as lamination are preserved. The presence of

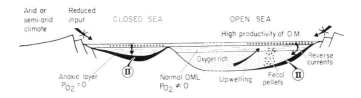

TYPICAL HABITAT OF MARINE OM

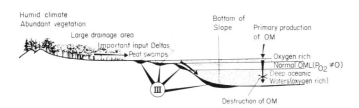

TYPICAL HABITAT OF MODERATELY DEGRADED TERRESTRIAL OM

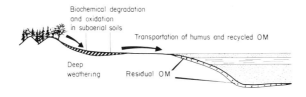

WIDESPREAD OCURRENCE OF RESIDUAL OM

FIG. 2. Principal environments of deposition of the main types of organic matter (after Tissot, 1979).

laminated organic sediments, however, cannot be used alone as proof of anoxic bottom conditions as the ability of organisms to 'plough' the sediments depends on the sedimentation rate (Habib 1982).

Mineralogical data must also be taken into consideration. Sediments rich in marine OM generally have relatively high phosphate contents, though no phosphorites of economic value have been identified (Arthur & Jenkyns 1981), sediments containing terrestrial OM are generally poor in phosphate.

Organic-rich sediments are often rich in pyrite, especially the argillaceous lithologies. But chalks which are light-coloured, deeply burrowed and organic-poor also frequently contain large clusters of pyrite or marcassite. These clusters formed in anoxic micro-environments generally localized around large fossils. OM-depleted but pyrite-rich deposits may exist as well. Therefore pyrite is a somewhat ambiguous environmental indicator.

Nor is sediment colour a specific indicator of anoxia as the darkness of the sediment does not necessarily follow the OM content. Petroleum geologists well know that both dark and light sediments may have high or low TOC.

In summary it can generally be assumed that deeply burrowed, white sediments are usually OM-poor and have been deposited under oxic conditions. Whilst thinly-laminated, dark-coloured sediments with high pyrite, phosphate, TOC contents and OM of dominantly marine origin have been deposited in anoxic environments. Medium grey deposits containing terrestrial or residual OM deserve closer attention, including detailed sedimentological examination. Such may have been deposited under water of medium to low oxygen contents.

Modern anaerobic (=anoxic) sediments are restricted either to isolated basins whose bottom waters are very slowly renewed (euxinic basins: Degens & Ross 1974), or to sea floors localized below the oxygen minimum layer (OML), which develop under productive surface waters along continental margins (Wyrtki 1971; Arthur & Schlanger, 1979). Both types of anaerobic environments can occur in large isolated basins or even in the open ocean but neither can be applied indiscriminately to the past without specific evidence. Deep-sea drilling in the Black Sea, for example, has shown that at least three cycles of cold-oxia/warm-anoxia conditions in the bottom waters occurred during just the Pleistocene (Muratov *et al.* 1978). Present-day anoxic environments are not very frequent, none are comparable to the 10 Myr periods of anoxia which affected the Central Eastern Atlantic during the Cretaceous.

Types of occurrence of North Atlantic black shales

The main characteristics of the sediments studied here concern their cyclic or acyclic character, sedimentary figures, mineralogies and organic contents. Examples of Atlantic black shale types are presented below together with two attempts at classification which take into account either the mode of emplacement of the associated sediments (Table 1a) or the level of anoxia on the sea bottom (Table 1b).

I—Sediments of simple anaerobic environments

These are clearly characterized by a high organic matter content (TOC $> 1\%$) of planktonic origin.

First case: cyclic anoxic sediments deposited in a restricted basin (Fig. 3 IA)

All lithological types of the cycle have a high TOC with marine organic matter. Examples can be found in the central Eastern Atlantic, between the median ridge and Africa, where euxinic conditions persisted during most of the Albian

TABLE 1a: *Main typical modes of emplacement of North Atlantic black shales.* (Anoxic and anaerobic are used in a strictly synonymous sense.)

I Black shales implied in cyclic sedimentation (usual situation)

IA Interbedding by redepositional processes:
  1st case: Anoxic sediment redeposited in anoxic environment.
  2nd case: Oxic sediment redeposited in anoxic environment.
  3rd case: Slightly anoxic to oxic sediment redeposited within oxic environment.

IB Interbedding by cyclic alteration of the environmental conditions:
  1st case: alternating oxic/anoxic environments in carbonate rich environments
  2nd case: alternating oxic/anoxic environments in carbonate depleted environments
  3rd case: alternating black and light coloured shales in oxic or slightly anoxic environments.

II Black Shales implied in acyclic sedimentation (unusual)

  1st case: Strongly anoxic sediments of the Cenomanian–Turonian events.
  2nd case: massive terrigenous influx in oxic environment.

TABLE 1b: *Main types of occurrences of North Atlantic black shales with respect to the oxygen content in the depositional environment (see also Fig. 3)*

I *Sediments deposited under completely anaerobic conditions.*
  1st case: anoxic sediment redeposited in an anoxic environment
  2nd case: acyclic sediment deposited during the Cenomanian–Turonian anoxic event.

II *Couplets of oxic/anoxic layers resulting from redepositional processes.*
  1st case: oxic sediment redeposited in an anoxic environment
  2nd case: anoxic sediment redeposited in an oxic environment.

III *Couplets of oxic/anoxic layers resulting from cyclic changes in bottom water conditions.*
  1st case: associated carbonate rich sediments
  2nd case: associated carbonate depleted sediments.

IV *Sediments deposited in oxic or slightly anoxic environments.*
  1st case: cyclic light and dark coloured argillaceous mudstones
  2nd case: redeposited dark coloured siltstone within an oxic environment
  3rd case: acyclic black argillaceous mudstones.

and Cenomanian (Tissot *et al.* 1979). For example, cores 47 to 41 of Hole 369A contain alternating carbonaceous and calcareous siltstones and mudstones of Early to Late Albian age. The average thickness of the siltstone layers is 0.6 m and of mudstones is 0.3 m.

The siltstones correspond to the 'allochtonous' part of the sequence. They were probably laid down in a very quiet environment and represent periodic influxes of calcareous silty mud and relatively coarse terrestrial detritus of shallow water origin, which were carried by low-density velocity currents. The detrital character of the siltstones is shown by the relative size and abundance of quartz grains, bioclasts and foraminiferan debris, and by their organic geochemistry (Fig. 3).

Black mudstone, on the other hand, corresponds to the 'autochtonous' part of the sequence. They are thinly laminated and only contain marine organic matter ($1\% < TOC < 9\%$). Their average calcite content is lower and their clay mineral content is higher than those of the siltstones. The black mudstones have been deposited under typically anoxic conditions and have resulted from the slow settling of argillaceous particles, together with fine calcitic and phosphate fragments.

The transition between the two lithologies is gradational through laminations on a centimetre scale. Where both marine and residual organic matter are present the sediment is bioturbated. This shows that the bottom currents which transported the siltstones were introducing enough oxygen to the sea floor to allow benthos to become very temporarily established.

Second case: sediments deposited during a general period of anoxia (Fig. 3 IB)

Evidence from a very wide area indicates that an anoxic interval occurred at the Cenomanian–Turonian boundary (Graciansky, Deroo *et al.* 1984). It resulted in the deposition of carbonaceous shales containing marine organic matter (TOC $< 39\%$) over enormous areas from the deep North Atlantic Ocean to marginal and epicontinental seas of North America, North Africa and Western Europe.

Site 105 (North American Lower Continental Rise Hills) provides a typical section through the Cenomanian–Turonian black shale horizon (Fig. 3 IB). Going up through the sequence carbonaceous shales progressively dominate over light greenish-grey oxic sediments. The anoxic layer in its turn is sharply overlain by reddish oxic sediments.

The widespread anoxic event is apparently coeval with the maximum extent of a world-wide transgression. In some parts of Italy it may have only lasted 0.7–0.35 Myr (Arthur & Premoli Silva 1982; Graciansky, Deroo *et al.* 1984). In this region the corresponding horizon is the *Livello Bonarelli* and is characterized by cyclic sedimentation (Wezel 1979). The same has been observed in the North Sea (Hart & Bigg 1981) but not in the deep Atlantic (as discussed in this paper).

II—Couplets of oxic/anoxic layers resulting from redepositional processes: oxic sediments redeposited within an anoxic environment (Fig. 3 IIA)

Examples can be found in the central Eastern Atlantic, in the late Barremian to early Aptian sediments of the Moroccan continental rise (Site 370, Cores 35 to 32). In this area an anaerobic environment prevailed at the sea floor into which oxic sediments from shallow environments were carried as turbidites.

The observed sedimentary cycles are typical calcareous turbidites (Fig. 3 IIA). The lower and coarser part of the elementary cycles show the standard features of graded bedding with parallel or wavy lamination. Debris are in order of abundance: echinoderm ossicles, quartz grains,

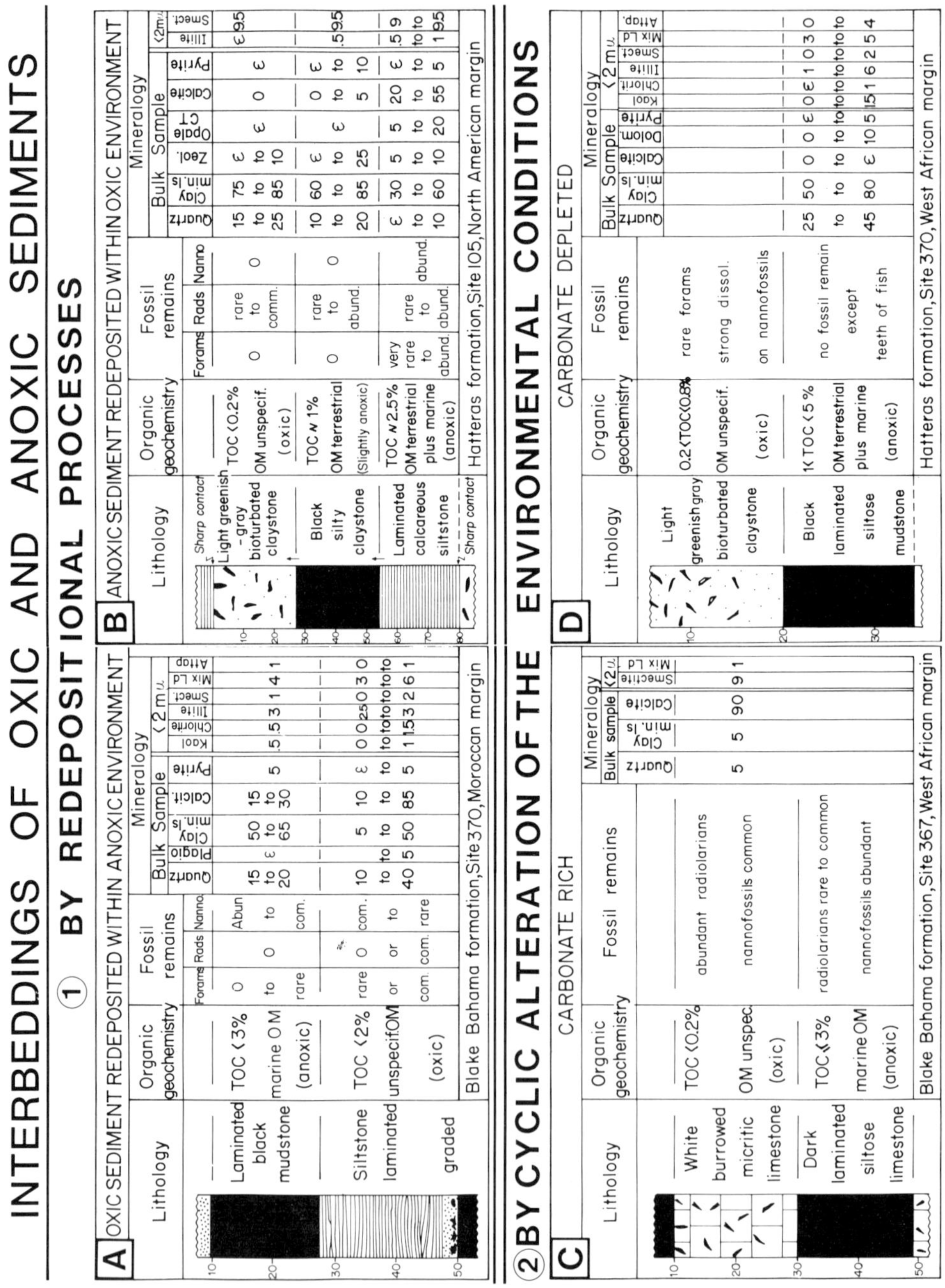
INTERBEDDINGS OF OXIC AND ANOXIC SEDIMENTS
① BY REDEPOSITIONAL PROCESSES
A OXIC SEDIMENT REDEPOSITED WITHIN ANOXIC ENVIRONMENT
Lithology
Organic geochemistry
Fossil remains
Mineralogy
Bulk Sample
<2mμ
Laminated black mudstone
TOC <3%
marine OM
(anoxic)
Siltstone laminated graded
TOC <2%
unspecif.OM
(oxic)
Blake Bahama formation, Site 370, Moroccan margin
B ANOXIC SEDIMENT REDEPOSITED WITHIN OXIC ENVIRONMENT
Sharp contact
Light greenish-gray bioturbated claystone
TOC <0.2%
OM unspecif.
(oxic)
Black silty claystone
TOC ≈ 1%
OM terrestrial
(Slightly anoxic)
Laminated calcareous siltstone
TOC ≈ 2.5%
OM terrestrial plus marine
(anoxic)
Sharp contact
Hatteras formation, Site 105, North American margin
② BY CYCLIC ALTERATION OF THE ENVIRONMENTAL CONDITIONS
C CARBONATE RICH
White burrowed micritic limestone
TOC <0.2%
OM unspec.
(oxic)
abundant radiolarians
nannofossils common
Dark laminated siltose limestone
TOC ≤3%
marine OM
(anoxic)
radiolarians rare to common
nannofossils abundant
Blake Bahama formation, Site 367, West African margin
D CARBONATE DEPLETED
Light greenish gray bioturbated claystone
0.2<TOC<0.8%
OM unspecif.
(oxic)
rare forams
strong dissol.
on nannofossils
Black laminated siltose mudstone
1<TOC<5%
OM terrestrial plus marine
(anoxic)
no fossil remain except teeth of fish
Hatteras formation, Site 370, West African margin

FIG. 31.

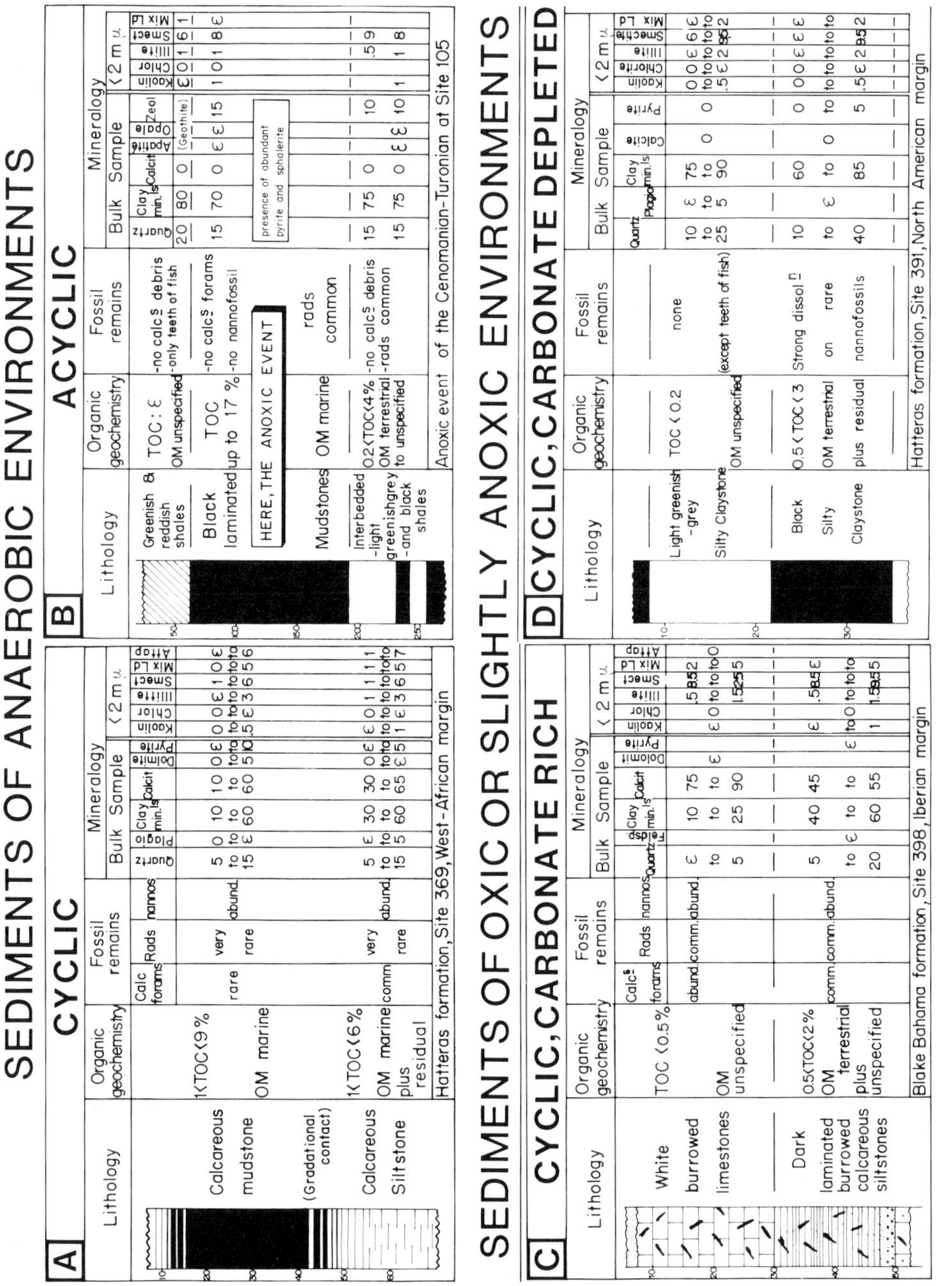

SEDIMENTS OF ANAEROBIC ENVIRONMENTS

A | CYCLIC

Lithology	Organic geochemistry	Fossil remains			Mineralogy															
					Bulk Sample									⟨ 2 m u					
		Calc forams	Rads	nannos	Quartz	Plagio	Clay min.¹ˢ	Calcit	Dolomite	Pyrite	Kaolin	Chlor	Illite	Smect	Mix Ld	Attap	Kaolin	Chlor	Illite	Smect	Mix Ld	Attap
Calcareous mudstone	1⟨TOC⟨9 % OM marine	rare	very rare	abund.	5 to 15	0 to ε	10 to 60	10 to 60	0 to 5	ε 0.5	0 to ε	0 to 3	ε 6	1 5	0 6	ε					
(Gradational contact)																					
Calcareous Siltstone	1⟨TOC⟨6 % OM marine plus residual	comm	very rare	abund.	5 to 15	ε 5	30 to 60	30 to 65	0 ε	ε 5	ε 1	0 to ε	1 3	1 6	1 5	1 7					

Hatteras formation, Site 369, West-African margin

B | ACYCLIC

Lithology	Organic geochemistry	Fossil remains	Mineralogy											
			Bulk Sample							⟨ 2 m u				
			Quartz	Clay min.¹ˢ	Calcit	Apatite	Opale	Zeol	Kaolin	Chlor	Illite	Smect	Mix Ld
Greenish & reddish shales	TOC: ε OM unspecified	-no calcˢ debris -only teeth of fish	20	80	0	(Geothite)			ε	0	1	6	1
Black laminated	TOC up to 17 %	-no calcˢ forams -no nannofossil	15	70	0	ε	ε	15	1	0	1	8	ε
HERE, THE ANOXIC EVENT			presence of abundant pyrite and sphalerite										
Mudstones	OM marine	rads common											
Interbedded -light greenishgrey -and black shales	0.2⟨TOC⟨4% OM terrestrial to unspecified	-no calcˢ debris -rads common	15 15	75 75	0 0	ε	ε	10 10	1		.5 1	9 8	

Anoxic event of the Cenomanian-Turonian at Site 105

SEDIMENTS OF OXIC OR SLIGHTLY ANOXIC ENVIRONMENTS

C | CYCLIC, CARBONATE RICH

Lithology	Organic geochemistry	Fossil remains			Mineralogy												
					Bulk Sample					⟨ 2 m u							
		Calcˢ forams	Rads	nannos	Quartz	Feldsp	Clay min.¹ˢ	Calcit	Dolomit	Pyrite	Kaolin	Chlor	Illite	Smect	Mix Ld	Attap	
White burrowed limestones	TOC ⟨0.5% OM unspecified	abund.	comm.	abund.	ε to 5		10 to 25	75 to 90	ε	ε 1.5	0 2	0 5	8 5	5	2		
Dark laminated burrowed calcareous siltstones	0.5⟨TOC⟨2% OM terrestrial plus unspecified	comm.	comm.	abund.	5 to 20	ε	40 to 60	45 to 55	ε 1	ta 1.5	0 9	5 5	8 5	ε			

Blake Bahama formation, Site 398, Iberian margin

D | CYCLIC, CARBONATE DEPLETED

Lithology	Organic geochemistry	Fossil remains	Mineralogy									
			Bulk Sample					⟨ 2 m u				
			Quartz	Plagio	Clay min.¹ˢ	Calcit	Pyrite	Kaolin	Chlorite	Illite	Smectite	Mix Ld
Light greenish -grey Silty Claystone	TOC ⟨ 0.2 OM unspecified	none (except teeth of fish)	10 to 25	ε to 5	75 to 90	0	0	0 to .5	0 to ε	ε to 2	6 to 9	ε to 2
Black Silty Claystone	0.5 ⟨ TOC ⟨ 3 OM terrestrial plus residual	Strong dissol □ on rare nannofossils	10 to 40	ε	60 to 85	0 5	0 to .5	0 to ε	0 to 2	ε to 9	ε to 5	ε to 2

Hatteras formation, Site 391, North American margin

FIG. 3 II. Types of occurrences of North Atlantic black shales.

mollusc fragments, calcareous sandstones and grains of calcareous micrite. The upper part of individual cycles comprise dark mudstones, which are mostly argillaceous with scattered quartz grains and echinoderm fragments. Except for nannoplankton, fossils are rare. Depending on the cycle, calcite contents range between 0 and 70%.

TOC ranges from 0.4% in winnowed quartzose sand laminae to 2.3% in calcarenites. OM is residual or of terrestrial origin in such reworked sediments from the base of turbiditic cycles. In contrast the hemipelagic parts of the cycles, which have comparable TOC contents of 1–3%, contain phytoplanktonic OM.

The nature of the sedimentary influx shows that the reworked material originated across the continental shelf: from the outer shelf or upper slope (abundant crinoid ossicles), from the inner shelf (micritized calcareous fragments) and from the continent itself (quartz grains and terrestrial plant debris). The reworked sediments were transported into anaerobic environments which were favourable for the preservation of marine OM. The water and sediment movements involved were not strong enough to cause either dilution of the marine OM, except during deposition of the reworked sediments, or reoxygenation of the anoxic bottom waters.

III—Couplets of oxic/anoxic layers resulting from cyclic changes in bottom waters conditions

First case: carbonate depleted sediments
(Fig. 3 IID)

Interbeds of carbonaceous/non-carbonaceous claystones occur in the Hatteras formation (Jansa *et al.* 1979) at the foot of the North American continental margin. The lithologies are quite homogeneous except for their organic geochemistry. In the carbonaceous layers (TOC contents: 1.5%–3%) terrestrial OM is more abundant than marine OM. These layers must have resulted from temporary but recurrent anoxia in the basin.

A typical example was encountered in Hole 391C. Core 10, Section 1 to Core 6, Section 4 (Upper Aptian to Middle Albian) from this hole consist of light greenish-grey and black argillaceous mudstones. The quartz and the predominance of argillaceous material suggest that slow deposition occurred in a quiet environment; there is no evidence of any redeposition. The varied clay mineral association including kaolinite, illite, chlorite and smectite (smectite is dominant) and the presence of terrestrial OM indicate the detrital origin of the sediments. The low calcite content,

the absence of foraminiferans and the strong dissolution of nannofossils show that deposition took place near the CCD.

Second case: complex interbeds of calcareous/non-calcareous and carbonaceous/non-carbonaceous sediments

Such interbeds (Fig. 3 IIB) can be observed in the Hatteras formation on the American side of the North Atlantic. In addition to the alternating light greenish grey claystones and black claystones (as described in the previous case) dark calcareous-carbonaceous siltstones are present. The deposition of such a complex assemblage has no simple and definitive explanation. An example (Fig. 3 IIB, occurs at Site 105, Core 12 to Core 10 *pro parte* (late Albian to earliest Cenomanian).

Bottom waters were probably not anoxic but their oxygen contents must have fluctuated allowing (i) the preservation of some terrestrial organic matter (TOC <5%) in the black claystones (ii) proliferation of burrowing organisms during the deposition of the light greenish-grey claystone. The very low TOC contents (<0.2%) of the light greenish-grey claystone can be explained either by a variation in the influx of terrestrial plant debris or by temporary high oxygen level in the bottom waters.

In the calcareous (10% <$CaCO_3$ <60%) carbonaceous siltstones current lamination and micro-graded bedding indicate that this lithology has been redeposited from shallower environments. Their final depth of deposition must have been located near the carbonate compensation depth, for they have calcite contents of 60%, compared to <5% for the non-calcareous sediments and, like the other lithologies, contain calcareous micro- and nannofossils which show signs of dissolution.

The calcareous-carbonaceous (TOC <3.5%) siltstones contain dominantly terrestrial OM, but, in a few samples, this is associated with marine OM which must have been deposited during just a few episodes of severe anoxia. Alternating dark and light coloured sediment on a decimetre scale would have resulted from ocean-wide fluctuations in the redox conditions in the bottom sea waters, as at Site 391 (see Case III-1). According to this interpretation the only redeposited sediments are the calcareous laminae which are interbedded with the black argillaceous laminae on a millimetre scale within the calcareous-carbonaceous siltstone. An alternative interpretation is that both the calcareous and non-calcareous sediments were redeposited as a unit like a mudflow. This view is supported by the erosional contacts at the base of the calcareous siltstones and on the contrary by their gradational tops. This interpretation which has been retained on Fig. 3 IIB suggests that the redeposited black sediment may have originated from within a shallower mid-water oxygen minimum layer which was favourable to OM preservation. Partial oxidation of OM and dissolution of carbonate particles could have resulted from reaction of the carbonaceous and calcareous muds with oxygenated but carbonate depleted bottom waters during the last phase of the redepositional processes. If such an explanation is acceptable the intercalation of calcareous-carbonaceous siltstones would be considered as the result of redeposition of anoxic sediment within an oxic environment. In fact the presence of abundant zeolite (clinoptilolite) and of traces of opal–CT replacing radiolarians indicates relatively high organic productivity which did not result in the preservation of marine organic matter. A similar interpretation may apply to the Albian of Hole 417D (Bermuda Rise), where red (= stained by haematite), light greenish grey and black mudstones are associated (Donelly *et al.* 1979). Marine or terrestrial organic matter is present in the darker lithologies. Rapid and strong variations of the environmental conditions seem to be related to the elevated position of the sites on the mid-Atlantic ridge during mid-Cretaceous times. A model for such fluctuations has been advanced by Gardner *et al.* (1975), Dean & Gardner (1982).

IV—Black shale of possible oxic environments

First case: acyclic argillaceous mudstones

At Site 105, Core 19 (Valanginian–Hauterivian boundary) below the North American lower continental rise hills, a 10 m thick sequence of argillaceous black shales is interbedded within the limestones of the Blake Bahama Formation (Jansa *et al.* 1979). In spite of a low calcite content (< 15%) which originates mainly from nannofossils, the depth of deposition was far above the CCD (Graciansky *et al.* 1982). The varied association of illite, chlorite and smectite (Zemmels *et al.* 1972) and the presence of terrestrial OM (1 < TOC < 3%) indicates the dominantly terrigenous origin of the sediment.

Radiolarians, which are generally replaced by opal–CT and by clinoptilolite, are abundant and concentrated along millimetre thick laminae. Their abundance shows that the marine organic productivity was high but the relative lack of OM preservation suggests that the oxygen contents were relatively high in the bottom waters.

Second case: cyclic argillaceous mudstones

The Hatteras formation at Site 391 (North American margin), or at Site 398 (Cores 103 to 88: latest Albian to middle Albian; Vigo Seamount, Iberian continental margin) provides typical examples of interbedded black and olive grey claystones. Their consistently very low calcite contents (< 5%) show that they were probably deposited below the carbonate compensation depth. The dark colour is mainly due to scattered micropyrite. TOC content is less than 1% and systematically lower in the olive sediments than in the black ones. The OM is dominantly terrestrial.

At sites with high accumulation rates, such as site 398, it is hardly possible to evaluate the degree of anoxia in the bottom water. Even if anoxia were severe the marine OM could have been diluted by the high detrital and terrestrial OM influxes. On the other hand, if the oxygen levels were high enough to allow degradation of the marine OM, a moderate amount could have been preserved as a result of the high sedimentation rates. But the idea of aerobic bottom water cannot be excluded, the terrestrial OM being protected from alteration by the rapid transportation, sedimentation and burial.

Third case: cyclic black and white calcareous mudstones (Fig. 3 IC)

Interbedded black calcareous laminated siltstones and white massive limestones occur at the base of Hole 398D (Cores 138–131, late Hauterivian to early Barremian), beneath the Iberian continental margin (Fig. 3 IC). High calcite contents show that the depth of deposition was above the CCD.

The black siltstone is laminated as a result of being deposited from low density currents in a very quiet environment (Graciansky & Chenet 1979). Their dark colour is due to both micropyrite and plant debris. TOC contents range from 0.5 to 2%. The more carbonaceous sediments contain either residual or terrestrial OM.

The white limestone is very fine grained and is strongly bioturbated. Main components are calcareous nannofossils ($CaCO_3$ is 90%), calcitized radiolarians and rare grains of phosphate. It contains less than 0.5% TOC. The origin of the OM is not recognizable due to alteration. The limestones have obviously been deposited in a well oxygenated environment. The conditions could have fluctuated, becoming slightly reducing at times, but it seems that the relatively high oxygen contents were maintained even during the deposition of the darker sediments (Deroo *et al.* 1978).

The main Cretaceous stratigraphic units and major unconformities in the North Atlantic

Definition of the main units and of their boundaries (Figs 4 and 5)

Our recent revision of the North Atlantic stratigraphy based on foraminiferans, nannofossils, radiolarians and partly on palynology (Müller *et al.* 1983–84) together with organic geochemistry data (Herbin & Deroo 1982), recognizes three main Cretaceous formations. These are separated by two major unconformities each of which corresponds to a major palaeoceanographic event. The older event (*E1*) is dated as late Aptian, and the most recent event (*E2*), which is already well known (Jansa *et al.* 1979), as Cenomanian–Turonian (Table 2; Fig. 4).

Four main formations have been identified on the North American margin by Hollister *et al.* (1972) and Jansa *et al.* (1979). Analogous formations have been drilled along the West European and African margins. These have resulted from similarities in the sedimentological and tectonic evolution of both sides of the North Atlantic ridge (Lancelot 1977). We, therefore, consider

the Plantagenet Formation (Turonian–Senonian), the Hatteras Formation (late Aptian–Cenomanian) and the Blake–Bahama Formation (Berriasian to early Aptian) to extend all over the North Atlantic (Table 2). Each one of these formations can be identified by the TOC content and by the type of the OM resulting from rockeval. pyrolysis data (Fig. 5) as well as from estimates of accumulation rate.

Accumulation rate data

We use accumulation rate diagrams in identifying the stratigraphic characteristics of the four formations and of their boundaries. Accumulation rates have been re-calculated using our revised dating but without decompacting the sediments. This means that rates shown on the graphs (Figs 6 to 8) must not be confused with sedimentation rates. Accumulation rates in metres per million years (m/Myr) are plotted versus age in million years. One of these graphs relates to the Eastern North Atlantic (European and African side); Fig. 6 the Western North Atlantic (American side; Fig. 7) and the Cretaceous mid-oceanic ridge (Fig. 8). The graphs show several intervals with low accumulation rates (LAR) of generally less than 1 to 2 m/Myr.

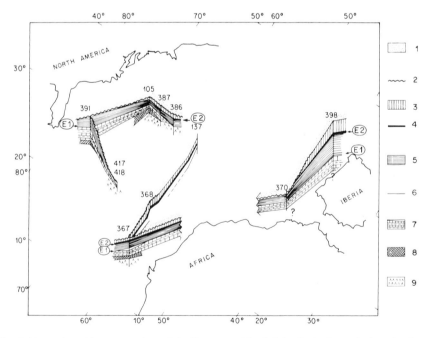

FIG. 4. Synthetic stratigraphic cross sections of the Cretaceous North Atlantic. 1: Cenozoic deposits; 2: erosional surface at the base of the Cenozoic; 3: Plantagenet Formation; 4: Carbonaceous shales of Event *E2*; 5: Hatteras Formation; 6: Event *E1*; 7: Blake Bahama Formation; 8: Cat Gap Formation; 9: basalts.

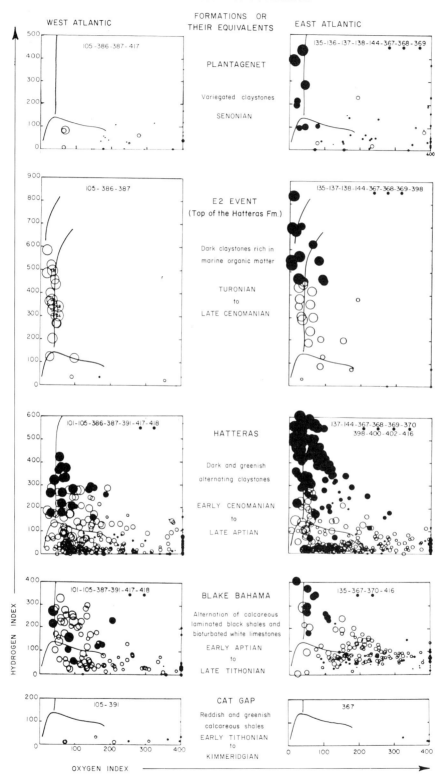

FIG. 5. Organic geochemistry diagrams of pyrolysis related to the sediments investigated (from Herbin *et al.*, 1982). Size of circles is proportional to the TOC contents.

TABLE 2. *The main sedimentary formations of the Cretaceous age in the Northern Atlantic: their ages and characteristics*

Ages		Formation	Facies	Geographical extent
65				
Maästrichtian 72		Plantagenet	Varicoloured shales	American and African sides recurrent carbonaceous shales on the African side
Campanian 83				
Santonian Coniacian 88				
Turonian 91				
Cenomanian 95		Event E2	General stagnation; sedimentary condensation	Widespread distribution even in epeiric seas
Albian	L	Hatteras	Interbedded greenish and black claystones	Characteristic of the deep Atlantic
	M			Important terrigenous influx on the Tethyan margins and on top of the Atlantic margins
	E		Redeposited calcareous siltstones	
107				
Aptian 112		Event E1	Rise of the CCD; sedimentary condensation	Widespread distribution even in the Tethyan realm
Barremian 114				
Hauterivian 119		Blake–Bahama	Interbedded white micritic limestone and black calcareous silty mudstone	Possible extension to the whole Atlantic and Tethyan realms (except on the Urgonian reefs)
Valanginian 126				
Berriasian 130				

The older LAR interval dated Portlandian is observed on the American (Site 105) and on the African sides (Site 367 and 416). The earlier Cretaceous LAR interval is dated Barremian at Sites 367, 370, 416, 398 on the eastern side and late Hauterivian–early Barremian on the American side (sites 101, 105, 397, 391). It does not correspond to any distinct lithological unit. The middle Cretaceous LAR interval is observed at every DSDP site and coincides with our Event *E1*.

On the American side it is dated as late Aptian at sites 101, 105 and 387 and early late Aptian at site 391 (Fig. 7), while along the Eastern Atlantic margins it is late Aptian at site 370 and early late Aptian at Sites 367 and 402. At Site 398 (Iberian margin) the LAR is latest Aptian because of the peculiar structural position of the site and especially high accumulation rate in the early Cretaceous. It is even recognizable on the mid-ocean ridge at Site 417 in the late Aptian. With the exception of Site 398 event *E1* is centered on the lower part of the late Aptian (Gargasian) which corresponds to a low stand of sea level of eustatic origin on the Vail curve (Vail *et al.* 1977; Vail & Mitchum 1979).

The younger LAR interval occurred mainly during the middle and the late Cenomanian (plus the Turonian *pro parte* at sites 137, 367, 369). It is recorded at every site except for sites 101, 370, 391 and 402, where Cenozoic erosion occurred, and site 386 where a continuous Cenomanian series occurs probably as a result of deposition in a depression on the flank of the Bermuda Rise (Donelly *et al.* 1979). This LAR interval coincides exactly with Event *E2*. At its beginning it is coeval with a low stand of sea level on the Vail curve. Later it corresponds to a progressive transgression of Cenomanian age. It ends in the early Turonian when the maximum transgression was reached.

Events *E1* and *E2* which are marked by low accumulation rates seem to record phenomena of global importance. Therefore they may be used to delineate the main sedimentary units. This conclusion, together with the observed lithological similarities allowed us to extend to the whole Atlantic the stratigraphical formations previously defined by others along the North American margin.

The Blake–Bahama Formation (Table 2) is separated from the Upper Jurassic Cat Gap

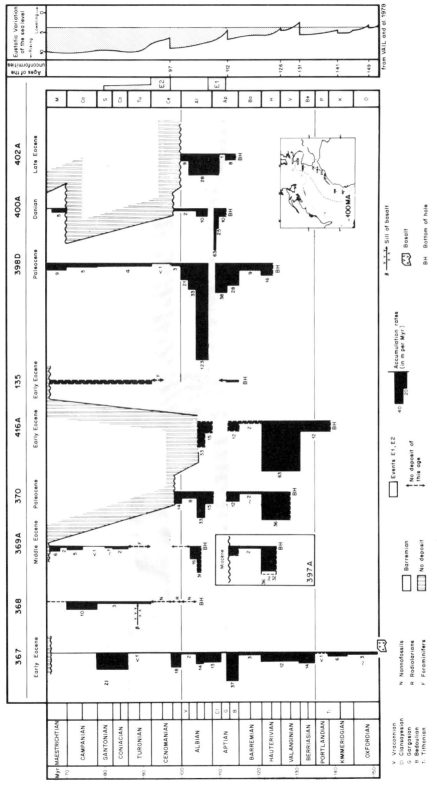

FIG. 6. Sediment accumulation rate diagrams, DSDP bore-holes in the Eastern North Atlantic.

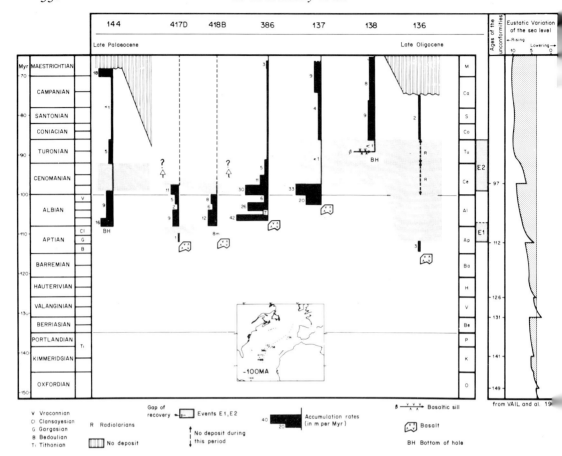

FIG. 7. Sediment accumulation rate diagrams, DSDP bore-holes in the Western North Atlantic.

Formation by the Portlandian LAR interval. The Blake–Bahama Formation comprises mainly interbedded micritic limestones and calcareous silty mudstones. The accumulation rate was relatively low in the late Hauterivian and Barremian but higher during the deposition of the upper part of the formation at Sites 367, 370, 387, 391, 398.

The Hatteras Formation is separated from the underlying Blake–Bahama Formation by the LAR interval dated early late Aptian (event *E1*). Main lithologies are claystones of olive-grey, black or rarely reddish colour interbedded with redeposited calcareous siltstones. Its high accumulation rates are due to the interbeds of turbiditic layers. They have been dated generally as early Cenomanian except for sites 105, 370, 391, 398 where they are middle Albian and record important temporary terrigenous influxes.

The Hatteras Formation ends with the middle–late Cenomanian LAR which corresponds to the deposition of a layer of ocean-wide extension,

with a high TOC content and containing marine OM. This layer is characteristic of a marked anoxic event (Event *E2*).

The Plantagenet Formation comprises mainly reddish vari-coloured silty claystones in the deep ocean and reddish foraminiferal nannofossiliferous chalks at shallower less than 10 m/Myr and often 2 m/Myr.

Mineralogical data

Our biostratigraphy and organic geochemistry have been complemented by determinations of the clay mineral associations. All these studies were performed on the same samples when size allowed. Such determinations contribute to the definition of the three geological Formations: Blake–Bahama, Hatteras, Plantagenet (Table 3 and Fig. 9).

The result was that the clay mineralogy is similar even in different but adjacent lithologies. Also the mineral assemblages were similar what-

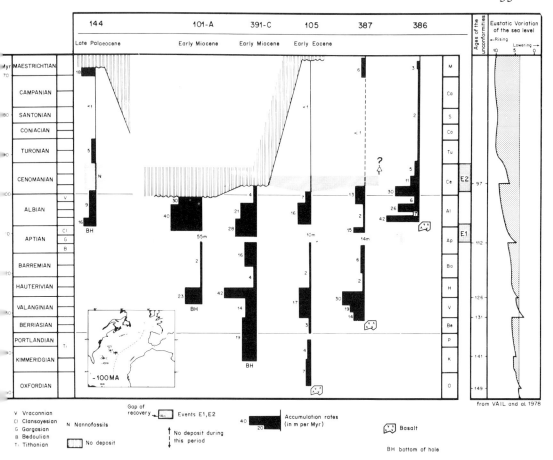

FIG. 8. Sediment accumulation rate diagrams, DSDP bore-holes in the Mid-North Atlantic.

ever their present depths below the sea floor. This suggests that burial depth was not sufficient to bring about any mineralogical transformation.

On the basis of the distribution of the various clay assemblages, the North Atlantic can be divided into two sub-basins. The Western sub-basin includes sites 105, 387 and 391 while mineralogical data for the Eastern sub-basin, along the European and African margins, comes from sites 137, 367, 369, 370, 386, 398, 400, 417, 548, 549 and 550. The clays of this Eastern sub-basin have a more pronounced detrital character than the Western one in the sense that they are more diverse.

The distinction between these two sub-basins is consistent with that one drawn by Tissot *et al.* (1979) on the basis of organic geochemical data. The western sub-basin was probably relatively oxygenated during Aptian–Albian times due to temporary communication with the Pacific. The eastern sub-basin on the contrary was restricted for a long time until late Santonian times.

The 'fence' between the two sub-basins does not coincide geographically with the mid-ocean ridge in the Cretaceous. But the present day Bermuda rise could have provided a convenient barrier during mid-Cretaceous times. Holes 384 and 385 (Tucholke & Vogt 1979; Donelly *et al.* 1979) have shown that an anomalous ridge of Albian age extended further northward from the New England Seamounts. A southern extension of the Bermuda rise has not been demonstrated but cannot be excluded for the Cretaceous. These types of barrier, which are illustrated in Fig. 9 by a mid-ocean ridge with an asymmetric profile, have been proposed independently by Chamley & Debrabant (1982).

The evolution of the clay mineral association during Cretaceous times can be divided into four main phases. The first three may document the asymmetry of the basin with respect to the sedimentary supply. The fourth corresponds to the homogeneity of the sedimentary environments during Senonian times.

TABLE 3. *Cretaceous clay mineral assemblages in the North Atlantic*

	Ages	Formations	S Western sub-basin N	N Eastern sub-basin S
65				
	Maästrichtian		Uniform clay assemblages from the West to the East	
72		Plantagenet	Assemblage 5 varied, with smectite, kaolinite, illite plus occasional chlorite and mixed layer clays	
	Campanian			
83	Santonian			
88	Coniacian		end of the phase of anoxia	
91	Turonian	Event E2		
95	Cenomanian			Permanent anoxia
				3a: smectite, illite, chlorite, mixed layer clays (plus kaolinite on the African margin) attapulgite reappears (Bermuda transect)
	Albian	Hatteras	Cyclic periods of anoxia 3b: smectite dominating over scarce illite and occasional kaolinite	
107				2a: illite, mixed layer clays
	Aptian	Event E1		
112				
114	Barremian			
	Hauterivian	Blake–Bahama	1b: smectite plus occasional illite and mixed layer clays	1a: kaolinite, chlorite, illite, smectite, mixed layer clays, attapulgite
119				

During the first phase, prior to the earliest Aptian, the few available data indicate this asymmetry. On the American side (Hole 391C, Blake Bahama Basin) smectite plus occasional illite and mixed layered clays are present in various proportions (*assemblage 1b*). On the African side (Site 370, Deep Basin of Morocco) kaolinite, chlorite, illite, smectite, mixed layer clays and attapulgite are present. This type of assemblage (*named 1a*) is similar to that found at Site 398 (Iberian margin; Chamley *et al.* 1979).

During the second phase (Aptian–middle Albian) numerous data clearly show the difference between the two sub-basins. The mineralogical composition of the bulk sediment changes dramatically across event *E1* (late Albian), in particular the calcite content generally diminishes, but no change occurs in the clay mineral assemblages.

In the Eastern sub-basin an admixture of illite, mixed layer clays and kaolinite is present at the foot of the African margin (*assemblage type 2a*). In the western sub-basin, smectite is dominant over other minerals. Smectites are mostly terrigenous in origin but could partly result from neoformation in the sediment.

The observed difference between the two sub-basins has been explained by different climatic regimes over Africa and America (Tissot *et al.*

1979). A tectonic and morphological explanation can be also envisaged. The varied mineralogical assemblage of the Eastern sub-basin may be linked to an episode of important syntectonic detrital supply recorded in the Western Tethyan ranges (North Africa, Southern Spain; Grandjacquet & Mascle 1978) and dated Lower Cretaceous.

The sediments deposited during the beginning of the third phase (late Albian–early Cenomanian) are not distinct from the immediately underlying ones as all belong to the Hatteras formation, and the change in the clay mineral assemblage was not accompanied by a clear lithological change. The difference between the eastern and the western sub-basins, though, is still apparent.

In the western sub-basin the nearly pure smectite assemblage evolves progressively towards a more terrigenous association. Kaolinite appears with smectite (*association 3b*) first in the South (Site 391) and then in the North (Site 105). Late, vari-coloured, mostly reddish shales appear as interbed within the typical black shales. This coincides with the development of a new association (*association 5*) including kaolinite, illite, occasional, minor chlorite and/or mixed layer clays in addition to the dominant smectite.

In the eastern sub-basin the changes are the reverse of those observed in the western sub-

TURONIAN - EARLY SENONIAN

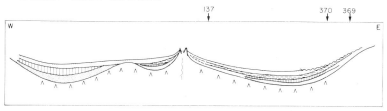

LATE ALBIAN - EARLY CENOMANIAN

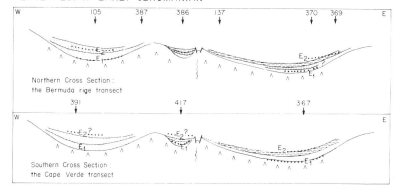

APTIAN - MIDDLE ALBIAN

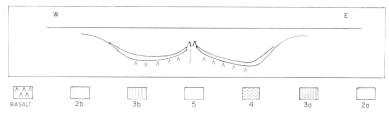

FIG. 9. Diagrammatic cross section showing the succession of clay mineral assemblages in the Central North Atlantic. Assemblages *1a* (kaolinite, chlorite, illite, smectite, mixed layer clays and attapulgite) and *1b* (smectite dominating plus illite and mixed layer clays) are not represented on this figure. *2a:* illite + mixed layer clays. *2b:* dominant smectite plus scarce illite. *3a:* attapulgite present and smectite dominant; illite and mixed layer clays vanish. Occasional chlorite. *3b:* smectite dominant over kaolinite and illite. *4:* dominant smectite plus scarce illite. *5:* smectite dominant over kaolinite and illite plus occasional chlorite and mixed layer clays.

Phase 2 corresponds to assemblages *2a* and *2b*. *Phase 3* corresponds to assemblages *3a*, *3b* and *4*. *Phase 4* corresponds to assemblage *5*. The oceanic rise which is figured at the west of the mid-oceanic ridge constitutes a fence with respect to the distribution of the clay minerals in the ocean. It disappeared in the Late Cretaceous by when assemblage 5 was deposited. The boundaries between the different units shown on this figure are diachronous in comparison with events *E1* and *E2*. The deposition of assemblages *2a* and *5* (eastern sub-basin) began earlier in the north than in the south. The deposition of assemblages *2b* and *5* (western sub-basin), however, began sooner in the south than in the north.

basin. The previous diverse clay assemblage progressively disappears. First smectite is associated with attapulgite (*association 3a*), then it occurs nearly alone (*association 4*). This smectite is probably largely reworked from restricted epeiric or intracontinental basins (e.g. Chamley 1979). Several observations indicate that eastern Atlantic sub-basin was confined during Albian, Cenomanian and (?) Turonian times, i.e. the low

sediment accumulation rates, the high TOC contents, the marine origin of the organic matter, and the abundant development of diagenetic minerals such as dolomite, rhodochrosite and baryte. Such conditions would have favoured the diagenetic reorganization of primary clay minerals to smectites and/or attapulgite, but the effect of such processes are not yet clear. The diverse clay mineral assemblage of Site 367 in the Cape

Verde Basin, is an exception to the generalization, being characterized by a diverse clay mineral assemblage of smectite, illite, kaolinite and mixed layer clays. This might be due to coeval tectonic activity along the Romanche fracture zone (Chamley & Robert 1979).

The fourth phase which begins at the end of event *E2*, lasted from late Turonian to Senonian times. The drastic lithological change observed across event *E2* is also reflected by the clays.

The clay assemblages of the Plantagenet Formation display more clear detrital characteristics than do the clays of the Hatteras Formation. Smectites are associated with kaolinite, illite and locally with chlorite and mixed layer clays. This association first probably appeared in the middle or late Albian at Site 391. It invaded, first the western North Atlantic sub-basin, and then progressively the eastern sub-basin from the north to the south. Site 367 (Cape Verde basin), the southernmost site of the eastern sub-basin, was the site at which the association last appeared in late Santonian time. This illustrates how the evolutions of the South Atlantic and Cape Verde Basin paralleled each other, both being subject to severely restricted conditions for a long time.

The reddish shales in the Plantagenet Formation reflect oxidizing bottom water conditions and contain detrital clay minerals (see above). The difference in the clay assemblages of the eastern and the western sub-basin, which was apparent in the older sediments, progressively disappears and is not recognizable by the late Santonian in the southeast. This shows that the local confinement and/or the restriction of the bottom waters, which were characteristic of the previous phases, was definitely replaced by free circulation which has persisted until the present.

Palaeoenvironmental reconstructions for the North Atlantic during Cretaceous times

The palaeogeographic evolution of the North Atlantic can be divided into three phases each one corresponding to the deposition of the Blake–Bahama, Hatteras and Plantagenet Formations. Events *E1* and *E2* which separate these three phases record dramatic palaeoceanographic changes of global importance (Figures 10–13).

The Blake–Bahama phase

During the Blake–Bahama Phase (Fig. 10) interbeds of white micritic limestones and black calcareous silty mudstones (lowermost Cretaceous to early Aptian) were deposited. These have been observed at Sites 101, 105, 387, 391 (American Side of the Atlantic), 398 and 400 (European margin) and 135, 367, 370 (African Side). Comparable lithologies exist in the Tethyan Lower Cretaceous (Graciansky *et al.* 1981).

During this phase there was no marked difference in the environmental conditions between the western and eastern Atlantic sub-basins, although the clay mineral supply to each differed (see above).

The evolution of redox conditions on the sea floor with time during the Blake–Bahama phase involved gradual changes from well aerated to periodically restricted environments. The underlying Cat Gap Formation (late Jurassic) at sites 105, 367 and 391 consists mainly of marly limestone of light colour with TOC contents lower than 0.9% and altered (= residual) organic matter. Oxic environments lasted up to, at least, early Tithonian times. Then anoxic conditions began to occur in both the western and eastern parts of the ocean at sites 105, 367, 387, 391, 417 and 418. Evidence of this change is provided by the black silty mudstones which contain high TOC contents (2–5% and even 10% for Sites 417 and 418) and marine organic matter. They are regularly interbedded with white micritic limestones which were deposited in oxic environments and contain low TOC (< 0.2%) and residual OM.

This sort of interbedding may result from the redeposition of oxic sediments by turbiditic processes within anoxic environment as at Sites 370, 391, 397. Temporary oxygenation was probably induced by the turbiditic influx (see above, sedimentary cycles of types II, first case).

In the other cases where redepositional processes have been observed the organic matter content is too low to enable an interpretation of the redox conditions on the sea floor. If oxic conditions prevailed on the sea floor—which cannot be demonstrated—the minor terrestrial organic matter which is still present might have been preserved from alteration by rapid transportation and burial.

A third kind of situation occurs at Site 105 where alternation of white micritic limestones and black shales is not due to redeposition but probably results from cyclic changes of the conditions on the sea floor (Dean *et al.* 1977; Arthur & Natland 1979; McCave 1979; Cotillon *et al.* 1979; Darmedru *et al.* 1982). The causes of these changes are not fully understood yet. The period of each cycle is between 10,000 and 50,000 years. The cyclic character may be related to cyclic perturbations of the earth's orbital parameters which are of similar duration (Schwarzacher & Fisher 1982; de Boer 1982).

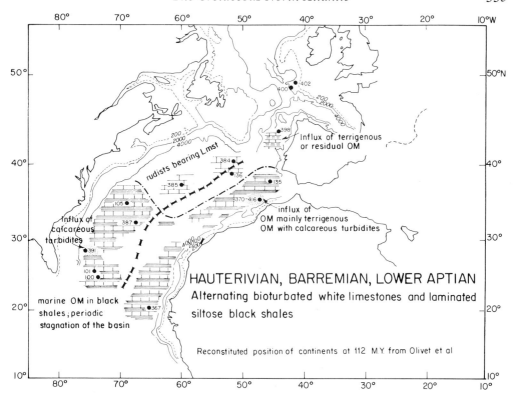

FIG. 10. Distribution of facies in the deep Atlantic during Hauterivian, Barremian and Early Aptian times (Blake–Bahama phase). During the Blake–Bahama phase, there was no marked difference in the environmental conditions between the western and the eastern parts of the North Atlantic. The characteristic interbeddings of white micritic limestones and of black calcareous silty mudstone is known even in the Tethyan realm (Graciansky *et al.*, 1981). At most sites sea floor conditions were cyclically oxic and anoxic. At the foot of the Moroccan margin, the major terrigenous influx of organic matter has probably obscured the presence of marine organic matter. On the Iberian margin (site 398) the rapid transportation and burial of the terrigenous organic matter has led to a situation which does not permit the interpretation of the redox conditions on the sea floor. Reconstruction of the situation of continents and DSDP sites for 112 Myr from J. L. Olivet *et al.*, 1982.

Events E0 and E1

Calcareous sediments of the Blake–Bahama Formation are overlain by purely argillaceous sediments, eventually interbedded with calcareous turbidites of the Hatteras Formation dated as latest Aptian to Cenomanian age. This sharp lithological change corresponds to a rapid rise of the carbonate compensation depth (Thierstein 1979; Sigal 1979; Müller *et al.* 1983–1984) and to a generalized unconformity, both of which defining our Events E0 and E1. In several places the Blake–Bahama Formation has graded to the Hatteras Formation through two steps which, elsewhere, cannot be clearly separated.

At site 398 the sea bottom crossed the CCD towards the Barremian–Aptian boundary (Event E0); a sedimentary gap was dated latermost Aptian (Clansayes beds partly missing) and

corresponded to a marked lithological change (Event E1). At site 367, reddish claystones of early Aptian age are separated from the Blake Bahama Formation below and from the Hatteras Formation above by unconformities and marked lithological changes corresponding respectively to our Events E0 below and E1 above. At site 367 the early deepening of the Cape Verde basin (Chenet & Francheteau 1979) is accompanied by the deposition of carbonate-depleted reddish shales dated as early Aptian and bracketed by Events E0 and E1. Both are recorded by sharp lithological changes between these sediments and equivalents of the Blake–Bahama Formation below and the Hatteras Formation above. At site 398, a lithological change from mainly calcareous to mainly argillaceous sediments is dated as latermost Barremian (Event E0) and precedes the transition from the Blake–Bahama Formation to

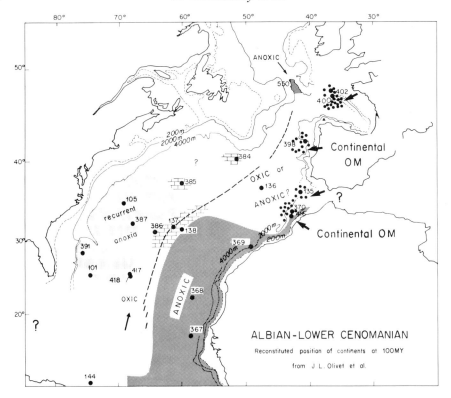

FIG. 11. Distribution of environments in the North Atlantic during Albian–early Cenomanian times (Hatteras phase). During the Hatteras phase, the mid-ocean ridge played the role of a 'fence' separating the western and eastern sub-basins. On the ridge, the sedimentary environment was probably oxic, with a few exceptions and sea bottoms were shallower than the CCD. West of the ridge slightly oxic conditions generally prevailed in spite of high organic productivity indicated by the relative abundance of radiolarians. East of the ridge, the anoxia was permanent and intense in the southern part, this anoxia resulting more from 'euxinic' conditions than from a high organic productivity as shown by the relative scarcity of the radiolarians. Farther north on the Iberian and Armorican margins oxic or slightly anoxic conditions prevailed. Nevertheless on the Porcupine Abyssal plain of Ireland (site 550) anoxic environments recurred during the Cenomanian. Reconstruction of the situation of the continents and DSDP sites for 100 Myr from Olivet *et al.*, 1972.

the typical Hatteras formation dated at Late Aptian (Event *E1*).

In other places only Event *E1* is fully characteristic: at site 370, the unconformity of Event *E1* corresponds to a sedimentary gap dated as late Aptian and earliest Albian and at Site 417 as latest Aptian to earliest Albian. In other holes, lack of cores and/or poor recovery did not allow us to demonstrate directly the existence of a gap. Nevertheless the sedimentation rates become systematically lower towards the Event *E1* interval (Sites 101, 105, 367, 387, Fig. 1).

At sites 101, 105 and 387 the low accumulation rates of Event *E1* coincide with relatively high TOC values and the presence of marine organic matter. This relationship is not observed for intervals which were deposited by turbiditic processes: this type of sedimentation probably

diluted any marine OM which was being deposited.

Event *E1* occurred in the late Aptian along the European and African Atlantic margins, and the northern Tethyan margin (Graciansky *et al.* 1981). During Event *E1*, carbonate build-ups ('Urgonian') along the Tethyan and the American margin or shelf edges were overwhelmed by huge masses of detrital sediments which originated from the continents (Schlee & Jansa 1981; Graciansky *et al.* 1981).

The Hatteras phase

During the Hatteras phase (Fig. 11) alternating black and greenish shales were deposited. In some areas beige to reddish shales occur bearing

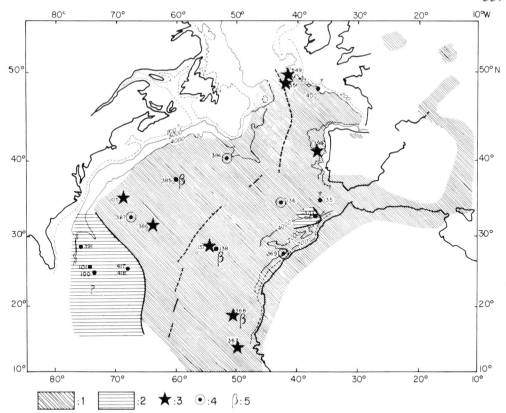

FIG. 12. Distribution of anoxic facies around the Cenomanian Turonian boundary (Event *E2*). The distribution over the American continent is not shown because of insufficient data but it is present in the Western interior. Radiolarian cherts from sites 137, 398, 417, 549 and 551 indicate some localized high productivity during Event *E2*.

witness to temporary oxic environments. The consistently low carbonate contents are characteristic of a high CCD.

At the end of Event *E1*, sedimentation resumed in late Aptian or in early Albian times. But on the Cretaceous mid-ocean ridge the earliest deposits are dated late Albian at site 137 and early middle Albian at Site 386 where they directly overlie the basalts.

The initiation of the Hatteras phase is marked by a sudden increase in accumulation rates due to a marked influx of clay-quartzose terrigenous material. Later in the Albian the sedimentary supply included foraminiferal and nannofossil carbonates transported by turbiditic processes. These calci-turbidites tended to decrease in importance during the Cenomanian at sites 105, 369 and 398 resulting in a progressive lowering of the accumulation rate prior to Event *E2*. At sites 137, 367, 386, 387, 398 and 417, on the contrary, the calci-turbidite persisted and the accumulation rate remained high as late as Event *E2*.

From organic geochemical data (Tissot *et al.* 1979) three domains can be distinguished in the North Atlantic during the Hatteras phase.

(a) The western Atlantic sub-basin between the American margin and the Bermuda Rise where periodic episodes of anoxia probably occurred (see above, types of sedimentary cycles, part III, case 2). Interbedded greenish and black shales are characteristic of this area. The greenish shales (TOC contents <0.3% and hydrogen indices <300) were deposited in oxic environments. The interbedded black shale generally have low TOC contents and contain terrestrial and/or residual OM except in a few layers in which TOC contents are <4.5% and marine OM occurs.

(b) On the Cretaceous mid-ocean ridge the sedimentary environments was probably oxic. The Hatteras sediments of sites 137, 386, 417, 418 all have very low TOC contents except the Middle and Late Albian ones of site 417 and 418 which include several anoxic layers (2% <TOC <8%; hydrogen indices <400).

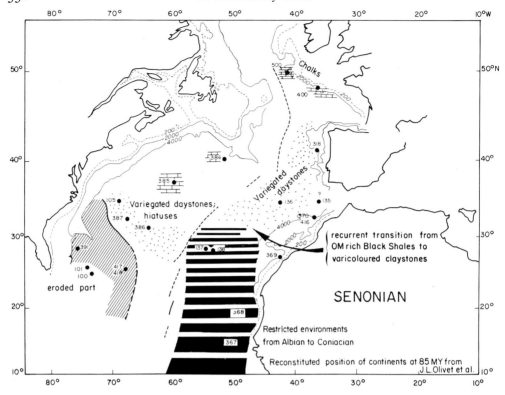

FIG. 13. Distribution of facies and environments during the Senonian (Plantagenet phase). After the generalized anoxia of Event *E2* in the Early Turonian, deposition in the North-Atlantic became as diverse as it had been during the Albian, with deposition of different lithologies in the eastern and western sub-basins. East of the ridge all the recovered sediments were deposited below the CCD except for the foraminiferal and nannofossiliferous chalks of sites 400, 549, 500 and 551. The degree of intensity and persistence of bottom-water anoxia observed in the Albian decreased from South to North, in places anoxia persisting until the Santonian, but with progressive and recurrent ventilation. West of the Mid-ocean ridge, environments were definitely oxic. At sites 101, 391, 417 and 418, Cenozoic erosion has removed any Upper Cretaceous sediments.

(c) The southern part of the eastern sub-basin between the African margin, the mid-ocean ridge and the Canaries remained permanently anoxic during the Hatteras phase. The immediately post-Event *E1* (Lower to early middle Albian) sediments contain associated terrestrial and marine organic matter as a result of significant terrigenous supply into the anoxic basin. Later in the Albian and in the Cenomanian, only marine organic matter accumulated giving rise to sediments at Sites 367, 368, 369 and 370 with TOC contents as high as 30% and hydrogen index up to 600: such values are characteristic of severe anoxic conditions.

The northern part of the eastern Atlantic sub-basin deserves special discussion. At site 370 off Morocco interbeds of oxic and anoxic layers could have resulted from redepositional processes. This interpretation implies redeposition of anoxic sediments previously deposited under the

oxygen minimum layer ('OML') at mid-water depth (see above, types of occurrences, part III, case 2). Another interpretation is that the anoxic layers record fluctuations of the oxygen contents of the bottom waters. If this is so, the evolution of the domain between the Canary ridge and the Newfoundland–Gibralter line is similar to that of the western sub-basin.

Further north along the European margin at site 398 (Iberian margin) and 400–402 (Armorican margin) only terrestrial organic matter is preserved in the sediments which have low TOC contents. The relatively high accumulation rate and the resistance of terrestrial OM to oxidation does not allow us to decide if the OM was preserved in a weakly anoxic environment or if it was preserved in an oxic environment as a result of rapid transportation and burial.

To the north, at the foot of the Irish continental margin, evidence from site 550 shows that oxic and anoxic conditions alternated during the Cenomanian (Graciansky *et al.* 1984).

Event E2

The top of the Hatteras Formation is marked by an ocean-wide non-conformity (Fig. 12). This non-conformity may correspond to an erosional surface of Cenozoic age as at sites 391, 401, 417, 418 (Tucholke & Mountain 1979) 340, 400, 402 and 416 in which case the Turonian and Senonian have been lost. At site 534, early Maästrichtian variegated claystones overlie carbonaceous claystone of Vraconian age (Sheridan *et al.* 1983). At the other sites where the post-Cenomanian Cretaceous is preserved, the dark shales of the Hatteras Formation are separated from the reddish and vari-coloured sediments of the overlying Plantagenet Formation by a sedimentary gap or a markedly condensed sequence.

The dating of Event *E2* has been more difficult than that of Event *E1*. This is mainly due to the low carbonate content of Cenomanian–Turonian sediments and as a consequence, of the poor preservation of calcareous nannofossils and foraminiferans. Nevertheless Event *E2* was estimated to have lasted for a part of the Cenomanian at sites 105, 135 and 137, the late Cenomanian through the Turonian at sites 367, 549 and 550, and the late Cenomanian through the Coniacian at sites 136 and 369. It may correspond to a gap which could have resulted from non-deposition and/or erosion. At site 550 the late, middle Cenomanian and Turonian are simply missing. At site 369 this is clearly the result of erosion; white chalks of Coniacian age directly overlie carbonaceous shales of Late Albian age. The missing stages are represented by Albian and Cenomanian contorted layers, phacoids and pebbles of carbonaceous shales which occur as displaced sediments within the Coniacian chalks. Elsewhere Event *E2* is represented by a condensed interval of carbonaceous shales which are often associated with radiolarian cherts. The accumulation rates of these layers are generally less than 1 m/Myr (or even 0.2 m/Myr as at site 105). The sediments are generally pyritic and phosphatic and are laminated on a millimetre or submillimetre scale. Their TOC contents are greater than 2% and on average reach 10%.

Carbon-rich samples (TOC contents 20–25%) from site 105 (American margin) have hydrogen indices of up to 600 and ones from the African side (TOC contents 39%) have indices of up to 800 (Herbin *et al.* 1982). Such samples are also enriched in metals such as Ba, Pb, Cu and Ni. The sediments deposited during Event *E2* characteristically have very low accumulation rates

and high concentrations of marine organic matter resulting from marked reducing conditions. This is true for those from the deep Atlantic ocean as well as those from the large marginal or epicontinental seas of North America, Africa and Europe, such as the western Tethys (Graciansky *et al.* 1983) and the North Sea (Hart & Bigg 1981).

The Plantagenet phase

Along the American side of the North Atlantic any deposits of the Plantagenet Formation (Fig. 13) which did exist have been removed by Cenozoic erosion at sites 100, 101, 391, 417 and 418.

Three observations can be made about the Plantagenet Formation that has been preserved. (a) Foraminiferal and nannofossiliferous chalks were deposited at sites 384, 385, 400 and 549 in moderate water depths. This indicates a relative lowering of the CCD after Event *E2*. Carbonate depleted shales were deposited in deeper waters. (b) These deeper-water shales are generally brownish to bright reddish in colour, have TOC contents as low as 0.1–0.3%, and contain unspecified organic matter. They, therefore, characterize the oxic environments which succeeded the generalized oceanic stagnation of Event *E2* (sites 105, ?135, 136, 386 and 387). (c) However, at the foot of the African margin (sites 137, 138, 367 and 368) carbonaceous shales with marine OM continued to be deposited as late as the Coniacian, interbedded with shales of greenish to reddish colour. Such interbeds indicate that recurrent oxygenation occurred progressively in the previously anoxic basin located between the mid-ocean ridge, the Canary islands and West-African margin. Definitely oxic sedimentation only occurred during the late Senonian.

Summary and discussion

The depositional phases and sedimentary events which occurred during the Cretaceous North Atlantic, following the deposition of the oxic calcareous shales and mudstones of the Cat Gap formation (Late Jurassic), can be summarized as follows:

(a) *The Blake–Bahama phase* (Valanginian– early Aptian)

The Blake–Bahama Formation consists of alternating white calcareous mudstones and dark grey shales which were mostly deposited under oxic conditions, except during several anoxic episodes which were more numerous along the eastern than the western side of the Atlantic.

(b) *Event E1*

This corresponds to a non-conformity which is characterized by lowered sedimentation rates and, in some places, by a sedimentary hiatus. It is also coeval with rapid rise of the CCD (Thierstein 1979; Sigal 1979), but it is not coincident with any change in clay mineral assemblages.

(c) *The Hatteras phase* (late Aptian–late Cenomanian)

The initiation of this phase is marked by the relatively rapid deposition of argillaceous shales which typically consist of greenish and black interbeds. The dark colour results from micropyrite, often associated with terrestrial vegetal debris. Fine scale lamination and marine OM occur throughout sediments from the area between the Canaries, the mid-Ocean ridge and the African margin. In the Western part of the North-Atlantic phytoplanktonic OM is only present in a few layers. Marine OM is rare at the foot of the Moroccan (site 370), Iberian (site 398) and Armorican (site 400) margins, but it is present to the North, off Ireland (site 500). Such differences in organic preservation illustrate the variety of redox conditions which prevailed in the North-Atlantic basin during the Hatteras phase.

(d) *Event E2*

This second non-conformity is of major importance. It corresponds to low sedimentation rates and/or to a sedimentary gap of variable duration (middle Cenomanian–earliest Turonian). It is immediately preceeded by, or coincident with the deposition of a black shale horizon with high contents of marine OM. This unique horizon was deposited not only in the deep Atlantic Ocean but also in the adjacent epeiric seas of North America, North Africa and Western Europe and in the Western Tethys. It represents a period of widespread but temporary oceanic stagnation (Graciansky *et al.* 1983).

(e) *The Plantagenet phase* (Turonian–Senonian)

This is marked by the deposition of oxic vari-coloured shales except in the Canaries–African part of the basin where recurrent anoxic layers were deposited up to the late Coniacian. The

sediment supply was more terrigenous in nature than during the Hatteras phase.

The black shales of the Central and North Atlantic are far from being uniform in their lithological, chrono-stratigraphical, geochemical or depositional characteristics. The simple 'euxinic' model, corresponding to the deposition of 'sapropels' in an anoxic environment, can be applied to the Canary–Africa part of the basin, but is not necessarily applicable to black shales from other regions. The black colour of the shales, indeed, is not always due to high TOC contents. Abundant micropyrite in a shale may be partly responsible for the colour. Although anoxic environments are favourable for the preservation of any kind of OM, high TOC values are not necessarily indicative of anoxia, they may result from terrestrial OM which can accumulate under oxic conditions. OM-rich layers most commonly occur with layers which are organic carbon lean. (Dean & Gardner 1982; Einsele & Zeilacher 1982). These intercalations may result from redepositional environments periodically altered as when oxic sediments are periodically transported down-slope into anoxic bottom waters.

In other cases the interbeds of oxic and anoxic sediments can be related to cyclic climatic events. In the case of the Pleistocene Mediterranean, for instance, the succession of pluvial and dry climatic phases on the adjacent land has been evoked to explain the rhythmic sapropel layers in the Mediterranean (Rossignol-Strick *et al.* 1982). Indeed it has been suggested that regularly spaced lithological changes can be related to regular fluctuation of the velocity of ocean water circulation in response to shifts of the caloric equator due to astronomic influences (de Boer 1982). The duration of the observed cycles has been estimated at 20,000 to 50,000 yrs (Deroo *et al.* 1982; Arthur & Premoli Silva 1982). This is of the order of the duration of cyclic perturbation of the Earth's orbit which would be at the origin of many cyclical sedimentary processes (see Schwarzacher & Fischer 1982 for Tethyan examples).

Events *E1* and *E2* are especially significant as they respectively corresponded to the initiation and to the conclusion of typical black shale episode in the North Atlantic.

Event *E1* dated late Aptian in most cases occurred in the deep ocean at exactly the time when the Urgonian sub-reefal limestones of the marginal and epeiric adjacent seas, including the western Tethys (Graciansky *et al.* 1981) were replaced by dark calcareous shales. Moullade & Guerin (1981) from microfossil and ammonite data and Lancelot (1980) have argued that shallow South Atlantic waters could have penetrated the North Atlantic at approximately this time. A rapid regression-transgression of eustatic origin (Vail *et al.* 1979) occurred during this period.

Event *E2* (middle Cenomanian–early Turonian) corresponds to a rapid lowering of the CCD and to a condensed sedimentation or to a hiatus. It is marked by the more pronounced phase of anoxia which is very apparent from the lithological column. For instance, organic matter is abundant (TOC values up to 39%) in sediments at the foot of the African margin. The enormous geographical extent of the anoxic conditions (Graciansky *et al.* 1983), which affects epeiric seas in North America, West Africa and Western Europe and the Western Tethys (*Livello Bonarelli*, Arthur & Premoli Silva 1982) and possibly parts of the Pacific (Moberly *et al. in press*) shows that the observed concentration of OM records a period of ocean-wide stagnation and that deep sea environments can be as sensitive to modifications in environmental conditions as shallower ones.

The Cenomanian–Turonian black shale horizon may simply be related to the Lower Turonian high stand of sea level (?450 m above present day; Hancock & Kauffman 1979), which is thought to have been of eustatic origin (Vail *et al.* 1977), and caused a wide scale transgression over the continents. It is plausible that the increased depositional surface area available for biogenic, and terrigenous sediments during the maximum transgression and the reduced surface area subjected to subaerial erosion, decreased the sediment available for deposition per unit area per unit time.

Jenkyns (1980) has proposed that the Cretaceous transgression was important in fostering marine anoxia. But all major transgressions, such as that of the Maästrichtian, do not necessarily induce ocean-wide anoxic events. High oceanic fertility seems to be related to high TOC contents in some instances, for example anoxic layers are interbedded within radiolarian cherts at sites 137, 398, 417 and 549 but not all. High fertility, as recorded by radiolarian-rich deposits, was not associated with the development of TOC-rich anoxic layer at the foot of the African margin. As pointed out by Arthur & Premoli-Silva (1982) we still do not understand the causes of this expansion of the oxygen minimum zone nor its apparent correlation with the eustatic sea level at the Cenomanian–Turonian boundary.

Climatic variations, transgressions and regressions of eustatic origin, displacements of oceanic water masses together with continental drift are among the processes which must be evoked for interpreting the geochemistry of the Cretaceous black shales which constitute themselves a very varied group. There is probably no unique cause which could explain their formation. More probably each deposit results from a coincidence of several favourable factors. Unfortunately we are neither able to evaluate the relative importance of each one nor be sure that we know them all.

ACKNOWLEDGEMENTS: This study was sponsored by the Centre National Pour l'Exploitation des Océans (Contract CNEXO No. 78-5669, Palaeoenvironment of Black Shales in the North Atlantic) and partly by the Centre National de la Recherche Scientifique. (Action Thématique Programmée IPOD). Laboratory studies have been performed at the Institut Français du petrole under a contract with the Comité d'Etudes Pétrolières Marines (CEPM) and at Ecole Nationale Supérieure des Mines de Paris. Re-description of cores and appropriate sampling have been accomplished at the Lamont Doherty Geological Observatory thanks to the approval of Chief Scientist of the Deep Sea Drilling Project and the help of the curatorial staff of the East Coast Repository.

Fruitful discussions have been held with M. Arthur, M. Bourbon, H. Chamley, P. Y. Chenet, R. Cunningham, P. Decommer, J. Francheteau, D. Habib, F. Mélières, G. Pautot, Y. Reyre, J.-C. Sibuet, M. Thiry and E. L. Winterer. Much care has been taken by Andy Fleet over the editing of the final form of this paper.

References

ARTHUR, M. A. 1979. Paleoceanographic events—recognition, resolution, reconsideration. *Rev. of Geo. and Space Phys.*, **17**, No. 7, 1474–1494.

—— 1979. North Atlantic Cretaceous black shales: the record at Site 398 and a brief comparison with other occurrences. *In:* SIBUET, J.-C. & RYAN, W. B. F. *et al.*, *Init. Rep. of the Deep Sea Drilling Project*, **47**, Part 2, Washington, D.C. (U.S. Government Printing Office), 719–751.

—— & JENKYNS, H. C. 1981. Phosphorites and paleoceanography. *In:* BERGER, W. H. (ed.), Ocean geochemical cycles, *Proc. 26th Int'l Cong. Oceanologica Acta*, Spec. Issue, 83–96.

—— & NATLAND, J. H. 1979. Carbonaceous sediments in the north and south Atlantic: the role of salinity in stable stratification of early Cretaceous basins. *In:* TALWANI, M., HAY, W. & RYAN, W. B. F. (eds), *Deep Drilling Results in the Atlantic Ocean: Continental Margins and Paleoenvironment*, Washington D.C. American Geophysical Union, 375–401.

—— & PREMOLI SILVA, I. 1982. Development of widespread organic carbon rich strata in the Mediterranean Tethys. *In:* SCHLANGER, S. O. & CITA, M. B. (eds) *Nature and Origin of Cretaceous Carbon-Rich Facies*, Acad. Press, 7–54.

ARTHUR, M. A. & SCHLANGER, S. O. 1979. Cretaceous 'oceanic anoxic events' as causal factors in development of reef-reservoired giant oil fields. *Bull. Am. Assoc. Petr. Geol.*, **63**, 870–885.

BENSON, W. E. & SHERIDAN, R. E. *et al.* 1978. *Init. Rep. of the Deep Sea Drill. Proj.*, **44**, Washington D.C. (U.S. Government Printing Office).

BERNOULLI, D. & JENKYNS, H. C. 1974. Alpine, Mediterranean and central Atlantic Mesozoic facies in relation to the early evolution of the Tethys. *In:* DOTT, R. H. & SHAVER, R. H. (eds), *Modern and Ancient Geosynclinal Sedimentation, SEPM Spec. Publ.*, **19**, 129–160.

DE BOER, P. 1982. Some remarks about the stable isotope composition of cyclic pelagic sediments from the Cretaceous in the Apennines (Italy). *In:* SCHLANGER, S. O. & CITA, M. B. (eds), *Nature and Origin of Cretaceous Carbon-rich Facies*, Academic Press, 129–144.

BRALOWER, T. & THIERSTEIN, H. R. 1982. Mid-Cretaceous black shales: a result of excessive fertility or global anoxia? *Bull. Am. Assoc. Petr. Geol.* **66–5**, 552.

BROSSE, E. 1983. Geochimie minérale de sédiments à facies black-shales, Cretacé 'moyen' de l'Atlantique Nord, sites 386 et 391. *Rev. Instr. Fr. Petrole*, **38**, 3, 299–328.

CHAMLEY, H. 1979. North Atlantic clay sedimentation and palaeoenvironment since the late Jurassic. *In:* TALWANI, M., HAY, W. & RYAN, W. B. F. (eds) *Deep Drilling Results in the Atlantic Ocean: Continental Margins and Paleoenvironments.* Washington, D.C., American Geophysical Union, 342–361.

——, DEBRABANT, P. *et al.* 1979. Mineralogy and geochemistry of Cretaceous and Cenozoic Atlantic sediments of the Iberian Peninsula (site 398, DSDP leg 47B). *In:* SIBUET, J.-C., RYAN, W. B. F. *et al., Initial Reports of DSDP*, **47** (2), Washington, D.C.

—— & DEBRABANT, P. 1982. L'Atlantique Nord à l'Albien; influences américaines et africaines sur la sédimentation. *C.R. Acad. Sc.*, Paris, **294**, D, 525–528.

—— & ROBERT, C. 1979. Late Cretaceous to early Paleogene environmental evolution expressed by the Atlantic clay sedimentation. *In:* COPENHAGEN, W. K., CHRISTENSEN & BIRKELUND, T. (eds) *Cretaceous-Tertiary Boundary Events*, II, 71–77.

CHENET, P. Y. & FRANCHETEAU, J. 1979. Bathymetric reconstruction method: application to the central Atlantic basin between 10°N and 40°N. *In:* DONELLY, T. *et al.* (eds) *Init. Rep. of the Deep Sea Drill. Proj.* **51**, **52**, **53**, Part 2, Washington D.C. (US Government Printing Office), 1501–1514.

COTILLON, P., FERRY, S., GAILLARD, C., JAUTEE, E., LATREILLE, G. & RIO, M. 1979. A la recherche des facteurs oscillants de la sédimentation marine ancienne par l'étude des alternances marno-calcaires. *C.R. Acad. Sc.* Paris, **289D**, 1121–1124.

DARMEDRU, C., COTILLON, P. & RIO, M. 1982. Rythmes climatiques et biologiques en milieu marin pélagique. *Bull. Soc. Geol. Fr.*, 7, XXIV, 3, 627–640.

DEAN, W. E., BARRON, E. J. & BOYCE, R. E. 1981. A Cretaceous black-shale deposition within an oxidized red clay, turbidite environment southern Angola Basin, South Atlantic Ocean. *Bull. Am. Assoc. Petr. Geol.* **65**, 917.

—— & GARDNER, J. V. 1982. Origin and geochemistry of redox cycles of Jurassic to Eocene age, Cape Verde Basin (DSPD Site 367), continental margin of North-west Africa. *In:* SCHLANGER, S. O. & CITA, M. B. (eds), *Nature and Origin of Cretaceous Carbon-Rich Facies*, Academic Press. 55–78.

——, GARDNER, J. V., JANSA, L. F., CEPEK, P. & SEIBOLD, E. 1978. Cyclic sedimentation along the continental margin of northwest Africa. *In:* LANCELOT, Y., SEIBOLD, E. *et al. Init. Rep. of the Deep Sea Drill. Proj.* **41**, Washington, D.C. (US Government Printing Office), 965–989.

DEGENS, E. T. & ROSS, D. A. (eds) 1974. The Black Sea—geology, chemistry and biology. *Mem. Am. Ass. of Petrol. Geol.*, **20**, 1–633.

DEROO, G., GRACIANSKY, P.-C. DE, HABIB, D. & HERBIN, J.-P. 1978. L'origine de la matière organique dans les sédiments crétacés du site IPOD 398 (Haut-fond de Vigo): corrélations entre les données de la sédimentologie, de la géochimie organique et de la palynologie, *Bull. Soc. Geol. Fr.* 7, t. XX, No. 4, 465–469.

——, HERBIN, J. P. & HUC, A. Y. 1982. Organic geochemistry of Cretaceous black shales from DSDP Site 530, Leg 75, Eastern South Atlantic. *In:* HAY, W. W., SIBUET, J.-C. *et al. Init. Rep. of the Deep Sea Drill. Proj.*, **75**, Washington D.C. (US Government Printing Office). pp. 983–1000.

——, HERBIN, J.-P., ROUCACHE, J. & TISSOT, B. 1979. Organic geochemistry of Cretaceous shales from DSDP Site 398, Leg 47B, eastern North Atlantic. *In:* SIBUET, J.-C., RYAN, W. B. F. *et al. Init. Rep. of the Deep Sea Drill. Proj.* **47**, Part 2, Washington D.C. (US Government Printing Office), 513–522.

DONELLY, T., FRANCHETEAU, J., BRYAN, W., ROBINSON, P., FLOWER, M. & SALISBURY, M. 1979. *Init. Rep. of the Deep Sea Drill. Proj.* vol. **51**, **52**, **53**, Washington D.C. (US Government Printing Office).

DOUGLAS, R. G. 1981. Paleoecology of continental margin basins: a modern case history from the Borderland of Southern California. *In:* DOUGLAS, R. G., COLBURN, I. P. & GORSLINE, D. S. (eds), *Depositional Systems of Active Continental Margins Basins; Short Course Notes.* Pacific Section SEPM, 121–156.

ESPITALIE, J., LAPORTE, J. L. *et al.* 1977. Méthode rapide de caractérisation des roches mères de leur potentiel pétrolier et de leur degré d'évolution, *Rev. Inst. Fr. Petrole*, **32**, 23–42.

FISCHER, A. G. & ARTHUR, M. A. 1977. Secular variations in the pelagic realm. *In:* COOK, H. E. & ENOS, P. (eds) Deep water carbonate environments, *SEPM Spec. Publ.* **25**, 19–50.

GARDNER, J. V., DEAN, W. E., JANSA, L. & SEIBOLD, E. 1977. Sediments recovered from the northwest African continental margin, Leg 41, Deep Sea Drilling Project. *In:* LANCELOT, Y., SEIBOLD, E. *et al. Init. Rep. of the Deep Sea Drill. Proj.* 41, Washington D.C. (US Government Printing Office), 1121–1134.

GRACIANSKY, P.-C. DE 1982. Les formations d'âge Crétacé de l'Atlantique Nord et leur matière organique: paléogéographie et milieux de dépôt. *Rev. Inst. Fr. Petrole*, **37**, 275–337.

——, BOURBON, M., LEMOINE, M. & SIGAL, J. 1981. The sedimentary record of mid-Cretaceous events in the western Tethys and central Atlantic oceans and their continental margins. *Eclogae. Geol. Helv.* **74**/2, 353–367.

—— & CHENET, P. Y. 1979. Sedimentological study of cores 138 to 56 (upper Hauterivian to middle Cenomanian): An attempt at reconstruction of paleoenvironments. *In:* SIBUET, J.-C., RYAN, W. B. F. *et al. Init. Rep. of the Deep Sea Drill. Proj.* **47**, Part 2, Washington, D.C. (US Government Printing Office), 403–418.

——, DEROO, G. *et al.* 1984. A stagnation event of ocean-wide extent in the upper Cretaceous, *Nature,* **308**, 346–9.

——, POAG, C. W. *et al.* 1982. The Goban Spur Transect: a precursor to ocean margin drilling. *Geotimes,* **27**, No. 5. 23–25.

——, —— *et al.* 1984. *Init. Rep. of the Deep Sea Drill. Proj.* 80, Washington D.C. (US Government Printing Office).

GRANDJACQUET, C. & MASCLE, G. 1978. The structure of the Ionian sea, Sicily and Calabria, Lucania. *In:* NAIRN, E. M., KAYNES, W. H. & STEHLI, F. G. (eds), *The Ocean Basins and Margins,* vol. 4B. Plenum Press, 257–329.

HABIB, D. 1982. Sedimentation of black clay organic facies in a Mesozoic oxic North Atlantic. *In: Proc. Third North Amer. Paleont. Conv.* **1**, 217–220.

HANCOCK, J. M. & KAUFFMAN, E. G. 1979. The great transgressions of the late Cretaceous. *J. Geol. Soc. London.* **136**, 175–186.

HART, M. B. & BIGG, P. J. 1981. Anoxic events in the late Cretaceous chalk seas of north-west Europe. *I.G.C.P. Project,* **58**, 177–185.

HAYES, D. E., PIMM, A. C. *et al.* 1972. *Init. Rep. of the Deep Sea Drill. Proj.* 14, Washington D.C. (US Government Printing Office).

HERBIN, J.-P. & DEROO, G. 1982. Sédimentologie de la matière organique dans les formations du Mésoz-oïque de l'Atlantique Nord. *Bull. Soc. Géol. Fr.* 7, XXIV, 4, 497–510.

HOLLISTER, C. D., EWING, J. L. *et al.* 1972. *Init. Rep. of the Deep Sea Drill. Proj,* 11, Washington D.C. (US Government Printing Office).

JANSA, L. F., ENOS, P., TUCHOLKE, B. E., GRADSTEIN, F. M. & SHERIDAN, R. E. 1979. Mesozoic-Cenozoic sedimentary formations of the North American basin: Western North Atlantic. *In:* TALWANI, M., HAY, W. & RYAN, W. B. F. (eds) *Deep Drilling Results in the Atlantic Ocean: Continental Margins and Paleoenvironment.* American Geophysical Union, Washington, D.C., 275–296.

JENKYNS, H. C. 1980. Cretaceous anoxic events: from continents to oceans, *J. Geol. Soc. London,* **137**, 171–188.

LANCELOT, Y. 1980. Birth and Evolution of the 'Atlantic Tethys'. (Central North Atlantic) *Mem. B.R.G.M.,* No. **115**, *Géologie des chaines alpines issues de la Tethys,* and *Colloque C5 du 26e Congrés Géologique International,* 214–223.

—— & SEIBOLD, E. 1977. The evolution of the central

northeastern Atlantic—summary of results of DSDP Leg 41, *Init. Rep. of the Deep Sea Drill. Proj.* 51, Washington D.C. (US Government Printing Office). 1215–46.

—— & WINTERER, E. L. 1980. *Init. Rep. of the Deep Sea Drill. Proj.* **50**, Washington D.C. (US Government Printing Office).

MCCAVE, I. N. 1979. Depositional features of organic-carbon-rich black and green mudstones at DSDP Sites 386 and 387, western North Atlantic. *In:* TUCHOLKE, B. E., VOGT, P. R. *et al. Init. Rep. of the Deep Sea Drill Proj.* **43**, Washington D.C. (US Government Printing Office), 411–420.

MOBERLEY, R., SCHLANGER, S. O. *et al. Init. Rep. of the Deep Sea Drill. Proj.* **89**, Washington D.C. (US Government Printing Office).

MONTADERT, L., ROBERTS, D. G. *et al.* 1979. Sites 399, 400, and Hole 400A. *In:* MONTADERT, L., ROBERTS, D. G. *et al. Init. Rep. of the Deep Sea Drill. Proj.* **48**, Washington D.C. (US Government Printing Office), 35–71.

MOULLADE, M. & GUERIN, S. 1981. Le problème des relations de l'Atlantique Sud et de l'Atlantique Central au Crétacé moyen: nouvelles données microfauniques d'après les forages DSDP, *Bull. Soc. Geol. Fr.,* 7, XXIV, 3, 511–518.

MÜLLER, C., SCHAAF, A. & SIGAL, J. 1983–1984. Biostratigraphie des formations d'âge Crétacé dans les forages du DSDP dans l'Atlantique Nord, *Revue Inst. Fr. Petrole,* **38**, 6, 683–708 and **39**, 1, 3–23.

MURATOV, M. V., NEPROCHOV, Y. P., ROSS, D. A. & TRIMONIS, E. S. 1978. Basic features of the Black Sea Late Cenozoic History based on results of Deep Sea Drilling, Leg 42B. *In:* ROSS, D. A., NEPROCHOV, Y. P. *et al. Init. Rep. of the Deep Sea Drill. Proj.* **42**, Part 2, 1141–1148, Washington D.C. (US Government Printing Office).

OLIVET, J. L., BONNIN, J., BEUZART, P. & AUZENDE, J.-M. 1982. Cinématique de l'Atlantique Nord et Central CNEXO, BEICIP (ed), Paris.

——, ——, & —— 1982. Cinématique des plaques et paléogéographie: une revue. *Bull. Soc. Géol. Fr.,* 7, XXIV, 5–6, 875–892.

ROSSIGNOL-STRICK, M., NESTEROFF, W., OLIVE, P. & VERGNAUD-GRAZZINI, C. 1982. After the deluge: Mediterranean stagnation and sapropel formation. *Nature,* **295**, No. 5845, 105–110.

RYAN, W. B. F. & CITA, M. B. 1977. Ignorance concerning episodes of ocean-wide stagnation. *Mar. Geol.,* **23**, 197–215.

SCHLANGER, S. O. & CITA, M. B. 1982. Nature and origin of Cretaceous carbon-rich facies. *Academic Press,* 229 p.

—— & JENKYNS, H. C. 1976. Cretaceous oceanic anoxic events: causes and consequences. *Geol. en Mijnbouw,* **55**, 179–184.

SCHLEE, J. & JANSA, L. F. 1981. The paleoenvironment and development of the eastern North American Continental margin, *26th Int'l Geol. Cong., Paris, Colloque C3, Oceano. Acta,* 71–80.

SCHWARZACHER, W. & FISCHER, A. G. 1982. Limestone-shale bedding and perturbations of the earth's orbit. *In:* EINSELE, G. & SEILACHER, A. (eds), *Cyclic and Event Stratification,* Springer-Verlag, 72–95.

SHERIDAN, R. E. & GRADSTEIN, F. M. 1983. *Init. Rep. of the Deep Sea Drill. Proj.* **76**, Washington D.C. (US Government Printing Office).

SIBUET, J.-C. & RYAN, W. B. F. 1979. *Init. Rep. of the Deep Sea Drill. Proj.* **47B**, Washington D.C. (US Government Printing Office).

SIGAL, J. 1979. Chronostratigraphy and ecostratigraphy of cretaceous formations recovered on DSDP leg 47B, site 398. *In:* SIBUET, J.-C. & RYAN, W. B. F. *et al. Init. Rep. of the Deep Sea Drill. Proj.* **47**, Part 2. Washington D.C. (US Government Printing Office), 287–326.

SUMMERHAYES, C. P. 1981. Organic facies of middle cretaceous black shales in deep north Atlantic. *Bull. Am. Assoc. Petr. Geol.*, **65**, 2364–2380.

TISSOT, B., DEROO, G. & HERBIN, J.-P. 1979. Organic matter in cretaceous sediments of the north Atlantic: contribution to sedimentology and paleogeography. *In:* TALWANI, M., HAY, W. & RYAN, W. B. F. (eds), *Deep Drill. Results in the Atlantic Ocean: Cont. Marg. and Paleoenvir.*, Washington D.C., American Geophysical Union, 362–374.

THIERSTEIN, H. R. 1979. Paleoceanographic implications of organic carbon and carbonate distribution in Mesozoic Deep Sea sediments. M. Ewing, Series 3. *In:* TALWANI, M., HAY, W. & RYAN, W. B. F. (eds) *Deep Drilling Results in the Atlantic Ocean: Continental Margins and Paleoenvironment.* Washington D.C., American Geophysical Union, 249–274.

TUCHOLKE, B. E. & VOGT, P. R. 1979. Western North Atlantic: Sedimentary evolution and aspects of tectonic history. *In:* TUCHOLKE, B. E., VOGT, P. R. *et al. Init. Rep. of the Deep Sea Drill. Proj.* **43**, Washington D.C. (US Government Printing Office), 791–825.

—— & —— *et al.* 1979. Site 387: Cretaceous to Recent sedimentary evolution of the western Bermuda rise. *In:* TUCHOLKE, B. E., VOGT, P. R. *et al. Initial Reports of the Deep Sea Drilling Project*, **43**, Washington D.C. (US Government Printing Office), 323–391.

—— & MOUNTAIN, G. S. 1979. Seismic stratigraphy lithostratigraphy and paleosedimentation patterns in the north American Basin. *In:* TALWANI, M., HAY, W. & RYAN, W. B. F. (eds) *Deep Drilling Results in the Atlantic Ocean: Continental Margins and Paleoenvironment*, American Geophysical Union, Washington D.C., 58–86.

VAIL, P. R. & MITCHUM, R. M. Jr. 1979. Global cycles of sea level change and their role in exploration, *10th World Petrol. Congr., Bucarest.*

——, —— & THOMPSON, S. 1977. Global cycles of relative changes of sea level, *Mem. Am. Assoc. Petrol. Geol.* No. **26**, 83–98.

WAPLES, D. W. 1984. A reappraisal of anoxia and organic richness, with emphasis on the Cretaceous North-Atlantic. *In:* GRACIANSKY, P.-C. DE, POAG, C. W. *et al. Init. Rep. of the Deep Sea Drill. Proj.* **80**, Washington D.C. (US Government Printing Office). 999–1018.

WEZEL, F. C. 1979. The Scaglia Rossa Formation of Central Italy: results and problems emerging from a regional study. Ateneo Parmense, *Acta Naturalia.* **15**, 243–259.

WYRTKI, K. 1962. The oxygen minimum in relation to ocean circulation. *Deep Sea Res.* **9**, 11–23.

ZEMMELS, I., COOK, H. E. & HATHAWAY, J. C. 1972. X-ray mineralogy studies Leg 11. *In:* HOLLISTER, C. D., EWING, J. I. *et al. Init. Rep. of the Deep Sea Drill. Proj.*, Vol. **11**. Washington D.C. (US Government Printing Office), 729–790.

P. C. DE GRACIANSKY, Ecole des Mines, 60 Bd St Michel, F-75272 Paris, France.

E. BROSSE, G. DEROO & J.-P. HERBIN, Institut Francais du Petrole, 1 Ave. de Bois Préau, F-92506 Rueil-Malmaison, France.

C. MÜLLER, 1 Rue Martignon F-92500 Rueil-Malmaison, France.

J. SIGAL, Collège de France, Station Marcellin Berthelot F-92360 Meudon-la-Forêt, France.

A. SCHAAF, Institut de Géologie, 1 Rue Blessig, F-67084 Strasbourg, France.

Organic carbon and metal accumulation rates in Holocene and mid-Cretaceous sediments: palaeoceanographic significance

T. J. Bralower & H. R. Thierstein

SUMMARY: The proportion of the organic carbon produced in oceanic surface waters that is buried in the underlying sediments is highly variable. The organic-carbon preservation factor, the proportion of preserved to produced organic carbon, is much higher in anoxic than in oxic deep waters. Predictability of organic-carbon preservation factors from sedimentary evidence would enable estimation of past primary production rates from measurable accumulation rates of organic carbon in ancient sediments.

Accumulation rate patterns of organic carbon, transition metals, and excess transition metals in Holocene and mid-Cretaceous sediments are evaluated as predictors of organic-carbon preservation factors. Holocene transition-metal accumulation rates are controlled dominantly by bulk accumulation rates. Euxinic deep water environments, characterized by high organic-carbon preservation factors, are more successfully identified by sedimentological than by geochemical criteria.

Sedimentological evidence from several mid-Cretaceous intervals implies widespread deep-water anoxia, high organic-carbon preservation factors, and correspondingly low primary productivity for large parts of the mid-Cretaceous oceans.

Why were the source rocks of over half of the world's giant oil fields deposited during the mid-Cretaceous (Irving et al. 1974)? This question remains one of the major palaeoceanographic enigmas (Ryan & Cita 1977; Schlanger & Cita 1982). There is clearly great economic significance to the question of whether oceanic fertility or terrigenous organic-carbon supply were high, whether deep waters were locally anoxic (i.e. less than about 0.5 ml/l of dissolved oxygen) or whether entire basins became euxinic (i.e. contained dissolved H_2S), because each of these mechanisms may have led to a different geographic distribution of potential hydrocarbon source rocks. Dark coloured bituminous sediments of mid-Cretaceous (Aptian–Cenomanian) age have been recovered from all the major ocean basins and are observed in numerous land exposures (Jenkyns 1980). These rocks, often described by the loosely defined term 'black shale', have been studied using many different approaches (e.g. Dean et al. 1978; Arthur 1979; Chamley et al. 1979; Thierstein 1979a; Tissot et al. 1979; Brumsack 1980; Graciansky et al. 1982; Ibach 1982).

Three hypotheses for the origin of these bituminous sediments have been proposed: (1) High palaeofertility of oceanic surface waters (Schlanger & Jenkyns 1976; Thiede & van Andel 1977; Parrish & Curtis 1982); (2) high supply of terrestrial organic carbon from the continents associated with high mid-Cretaceous sealevels (Habib 1979; Jenkyns 1980); and (3) increased preservation of organic carbon in climatically and tectonically induced anoxic deep waters

(Lancelot et al. 1972; Fischer & Arthur 1977; Thierstein & Berger 1978; Arthur & Natland 1979; Brumsack 1983; Waples 1983). The arguments for high palaeofertility caused by upwelling have been based on palaeogeographic setting (Ryan & Cita 1977; Parrish & Curtis 1982), kerogen composition (Summerhayes 1981), nannofossil assemblages (Roth & Bowdler 1981) and sedimentology (Thiede et al. 1982). Based on lithologic criteria and on an assumed lowered oceanic convection, it has also been proposed that the palaeoproductivity of Cretaceous surface waters may have been relatively low (Fischer & Arthur 1977; Berger 1979).

We report on an attempt to analyse and compare processes of organic-carbon and metal accumulation in Holocene and mid-Cretaceous marine sediments. The use of accumulation rates, rather than concentrations, requires stratigraphic time control, but eliminates the influence of diagenetic loss of porosity and allows identification of changes in the accumulation rates of components of interest versus those of dilutants. This last aspect in particular is of considerable concern in sedimentary intervals with highly variable carbonate contents.

Our approach is based on an analysis of the relationship between the organic-carbon accumulation rates observed in Holocene marine sediments from various settings (Fig. 1) and the estimated primary carbon fixation rates in overlying surface waters. This relationship is characterized by the organic-carbon preservation factor (Müller & Suess 1979), which is expressed as the percentage of the organic carbon produced in

From: BROOKS, J. & FLEET, A. J. (eds) 1987, Marine Petroleum Source Rocks
Geological Society Special Publication No. 26 pp. 345–369.

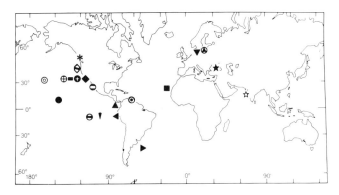

Fig. 1. Location of Holocene surface sediments. Site symbols as in Figs 2, 10.

surface waters that accumulates in the underlying sediments (Table 1). Organic-carbon preservation factors in Holocene environments vary from a low of less than 0.001% up to over 25%, i.e. over four orders of magnitude. The range of estimated primary production rates, on the other hand, varies over only one and a half orders of magnitude (Table 2, Fig. 2). Processes related to the transport of organic carbon from the photic zone through the benthic transition layer evidently determine the patterns of organic-carbon burial.

Since processes affecting the preservation of organic carbon have such a significant effect on the patterns of organic-carbon burial, the question arises whether we can put a value on the magnitude of the organic-carbon preservation factor from other sedimentary evidence. If this were possible, we could estimate the primary production rate of the surface waters of ancient oceans from the accumulation rate of organic carbon in the sediment, which can be determined by stratigraphic means.

Because one of the dominant processes leading to high organic-carbon preservation factors is the lack of oxygen in deep waters, we have specifically tested the hypothesis, that euxinic deep-water environments, and related past movements of the redoxcline through the water column, may have led to excessively high accumulation rates of transition-metal sulphides. Precipitation of transition-metal sulphides in euxinic deep waters (referred to here as euxinic hydrogenous precipitation) has been identified as a possibly significant process (e.g. Brewer & Spencer 1974; Degens & Stoffers 1977; Holland 1979; Brumsack 1980) responsible for the well-known metal enrichment of bituminous rock deposits throughout the geological record (e.g. Vine & Tourtelot 1970).

In the following we review and compare the processes and patterns of organic carbon accumulation in Holocene and mid-Cretaceous marine sediments. We then discuss the processes of metal enrichment in Holocene marine deposits and their applicability for palaeoenvironmental interpretations of mid-Cretaceous bituminous intervals.

TABLE 1. *Calculation of organic-carbon preservation factors and accumulation rates* ($R_{comp.}$) *of sediment components. (S is the sedimentation rate; P_d, P_w refer to dry and wet bulk density; Φ is the porosity; $X_{comp.}$ is the concentration of the component (organic carbon, carbonate, transition metal), RC_{org} is the accumulation rate of organic carbon).*

---

1 Preservation factor

$$= \frac{\text{Organic carbon accumulation rate}}{\text{Primary production rate}}$$

$$P.F. (\%) = \frac{RC_{org} \, (g/cm^2/ka) \times 1000}{P.P. \, (gC/m^2/a)}$$

2 Bulk accumulation rate $(RB) = S(P_w - 1.025\Phi)$

   Bulk accumulation rate $(RB) = S(P_d(1 - \Phi))$

3 Component accumulation rate $(R_{comp}) = RB \times X_{comp.}$

Methods

Although many of the measurements used in our interpretations are taken from the literature, we have made organic carbon, calcium carbonate, transition metal and Al measurements as part of this study. Samples were air-dried, ground in a spex mill and homogenized. Percent organic carbon was determined both in our lab and by P. H. Roth (University of Utah) using a Leco carbon analyser. This technique also yielded percent calcium carbonate which was corrobo-

TABLE 2. *Geographic, hydrographic, and sedimentary analytical data of Holocene sites.*

Region	Station	Lat.	Long.	Water Depth	R_{prod}	O_2	Depth in core	P_d	Φ	S	R_{bulk}	C_{org}	$CaCO_3$	RC_{org}	$RCaCO_3$	P.F.	Lam.
				m	g/m²/a	ml/l	cm	g/cm³	%/100	cm/ka	g/cm²/ka	%	%	g/cm²/ka	g/cm²/ka	% of R_{prod}	
Central Pacific	10127-2	13 42N	151 39W	5686	50	4.0	0-2	2.65	0.86	0.19	0.070	0.28	1	0.0002	0.0007	0.004	N
Central Pacific	10132-1	6 13N	148 57W	5004	50	4.0	0-4	2.65	0.80	0.58	0.307	0.22	32	0.0007	0.098	0.014	N
Central Pacific	10140-1	9 15N	148 45W	5144	50	4.0	0-2	2.49	0.85	0.41	0.153	0.33	1	0.0005	0.0015	0.010	N
Central Pacific	10141-1	9 07N	148 47W	5189	50	4.0	0-2	2.49	0.85	0.36	0.134	0.31	1	0.0004	0.0013	0.008	N
Central Pacific	10145-1	4 00N	144 49W	4599	100	4.0	0-2	2.65	0.80	0.32	0.170	0.21	74	0.0004	0.126	0.004	N
Central Pacific	10147-1	3 50N	145 02W	4619	100	4.0	0-2	2.65	0.80	0.43	0.228	0.23	72	0.0005	0.164	0.005	N
Central Pacific	10175-1	9 19N	146 01W	5164	50	4.0	0-2	2.48	0.84	0.23	0.091	0.40	1	0.0004	0.0009	0.008	N
Oregon Margin	7610-8	44 36N	126 20W	2060	100	—	0-1	2.42	0.88	10.0	2.90	1.50	—	0.044	—	0.44	N
Panama Basin	P-2	1 25S	92 59W	3510	365	2.4	0-30	—	—	—	1.83	0.60	60	0.011	1.10	0.030	N
Panama Basin	P-6	0 52N	86 08W	2712	183	2.4	0-40	—	—	—	3.10	0.71	73	0.022	2.26	0.12	N
East Pacific Rise	Y71-45P	11 05N	110 06W	3096	120	4.0	5-10	—	—	—	0.650	0.83	81	0.0054	0.527	0.045	N
Bauer Deep	Y71-36MG	10 08S	102 51W	4541	130	4.0	0-35	—	—	—	0.030	0.21	1	0.0001	0.0003	0.0008	N
Canary Basin	12392-1	25 10N	16 51W	2575	75	4.93	2-10	2.71	0.64	4.70	4.59	0.35	40	0.016	1.84	0.21	N
Canary Basin	12310-3	23 30N	18 43W	3076	90	5.15	0-2	2.71	0.76	2.50	1.63	0.34	57	0.0055	0.929	0.061	N
Canary Basin	12327-4	23 08N	17 44W	2037	130	3.36	0-1	2.71	0.85	6.00	2.44	1.34	42	0.033	1.02	0.25	N
Canary Basin	12328-4	21 09N	18 34W	2798	250	5.15	0-1	2.71	0.79	12.7	7.23	1.66	36	0.120	2.60	0.48	N
Canary Basin	12329-4	19 22N	19 56W	3315	90	5.38	0-2	2.71	0.77	2.00	1.25	0.61	64	0.0076	0.800	0.084	N
Canary Basin	12336-1	16 14N	20 26W	3645	75	5.87	0-2	2.71	0.75	2.20	1.49	0.44	54	0.0066	0.805	0.088	N
Canary Basin	12337-4	15 58N	18 07W	3085	160	5.15	0-2	2.71	0.79	4.00	2.28	1.46	12	0.033	0.274	0.21	N
Canary Basin	12347-1	15 50N	17 51W	2710	175	5.15	0-1	2.71	0.79	9.10	5.18	2.34	8	0.121	0.414	0.69	N
Canary Basin	12345-4	15 29N	17 22W	966	210	2.69	0-1	2.71	0.79	7.30	4.15	3.67	12	0.152	0.498	0.72	N
Canary Basin	12344-3	15 26N	17 21W	711	210	2.25	0-2	2.71	0.79	7.30	4.15	2.59	19	0.107	0.789	0.51	N
Canary Basin	13209-2	12 29N	20 03W	4713	70	5.99	0-10	2.71	0.79	2.00	1.14	0.51	—	0.0058	—	0.083	N
Argentine Basin	V-15-141	45 44S	50 45W	5934	100	5.15	0-1	2.60	0.63	3.30	3.17	0.72	—	0.023	—	0.23	N
Argentine Basin	V-15-142	44 54S	51 32W	5885	100	5.15	0-2	2.60	0.63	3.80	3.66	0.92	—	0.034	—	0.34	N
Black Sea	1462K	43 02N	33 02E	2186	73	7.0*	0-30	2.65	0.79	10.0	5.57	4.52	56	0.252	3.12	3.5	L
Black Sea	1474K	42 23N	37 36E	2117	30	7.0*	0-25	2.65	0.79	10.0	5.57	5.00	45	0.279	2.51	9.3	L
West India Margin	KK187	9 30N	75 30E	2121	300	2.73	0-10	2.50	0.85	11.4	4.28	3.40	28	0.146	1.20	0.49	N
West India Margin	KK188	9 30N	75 30E	988	300	0.06	0-2	2.50	0.81	27.0	12.8	6.60	36	0.845	4.61	2.8	L
West India Margin	KK210	17 30N	71 00E	495	300	0.87	0-20	2.50	0.86	11.0	3.85	4.50	63	0.173	2.43	0.58	L
Kiel Bay	13947	54 32N	10 04E	28	160	Var	0-20	2.60	0.85	140	54.6	4.91	17	2.68	—	17	N
Kiel Bay	13939	54 32N	10 04E	28	160	Var	0-20	2.60	0.85	140	54.6	5.16	18	2.82	—	18	N
Kiel Bay	12897	54 31N	10 02E	28	160	Var	0-20	2.60	0.84	140	58.2	4.87	18	2.83	—	18	N
Bornholm Basin	K1-878	55 18N	15 02E	71	60	Var	0-34	2.54	0.85	100	38.1	4.54	29	1.73	—	29	L
Cariaco Trench	147A	10 43N	65 10W	892	170	0.5*	0-350	2.40	0.85	50.0	18.0	5.50	6	0.990	1.08	5.8	L
Peru Shelf	7706-39	11 15S	77 57W	186	500	0.5	0-3	1.89	0.88	140	31.8	12.5	2	3.98	0.636	8.0	L
Peru Shelf	7706-36	13 37S	76 51W	370	400	0.5	0-3	1.93	0.86	66.0	17.8	21.2	2	3.77	0.356	9.4	L
Saanich Inlet		48 35N	123 30W	200	200	Var	0-250	—	—	—	93.0	3.58	1	3.33	0.930	17	L
Santa Barbara Basin		34 14N	120 02W	575	300	0.2	0-20	—	—	—	90.0	3.13	10	2.82	9.00	9.4	L
Santa Monica Basin		33 45N	118 52W	930	300	0.2	0-25	—	—	—	24.0	3.98	16	0.955	3.84	3.2	L
San Pedro Basin		33 30N	118 19W	890	300	0.2	0-32	—	—	—	28.0	3.73	9	1.04	2.52	3.5	L
Soledad Basin		25 14N	112 41W	520	300	0.2	0-28	—	—	—	40.0	6.46	20	2.58	8.00	8.6	L
Gulf of California	BAV76B29	26 42N	111 25W	635	200	0.3	0-200	—	—	—	33.0	4.39	20	1.45	6.60	7.3	L

Included are station latitude, longitude and water depth, surface water primary production rate (R_{prod}), bottom water dissolved oxygen content (O_2; * indicates permanent H_2S concentration, Var indicates waters containing H_2S seasonally), depth in core of sedimentary measurements and stratigraphy, dry bulk density (P_d) and porosity (Φ) of sediment, sedimentation rate (S) and bulk accumulation rate (R_{bulk}), average organic carbon (C_{org}) and carbonate ($CaCO_3$) contents, sedimentary accumulation rates of organic carbon (RC_{org}) and carbonate ($RCaCO_3$), preservation factor of organic carbon (P.F.) and presence (L) or absence (N) of sedimentary lamination (Lam.). — indicates unavailable data. For data sources see Table 3.

rated on identical samples using the carbonate bomb technique (Hülsemann 1966). Transition metals Cu, Ni and Zn were measured in our lab and by H.-J. Brumsack (Göttingen) using atomic absorption spectrophotometry. Al and some Ni measurements were made by X-ray fluorescence. Full analytical procedures, precisions and accuracies are given in Bralower (1984).

Holocene organic-carbon accumulation

Sedimentary accumulation rates

In our analysis of Holocene organic-carbon accumulation (Table 2) we have included the basic data set of Müller & Suess (1979). In order to make our Holocene calibration more complete, we have collected additional relevant sedimentary data from environments with more restricted hydrographic conditions (e.g. Black Sea, Cariaco Trench, Saanich Inlet, Bornholm Basin, California Borderland Basins and Gulf of California) and from open ocean areas with more varied hydrographies and fertilities (West India Margin, Panama Basin, East Pacific Rise and Bauer Deep). Table 3 documents the sources of the various categories of data.

A comparison of the Holocene accumulation rates of organic carbon determined in surface sediments with the estimated primary production rate of the respective overlying surface waters is shown in Fig. 2. The primary production rates measured and estimated for the various areas covered by the present data set range over one and a half orders of magnitude. The sedimentary

organic-carbon accumulation rates were derived from the organic-carbon contents measured in the surface sediments and the bulk accumulation rate determined from the stratigraphy in the upper few tens of centimetres in the sediment cores. The derived accumulation rate applies, therefore, to the generally bioturbated benthic transition layer, which may have an average age of up to a few thousand years.

Despite the fact that measurements of primary productivity are difficult to make (e.g. De Vooys 1979) and that many of the values we use are interpolated estimates, a general increase of sedimentary organic-carbon accumulation rate with increasing primary productivity is observed.

The diagonal lines in Fig. 2 give trends of equal organic-carbon preservation factors. These are higher than 1% in areas of high productivity and water depths of less than 1 km. Organic-carbon preservation factors are less than 0.5% in slowly accumulating sediments at abyssal depths, even where primary productivity is relatively high, such as in the Panama Basin. The most significant exception is the Black Sea, which has euxinic deep waters.

The exponential relationship between organic-carbon accumulation rate and sedimentation rate, which was pointed out by Heath *et al.* (1977) and Müller & Suess (1979) is confirmed in our data set (Fig. 3). We have, however, used bulk accumulation rates rather than sedimentation rates for the purpose of our comparison with diagenetically compacted mid-Cretaceous sediments. The variables in Fig. 3 are partially dependent. The organic-carbon accumulation rate, however, increases more rapidly than the bulk accumulation rate (slope greater than unity)

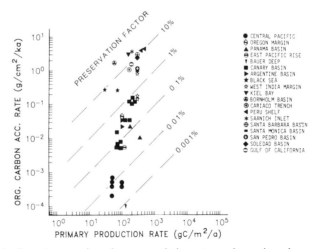

FIG. 2. Primary production rates, organic-carbon accumulation rates, and organic-carbon preservation factors in Holocene sites.

TABLE 3. *References for sources of Holocene data listed in Tables 2 and 6. Categories are primary production data* (Rp), *oxygen contents of bottom waters and presence or absence of sedimentary lamination* (O_2/Lam), *physical properties* (P/Φ), *sedimentation rate or bulk accumulation rate* (S/RB) *and sedimentary measurements of organic carbon, carbonate and transition metals* (C_{org}, $CaCO_3$, Metal).

Region	RP	O_2/Lam	P/Φ	S/RB	C_{org}	$CaCO_3$	Metal/Al
Central Pacific	1	2,3	1	1	1	1,4	—
Oregon Margin	1	—	1	1	1	—	—
Panama Basin	5	2,6	—	7	7	7	—
East Pacific Rise	8	2	9	9	10	10	9
Bauer Deep	8	2	9	9	10	10	9
Canary Basin	1	11	1	1	1	12,13,14	15,16
Argentine Basin	1	17	1	1	1	—	—
Black Sea	18	19,20	21	20	20,22,23	20,22	16
West India Margin	24	25,26	27,28	26	27	27	27
Kiel Bay	1	29	1	1	1,30	—	30
Bornholm Basin	31	32,33	32	32	32	—	32
Cariaco Trench	34	35,36	35	37	16	16	16
Peru Shelf	38	39	1	1	1	40	40
Saanich Inlet	41	42,43	44	44	45	45	45
Santa Barbara Basin	46	47,48	—	49	49	49	49
Santa Monica Basin	46	47,50	—	49	49	49	49
San Pedro Basin	46	47,50	—	49	49	49	49
Soledad Basin	46	—	—	49	49	49	49
Gulf of California	51	52,53	—	53	53	53	53
Central North Pacific	—	—	—	54	—	—	55
Average pelagic lithologies							
Calcareous ooze	—	—	56	56	57	—	58
Siliceous ooze	—	—	59	59	57	—	60
Red clay	—	—	61	62	63	—	58

1. Müller and Suess, 1979
2. Craig *et al.*, 1981
3. Reid, 1965
4. Müller and Mangini, 1980
5. Moore *et al.*, 1973
6. Bennett, 1963
7. Pedersen, 1983
8. van Andel *et al.*, 1975
9. Dymond and Veeh, 1975
10. Kendrick, 1973
11. Weichart, 1974
12. Diester-Haass, 1975
13. Müller, 1975
14. Thiede, 1977
15. Hartmann *et al.*, 1976
16. Bralower, 1984
17. Bainbridge, 1981
18. Shimkus and Trimonis, 1974
19. Fonselius, 1974
20. Ross and Degens, 1974
21. Manheim and Chan, 1974
22. Hirst, 1974
23. Pelet and Debyser, 1977
24. Platt and Subba Rao, 1975
25. Stackelberg, 1972
26. Zobel, 1973
27. Marchig, 1972
28. Assumed density
29. G. Wefer, pers. comm.
30. Erlenkeuser *et al.*, 1974
31. Kaiser and Schulz, 1975
32. Suess and Erlenkeuser, 1975
33. Grasshoff and Voipio, 1981
34. Deuser, 1973
35. Edgar, Saunders *et al.*, 1973
36. Richards, 1976
37. Spiker and Simoneit, 1982
38. Suess, 1980
39. Reimers, 1981
40. Dymond, 1981
41. Parsons *et al.*, 1969
42. Richards, 1965
43. Gucluer and Gross, 1964
44. Matsumoto and Wong, 1977
45. Presley *et al.*, 1972
46. Koblentz Mishke *et al.*, 1970
47. Emery, 1960 (p. 108)
48. Berger and Soutar, 1970
49. Bruland *et al.*, 1974
50. Douglas, 1981
51. Zeitzschel, 1969
52. Calvert, 1964
53. Donegan, 1982
54. Janecek and Rea (in press)
55. Corliss *et al.*, 1982
56. Berger and Killingley, 1982
57. Lisitzin, 1972 (p. 168)
58. Turekian and Wedepohl, 1961
59. Johnson, 1975
60. Leinen and Stakes, 1979
61. Horn *et al.*, 1974
62. Berger, 1974
63. Seibold and Berger, 1982 (p. 263)

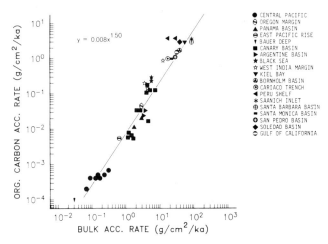

FIG. 3. Organic-carbon accumulation rate increases exponentially with increasing bulk accumulation rate in Holocene environments. (Correlation coefficient r = 0.977.)

indicating that the correlation is not fortuitous. The observed relationship suggests that higher burial rates inhibit the combustion rate of organic carbon in the benthic transition layer. Additionally, coastal sites with high bulk accumulation rates generally have high primary productivities and low oxygen contents (Table 2). These factors also enhance organic-carbon accumulation rates. What is the relative importance of the various processes and conditions, such as water depth, bulk accumulation rate, particle transport mechanisms, oxygen content in the water column, type of organic carbon supplied, and diagenesis, all of which influence the organic-carbon accumulation rates in marine sediments?

Primary production and fluxes in the water column

The primary production rates of organic carbon range from low values of 30–50 g $C/m^2/a$ in the central Black Sea and the subtropical central gyres to high values of up to 1000 g $C/m^2/a$ in coastal and oceanic upwelling areas (e.g. Koblentz-Mishke *et al.* 1970; Shimkus & Trimonis 1974; Reimers 1981). Uncertainties in these estimates originate from inherent diurnal, seasonal, and small-scale geographic variations, as well as from differences in measurement techniques employed.

The most compelling evidence for the fate of organic carbon in the water column comes from sediment trap data. Fig. 4 illustrates organic carbon fluxes in the water and upper sediment columns of three different sedimentary environments. The proportion of organic carbon synthesized by primary producers, which leaves the

photic zone, has been variably estimated to be between about 10% and 30% (e.g. Degens & Mopper 1976; Suess 1980). Most of the organic matter produced in the euphotic zone is thus recycled through processes such as grazing and respiration. The present consensus from studies of transport mechanisms in the deeper water column is that rare, relatively large particles account for most of the vertical transport (Lal 1977; Spencer *et al.* 1978). Sizes and types of particles (inorganic aggregates and faecal pellets) may vary in a systematic way geographically and with water depth (Shanks & Trent 1980; Suess

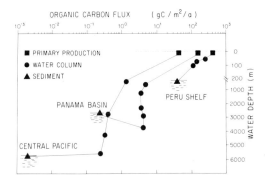

FIG. 4. Primary production, water column fluxes, and sedimentary accumulation rates of organic carbon in a coastal environment and in high and low fertility oceanic areas. Peru Shelf data from Suess (1980; p, w, s). Panama Basin data from Moore *et al.* (1973; p); Spencer *et al.* (1981; w) and Pedersen (1983; s). Central Pacific data from Müller and Suess (1979; p, s) and Honjo (1980; w). (p, w, s indicate sources of primary production, water column flux and sedimentary accumulation rate data respectively).

1980; Dunbar 1981). As illustrated in Fig. 4, the total decrease in measured organic-carbon fluxes within the deep water column is less than one order of magnitude at any particular site (Dunbar 1981). The somewhat higher constant rate losses inferred by Suess (1980) resulted from a data set which included profiles from coastal and open ocean areas which have vastly different surface fertilities and deep-water oxygen profiles. The water column preservation factor is highest in coastal areas, such as the Peru Shelf. It is lower in open ocean high fertility areas, such as the Panama Basin, and it is lowest in open ocean low fertility areas, such as the central Pacific (Fig. 4). This gradient may be associated more with decreasing intensity of oxygen minimum zones and possibly changing particle transport mechanisms, than with water depth *per se*.

Diagenetic losses

The differences in the organic-carbon fluxes as measured in the deepest traps and in the underlying sediments appear to vary regionally (Fig. 4). Most of the measurements used in our data set for the calculation of Holocene organic-carbon accumulation rates were made at the top of the sediment column. With the exception of a few cores raised from euxinic and highly anoxic deep-water environments (Black Sea, Cariaco Trench, Bornholm Basin, Saanich Inlet, Santa Barbara, Santa Monica and San Pedro Basins, Gulf of California) all core tops are bioturbated and the measurements are thus representative of the benthic transition layer, which includes the uppermost 5–10 cm of sediment. Our calculated organic-carbon accumulation rates, therefore, have been decreased by early diagenetic losses of organic carbon.

The residence time of particulate matter in the water column is estimated to be weeks or months (Lal 1977), whereas the residence time in the bioturbated surface sediment layer is hundreds to thousands of years (e.g. Erlenkeuser 1980). The relative amount of oxidative degradation of organic matter should therefore be most significant in the benthic transition layer. What is the magnitude of these early diagenetic losses? And how significant are organic carbon losses during later burial diagenesis?

The sequence of the most important early diagenetic biochemical degradation reactions has been evaluated experimentally by measuring dissolved oxidants and nutrients in pore waters of marine sediment cores (e.g. Berner 1974; Toth & Lerman 1977; Froelich *et al.* 1979; Müller & Mangini 1980). This sequence proceeds from dissolved oxygen consumption through denitrifi-

cation, reduction of manganese oxides, iron oxides, sulphate and eventually fermentation with methane production.

In oxic deep-water environments the extent of biochemical degradation of organic carbon is mostly a function of sedimentation rate. Below a sedimentation rate of about 1 cm per 1000 years the sediment column remains completely oxic (Heath *et al.* 1977; Müller & Mangini 1980) and organic-carbon contents are usually less than 0.2% (Grundmanis & Murray 1982). At higher sedimentation rates the supply of organic matter is high enough to exhaust all available oxygen and nitrate at a depth of a few tens of centimetres in the sediment (e.g. Hartmann *et al.* 1973; Toth & Lerman 1977; Froelich *et al.* 1979). Dissolved sulphate is usually absent below 1 to 10 metres (Curtis 1980).

In anoxic and particularly in euxinic environments, biochemical degradation of organic matter is less efficient and more incomplete for several reasons: lack of bioturbation in the surface sediment layer inhibits the supply of oxidants into the sediment; many products from bacterial metabolism are toxic, resulting in lowered bacterial activity; anaerobic decomposition reactions are thermodynamically inefficient (Brooks 1978; Tissot & Welte 1978; Froelich *et al.* 1979; Demaison & Moore 1980). As a result of these processes combustion rates decrease rapidly below the benthic transition layer in anoxic sediment columns, microbial populations decline, organic decomposition eventually ceases, and reactive as well as refractory organic substances become permanently buried.

In environments with sedimentation rates of more than about a centimetre per thousand years, which become rapidly anoxic below the benthic transition layer, the diagenetic organic-carbon losses below that layer appear to be no more than another 20 to 30 percent, and below about 50 cm depth the organic-carbon contents remain virtually constant (Bordovsky 1965; Hartmann *et al.* 1973; Heath *et al.* 1977; Murray *et al.* 1978; Berner 1982). Absence of any significant organic-carbon losses deeper in anoxic sediment columns is supported by the lack of systematic decreases in organic-carbon contents with depth in numerous DSDP holes from various environments with average sedimentation rates of greater than about a centimetre per thousand years, such as the Cariaco Trench (Saunders *et al.* 1973), Black Sea (Mopper *et al.* 1978; Erdman & Schorno 1978), Gulf of California (Deroo & Herbin 1983), Caribbean Sea and eastern equatorial Pacific (Gardner 1982). Significant diagenetic organic-carbon losses in many black shale sequences also appear unlikely because they would imply unreasonably high original organic-carbon contents (Bralower 1984).

Terrigenous organic matter

Numerous attempts have been made to recognize the sources of organic matter buried in marine sediments. The most commonly used methods are carbon isotopes (e.g. Gormly & Sackett 1977; Hedges & van Geen 1982), microscopic kerogen analysis (e.g. Habib 1979; Durand 1980), and elemental analyses (e.g. Tissot *et al.* 1979). Difficulties arise in older and in slowly accumulating sediments, because progressive diagenesis tends to obscure the original differences between terrigenous and marine organic matter (e.g. Tissot & Welte 1978; Brooks 1981). A survey of the literature on the composition of organic matter in Holocene marine sediments suggests that generally at least half, and usually considerably more, of the total organic carbon is of marine origin. This has specifically been documented in all sediments containing 1% organic carbon or more in the following areas: Central Atlantic (Caratini *et al.* 1978, 1979), Black Sea (Pelet & Debyser 1977), Cariaco Trench (Caratini *et al.* 1978), Saanich Inlet (Brown *et al.* 1972), California Borderland Basins (Summerhayes 1981), Gulf of California (Deroo & Herbin 1983). Even in cores from the Amazon cone area, where the riverine influx of terrigenous organic material from a tropical rain forest is extremely high, Holocene sediments are dominated by amorphous, marine derived kerogen (Caratini *et al.* 1978).

Mid-Cretaceous organic-carbon accumulation

The number of mid-Cretaceous sequences available for analyses is limited by the prerequisites of adequate sample density and core recovery, availability of physical property measurements and the preservation of carbonate micro- and nannofossils used for time control (Fig. 5).

Biochronology

Included in our comparison are sediment sequences of Aptian, Albian and Cenomanian age. The thicknesses of the intervals were determined by calcareous nannofossil stratigraphy, for which a reasonably well established zonation exists (Thierstein 1973, 1976; Manivit *et al.* 1977). The *Chiastozygus litterarius* and *Parhabdolithus angustus* Zones cover the Aptian, the *Prediscosphaera cretacea* and *Eiffellithus turriseiffeli* Zones cover the Albian and the *Lithraphidites acutum* Zone covers the Cenomanian Stage. Whenever available, published planktic foraminiferal assemblages were used to verify ages and thicknesses of these intervals. The radiometric age calibration used for the stage boundaries is that of Harland *et al.* (1982). To estimate the relative durations of nannofossil zones within the Aptian and Albian Stages, averages of the relative thicknesses of the nannofossil zones from several sections of reasonably consistent lithology were used. The sediments within each section were assumed to have accumulated at constant rates. For the Aptian

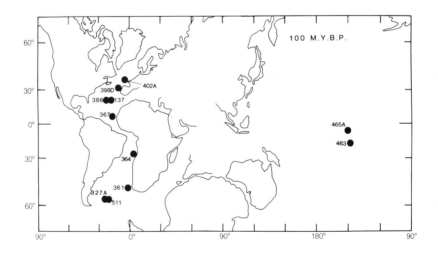

FIG. 5. Location of analysed mid-Cretaceous intervals from various DSDP Sites.

TABLE 4. *Palaeobathymetric, stratigraphic and analytical data of mid-Cretaceous intervals.*

Site	Cores	Nanno-Zone	Paleo-Depth	Sub. Depth	Total	Time	S	P_w	Φ	R_{bulk}	C_{org} %			$CaCO_3$ %			RC_{org}	$RCaCO_3$
			m	m	m	ma	cm/ka	g/cm³	%/100	g/cm²/ka	n	X	σ	n	X	σ	g/cm²/ka	g/cm²/ka
137	7-1/16-1	L acut.	3100	256–376	120	6.5	1.85	1.85	0.40	2.68	32	0.28	0.48	32	47.9	23.0	0.0075	1.28
327A	16-1/21-4	P cret.	500	185–314	129	6.6	1.95	2.00	0.45	3.02	6	0.15	0.05	6	39.3	12.5	0.0045	1.19
361	26cc/32-2	P ang.	2750	953–1062	109	3.6	3.03	2.15	0.25	5.73	13	4.70	4.53	19	3.5	4.2	0.269	0.201
364	24-2/33cc	E turr.	1050	674–853	179	8.9	2.01	2.40	0.50	3.80	20	0.22	0.37	30	48.6	26.6	0.0084	1.85
364	34-1/41-2	P cret.	950	872–1007	135	6.6	2.05	2.40	0.45	3.98	12	1.28	1.35	20	63.6	20.5	0.051	2.53
364	41-3/42cc	P ang.	875	1008–1033	25	3.6	0.69	2.30	0.47	1.26	5	8.06	8.45	7	42.1	22.9	0.102	0.530
367	18-1/20-2	L acut.	4500	631–689	58	6.5	0.89	1.85	0.40	1.28	6	21.32	5.38	4	15.4	10.2	0.273	0.197
367	20-4/22-5	E turr.	4430	689–729	40	8.9	0.45	1.97	0.45	0.68	21	7.80	4.75	11	4.3	3.7	0.053	0.030
386	44-4/49-3	L acut.	3150	751–810	59	6.5	0.91	2.05	0.39	1.50	20	0.61	0.68	21	7.3	23.2	0.0092	0.110
386	50-2/57cc	E turr.	3050	810–888	78	8.9	0.88	1.94	0.43	1.32	21	1.35	0.74	21	29.1	22.5	0.018	0.384
386	58-1/65-1	P cret.	2500	888–956	68	6.6	1.03	1.85	0.49	1.39	29	2.00	3.01	29	11.6	20.2	0.028	0.161
398D	57-2/60cc	E turr.	2900	957–993	36	8.9	0.40	2.10	0.33	0.70	14	0.60	0.54	14	29.8	4.5	0.0042	0.209
398D	61-1/97cc	P cret.	2750	993–1354	361	6.6	5.47	2.10	0.33	9.63	17	1.63	1.76	17	8.7	12.8	0.157	0.838
402A	5-1/33-5	P ang.	900	175–449	274	3.6	7.61	2.40	0.22	16.51	44	1.17	0.48	44	33.2	11.3	0.193	5.48
463	56-1/69-1	P ang.	350	485–606	121	3.6	3.36	2.40	0.20	7.39	14	0.46	0.21	47	63.0	20.8	0.034	4.66
463	69cc/78cc	C litt.	250	606–699	93	2.4	3.88	2.30	0.20	7.72	14	0.79	0.46	39	35.2	29.4	0.061	2.72
465A	28-1/40-1	E turr.	500	297–414	117	8.9	1.31	2.30	0.20	2.75	14	3.69	2.37	36	65.6	24.4	0.101	1.80
511	50-2/56-1	P cret.	500	434–491	57	6.6	0.86	2.00	0.40	1.37	8	0.10	0.07	7	31.0	18.2	0.0014	0.425

Included are upper- and lower-most cores of nannofossil zone/interval (see Fig. 6), paleodepth, cored sub-bottom depth of interval and total recovery length (Total), duration of interval (Time), sedimentation rate, wet bulk accumulation rate (P_w), porosity, bulk accumulation rate, sedimentary organic carbon and carbonate contents (n, X, σ are number of measurements, mean and one standard deviation respectively), and organic-carbon and carbonate accumulation rate. Other symbols as in Table 2. For data sources see Table 5.

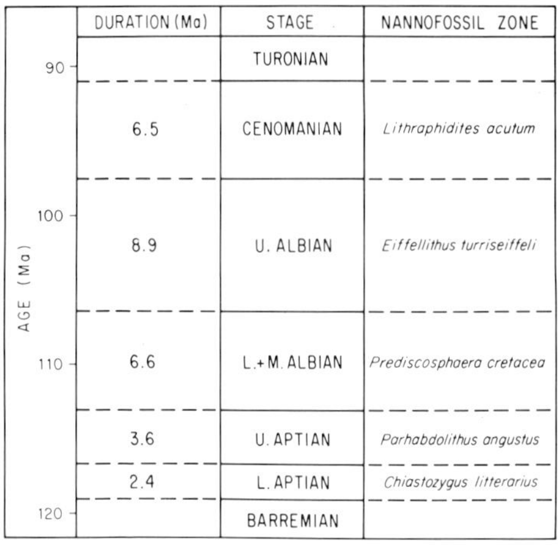

DURATION (Ma)	STAGE	NANNOFOSSIL ZONE
	TURONIAN	
6.5	CENOMANIAN	*Lithraphidites acutum*
8.9	U. ALBIAN	*Eiffellithus turriseiffeli*
6.6	L.+M. ALBIAN	*Prediscosphaera cretacea*
3.6	U. APTIAN	*Parhabdolithus angustus*
2.4	L. APTIAN	*Chiastozygus litterarius*
	BARREMIAN	

(Left axis: AGE (Ma): 90, 100, 110, 120)

FIG. 6. Mid-Cretaceous biochronology used (for details see text).

these were from Site 463 (Table 4) and the Route d'Angles section in southeastern France (*C. litterarius* Zone 15 m thick, *P. angustus* Zone 26 m thick; Thierstein 1973) and for the Albian they were from Sites 386 (Table 4), 463 and 464 (Roth 1981) and the Col de Palluel section in southeastern France (Thierstein 1973). The ratios between the adjacent zonal thicknesses in each of the sections were averaged for each stage (Thierstein 1979b) and then normalized to the duration of the entire stage given by Harland *et al.* (1982). The resulting calibration is shown in Fig. 6. The duration of the Cenomanian Stage of 6.5 Ma given in Harland *et al.* (1982) is 2 Ma longer than proposed by Obradovich & Cobban (1975), 1.5 Ma shorter than proposed by van Hinte (1976), and 2.5 Ma longer than proposed by Kennedy & Odin (1982). The duration of 15.5 Ma for the Albian Stage given in Harland *et al.* (1982) is 7.5 Ma longer than proposed by van Hinte (1976), 2.5 Ma shorter than proposed by Obradovich & Cobban (1977), 11.5 Ma shorter than proposed by Lanphere & Jones (1978), and 3.5 Ma longer than proposed by Kennedy & Odin (1982). The duration of the Aptian Stage of 6 Ma given in Harland *et al.* (1982) is 1 Ma shorter than proposed by van Hinte (1976), 7 Ma shorter than proposed by Lanphere & Jones (1978), and 1 Ma longer than proposed by Kennedy & Odin (1982). It appears unlikely that Harland *et al.* (1982) have overestimated the age durations of the individual mid-Cretaceous stages by more than 30%, but they may possibly have underestimated these durations by up to 100%. In the latter case, our accumulation rate calculations may be too high by up to a factor of two. These errors are by far the largest among the parameters we used to compute accumulation rates in mid-Cretaceous intervals.

Mid-Cretaceous accumulation rates

We calculated bulk accumulation rates by the same method as described by van Andel *et al.* (1975). Sources of biostratigraphic data as well as those of physical properties, organic-carbon and calcium carbonate contents are documented in Table 5. Organic-carbon and carbonate accumulation rates were computed from average contents within the intervals defined by the biostratigraphic zones (Table 4). Palaeodepth estimates are from Thierstein (1979a), and

TABLE 5. *References for sources of mid-Cretaceous data listed in Table 4. Included are sources of nannofossil stratigraphy and relevant sedimentary data.*

Site	Nanno-strat.	P/Φ	C_{org}	CaCO$_3$
137	1	2	3	3
327A	4	5	6	6
361	7	8	8	8
364	7	8	8	8
367	9,10,11	12	3,13,14	3,14
386	15	16	14,17	14,17
398D	18	19	14,19	14,19
402A	20	21	3	3
463	22	23	14	14,24
465A	22	23	14	14,24
511	25	26	26	26

1 Roth and Thierstein, 1972
2 Hayes, Pimm *et al.*, 1972
3 DSDP data bank
4 Wise and Wind, 1976
5 Barker, Dalziel *et al.*, 1976
6 Cameron, 1976
7 Proto-Decima *et al.*, 1978
8 Bolli, Ryan *et al.*, 1978
9 Bowdler, 1978
10 Čěpek, 1978
11 Thierstein, 1979a
12 Trabant, 1978
13 Brumsack, 1979
14 Bralower, 1984
15 Okada and Thierstein, 1979
16 Tucholke, Vogt *et al.*, 1979
17 Cameron, 1979
18 Blechschmidt, 1979
19 Sibuet, Ryan *et al.*, 1979
20 Müller, 1979
21 Montadert, Roberts *et al.*, 1979
22 Roth, 1981
23 Thiede, Vallier *et al.*, 1981
24 Dean, 1981
25 Wise, 1983
26 Ludwig, Krasheninikov *et al.*, 1983

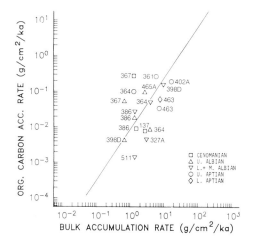

FIG. 7. Bulk and average organic-carbon accumulation rates of mid-Cretaceous intervals, and regression line describing Holocene trend (from Fig. 3).

Roth (1981), and include uncertainties of about ± 300 m.

The mid-Cretaceous organic-carbon accumulation rates are averages computed from numerous concentration measurements taken from within the intervals defined by the nannofossil zones. In consideration of the often highly variable organic-carbon contents within any one interval, we have adjusted our sampling strategy to include all lithologies present at approximately the proportional frequencies. If during certain parts of any interval the accumulation rates of organic carbon were higher than our mean, they must have been proportionally lower during the remaining parts. Further analyses of range,

frequency and geographic distribution of organic carbon variability appear desirable, but are beyond the scope of this paper.

The ranges of observed average mid-Cretaceous bulk- and organic-carbon accumulation rates (Fig. 7) are similar to those observed in Holocene open ocean and continental margin environments located above the calcium carbonate compensation depth (see Fig. 3) which is currently at about 4.5 to 5.5 km water depth (Berger 1974). The scatter of the mid-Cretaceous average accumulation rate patterns, however, is very wide compared to the relatively tight correlation observed in Holocene environments. It is evident that, in great contrast to the Holocene, factors other than bulk accumulation rates must have dominated the distribution of organic-carbon sinks in mid-Cretaceous oceans. The most likely reasons for the increased scatter in the mid-Cretaceous are regional and temporal variability in fertility and deep-water ventilation. The clustering of data points in Fig. 7 appear to be mostly site-specific but no basin-wide clusters can be detected. The scattered points do not cluster stratigraphically, suggesting no systematic bias in our relative time estimates for the nannofossil zones.

A comparison of the depth partitioning of organic-carbon accumulation rates in the middle Cretaceous and the Holocene is revealing (Fig. 8). Bulk accumulation rate versus depth relationships are quite similar in oceanic Holocene sites to those observed in the middle Cretaceous (Bralower 1984). Because of their strong correlation with bulk accumulation rates, organic-carbon accumulation rates in the Holocene also are strongly depth dependent. Notable exceptions

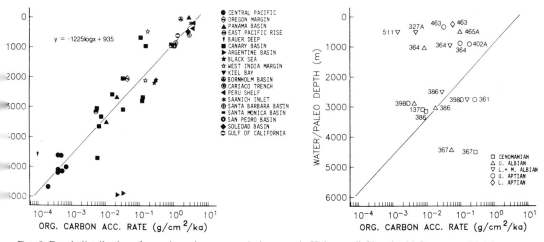

FIG. 8. Depth distribution of organic-carbon accumulation rates in Holocene (left) and mid-Cretaceous (right) sites. Both graphs show the regression line for the Holocene data (r = 0.892).

are the turbidite sequences in the Argentine Basin. Middle Cretaceous intervals from shallow palaeodepths show a comparatively low organic-carbon accumulation rate suggesting much less pronounced shallow oxygen minimum zones and lower bulk accumulation rates than are observed today in coastal areas. The Lower Albian interval at Site 398D, and the Upper Aptian interval at Site 361 show high bulk accumulation rates and high terrigenous kerogen supply (Summerhayes 1981; Foresman 1978) leading to enhanced organic-carbon accumulation rates (Fig. 8). The most significant non-analogue situation in comparison to the Holocene is found at Site 367 (Figs 7 and 8), where excessive organic-carbon accumulation at great depths must have resulted from strong oxygen depletion of abyssal waters.

Transition-metal accumulation

Inorganic metal sulphide precipitation or scavenging of metals by sinking particles at and below the redox boundary between oxic surface waters and hydrogen-sulphide containing deep waters have been proposed as mechanisms leading to the well-known metal enrichments in bituminous sediments, which are observed throughout the geological record (Vine & Tourtelot 1970; Brewer & Spencer 1974; Degens & Stoffers 1977; Holland 1979; Brumsack 1980, 1983). Can such observed sedimentary associations be used to recognize euxinic deep-water environments, which are characterized by high organic-carbon preservation factors? To test this rather exciting possibility, we have determined and examined the Holocene transition-metal accumulation rates from a large range of marine environments. Previous studies have emphasized differences in the concentrations of metals in various marine sediments, and those which included interpretations of metal accumulation rates, were focussed on particular environments (e.g. Boström *et al.* 1973; Dymond & Veeh 1975).

Oceanic cycling of metals

Transition metals are chemically associated with solid sedimentary materials through adsorptive bonding onto particle surfaces, through coprecipitation in lattice sites of authigenic minerals, and through complexing with organic compounds (Gibbs 1973; Saxby 1973; Förstner & Wittman 1979). The major sinks in the oceanic transition-metal cycles are hydrothermal, oxic and euxinic hydrogenous precipitation, and incorporation in organic and detrital particles (Fig. 9; Chester & Aston 1976).

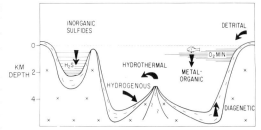

FIG. 9. The cycling of transition metals in the oceans.

The detrital input of transition metals by rivers, wind and ice consists mostly of rock fragments and mineral weathering residue. The transition-metal contents of terrigenous detritus are relatively constant in unpolluted areas (Chester & Aston 1976) and can be represented by the 'average shale' of Turekian & Wedepohl (1961) and Wedepohl (1970).

Metal enriched sediments occurring along oceanic spreading centres show a considerable range of concentrations and accumulation rates of mostly Fe and Mn, and to a minor extent of the transition metals Co, Cu, Ni, and Zn (e.g. Chester & Aston 1976; Dymond 1981; McMurtry *et al.* 1981). Hydrothermally influenced metal deposits are often less enriched in the transition metals Co, Cu, Ni, and Zn than hydrogenous deposits (e.g. Dymond & Veeh 1975). Subsurface mixing of hydrothermal solutions with ground water may lead to depletion of trace metals in existing hot-spring waters as is observed at the Galapagos spreading centre (Edmond *et al.* 1979).

Hydrogenous deposits are those derived from seawater components by inorganic reactions in the water column or benthic transition layer. Oxic hydrogenous activity occurs at or close to the sediment–water interface in slowly accumulating abyssal environments and results in Fe- and Mn-oxide and -hydroxide deposits (Chester & Aston 1976; Dymond 1981; McMurty *et al.* 1981). Euxinic hydrogenous processes occur in the water column at the O_2–H_2S interface and lead to coprecipitation of transition metals with sulphide phases (Kaplan *et al.* 1969; Brewer & Spencer 1974).

The organic tissue of plankton is enriched in many transition elements relative to sea water (Martin & Knauer 1973). Sinking organic matter may therefore be a significant carrier for transition metals to marine sediments (Boström *et al.* 1974).

Diagenetic remobilization of transition metals may occur at changes in redox potential, during dissolution of minerals, and during bacterial degradation of organic matter (Price 1976). Once transition metals such as Cu, Ni and Zn are co-precipitated as sulphides (hydrogenously or di-agenetically), they are insoluble, even under anoxic conditions (Brooks *et al.* 1969; Calvert 1976). Where dissolved transition metals reach detectable levels in anoxic pore waters, their concentrations appear to be very low (Presley *et al.* 1972) and they tend to occur as organic complexes in dissolved humic compounds (Nissenbaum *et al.* 1972). Thus, once precipitated as sulphides and buried tens of centimetres below bioturbated surface layers, large-scale diagenetic displacement of transition metals, with the exception of Mn, through the sediment column appears unlikely. However, a quantitative evaluation of potential diagenetic metal enrichments in ancient reducing sediment columns is clearly desirable.

Holocene transition-metal accumulation rates

The preceding review suggests that the importance of various oceanic processes governing the accumulation rates of metals in Holocene marine sediments is highly variable geographically. Thus it is essential to evaluate metal accumulation rates from as many Recent environments as possible before comparisons and interpretations of patterns in ancient sediments are attempted. To be useful for such a comparison, a sediment core needs to be dated stratigraphically and concentration measurements of various metals, organic carbon, and carbonate, preferably from the same samples, must be available. Such integrated data are notoriously scarce in the literature. We have included most of these previously described and analysed cores in our Holocene data set (Table 6, Fig. 1). We report new measurements of organic carbon, carbonate, and metal contents in sediments from the Cariaco Trench and the Black Sea. We have also analysed *Ni* in cores from the Canary Basin, which were previously studied by Hartmann *et al.* (1976).

Although most samples are enriched in organic carbon, they cover a wide range of sedimentation rates and of organic-carbon, carbonate, and detrital accumulation rates. Moreover, the sites represent a wide range of hydrographic conditions from well oxygenated (e.g. Canary Basin), to anoxic (e.g. Santa Barbara Basin), to seasonally (e.g. Saanich Inlet) and permanently euxinic deep-water conditions (e.g. Black Sea). The sites also span a wide range of primary production rates.

The transition metals we use in our interpretations are Cu, Ni and Zn because analytical procedures for their determination are well established and because these three transition metals are among the most commonly measured.

They are therefore the most readily available in the literature and allow assembly of a comparatively large Holocene calibration data set. By interpreting the combined accumulation rates of Cu, Ni and Zn, we are attempting to analyse the average trace metal behaviour. We have included one site each from the East Pacific Rise and Bauer Deep to identify possible accumulation rate anomalies due to hydrothermal and hydrogenous processes. For comparison purposes we have added average estimates for bulk and metal accumulation rates for additional facies (siliceous ooze, calcareous ooze, red clay), although the measurements for the individual components were not all done on identical cores (Table 3).

The accumulation rate of combined Cu, Ni, and Zn is highly correlated with bulk accumulation rate (Fig. 10), the correlation coefficient reaching a value of $r = 0.967$. The high correlation indicates that, over the large range of bulk accumulation rates covered, transition-metal accumulation rates are dominated by detrital supply. We note that the hydrogenously dominated transition-metal accumulation rate of the Bauer Deep Site is among the lowest known, despite the fact that the metal contents in those sediments are exceptionally high. The fact that the Bauer Deep and the East Pacific Rise Sites lie close to the overall Holocene trend may be deceptive. Accumulation rate patterns of individual metals are very variable regionally in these areas (McMurtry *et al.* 1981) and the summation of the three metals may obscure meaningful anomalies in the accumulation rates of individual metals. Although metal accumulation rates of the East Pacific Rise Site are rather low compared to other Holocene settings, it should be noted that those in the anoxic, brine-filled Atlantis-II Deep in the Red Sea appear to be extremely high (Emery *et al.* 1969; Shanks & Bischoff 1980). The transition-metal accumulation rates show a comparably high correlation with organic-carbon accumulation rate ($r = 0.956$) and water depth, because both of these parameters are highly correlated with each other and with bulk accumulation rate (Figs 3, 8).

Mid-Cretaceous transition-metal accumulation rates

Chemical analyses of mid-Cretaceous sediments have demonstrated highly variable enrichments in metals and organic carbon (e.g. Lange *et al.* 1978; Chamley *et al.* 1979; Maillot & Robert 1980; Varenstsov 1981). Mid-Cretaceous transition-metal enrichments have been interpreted as hydrothermally derived (Murdmaa *et al.* 1979; Hein *et al.* 1982) or precipitated from euxinic

TABLE 6. Holocene and mid-Cretaceous transition metal data.

Column groups: **Average metal concentrations** — Cu ppm (X, σ), Ni ppm (X, σ), Zn ppm (X, σ), Al % (X, σ); then C_{org} %. **Excess conc. ppm** — Cu, Ni, Zn, Tot.; then C_{org} %. **Accumulation rates (mg/cm²/ka)** — Bulk, Cu, Ni, Zn, Tot., Ex., C_{org} %.

Region	Station	n	Cu X	σ	Ni X	σ	Zn X	σ	Al X	σ	C_{org} %	Ex Cu	Ex Ni	Ex Zn	Ex Tot.	C_{org} %	Bulk	Cu	Ni	Zn	Tot.	Ex.	C_{org} %
East Pacific Rise	Y71-45P	1	67	—	146	—	31	—	0.078	—	0.83	67	145	30	242	0.83	650	0.044	0.095	0.020	0.159	0.160	5.4
Bauer Deep	Y71-36MG	1	781	—	498	—	308	—	2.18	—	0.21	771	481	281	1533	0.21	30	0.023	0.015	0.009	0.047	0.046	0.1
Canary Basin	12328-4	1	45	—	63	—	84	—	5.03	—	1.66	23	24	21	68	1.66	7230	0.325	0.455	0.607	1.39	0.492	120
Canary Basin	12336-1	1	38	—	51	—	61	—	3.39	—	0.44	23	25	19	67	0.44	1490	0.057	0.076	0.091	0.224	0.100	6.6
Canary Basin	12337-4	1	47	—	85	—	120	—	8.09	—	1.46	11	23	19	53	1.46	2280	0.107	0.194	0.274	0.575	0.121	33
Black Sea	1462K	1	25	—	50	—	48	—	2.35	—	4.52	15	32	19	66	4.52	5570	0.139	0.279	0.267	0.685	0.368	252
Black Sea	1474K	1	81	—	100	—	114	—	7.05	1.11	5.00	50	46	26	122	5.00	5570	0.451	0.557	0.635	1.64	0.680	279
West India Margin	KK187	1	78	—	195	—	234	—	—	—	3.40	—	—	—	—	3.40	4280	0.334	0.835	1.00	2.17	—	146
West India Margin	KK188	1	82	—	120	—	225	—	—	—	6.60	—	—	—	—	6.60	12800	1.05	1.54	2.88	5.47	—	845
West India Margin	KK210	1	67	—	86	—	109	—	—	—	4.50	—	—	—	—	4.50	3850	0.258	0.331	0.420	1.01	—	173
Kiel Bay	A-GC	6	38	4	77	22	119	7	5.10	0.67	5.18	15	38	55	108	5.18	54600	2.07	4.20	6.50	12.8	5.90	2830
Bornholm Basin	K1-878	7	32	6	54	18	107	7	—	—	4.28	—	—	—	—	4.28	38100	1.22	2.06	4.08	7.36	—	1630
Cariaco Trench	147A	7	39	7	73	9	124	18	6.65	1.37	5.50	10	12	41	63	5.50	18000	0.702	1.31	2.23	4.24	1.13	990
Peru Shelf	7706-39	1	60	—	86	—	91	—	4.04	—	12.5	42	55	41	138	12.5	31800	1.91	2.73	2.89	7.53	4.39	3980
Peru Shelf	7706-36	1	74	—	157	—	96	—	3.73	—	21.2	58	128	50	236	21.2	17800	1.32	2.79	1.71	5.82	4.20	3770
Saanich Inlet	—	13	49	—	61	—	77	—	—	—	3.58	—	—	—	—	3.58	93000	4.56	5.67	7.16	17.4	—	3330
Santa Barbara Basin	—	12	29	1	43	6	105	4	4.98	0.39	3.13	7	5	43	55	3.13	90000	2.61	3.87	9.45	15.9	4.95	2820
Santa Monica Basin	—	11	40	2	57	4	117	12	6.84	0.32	3.98	10	4	32	46	3.98	24000	0.960	1.37	2.81	5.14	1.10	955
San Pedro Basin	—	11	44	3	48	8	118	4	6.37	0.21	3.73	16	0	39	55	3.73	28000	1.23	1.34	3.30	5.87	1.54	1040
Soledad Basin	—	13	35	2	55	5	71	5	3.16	0.25	6.46	21	31	32	84	6.46	40000	1.40	2.20	2.84	6.44	3.36	2580
Gulf of California	BAV76 B29	20	31	—	29	—	50	—	3.51	—	4.39	15	2	6	23	4.39	33000	1.02	0.957	1.65	3.63	0.76	1450
Central N. Pacific	GPC-3	1	190	—	155	—	140	—	10.0	—	—	146	78	15	239	—	320	0.061	0.050	0.045	0.156	0.076	—
Average lithologies																							
Av. calcareous ooze		—	30	—	30	—	35	—	—	—	0.25	—	—	—	—	0.25	934	0.028	0.028	0.033	0.089	—	2.3
Av. siliceous ooze		—	—	—	—	—	—	—	—	—	0.50	—	—	—	—	0.50	225	0.110	0.030	0.060	0.200	—	1.1
Av. red clay		—	250	—	225	—	165	—	—	—	0.10	—	—	—	—	0.10	67	0.017	0.015	0.011	0.043	—	0.1
Mid-Cretaceous Site	Zone																						
367	L acut.	2	208	46	259	73	1400	1160	8.23	0.63	18.60	41	90	128	259	18.60	1280	0.266	0.332	1.79	2.39	—	238
367	E turr.*	17	119	77	157	74	362	227	4.20	2.05	5.82	78	89	62	229	5.82	680	0.081	0.107	0.246	0.434	0.176	40
386	L acut.	8	97	42	121	64	114	81	4.16	1.85	0.51	56	105	52	213	0.51	1500	0.146	0.182	0.171	0.499	0.344	7.7
386	E turr.	5	74	22	137	137	104	29	—	—	0.88	146	149	184	479	0.88	1320	0.098	0.181	0.137	0.416	0.281	12
386	P cret.	12	163	87	179	120	233	233	3.94	1.29	2.06	—	—	—	—	2.06	1390	0.227	0.249	0.324	0.800	0.666	29
389D	E turr.	9	62	44	—	—	84	41	—	—	—	—	—	—	—	—	700	0.043	—	0.059	—	—	—
398D	P cret.	17	117	146	132	54	281	345	7.90	2.31	1.63	82	71	183	336	1.63	9630	1.13	1.27	2.71	5.11	3.24	157
465A	E turr.	10	31	21	42	22	236	189	2.46	3.06	2.80	20	23	205	248	2.80	2750	0.085	0.116	0.649	0.850	0.682	77

Number of measurements (n), (Cu, Ni, Zn, Al) concentrations (means ±1 standard deviation), excess transition-metal (individual and combined (Tot.)) contents, organic-carbon contents, bulk accumulation rates, individual and combined (Tot.) transition-metal accumulation rates, total excess transition-metal accumulation rates (Ex.) and

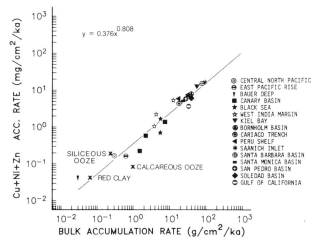

FIG. 10. Bulk accumulation rate and summed transition-metal accumulation rate in Holocene marine sediments. Regression line calculated using all data points except average lithologies (r = 0.967).

deep waters (Brumsack 1980; Thierstein *et al.* 1981).

Because of the considerable sample to sample variability, we have made new measurements of organic carbon, carbonate and metal concentrations on identical samples in eight mid-Cretaceous intervals with adequate biostratigraphic control (Bralower 1984). The organic-carbon measurements used to calculate accumulation rates are limited to those samples in which metal measurements were made (Tables 4 and 6). The eight intervals used are from North Atlantic Sites 367, 386 and 398D and Pacific Site 465A (Fig. 5) and the details are given in Bralower (1984).

Although considerable variability occurs, average transition-metal contents of mid-Cretaceous samples fall in the upper range of those measured in Holocene sediments (Table 6). Average accumulation rates of transition metals are consistently higher relative to the bulk accumulation rates in several mid-Cretaceous intervals when compared to the Holocene trend (Fig. 11). We therefore infer that at least some of the high metal contents in mid-Cretaceous bituminous intervals result from mechanisms other than the lack of sedimentary dilutants (Fig. 10). However because similarly high metal accumulation rates are not observed in Holocene pelagic and hemipelagic sediments, it is difficult with our data set to draw definite conclusions about the exact causes of mid-Cretaceous metal enrichments. Biological and euxinic hydrogenous processes appear likely explanations for the metal enrichments in black shales. In the following section we discuss a recently proposed attempt to differentiate among these sources.

Excess transition-metal accumulation rates

If the proportions of the transition metals introduced into marine sediments within the lattices of detrital minerals could be estimated and subtracted from the total transition-metal content, then the content and accumulation rates of the other, non-detrital (excess) transition-metal sources could be quantified. Previous studies (Thierstein *et al.* 1981; Brumsack 1983) have exposed a disparity in the relationship between the corrected (excess) transition-metal accumulation rate and the organic-carbon accumulation

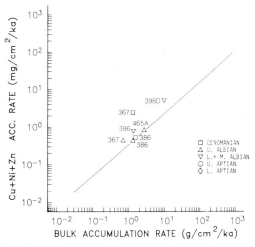

FIG. 11. Bulk accumulation rates and summed average transition-metal accumulation rates in various mid-Cretaceous intervals. Regression line describing Holocene trend from Fig. 10.

rate in different Holocene environments. Excess transition-metal accumulation rates are proportionally higher, relative to organic-carbon accumulation rates, in euxinic Black Sea Sites than they are in highly anoxic coastal upwelling sites. These anomalous transition-metal accumulation rates were perceived as a possible signature of the hydrogenous precipitation of metal sulphides in the Black Sea. We have tested this tenet in a wider range of environments including a coastal euxinic site (Cariaco Trench), deeper water oxic sites (Canary Basin) and in sites characterized by oxic hydrogenous (Bauer Deep) and hydrothermal (East Pacific Rise) metal precipitation.

To estimate the typical transition metal content of detritus, we have used the average of 200 shales with low organic carbon contents compiled by Wedepohl (1970). This shale standard has transition metal contents similar to those observed in the average suspended load of rivers entering the oceans (Chester & Aston 1976). To estimate the detrital amount of each transition metal in a sediment sample, we use the element Al the concentration of which in most surface sediments is largely controlled by the detrital input. In previous interpretations (e.g. Brumsack 1983) of excess transition-metal accumulation rates Fe has been used as the detrital index because of its greater availability in the published literature. However, since Fe can be sequestered from hydrothermal, hydrogenous and diagenetic precipitation, the excess transition-metal accumulation rate calculated in this way may also have

excluded some metal derived from non-detrital sources. The relative scarcity of published Al measurements has, however, led to the elimination of certain sites whose uncorrected transition-metal accumulation rates have been interpreted (Table 6).

We have used the measured Al content of the sediment and the metal/Al ratio of the average detrital shale standard to estimate the detrital proportion of any given transitional metal, i.e.:

$$\text{Excess Cu} = \text{Cu}_{\text{sample}} - \left(\text{Al}_{\text{sample}} \times \left[\frac{\text{Cu}}{\text{Al}}\right]_{\text{shale standard}}\right)$$

(Ratios of Cu, Ni and Zn to Al in the shale standard are 4.42, 7.70 and 12.46 respectively). In this way we have calculated the average excess transition-metal contents of sixteen Holocene Sites and six mid-Cretaceous intervals (Table 6). The excess transition-metal content is presumably associated with metal-organic compounds, although oxic- and euxinic-hydrogenous, hydrothermal, and diagenetic precipitation may also contribute. The excess transition-metal accumulation rates in Holocene cores and mid-Cretaceous intervals are shown in Fig. 12. Our present expanded Holocene data set includes oceanic and abyssal sites and thus allows a more differentiated interpretation than was possible in previous attempts (Thierstein *et al.* 1981). An overall correlation between excess-transition

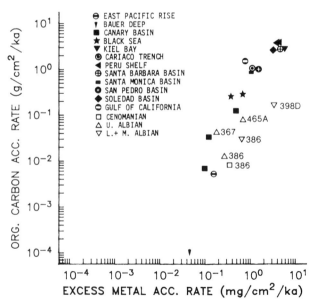

FIG. 12. Excess transition-metal (Cu, Ni, Zn) accumulation rates and organic-carbon accumulation rates in Holocene sediments and mid-Cretaceous intervals.

metal accumulation rate and organic-carbon accumulation rate exists and no Holocene site has an anomalously high excess transition-metal accumulation rate relative to the organic carbon accumulation rate. The correlation with organic-carbon accumulation rate (Fig. 12) indicates that metal-organic compounds control a significant proportion of the transition-metal flux to surface sediments. An examination of these organic carbon and transition-metal accumulation rate relationships indicates that no single process of metallogenesis appears to lead to a distinctly higher excess transition metal accumulation rate than any other. In particular, the observed relationships between the Black Sea, Cariaco Trench and the Canary Basin Sites suggests that euxinic hydrogenous precipitation does not leave an unequivocal signature on transitional-metal accumulation rate patterns. Euxinic hydrogenous precipitation may be limited by either sulphide, or more probably, by metal supply and thereby masked by the more significant detrital- and organic carbon-associated metal fluxes.

A comparison using Fe instead of Al as the detrital index has shown that the Fe-based excess transition-metal accumulation rates are lower than the Al-based ones by up to 50% but that the relative patterns are very similar to each other (Bralower 1984).

Generally, most of the mid-Cretaceous intervals show higher excess transition-metal accumulation rates relative to organic-carbon accumulation rates in comparison to Holocene Sites (Fig. 12). Hydrothermal activity has been or could be suspected in those mid-Cretaceous intervals which overlie volcanic basement, such as at Sites 386 and 465A. Euxinic hydrogenous and biological processes of metal enrichment may have operated in euxinic intervals such as the Cenomanian of Site 367. Diagenetic organic-carbon loss or metal enrichment through the precipitation of authigenic sulphide and carbonate minerals over long time intervals may also be a factor, although we have previously argued that it is unlikely that diagenetic changes have produced all of the differences between mid-Cretaceous and Holocene patterns. In addition, the possibly significant effects of petrology and hydrology of the detrital source terrain on the transition-metal contents of marine sediments need to be further investigated in Holocene nearshore settings. Perhaps several of these processes combined to produce the high transition-metal and excess transition-metal accumulation rates.

We conclude that transition-metal fluxes in oceanic sediments are highly variable and influenced by a number of processes which are difficult

to identify geochemically. Although hydrogenous transition-metal precipitation may occur in euxinic and anoxic basins, its signature in Holocene sediments cannot be detected unequivocally.

Palaeofertility in anoxic oceans

Fortunately other evidence is available which allows us to infer that ancient sediments were deposited in euxinic or oxygen deficient waters, where organic-carbon preservation factors were relatively high. Recently, for example, it has been shown that carbon/sulphur ratios of sediments appear to be strong indicators of ancient euxinic environments (Berner & Raiswell 1983; Leventhal 1983).

One of the most conclusive and readily available tracers for both anoxic and euxinic conditions, however, is the absence of benthic organisms and burrows in sediments. The lack of bioturbation leads to preservation of original laminations or sharp horizontal microbedding planes. The Holocene sediments recovered from euxinic or highly oxygen deficient deep-water environments are characterized by the complete absence of benthic fossils (e.g. Calvert 1964; Berger & Soutar 1970; Edgar *et al.* 1973; Ross & Degens 1974; Douglas 1981), by the excellent preservation of calcium carbonate shells such as aragonitic pteropods (Berger & Soutar 1970; Jung 1973) and by the presence of laminations (e.g. Calvert 1964; Edgar *et al.* 1973; Ross & Degens 1974; Douglas 1981). The laminations observed in Holocene sediments (Table 2) identify highly anoxic and euxinic deep-water environments with marine organic-carbon preservation factors of over 3% (Fig. 13).

Using this preservation factor index, we have determined primary production rates in three of the mid-Cretaceous intervals which are composed largely of laminated or microbedded bituminous sediments. In each of our mid-Cretaceous sections we have determined the relative proportions of laminated and microbedded versus burrowed intervals (for complete details, see Bralower & Thierstein 1984). The Upper Albian interval of DSDP Site 465A (equatorial Pacific) is laminated or microbedded throughout. Of the Cenomanian interval at DSDP Site 367 (eastern equatorial Atlantic), 85% is laminated or microbedded and over 70% of the Upper Albian interval at that site is laminated or microbedded. Other sections have significant proportions of bioturbated sediments, which must be partitioned out before primary production estimates can be derived (Bralower & Thierstein 1984).

If a conservative preservation factor estimate of 2%, taken from Holocene environments with

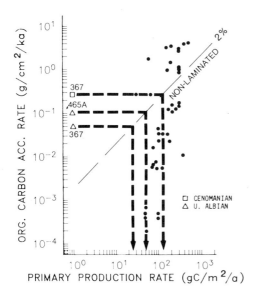

FIG. 13. Average primary productivity estimates for three mid-Cretaceous organic carbon-rich and dominantly laminated intervals are 25, 51 and 126 gC/ m²/a. Calculation based on measured sedimentary organic-carbon accumulation rates (corrected for small amounts of terrestrial kerogen) and an estimated organic-carbon preservation factor of 2%. Holocene sediments, indicated by dots, are non-laminated in settings with organic-carbon preservation factors below 2%.

(central N. Atlantic) (Bralower & Thierstein 1984). The highest primary production rates estimated for mid-Cretaceous oceanic intervals are still considerably lower than those measured in present-day high fertility areas.

Conclusions

1 Organic-carbon accumulation rates in Holocene marine sediments are dominantly controlled by sedimentation rate. Organic-carbon preservation factors are consistent environmental indicators. They are considerably higher in coastal areas and in basins with euxinic deep-waters (e.g. Black Sea) than in open ocean hemipelagic and pelagic regions. High organic-carbon preservation factors in ancient bituminous sediments can be predicted from the characteristic sedimentary structures of anoxic and euxinic basins such as lamination and microbedding. In such intervals, given reasonable stratigraphic time control, the organic-carbon accumulation rate divided by the organic-carbon preservation factor will yield a palaeoproductivity estimate.

2 Average organic-carbon accumulation rates in mid-Cretaceous intervals appear to be strongly influenced by factors other than sedimentation rate and water depth. Conservative estimates demonstrate that average productivity of mid-Cretaceous surface waters was never high by Holocene standards even in palaeo-upwelling settings.

3 Accumulation rates of the transition metals Cu, Ni and Zn in Holocene marine sediments are dominated by detrital and organic-matter supply. Precipitation of transition-metal sulphides in euxinic basins does not leave an unequivocal signature on Holocene metal accumulation rates. High mid-Cretaceous transition-metal accumulation rates have no clear modern analogue.

laminated or microbedded sediments, is applied to the Upper Albian at Site 465A and the Upper Albian and Cenomanian at Site 367, average primary production rates of 51, 25, and 126 g C/ m²/a respectively result (Fig. 13). Using a preservation factor of 2% instead of the 3% to 29% observed in Holocene environments with laminated sediments, allows for diagenetic organic-carbon losses of over 30%. More than at any of the other sites, the organic-carbon enrichments in these three intervals have previously been considered to have most likely resulted from high primary palaeoproductivity based on their palaeogeographic settings and the dominance of marine kerogen (Tissot *et al.* 1979; Summerhayes 1981; Thiede *et al.* 1982). Mid-Cretaceous intervals from other sites have lower organic-carbon accumulation rates, less upwelling-prone palaeogeographic settings, or show evidence for turbidite deposition and terrigenously derived kerogen. Their organic carbon enrichments are therefore even less likely to have been caused by high primary productivity. This is supported by palaeoproductivity estimates at DSDP Site 386

ACKNOWLEDGEMENTS: We gratefully acknowledge receipt of samples from Dr M. Hartmann (University of Kiel, Germany), the core collections of the Woods Hole Oceanographic Institution and the Deep Sea Drilling Project, funded by the National Science Foundation. Some of the organic carbon and trace element analyses were kindly made available to us by H.-J. Brumsack (University of Göttingen, Germany) and P. H. Roth (University of Utah). We thank H.-J. Brumsack, M. Kastner, and E. Suess for stimulating discussions, C. E. Reimers, D. Hirst and J. Thomson for helpful reviews of an earlier manuscript draft and J. E. Kaufman for laboratory assistance. Financial support was provided through National Science Foundation Grant OCE80-18515 and by Agip, Exxon, and Texaco oil companies.

References

ARTHUR, M. A. 1979. North Atlantic Cretaceous black shales: the record at Site 398 and a brief comparison with other occurrences. *In:* SIBUET, J.-C., RYAN, W. B. F. *et al. Init. Rep. Deep Sea Drilling Project*, v. **47**(2) U.S. Govt. Printing Office, Washington, D.C. 719–751.

—— & NATLAND, J. H. 1979. Carbonaceous sediments in the North and South Atlantic: the role of salinity in stable stratification of early Cretaceous basins. *In:* TALWANI, M., HAY, W. & RYAN, W. B. F. (eds) *Deep Drilling Results in the Atlantic Ocean; Continental Margins and Palaeoenvironment*, Maurice Ewing Series 3, Am. Geophys. Union Washington, D.C. 375–401.

BAINBRIDGE, A. E. 1981. *Geosecs Atlantic expedition. Volume 2. Sections and Profiles.* N.S.F. Washington D.C., 198 pp.

BARKER, P. F., DALZIEL, I. W. D. *et al.* 1976. *Init. Rep. Deep Sea Drilling Project, v.* **36**, U.S. Govt. Printing Office, Washington, D.C., 1080 pp.

BENNETT, E. B. 1963. An oceanographic atlas of the Eastern Tropical Ocean, based on data from Eastropic Expedition, October–December, 1955. *Inter-American Tropical Tuna Commission,* **8**, 31–165.

BERGER, W. H. 1974. Deep-sea sedimentation. *In:* BURK, C. A. & DRAKE, C. L. (eds), *The Geology of Continental Margins.* Springer-Verlag, New York, 213–241.

—— 1979. Impact of deep-sea drilling on paleoceanography. *In:* TALWANI, M., HAY, W. & RYAN, W. B. F. (eds) *Deep Drilling Results in the Atlantic Ocean; Continental Margins and Paleoenvironment,* Maurice Ewing Series 3, Am. Geophys. Union Washington, D.C. 297–314.

—— & SOUTAR, A. 1970. Preservation of plankton shells in an anaerobic basin off California. *Geol. Soc. Am. Bull.* **81**, 275–282.

—— & KILLINGLEY, J. S. 1982. Box cores from the equatorial Pacific: [14]C sedimentation rates and benthic mixing. *Marine Geol.* **45**, 93–125.

BERNER, R. A. 1974. Kinetic models for the early diagenesis of nitrogen, sulfur, phosphorus and silica in anoxic marine sediments. *In:* GOLDBERG, E. D. (ed.) *The Sea,* v. 5. Wiley, New York, 427–450.

—— 1982. Burial of organic carbon and pyrite sulfur in the modern ocean: its geochemical and environmental significance. *Am. Jour. Sci.* **282**, 451–473.

—— & RAISWELL, R. 1983. Burial of organic carbon and pyrite sulfur in sediments over Phanerozoic time: a new theory. *Geochim. Cosmochim. Acta,* **47**, 855–862.

BLECHSCHMIDT, G. 1979. Biostratigraphy of calcareous nannofossils: leg 47B, Deep Sea Drilling Project. *In:* SIBUET, J.-C., RYAN, W. B. F. *et al.,* Init. Rep. Deep Sea Drilling Project, v. **47**, pt. 2, U.S. Govt. Printing Office, Washington, D.C., 327–360.

BOLLI, H. M., RYAN, W. B. F. *et al.* 1978. *Init. Rep. Deep Sea Drilling Project,* **40**, U.S. Govt. Printing Office, Washington, D.C., 1079 pp.

BONATTI, E. 1975. Metallogenesis at oceanic spreading centers. *Annual Rev. Earth Planet. Sci.* **3**, 401–431.

BORDOVSKY, O. K. 1965. Accumulation and transformation of organic substances in marine sediments. *Marine Geol.* **3**, 3–114.

BOSTRÖM, K., KRAEMER, T. & GARTNER, S. 1973. Provenance and accumulation rates of opaline silica, Al, Ti, Fe, Mn, Cu, Ni and Co in Pacific pelagic sediments. *Chem. Geol.* **11**, 123–148.

——, JOENSUU, O. & BROHM, I. 1974. Plankton: Its chemical composition and its significance as a source of pelagic sediments. *Chem. Geol.* **14**, 255–271.

BOWDLER, J. L. 1978. *Mid-Cretaceous calcareous nannoplankton paleobiogeography and paleoceanography of the Atlantic Ocean.* Unpub. M.S. Thesis, Univ. of Utah, 182 pp.

BRALOWER, T. J. 1984. *Organic carbon and transition metal accumulation rates in Holocene and mid-Cretaceous marine sediments. Data and Techniques.* SIO Reference Series, **84** (214), 55pp.

BRALOWER, T. J. & THIERSTEIN, H. R. 1984. Low productivity and slow deep water circulation in mid-Cretaceous oceans. *Geology,* **12**, 614–618.

BREWER, P. G. & SPENCER, D. W. 1974. Distribution of some trace elements in Black Sea and their flux between dissolved and particulate phases. *In:* ROSS, D. A. & DEGENS, E. T. (eds) *The Black Sea — geology, chemistry and biology.* Am. Assoc. Petrol. Geol., Mem. **20**, 137–142.

BROOKS, J. 1978. Diagenesis of organic matter: some microbiological, chemical and geochemical studies of sedimentary organic matter. *In:* KRUMBEIN, W. E. (ed.) *Environmental biogeochemistry and geomicrobiology. Vol. 1. The aquatic environment.* Ann. Arbor Science, 287–308.

—— 1981. Organic maturation of sedimentary organic matter and petroleum exploration: a review. *In:* BROOKS, J. (ed.) *Organic Maturation Studies and Fossil Fuel Exploration.* Academic Press, London, 1–37.

BROOKS, R. R., KAPLAN, I. R. & PETERSON, M. N. 1969. Trace element composition of Red Sea geothermal brine and interstitial water. *In:* DEGENS, E. T. & ROSS, D. A. (eds) *Hot Brines and Recent Heavy Metal Deposits in the Red Sea.* Springer-Verlag, New York, 180–203.

BROWN, F. S., BAEDECKER, M. J., NISSENBAUM, A. & KAPLAN, I. R. 1972. Early diagenesis in a reducing fjord, Saanich Inlet, British Columbia.—III. Changes in organic constituents of sediment. *Geochim. Cosmochim. Acta,* **36**, 1185–1203.

BRULAND, K. W., BERTINE, K., KOIDE, M. & GOLDBERG, E. D. 1974. History of metal pollution in Southern California Coastal Zone. *Environ. Sci. and Tech.,* **8**, 425–432.

BRUMSACK, H.-J. 1979. *Geochemische Untersuchungen an kretazischen Atlantik-Schwarzschiefern der Legs 11, 14, 36 und 41 (DSDP).* Ph.D. Thesis Universtität zu Göttingen, 57 pp. (unpubl).

—— 1980. Geochemistry of Cretaceous black shales from the Atlantic Ocean (DSDP legs 11, 14, 36 and 41). *Chem. Geol.* **31**, 1–25.

—— 1983. A note on Cretaceous black shales and

recent sediments from oxygen deficient environments: paleoceanographic implications. *In*: SUESS, E. & THIEDE, J. (eds) *Coastal Upwelling; its sediment record. Part 1*. Plenum Press, New York, 471–484.

CALVERT, S. E. 1964. Factors affecting distribution of laminated diatomaceous sediments in Gulf of California. *In*: VAN ANDEL, T. H. & SHOR, G. G. Jr. (eds) *Marine Geology of the Gulf of California. Am. Assoc. Petrol. Geol. Mem.* **3**, 311–330.

—— 1976. The mineralogy and geochemistry of nearshore sediments. *In*: RILEY, J. P. & CHESTER, R. (eds) *Chemical Oceanography, v. 6*. Academic Press, London, 188–280.

CAMERON, D. H. 1976. Grain size and Carbon/Carbonate Analyses, Leg 36. *In*: BARKER, P. F., DALZIEL, I. W. D. *et al. Init. Rep. Deep Sea Drilling Project,* **36**, U.S. Govt. Printing Office, Washington, D.C., 1047–1050.

—— 1979. Grain size and carbon/carbonate analyses, Leg 43. *In*: TUCHOLKE, B. E., VOGT, P. R. *et al. Init. Rep. Deep Sea Drilling Project,* **43**, U.S. Govt. Printing Office, Washington, D.C., 1043–1047.

CARATINI, C., BELLET, J. & TISSOT, C. 1978. Etude microscopique de la matière organique: palynologie et palynofaciès. *In*: ARNOULD, M. & PELET, R. (eds) *Géochimie organique des sédiments marins profonds, Orgon II* (Ed. CNRS, Paris), 157–178.

——, BELLET, J. & TISSOT, C. 1979. Etude microscopique de la matière organique: palynologie et palynofaciès. *In*: ARNOULD, M. & PELET, R. (eds) *Géochimie organique des sédiments marins profonds, Orgon III* (Ed. CNRS, Paris), 215–265.

CĔPEK, P. 1978. Mesozoic calcareous nannoplankton of the eastern North Atlantic, Leg 41. *In*: LANCELOT, Y., SEIBOLD, E. *et al. Init. Rep. Deep Sea Drilling Project, v.* **41**. U.S. Govt. Printing Office, Washington, D.C., 667–687.

CHAMLEY, H., DEBRABANT, P., FOULON, J. *et al.* 1979. Mineralogy and geochemistry of Cretaceous and Cenozoic Atlantic sediments of the Iberian Peninsula (Site 398D, DSDP Leg 47B). *In*: SIBUET, J-C., RYAN, W. B. F. *et al., Init. Rep. Deep Sea Drilling Project,* **47**, pt. 2, U.S. Govt. Printing Office, Washington, D.C., 429–449.

CHESTER, R. & ASTON, S. R. 1976. The geochemistry of deep sea sediments. *In*: RILEY, J. P. & CHESTER, R. (eds) *Chemical Oceanography, v. 6*. Academic Press, London, 281–390.

CORLISS, B. H., HOLLISTER, C. D. *et al.* 1982. A paleoenvironmental model for Cenozoic sedimentation in the Central Pacific. *In*: SCRUTTON, R. A. & TALWANI, M. (eds) *The Ocean Floor*. Wiley, London, 277–304.

CRAIG, H., BROECKER, W. S. & SPENCER, D. 1981. *Geosecs Pacific Expedition. Volume 4. Sections and Profiles*. N.S.F. Washington D.C., 251 pp.

CURTIS, C. D. 1980. Diagenetic alteration in black shales. *J. Geol. Soc. London,* **137**, 189–194.

DEAN, W. E. 1981. Calcium carbonate and organic carbon in samples from deep sea drilling project sites 463, 464, 465 and 466. *In*: THIEDE, J., VALLIER, T. L. *et al.* 1981. *Init. Rep. Deep Sea Drilling Project.* **62**, U.S. Govt. Printing Office, Washington, D.C., 869–876.

——, GARDNER, J. V., JANSA, L. F., CĔPEK, P. & SEIBOLD, E. 1978. Cyclic sedimentation along the continental margin of Northwest Africa. *In*: LANCELOT, Y., SEIBOLD, E. *et al. Init. Rep. Deep Sea Drilling Project, v.* **41**. U.S. Govt. Printing Office, Washington, D.C. 965–989.

DEGENS, E. T. & MOPPER, K. 1976. Organic Material in Marine Sediments. *In*: RILEY, J. P. & CHESTER, R. (eds) *Chemical Oceanography, v. 6*. Academic Press, London, 59–113.

DEGENS, E. T. & STOFFERS, P. 1977. Phase boundaries as an instrument for metal concentrations in geological systems. *In*: KLEMM, D. D. & SCHNEIDER, H-J. (eds) *Time- and Strata-Bound Ore Deposits*. Springer-Verlag, Berlin, 25–45.

DEMAISON, G. J. & MOORE, G. T. 1980. Anoxic environments and oil source bed genesis. *Org. Geochem.,* **2**, 9–31.

DEROO, G. & HERBIN, J. P. 1983. The nature, origin, and distribution of organic material at Deep Sea Drilling Sites 482 through 485, Leg 65, in the Gulf of California. *In*: LEWIS, B. T. R., ROBINSON, P. *et al., Init. Rep. Deep Sea Drilling Project,* **65**, U.S. Govt. Printing Office, Washington D.C., 431–437.

DEUSER, W. G. 1973. Cariaco Trench: oxidation of organic matter and residence time of anoxic water. *Nature,* **242**, 601–603.

DE VOOYS, C. G. N. 1979. Primary Production in Aquatic Environments. *In*: BOLIN, B., DEGENS, E. T., KEMPE, S. & KETNER, P. (eds) *The Global Carbon Cycle*. Wiley, New York, 259–292.

DIESTER-HAASS, L. 1975. Sedimentation and climate in the Late Quaternary between Senegal and the Cape Verde Islands. *'Meteor' Forschungsergebnisse,* **20C**, 1–32.

DONEGAN, D. P. 1982. *Modern and ancient marine rhythmites from the sea of Cortez and California continental borderland: a sedimentological study*. M.S. thesis, Oregon State Univ., (Unpubl.) 123 pp.

DOUGLAS, R. G. 1981. Paleoecology of continental margin basins: a modern core history from the borderland of Southern California. *In*: DOUGLAS, R. G. (ed) *Deposition Systems of Active Continental Margin Basins: short course notes*. SEPM Pacific Section, 121–156.

DUNBAR, R. B. 1981. *Sedimentation and the history of upwelling and climate in high fertility areas of the northeastern Pacific Ocean*. Ph.D. Thesis, University of California, San Diego, (Unpubl.) 234 pp.

DURAND, B. 1980. *Kerogen*. Ed. Tecnip, Paris, France, 519 pp.

DYMOND, J. 1981. The geochemistry of Nazca plate surface sediments: an evaluation of hydrothermal, biogenic, detrital, and hydrogenous sources. *In*: KULM, L. D., DYMOND, J., DASCH, E. J. & HUSSONG, D. M. (eds) *Nazca plate: crustal formation and Andean convergence. Geol. Soc. Am. Mem.* **154**, 133–173.

—— & VEEH, H. H. 1975. Metal accumulation rates in the Southeast Pacific and the origin of metalliferous sediments. *Earth Planet. Sci. Lett.,* **28**, 13–22.

EDGAR, N. T., SAUNDERS, J. B. *et al.* 1973. *Init. Rep. Deep Sea Drilling Project,* **15**, U.S. Govt. Printing Office, Washington D.C.

EDMOND, J. M., MEASURES, C. *et al.* 1979. On the formation of metal rich deposits at ridge crests. *Earth Planet. Sci. Lett.,* **46**, 19–31.

EMERY, K. O. 1960. *The sea off Southern California, A modern habitat of petroleum.* Wiley, New York, 366 pp.

——, HUNT, J. M. & HAYS, E. E. 1969. Summary of hot brines and heavy metal deposits in the Red Sea. *In:* DEGENS, E. T. & ROSS, D. A. (eds) *Hot Brines and Recent Heavy Metal Deposits in the Red Sea.* Springer-Verlag, New York, 557–571.

ERDMAN, J. G. & SCHORNO, K. S. 1978. Geochemistry of carbon: Deep Sea Drilling Project, Legs 42A and 42B. *In:* ROSS, D. A., NEPROCHNOV, Y. P. *et al., Init. Rep. Deep Sea Drilling Project,* **42**, *pt. 2,* U.S. Govt. Printing Office, Washington, D.C., 717–721.

ERLENKEUSER, H. 1980. ^{14}C age and vertical mixing of deep-sea sediments. *Earth Planet. Sci. Lett.,* **47**, 319–326.

——, SUESS, E. & WILLKOMM, H. 1974. Industrialization affects heavy metal and carbon isotope concentrations in recent Baltic Sea sediments. *Geochim. Cosmochim. Acta,* **38**, 823–842.

FISCHER, A. G. & ARTHUR, M. A. 1977. Secular variations in the pelagic realm. *In:* COOK, H. E. & ENOS, P. (eds), *Deep Water Carbonate Environments.* SEPM Spec. Publ. **25**, 19–50.

FONSELIUS, H. 1974. Phosphorus in Black Sea. *In:* DEGENS, E. T. & ROSS, D. A. (eds) *The Black Sea—geology, chemistry and biology.* Am. Assoc. Pet. Geol. Mem. **20**, 183–199.

FORESMAN, J. B. 1978. Organic geochemistry DSDP Leg 40, continental rise of Southwest Africa. *In:* BOLLI, H. M., RYAN, W. B. F. *et al. Init. Rep. Deep Sea Drilling Project,* **40**, U.S. Govt. Printing Office, Washington D.C. 557–567.

FÖRSTNER, U. & WITTMAN, G. T. W. 1979. *Metal pollution in the aquatic environment.* Springer-Verlag, New York, 486 pp.

FROELICH, P. N., KLINKHAMMER, G. P., BENDER, M. L., LUEDTKE, N. A., HEATH, G. R., CULLEN, D., DAUPHIN, P. 1979. Early oxidation of organic matter in pelagic sediments of the eastern equatorial Atlantic: suboxic diagenesis. *Geochim. Cosmochim. Acta,* **43**, 1075–1090.

GARDNER, J. V. 1982. High resolution carbonate and organic-carbon stratigraphies for the late Neogene and Quaternary from the western Caribbean and eastern Equatorial Pacific. *In:* PRELL, W. L., GARDNER, J. V. *et al., Init. Rep. Deep Sea Drilling Project,* **68**, U.S. Govt. Printing Office, Washington, D.C., 347–364.

GIBBS, R. 1973. Mechanisms of trace metal transport in rivers. *Science,* **180**, 71–73.

GORMLY, J. R. & SACKETT, W. M. 1977. Carbon isotope evidence for the maturation of marine lipids. *In:* CAMPOS, R. & GONI, J. (eds) *Advances in Organic Geochemistry—1975.* Enadisma, Madrid, 321 pp.

GRACIANSKY, P. D. de, BROSSE, E. *et al.* 1982. Les formations d'âge Crétacé de l'Atlantique Nord et leur matière organique: paléogéographie et milieux de dépôt. *Rev. Inst. France Petrol.,* **37**, 275–336.

GRASSHOFF, K. & VOIPIO, A. 1981. Chemical Ocean-ography. *In:* VOIPIO, A. (ed) *The Baltic Sea.* Elsevier, New York, 183–213.

GRUNDMANIS, V. & MURRAY, J. W. 1982. Aerobic respiration in pelagic marine sediments. *Geochim. Cosmochim. Acta,* **46**, 1101–1120.

GUCLUER, S. M. & GROSS, M. G. 1964. Recent marine sediments in Saanich Inlet, a stagnant marine basin. *Limnol. Oceanog.* **9**, 359–376.

HABIB, D. 1979. Sedimentary origins of North Atlantic Cretaceous palynofacies. *In:* TALWANI, M., HAY, W. & RYAN, W. B. F. (eds) *Deep Drilling Results in the Atlantic Ocean; Continental Margins and Paleoenvironment,* Maurice Ewing Series 3, Am. Geophys. Union Washington, D.C. 420–437.

HARLAND, W. B., COX, A. V., LLEWELLYN, P. G., PICKTON, C. A. G., SMITH, A. G. & WALTERS, R. 1982. *A Geologic Time Scale.* Cambridge Univ. Press.

HARTMANN, M., MÜLLER, P. J., SUESS, E. & VAN DER WEIJDEN, C. H. 1973. *Oxidation of organic matter in recent marine sediments. 'Meteor' Forschungsergeb-nisse* **12C**, 74–86.

——, MÜLLER, P. J., SUESS, E. & VAN DER WEIJDEN, C. H. 1976. Chemistry of late Quaternary sediments and their interstitial waters from the NW African continental margin. *'Meteor' Forschungsergebnisse* **24C**, 1–67.

HAYES, D. E., PIMM, A. C. *et al.* 1972. *Init. Rep. Deep Sea Drilling Project, v. 14,* U.S. Govt. Printing Office, Washington, D.C., 975 pp.

HEATH, G. R., MOORE, T. C., Jr. & DAUPHIN, J. P. 1977. Organic carbon in deep-sea sediments. *In:* ANDERSEN, N. R. & MALAHOFF, A. (eds) *The Fate of Fossil Fuel CO$_2$ in the oceans.* Plenum, New York, 605–625.

HEDGES, J. I. & VAN GEEN, A. 1982. A comparison of lignin and stable carbon isotope compositions in Quaternary marine sediments. *Marine Chemistry,* **11**, 43–54.

HEIN, J. R., KOSKI, R. A. & MORGENSON, L. A. 1982. Uranium and thorium enrichment in rocks from the base of DSDP Hole 465A. Hess Rise, Central North Pacific. *Chem. Geol.* **36**, 237–251.

HIRST, D. M. 1974. Geochemistry of sediments from eleven Black Sea cores. *In:* DEGENS, E. T. & ROSS, D. A., *The Black Sea—geology, chemistry, and biology.* Am. Assoc. Petrol. Geol., Mem. **20**, 430–455.

HOLLAND, H. D. 1979. Metals in black shales—a reassessment. *Econ. Geol.* **7417**, 1676–1680.

HONJO, S. 1980. Material fluxes and modes of sedimentation in the mesopelagic and bathypelagic zones. *Jour. Mar. Res.* **38**, 53–97.

HORN, D. R., DELACH, M. N. & HORN, B. M. 1974. Physical properties of sedimentary provinces, North Pacific and North Atlantic Oceans. *In:* INDER-BITZEN, A. L. (ed) *Deep Sea Sediments.* Plenum, New York, 417–441.

HÜLSEMANN, J. 1966. On the routine analysis of carbonates in unconsolidated sediments. *J. Sed. Petrol.* **36**, 622–625.

IBACH, L. E. J. 1982. Relationship between sedimentation rate and total organic carbon content in ancient marine sediments. *Am. Assoc. Petrol. Geol. Bull.* **66**, 170–188.

IRVING, E., NORTH, F. K. & COUILLARD, R. 1974. Oil, climate, and tectonics. *Canadian Journal of Earth Sciences,* **11**, 1–17.

JANACEK, T. R. & REA, D. K. Eolian deposition in the Northeast Pacific Ocean: Cenozoic history of atmospheric circulation. *Geol. Soc. Am. Bull.*

JENKYNS, H. C. 1980. Cretaceous anoxic events: from continents to oceans. *J. Geol. Soc. London,* **137**, 171–188.

JUNG, P. 1973. Pleistocene pteropods—Leg 15, Site 147, Deep Sea Drilling Project. *In:* EDGAR, N. T., SAUNDERS, J. B. *et al. Init. Rep. Deep Sea Drilling Project,* U.S. Govt. Printing Office, Washington, D.C., 753–767.

JOHNSON, T. C. 1975. *Dissolution of siliceous microfossils in deep sea sediments.* Unpub. Ph.D. Thesis, University of California, San Diego, 163 pp.

KAISER, W. & SCHULZ, S. 1975. On primary production in the Baltic. *Merent. Julk./Havsforsk. Skr. No.* **239**, 29–33.

KAPLAN, I. R., SWEENEY, R. F. & NISSENBAUM, A. 1969. Sulfur isotope studies on Red Sea geothermal brines and sediments. *In:* DEGENS, E. T. & ROSS, D. A. (eds) *Hot Brines and Recent Heavy Metal Deposits in the Red Sea.* Springer-Verlag, New York, 474–498.

KENDRICK, J. W. 1973. *Trace element studies of metalliferous sediments in cores from the East Pacific Rise and Bauer deep, 10°S.* M.S. Thesis, Oregon State Univ., 117 pp. (Unpubl.)

KENNEDY, W. J. & ODIN, G. S. 1982. The Jurassic and Cretaceous time scale in 1981. *In:* ODIN, G. S. (ed) *Numerical Dating in Stratigraphy, v. 1.* Wiley, London, 557–592.

KOBLENTZ-MISHKE, O. J., VOLKOVINSKY, V. V. & KABANOVA, J. R. 1970. Plankton primary production of the world ocean. *In:* WOOSTER, W. S. (ed) *Scientific Exploration of the South Pacific,* 183–193.

LAL, D., 1977. The oceanic microcosm of particles. *Science,* **198**, 997–1009.

LANCELOT, Y., HATHAWAY, J. C. & HOLLISTER, C. D. 1972. Lithology of sediments from the Western North Atlantic Leg 11 of the DSDP. *In:* HOLLISTER, C. D., EWING, J. I. *et al. Init. Rep. Deep Sea Drilling Project,* v. **41**, U.S. Govt. Printing Office, Washington, D.C. 901–949.

LANGE, J., WEDEPOHL, K. H., HEINRICHS, H. & GOHN, E. 1978. Notes about the specific composition of 'Black Shales' from Site 367 (Leg 41). *In:* LANCELOT, Y., SEIBOLD, E. *et al., Init. Rep. Deep Sea Drilling Project* **41**, U.S. Govt. Printing Office, Washington, D.C., 875–877.

LANPHERE, M. A. & JONES, D. L. 1978. Cretaceous time scale from North America. *In:* COHEE, G. V. *et al.* (eds) *Geologic Time Scale, Am. Assoc. Petrol. Geol. Studies in Geology, No. 6,* 259–269.

LEINEN, M. & STAKES, D. 1979. Metal accumulation rates in the Central Equatorial Pacific during Cenozoic time. *Geol. Soc. Am. Bull., Part 1,* **90**, 357–375.

LEVENTHAL, J. S. 1983. An interpretation of carbon and sulfur relationships in Black Sea sediments as indicators of environments of deposition. *Geochim. Cosmochim. Acta,* **47**, 133–137.

LISITZIN, A. P. 1972. *Sedimentation in the world ocean. S.E.P.M. Spec. Publ.* **17**, 218 pp.

LUDWIG, W. J., KRASHENINIKOV, V. *et al. Site 511, summary. Init. Rep. Deep Sea Drilling Project,* **71**, U.S. Govt. Printing Office, Washington, D.C.

MCMURTY, G. M., VEEH, H. H. & MOSER, C. 1981. Sediment accumulation rate patterns on the northwest Nazca Plate. *Geol. Soc. Am. Mem.* **154**, 211–250.

MAILLOT, H. & ROBERT, C. 1980. Minéralogie et géochimie des sédiments Crétacés et Cénozoiques dans l'Océan Atlantique Sud. (Marge Africaine, dorsale Médio-Atlantique). *Bull. Soc. Geol. France,* **22**, 779–789.

MANHEIM, F. T. & CHAN, K. M. 1974. Interstitial waters of Black Sea sediments: New data and review. *In:* DEGENS, E. T. & ROSS, D. A., *The Black Sea—geology, chemistry and biology.* Am. Assoc. Petrol. Geol. Mem. **20**, 155–180.

MANIVIT, H., PERCH-NIELSEN, K., PRINS, B. & VERBEEK, J. W. 1977. Mid-Cretaceous calcareous nannofossil biostratigraphy. *Koninklijke Nederlandse Akademie van Wetenschappen, series B,* v. **80**, June 10, 169–181.

MARCHIG, V. 1972. Zur Geochemie rezenter sedimente des Indischen Ozeans. *'Meteor' Forschungsergebnisse.* **11C**, 1–104.

MARTIN, J. H. & KNAUER, G. A. 1973. The elemental composition of plankton. *Geochim. Cosmochim. Acta,* **37**, 1639–1653.

MATSUMOTO, E. & WONG, C. S. 1977. Heavy metal sedimentation in Saanich Inlet measured with ^{210}Pb technique. *Jour. Geophys. Res.* **82**, 5477–5482.

MONTADERT, L., ROBERTS, D. G. *et al.* 1979. *Init. Rep. Deep Sea Drilling Project,* **48**, U.S. Govt. Printing Office, Washington, D.C., 1183 pp.

MOORE, T. C., HEATH, G. R., KOWSMANN, R. O. 1973. Biogenic sediments of the Panama Basin. *Jour. Geol.,* **81**, 458–472.

MOPPER, K., MICHAELIS, W., GARRASI, C. & DEGENS, E. 1978. Sugars, amino acids, and hydrocarbons in Black Sea Sediment from DSDP Leg 42B cores. *In:* ROSS, D. A., NEPROCHNOV, Y. P. *et al., Init. Rep. Deep Sea Drilling Project,* **42**, pt. 2, U.S. Govt. Printing Office, Washington, D.C., 697–705.

MÜLLER, C. 1979. Calcareous nannofossils from the North Atlantic (leg 48). *In:* MONTADERT, L., ROBERTS, D. G. *et al. Init. Rep. Deep Sea Drilling Project,* **48**, U.S. Govt. Printing Office, Washington, D.C., 589–639.

MÜLLER, P. J. 1975. Diagenese stickstoffhaltiger organischer Substanzen in oxischen und anoxischen marinen Sedimenten. *'Meteor' Forschungsergebnisse,* **22C**, 1–60.

—— & MANGINI, A. 1980. *Organic carbon decomposition rates in sediments of the Pacific manganese nodule belt dated by* ^{230}*Th and* ^{231}*Pa. Earth Planet. Sci. Lett.* **51**, 94–114.

—— & SUESS, E. 1979. Productivity, sedimentation rate and sedimentary organic carbon in the oceans. 1. Organic carbon preservation. *Deep Sea Res.* **26A**, 1347–1362.

MURDMAA, I. O., GORDEEV, V. V., EMELYANOV, E. M., SHIRSHOV, P. P. & BAZILEVSKAYA, E. S. 1978.

Inorganic geochemistry of Leg 43 sediments. *In*:
TUCHOLKE, B. E., VOGT, P. R. *et al.*, *Init. Rep. Deep
Sea Drilling Project, v.* **43**, U.S. Govt. Printing
Office, Washington, D.C., 675–694.

MURRAY, J. W., GRUNDMANIS, V. & SMETHIE, W. M.
1978. Interstitial water chemistry in the sediments
of Saanich Inlet. *Geochim. Cosmochim. Acta*, **42**,
1011–1026.

NISSENBAUM, A., PRESLEY, B. J. & KAPLAN, I. R. 1972.
Early diagenesis in a reducing fjord, Saanich Inlet,
British Columbia: I. Chemical and isotopic changes
in major components of interstitial water. *Geochim.
Cosmochim. Acta*, **36**, 1007–1027.

OBRADOVICH, J. D. & COBBAN, W. A. 1975. A time
scale for the Late Cretaceous of the Western Interior
of North America. *Geol. Soc. Canada Spec. Paper,
no.* **13**, 31–54.

—— & COBBAN, W. A. 1977. Speculations on the Age
Span of the Albian Stage (Early Cretaceous). *Geol.
Soc. Am. Abstract,* **9**, 1345.

OKADA, H. & THIERSTEIN, H. R. 1979. Calcareous
nannoplankton. Leg 43, Deep Sea Drilling Project.
In: TUCHOLKE, B. E., VOGT, P. R. *et al. Init. Rep.
Deep Sea Drilling Project,* **43**, U.S. Govt. Printing
Office, Washington, D.C., 507–573.

PARRISH, J. T. & CURTIS, R. L. 1982. Atmospheric
circulation, upwelling and organic-rich rocks in the
Mesozoic and Cenozoic Eras. *Palaeogeog. Palaeoclim. Palaeoecol.* **40**, 31–66.

PARSONS, T. R., STEPHENS, K. & LE BRASSEUR, R. J.
1969. Production studies in the Strait of Georgia.
Part 1. Primary production under the Fraser River
Plume. February to May, 1967. *J. exp. mar. Biol.
Ecol.* **3**, 27–38.

PEDERSEN, T. F. 1983. Increased productivity in the
eastern equatorial Pacific during the last glacial
maximum (19,000–14,000 yr. B.P.). *Geology,* **11**, 16–
19.

PELET, R. & DEBYSER, Y. 1977. Organic geochemistry
of Black Sea cores. *Geochim. Cosmochim. Acta,* **41**,
1575–1586.

PLATT, T. & SUBBA RAO, V. 1975. *Primary production of
marine microphytes. In: Photosynthesis and Productivity in Different Environments, International Biological
Programme, v.* **3**, Cambridge University Press, 249–
280.

PRESLEY, B. J., KOLODNY, Y., NISSENBAUM, A. &
KAPLAN, I. R. 1972. Early diagenesis in a reducing
fjord, Saanich Inlet. British Columbia—II. Trace
element distribution in interstitital water and
sediment. *Geochim. Cosmochim. Acta,* **36**, 1073–
1090.

PRICE, N. B. 1976. Chemical diagenesis in sediments.
In: RILEY, J. P. & CHESTER, R. (eds) *Chemical
Oceanography,* **6**. Academic Press, London, 1–58.

PROTO-DECIMA, F., MEDIZZA, F. & TODESCO, L. 1978.
Southeastern Atlantic Leg 40 Calcareous nannofos-
sils. *In*: BOLLI, H. M., RYAN, W. B. F. *et al. Init.
Rep. Deep Sea Drilling Project,* **40**, U.S. Govt.
Printing Office, Washington, D.C., 571–634.

REID, J. L., Jr. 1965. Intermediate waters of the Pacific
ocean. *Johns Hopkins Oceanographic Studies, No. 2.*
Johns Hopkins Press, Baltimore, 85 pp.

REIMERS, C. E. 1981. *Sedimentary organic matter:*

distribution and alteration processes in the coastal
upwelling region off Peru. Ph.D. thesis, Oregon State
Univ. (Unpubl.) 219 pp.

RICHARDS, F. A. 1965. Anoxic basins and fjords. *In*:
RILEY, J. P. & SKIRROW, G. (eds) *Chemical
Oceanography* v. 1. Academic Press, New York,
611–655.

—— 1976. The Cariaco basin (Trench), *Oceanogr. Mar.
Biol. Am. Rev.* **13**, 11–67.

ROSS, D. A. & DEGENS, E. T. 1974. Recent sediments
of Black Sea. *In*: DEGENS, E. T. & ROSS, D. A. (eds)
*The Black Sea—geology, chemistry, and biology. Am.
Assoc. Pet. Geol., Mem.* **20**, 183–199.

ROTH, P. H. 1981. Mid-Cretaceous calcareous nannoplankton from the Central Pacific: Implications
for Paleoceanography. *In*: THIEDE, J., VALLIER,
T. L. *et al. Init. Rep. Deep Sea Drilling Project,* **61**,
U.S. Govt. Printing Office, Washington, D.C.,
471–489.

—— & THIERSTEIN, H. R. 1972. Calcareous nannoplankton: Leg 14 of the DSDP. *In*: HAYES, D. E.,
PIMM, A. C. *et al. Init. Rep. Deep Sea Drilling Project,*
14, U.S. Govt. Printing Office, Washington, D.C.,
421–485.

ROTH, P. H. & BOWDLER, J. 1981. Middle Cretaceous
calcareous nannoplankton biogeography and ocean-
ography of the Atlantic Ocean. *In*: WARME, J. E.,
DOUGLAS, R. G. & WINTERER, E. L. (eds) *The Deep
Sea Drilling Project: a Decade of Progress.* SEPM,
Spec. Publ. **32**, 517–546.

RYAN, W. B. F. & CITA, M. B. 1977. Ignorance
concerning episodes of ocean-wide stagnation. *Mar.
Geol.* **23**, 197–215.

SAUNDERS, J. B., EDGAR, N. T., DONNELLY, T. W. &
HAY, W. W. 1973. Cruise synthesis. *In*: EDGAR, N.
T., SAUNDERS, J. B. *et al. Init. Rep. Deep Sea Drilling
Project,* **15**, U.S. Govt. Printing Office, Washington,
D.C., 1077–1111.

SAXBY, J. D. 1973. Diagenesis of metal-organic complexes in sediments: formation of metal sulfides
from cysteine complexes. *Chem. Geol.* **12**, 241–288.

SCHLANGER, S. O. & CITA, M. B. 1983. *Nature and
Origin of Cretaceous Carbon-rich Facies.* Academic
Press, London, 229 pp.

SCHLANGER, S. O. & JENKYNS, H. C. 1976. Cretaceous
oceanic anoxic events: causes and consequences.
Geologie en Mijnbouw, **55**, 179–184.

SEIBOLD, E. & BERGER, W. H. 1982. *The Sea Floor.*
Springer-Verlag, New York, 288 pp.

SHANKS, A. L. & TRENT, J. D. 1980. Marine snow:
sinking rates and potential role in vertical flux.
Deep-sea Res. **27A**, 137–143.

SHANKS, W. C. III & BISCHOFF, J. L. 1980. Geochemistry, sulfur isotope composition and accumulation
rates of Red Sea geothermal deposits. *Econ. Geol.*
75, 445–459.

SHIMKUS, K. M. & TRIMONIS, E. S. 1974. Modern
sedimentation in the Black Sea. *Am. Assoc. Petrol.
Geol. Mem.* **20**, 249–278.

SIBUET, J.-C. & RYAN, W. B. F. 1979. *Init. Rep. Deep
Sea Drilling Project,* **47**, pt. 2, U.S. Govt. Printing
Office, Washington, D.C., 787 pp.

SPENCER, D. W., BREWER, P. G., FLEER, A., HONJO,
S., KRISHNASWAMI, S. & NOZAKI, Y. 1978. Chemical

fluxes from a sediment trap experiment in the Deep Sargasso sea. *Jour. Mar. Res.* **36**, 493–523.

—— and STIE members, 1981. The sediment trap intercomparison experiment: some preliminary data. *In*: ANDERSON, R. F. & BACON, M. P. (eds) *Sediment trap intercalibration experiment, Woods Hole Oceanographic Institution Technical Memorandum.* 1–81, 57–104.

SPIKER, E. C. & SIMONEIT, B. R. T. 1982. Radiocarbon dating of sediments from the Cariaco Trench, Deep Sea Drilling Project Site 147. *In*: WATKINS, J. S., MOORE, J. C. *et al. Init. Rep. Deep Sea Drilling Project,* **66**, U.S. Govt. Printing Office, Washington, D.C., 863–864.

STACKELBURG, V. V. 1972. Faziesverteilung in Sedimenten des indisch pakistanischen Kontinentalrandes. *'Meteor' Forschungsergebnisse.* **9C**, 1–73.

SUESS, E. 1980. Particulate organic carbon flux in the oceans—surface productivity and oxygen utilization. *Nature*, **288**, 260–263.

—— & ERLENKEUSER, H. 1975. History of metal pollution and carbon input in Baltic Sea sediments. *Meyniana*, **27**, 63–75.

SUMMERHAYES, C. P. 1981. Organic facies of middle Cretaceous black shales in deep North Atlantic. *Am. Assoc. Petrol. Geol. Bull.* **64**, 2364–2380.

THIEDE, J. 1977. Aspects of the variability of the glacial and interglacial North Atlantic eastern boundary current (last 150,000 years). *'Meteor' Forschungsergebnisse,* **28C**, 1–36.

THIEDE, J. & VAN ANDEL, T. H. 1977. The paleoenvironment of anaerobic sediments in the late Mesozoic South Atlantic Ocean. *Earth Planet. Sci. Lett.* **33**, 301–309.

—— & VALLIER, T. L. *et al.* 1981. *Init. Rep. Deep Sea Drilling Project,* **62**, U.S. Govt. Printing Office, Washington, D.C., 1120 pp.

—— DEAN, W. E. & CLAYPOOL, G. E. 1983. Oxygen deficient depositional paleoenvironments in the mid-Cretaceous tropical and sub-tropical Central Pacific Ocean. *In*: SCHLANGER, S. O. & CITA, M. B. (eds) *Nature and Origin of Cretaceous Carbon-rich Facies.* Academic Press, London, 79–100.

THIERSTEIN, H. R. 1973. Lower Cretaceous calcareous nannoplankton biostratigraphy. *Abl. Geol. B. A., Wien, Bd.* **29**, 52 pp.

—— 1976. Mesozoic calcareous nannoplankton biostratigraphy of marine sediments. *Mar. Micropaleontol.* **1**, 325–362.

—— 1979a. Paleoceanographic implications of organic carbon and carbonate distribution in Mesozoic deepsea sediments. *In*: TALWANI, M., HAY, W., RYAN, W. B. F. (eds): *Deep Drilling Results in the Atlantic Ocean; Continental Margins and Paleoenvironment, Maurice Ewing Series 3,* Am. Geophys. Union Washington, D.C., 249–274.

—— 1979b. Ratio averaging as a quantitative chronostratigraphic tool. *Geol. Soc. Am. Abstracts with programs,* 11/7, 527.

—— & BERGER, W. H. 1978. Injection events in ocean history. *Nature*, **276**, 461–466.

——, BRUMSACK, H.-J. & ROTH, P. H. 1981. Mid-Cretaceous black shales and ocean fertility. *Geol. Soc. Am. Abstracts with programs, v.* **13**, 565.

TISSOT, B. P. & WELTE, D. H. 1978. *Petroleum Formation and Occurrence.* Springer-Verlag, New York, 538 pp.

TISSOT, B., DEROO, G. & HERBIN, J. P. 1979. Organic matter in Cretaceous sediments of the N. Atlantic: contribution to sedimentology and paleogeography. *In*: TALWANI, M., HAY, W., RYAN, W. B. F. (eds) *Deep Drilling Results in the Atlantic Ocean; Continental Margins and Paleoenvironment. Maurice Ewing Series 3,* Am. Geophys. Union Washington, D.C., 362–374.

TOTH, D. J. & LERMAN, A. 1977. Organic matter reactivity and sedimentation rates in the ocean. *Am. Jour. Sci.* **277**, 465–485.

TRABANT, P. K. 1978. Synthesis of physical properties data from DSDP leg 41. *In*: LANCELOT, Y., SEIBOLD, E. *et al., Init. Rep. Deep Sea Drilling Project,* **41**, U.S. Govt. Printing Office, Washington, D.C., 1199–1215.

TUCHOLKE, B. E., VOGT, P. R. *et al.* 1979. *Init. Rep. Deep Sea Drilling Project,* **43**, U.S. Govt. Printing Office, Washington, D.C., 1115 pp.

TUREKIAN, K. K. & WEDEPOHL, K. H. 1961. Distribution of the elements in some major units of the Earth's crust. *Bull. Geol. Soc. Amer.* **72**, 175–192.

VAN ANDEL, T. H., HEATH, G. R. & MOORE, T. C. 1975. *Cenozoic history and paleoceanography of the central equatorial Pacific Ocean. Geol. Soc. Am., Mem.* **143**, 134 pp.

VAN HINTE, J. E. 1976. A Cretaceous time scale. *Am. Assoc. Petrol. Geol.* **60**, 498–516.

VARENTSOV, I. M. 1981. Geochemical history of post-Jurassic sedimentation in the central northwestern Pacific, southern Hess Riss, Deep Sea Drilling Project Site 465. *In*: THIEDE, J., VALLIER, T. L. *et al.* 1981. *Init. Rep. Deep Sea Drilling Project,* **62**, U.S. Govt. Printing Office, Washington, D.C., 819–832.

VINE, J. D. & TOURTELOT, E. B. 1970. *Geochemistry of black shale deposits—a summary report. Econ. Geol.* **65**, 253–272.

WAPLES, D. W. 1983. Reappraisal of anoxia and organic richness, with emphasis on Cretaceous of North Atlantic. *Am. Assoc. Petrol. Geol. Bull.* **67**, 963–978.

WEDEPOHL, K. H. 1970. *Environmental influences on the chemical composition of shales and clays. In*: AHRENS, L. H. (eds) *Physics and Chemistry of the Earth,* **8**, Pergamon, 305–333.

WEICHART, G. 1974. Meerschemische Untersuchungen im nordwestafrikanischen Auftriebsgebiet 1968. *Meteor Forschungsergebnisse.* **14A**, 33–70.

WISE, S. W. Jr. 1983. Mesozoic and Cenozoic calcareous nannofossils recovered by DSDP leg 71 in the Falkland Plateau Region, southwest Atlantic Ocean. *In*: LUDWIG, W. J., KRASHENINNIKOV, V. A. *et al. Init. Rep. Deep Sea Drilling Project, v.* **71**, U.S. Govt. Printing Office, Washington, D.C. 481–550.

WISE, S. W., Jr. & WIND, F. H. 1976. Mesozoic and Cenozoic calcareous nannoplankton recovered by DSDP leg 36 drilling on the Falkland Plateau, southeast Atlantic sector of the southern ocean. *In*: BARKER, P. F., DALZIEL, I. W. D. *et al. Init. Rep.*

Deep Sea Drilling Project **36**, U.S. Govt. Printing Office, Washington, D.C., 269–491.

ZEITZSCHEL, B. 1969. Primary productivity in the Gulf of California. *Marine Biology,* **3**, 201–207.

ZOBEL, B. 1973. Biostratigraphische Unter suchungen an Sedimenten des indisch-pakistanischen Kontinentalrandes (Arabisches Meer). *'Meteor' Forschungsergebnisse* **12C**, 9–73.

T. J. BRALOWER, Scripps Institution of Oceanography, University of California, San Diego, La Jolla, CA 92093, USA.

H. R. THIERSTEIN, Geologisches Institut, ETH-Zentrum, CH-8092, Zürich, Switzerland.

The Cenomanian–Turonian Oceanic Anoxic Event, I. Stratigraphy and distribution of organic carbon-rich beds and the marine δ^{13}C excursion

S. O. Schlanger, M. A. Arthur, H. C. Jenkyns & P. A. Scholle

SUMMARY: Marine strata deposited during late Cenomanian and early Turonian time display lithological, faunal, and geochemical characteristics which indicate that significant parts of the world ocean were periodically oxygen deficient. At, or very close to, the Cenomanian–Turonian boundary, between 90.5 and 91.5 million years ago, oxygen deficiencies were particularly marked over a period of less than 1 my. This short-lived episode of oceanic oxygen deficiency has been termed the Cenomanian–Turonian 'Oceanic Anoxic Event' (OAE). Marine sediments deposited during this event are, when compared with most of the Phanerozoic record, uncommonly rich in dark-grey to black, pyritic, laminated shales with total organic carbon contents that range from between 1 and 2% to greater than 20% which is largely of marine planktonic origin. The general lack of bioturbation in these beds is taken to indicate an absence of a burrowing fauna due to anoxic conditions. In coeval pelagic and shelf limestone sections the dark shales may be lacking; in such sections the Cenomanian–Turonian boundary is marked by δ^{13}C values of up to $+4.0\%_0$ or $+5.0\%_0$ in contrast to δ^{13}C values of $+2.0\%_0$ to $+3.0\%_0$ in limestones directly above and below the boundary. The high δ^{13}C values are taken to indicate an enrichment of the global ocean in ^{13}C values as a result of the preferential extraction of ^{12}C by marine plankton, the organic components of which were not recycled back to the oceanic reservoir during this period of enhanced organic-carbon burial. In many basins benthonic foraminiferal faunas are lacking in strata at or near the Cenomanian–Turonian boundary or consist of depauperate agglutinate faunas whereas diverse planktonic foraminiferal faunas and radiolarian remains are locally abundant. These zones free of benthonic foraminifera have been previously interpreted as the result of bottom-water oxygen deficiencies.

A correlation between high positive δ^{13}C values and manganese enrichment in shelf chalks has been pointed out by other workers; data presented here substantiates this correlation.

Sediments that display one or more of the above characteristics have been studied and identified from diverse basinal settings such as Pacific Basin mid-ocean plateaus, North American cratonic interior seaways, European shelf and interior seaways, circum-African embayments and seaways, Tethyan margins and the Caribbean region. The oxygen-deficient water masses are proposed to have taken the form of an expanded and intensified oxygen-minimum zone. Palaeobathymetric interpretation of strata from European and African shelf sequences and sections in the US Western Interior Basin show that shallow embayments, flooded by the rapid Cenomanian–Turonian transgression, were particularly favourable to deposition of anoxic sediments as were the neighbouring shelves and cratonic shallow seaways. The distribution of carbonaceous black shales and coeval light-coloured to red shallow-water limestones marked by a δ^{13}C 'spike' indicates that the upper surface of the widespread, intensified Cenomanian–Turonian oceanic oxygen-minimum zone was 100 to 200 metres below the surface of the sea in most areas; the lower surface was probably between 1.5 and 2.5 km below sea level. The main phase of the Cenomanian–Turonian OAE as exemplified by the Bonarelli Horizon in the Italian Apennines and the Black Band of Yorkshire and Humberside in England lasted less than 1 my. In some basins where coastal geometry and wind direction were effective in inducing strong upwelling conditions, the propensity for the deposition of carbon-rich facies increased and such facies were deposited in some predicted upwelling zones prior to and following the Cenomanian–Turonian OAE. However, the widespread distribution of anoxic sediments deposited synchronously during such a short-lived event indicates that such sediments are not simply the product of coincidental local climatic or basinal water mass characteristics but are the result of a global expansion and intensification of the Cenomanian–Turonian oxygen-minimum zone related to feedback between sea level rise and regional palaeoceanography. The palaeoceanography of the Cenomanian–Turonian OAE is discussed in detail in a companion paper by Arthur *et al.* 1987.

From: BROOKS, J. & FLEET, A. J. (eds) 1987, *Marine Petroleum Source Rocks*
Geological Society Special Publication No. 26 pp. 371–399.

Introduction

One of the prime results of the Deep Sea Drilling Project during the 1970s was the discovery that the major ocean basins, during Cretaceous time, were the sites of deposition of sediments anomalously rich in organic carbon in comparison to the average organic-carbon content of Phanerozoic sediments. A number of workers (Schlanger & Jenkyns 1976; Fischer & Arthur 1977; Thiede & van Andel 1977; Ryan & Cita 1977) noted this anomalous stratigraphic concentration of carbonaceous sediments, loosely described as 'black shales', and came to the general conclusion that whatever the mechanism involved, the Cretaceous oceans, from roughly Hauterivian through Santonian time, were locally or regionally oxygen deficient. Evidently a larger part of the organic carbon fixed in the upper mixed layer of the ocean by planktonic organisms in this time interval was not recycled, as now takes place in the ocean, and large amounts of terrestrially derived plant material were also sequestered in the sediments.

Examination of the stratigraphic occurrence of carbon-rich sediments by Schlanger and Jenkyns (1976) prompted them to postulate that there were two major time envelopes, late Barremian through Albian and late Cenomanian through early Turonian time, within which such sediments were concentrated. They further argued that during these times the oceanic oxygen-minimum layer had undergone a geographical and possibly a vertical expansion and intensification. Where this oxygen-minimum zone impinged on the sediment/water interface, carbon-rich sediments were laid down. They termed these periods Oceanic Anoxic Events (OAEs). Other workers (Ryan & Cita 1977) pointed out that during Coniacian–Santonian time, at least in the Atlantic, another period of widespread deposition of carbonaceous sediment took place. Three OAEs were recognized by Jenkyns (1980) (Fig. 1). The spread of oxygen-deficient waters in the world ocean was considered to be due to global high temperatures and low latitudinal temperature gradients which, coupled with the decreased solubility of oxygen in these warm waters, decreased the rate of reoxygenation of bottom waters (Fischer & Arthur 1977). A link with the great Cretaceous transgressions was also postulated by Schlanger and Jenkyns (1976). Two models were presented by these workers; the expanded oxygen-minimum model and a model which invoked the stagnation of entire ocean basins. Salinity stratification was also invoked (see Arthur & Natland 1979; Schlanger & Cita 1982, for reviews).

Early studies of the character of the organic carbon in these mid-Cretaceous strata suggested that the Aptian–Albian sediments contained abundant terrestrially derived plant material but that the Cenomanian–Turonian sediments were relatively rich in marine planktonic organic matter (Berger & von Rad, 1972; see Graciansky *et al.* 1982, for review). It further became apparent, due to the work of Scholle and Arthur (1980), that a strong positive $\delta^{13}C$ spike was associated with the Cenomanian–Turonian boundary (Fig. 2). These workers attributed the high—up to $+5.0\%_{oo}$—$\delta^{13}C$ values in pelagic and shelf limestones coeval with organic carbon-rich layers as being due to the sequestering in

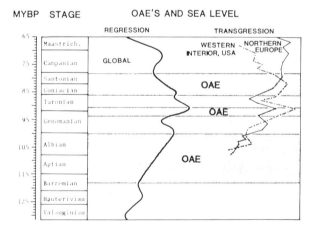

FIG. 1. Stratigraphic distribution of Cretaceous Oceanic Anoxic Events (OAE). The stippled pattern shows those time envelopes within which oxygen deficiencies in the oceanic water column were marked allowing deposition of strata rich in organic carbon or coeval limestones rich in ^{13}C (from Schlanger & Jenkyns 1976; Jenkyns 1980).

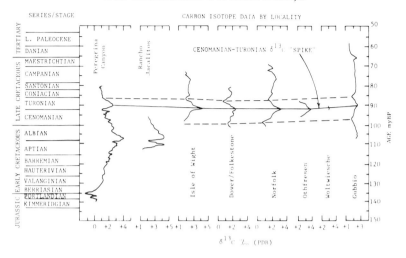

FIG. 2. Carbon isotope data showing $\delta^{13}C$ 'spikes' in Cretaceous sections. The marked $\delta^{13}C$ 'spike' correlative with the Cenomanian–Turonian boundary is taken as indicating that the enrichment of limestones in ^{13}C was the result of the sequestering of ^{12}C in organic carbon-rich beds deposited during the Cenomanian–Turonian OAE (modified from Scholle & Arthur 1980).

sediments of large amounts of marine-produced organic carbon, which is rich in ^{12}C, and the consequent enrichment of ^{13}C in the oceanic reservoir. By the late 1970s many workers recognized the link between carbon-rich Cretaceous sediments and the prolific nature of Cretaceous rocks as source beds (Irving *et al.* 1974; Arthur & Schlanger 1979; Tissot 1979; North 1979; Tissot *et al.* 1980; Summerhayes 1980; Demaison & Moore 1980).

The work presented in the present paper grew out of our realization that sediments of Cenomanian–Turonian age provided a good opportunity to study a short-lived, well-marked oceanographic event. In Part I we present the stratigraphic basis for our argument that there was a Cenomanian–Turonian OAE which has left a sedimentary record and a chemical trace in the form of strata anomalously rich in marine organic carbon or ^{13}C which mark deposits laid down at or very close to the Cenomanian–Turonian boundary in diverse geological settings on a global scale. We present our interpretations of the palaeoceanography of this period in Part II, a companion paper in this volume (Arthur *et al.*).

Stratigraphic framework

In any attempt to study Cenomanian–Turonian boundary sediments, either in general or from particular localities, two related problems become immediately apparent:

(1) on what faunal basis are these stratal units zoned as to relative age, and
(2) what are the absolute ages assigned to particular zones? In approaching this problem we have relied heavily on the work of Kauffman (1977), a recent review of the Cenomanian–Turonian boundary problem by Valentine (1982), Kennedy *et al.* (1981), the report (1979) of the Groupe de Travail Européen des Foraminifères Planctoniques (GTEFP), the work of G. Ernst *et al.* (1979) and Harland *et al.* (1982). The zonations and ages assigned for the purposes of this paper are summarized on Fig. 3. In sections where planktonic foraminifera are abundant, the rotaliporid extinction event is useful as a marker for the Cenomanian–Turonian transition beds. The GTEFP (1979) shows the last occurrence of *Rotalipora cushmani* as marking the base of the *Whiteinella archeocretacea* PRZ which straddles the Cenomanian–Turonian boundary; the first appearance of *Praeglobotruncana helvetica* being taken as a marker for basal Turonian beds. On the basis of macrofossils, in the US Western Interior Basin the Cenomanian–Turonian boundary is taken to be the boundary between the *Sciponoceras gracile* Zone and the *Inoceramus labiatus* Zone; the latter being taken by European stratigraphers as marking the basal Turonian. The *Actinocamax plenus* beds in Europe are taken as occurring in latest Cenomanian time. Horizon A is taken as being latest Cenomanian in age. In the description and discussion given below the dating of each section within this framework is discussed further.

1	2	3	4	5	6	7
	FORAM ZONES		**FORAM DATUM**	**MACROFOSSIL ZONES AND INDICES**		
MYBP	Mesogean	Boreal		NW Germany	U.K./France	U.S. Western Interior

STAGE — TURONIAN (U, M, L); CENOMANIAN (U, M)

MYBP scale: 89, 90, 91, 92, 93, 94

Mesogean foram zones:
- Marginotruncana schneegansi PRZ
- Praeglobotruncana helvetica TRZ
- Whitienella archeocretacea PRZ
- Rotalipora cushmani TRZ

Boreal foram zones:
- Marginotruncana coronata IZ
- M. sigali IZ
- P. helvetica IZ
- W. arch. PRZ
- Rotalipora cushmani TRZ

FORAM DATUM:
- FAD M. coro.
- LAD P. helv.
- FAD M. schn.
- FAD M. siga.
- FAD P. helv.
- FAD W. arch.
- LAD R. cush.
- LAD R. brot.

NW Germany (MACROFOSSIL ZONES):
- Inoceramus / 'Mytiloides'
- I. lamarcki
- I. cuvierii, I. typicalis
- M. hercynicus / M. subhercynicus
- M. labiatus
- M. mytiloides
- Neocardioceras juddii
- Actinocamax plenus (+ Metoic. geslinianum)
- Inoceramus pictus + Calycoceras naviculare
- Acanthoceras jukesbrownei

U.K./France:
- Subprionocyclus neptuni
- Collignoniceras woollgari IZ
- Mammites nodosoides
- Watinoceras coloradoense; I. labiatus
- HOR A
- Neocardioceras juddii
- Metoicoceras geslinianum (A. plenus)

U.S. Western Interior:
- M. latus
- M. hercynicus
- M. subhercynicus
- C. woollgari
- M. labiatus s.s.
- M. mytiloides; Mammites nodosoides
- M. opalensis; Watinoceras coloradoense
- Sciponoceras gracile
- Dunveganoceras albertense
- Dunveganoceras conditum
- Dunveganoceras pondi
- Plesiacanthoceras wyomingense
- Acanthoceras amphibolum

1.   from Harland, et al., 1982.
2,3,4.   from GTEFP, 1979.
5.   from Ernst, et al, 1979.
6.   from Kennedy et al., 1981.
7.   from Kauffman, 1977.

With reference to absolute ages on which, of course, sedimentation rate and event length arguments depend, various workers differ. According to the GTEFP report the Cenomanian–Turonian stage boundary is at 90 myBP. The time span allotted to the stratigraphic interval bounded by the top of the *Mytiloides nodosoides–I. labiatus* Zone and the base of the Plenus Marl is 89.5 to 90.5 myBP; within this interval the *W. archeocretacea* PRZ is shown to be less than 1 my in length. Van Hinte (1976) uses 86 to 100 myBP for the time spanned by both the Cenomanian and Turonian stages and places the boundary at 92 myBP: the time allotted to the interval from the top of the *I. labiatus* Zone to the base of the Plenus Marl is 3 my. Kauffman (1977) uses 87 to 94 myBP as the Cenomanian–Turonian time interval. As shown in subsequent sections of this paper the stratigraphic interval that includes the $\delta^{13}C$ 'spike' that marks the Cenomanian–Turonian OAE spans less than 1 my of time; the spike itself is probably a powerful correlation tool as postulated by Scholle and Arthur (1980). Following Harland *et al.* (1982), who place the Cenomanian–Turonian boundary at 91 myBP as shown on Fig. 3, the event took place between 90.5 and 91.5 myBP.

FIG. 4. Localities of European sections discussed in text: (1) South Ferriby pit, England; (2) Goban Spur, DSDP Sites 549–551; (3) North Sea, Sun Oil Well no. 22/1–2A; (4) Danish Central Graben; (5) Heligoland; (6) Wünstorf, Germany; (7) Salzgitter Anticline, Germany; (8) Shakespeare Cliffs, Dover, England; (9) Cap d'Antifer, France; (10) Gubbio, Italy; (11) Trento area, Italy; (12) Bürgenstock, Switzerland; (13) Ronda area, Spain.

Stratigraphy of the Cenomanian–Turonian oceanic anoxic event

Europe

Much of our field work was carried out in Europe because the Cenomanian–Turonian strata exposed there were deposited in a variety of basinal settings and the sections themselves have been studied intensively in terms of biostratigraphic control. In this section we review the stratigraphy locality by locality and synthesize the data into a coherent picture in terms of the palaeobathymetry of the sites of deposition of carbonaceous sediments laid down during the Cenomanian–Turonian OAE which coincided with the sharp transgression that flooded European shelves. Fig. 4 shows the localities discussed.

South Humberside, England (Locality 1, Fig. 4)

The Black Band of Yorkshire and Humberside has been regarded as a curious feature of the chalk sequence in England for many years (see Jefferies 1963; Hart & Bigg 1981 for review). The Black Band is well exposed in the South Ferriby Pit (Fig. 5). The lithologic contrast between the black, laminated marl and the white, heavily bioturbated chalks above and below the Black Band, and the smectitic character of the clays in the section led some workers (see Hallam & Sellwood 1968) to interpret the Black Band as a volcanic ash. Palaeontological studies by Hart & Bigg (1981) who place the Black Band in the *W. archeocretacea* Zone and elsewhere suggest that the band is the equivalent of bed 6 of the southern English Plenus Marl succession, point out that the unusual 100% agglutinated benthonic fauna of the Black Band '. . . represents a drastic change in bottom conditions.' Hart and Bigg further state that 'the fauna would appear to confirm the suggestion of Jenkyns (1980) and Schlanger & Jenkyns (1976) that the Black Band represents anoxic conditions on the sea floor.' Our carbon isotopic data (Fig. 5) clearly show that there is a strong and narrowly defined $\delta^{13}C$ spike immediately beneath and extending upwards into the Black Band. $\delta^{13}C$ values of $+2.7$ to $+2.9\%$ characterize the white chalks below the Black Band for a distance of the 5 metres sampled and values of $+3.0$ to $+3.3\%$ were found in the overlying chalks to a distance of 8 metres above

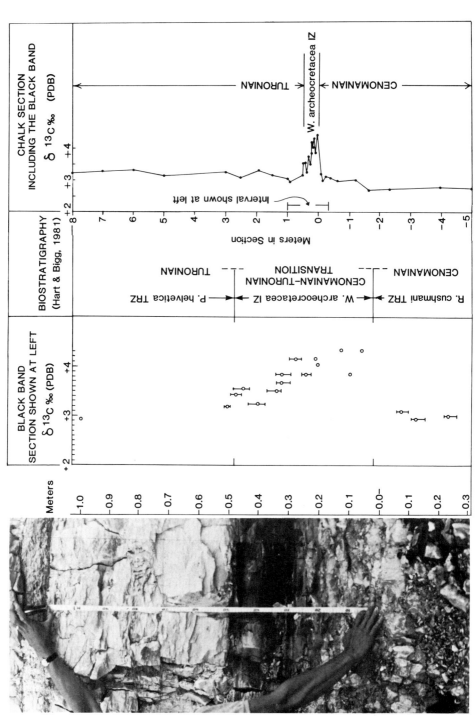

Fɪɢ. 5. Black Band exposed in South Ferriby Pit, Humberside, England. The carbonaceous, laminated, clay-rich band is in a thick section of white chalk of Cenomanian–Turonian age. The $\delta^{13}C$ 'spike' is restricted to the *W. archeocretacea* Zone which marks the Cenomanian–Turonian boundary. For a

the Black Band. The restriction of the high
(+3.5 to +4.3‰) $\delta^{13}C$ values to the *W. archeocretacea* Zone indicates the short duration of the
Cenomanian–Turonian oceanic anoxic event;
some of the lower $\delta^{13}C$ values in the upper part
of the Black Band s.s. may be due to diagenetically
produced light carbonate. The Black Band itself
contains from 1–1.5% total organic carbon in the
form of wisps of carbonaceous organic material
in thin laminae; fossils are sparse in contrast to
the fossil abundance in the chalk above and
below the Black Band (Fig. 6 a, b, c). The relative
paucity of organic carbon in the Black Band,
compared to other correlative sections in Europe,
and the small thickness of the band itself leads us
to conclude that the Black Band was deposited
near the upper limit of the oxygen-minimum zone
that lapped onto the shelf.

Goban Spur (Locality 2, Fig. 4)

During Leg 80 of the Deep Sea Drilling Project
several holes were drilled on the Goban Spur
which forms the edge of the west European shelf
(DSDP Scientific Staff 1982). Relevant to this
paper are results from Sites 549 and 551. A
section of black shale in a thick sequence of
Upper Cretaceous white chalks was encountered;
a situation similar to that seen in the section
exposed at South Ferriby Pit, Humberside. On
the Goban Spur the black shales are of late
Cenomanian to earliest Turonian age (*W. archeocretacea* zone after Hart 1985) and are described
as black, organic carbon-rich, laminated, radiolarian-rich mudstones with total organic carbon
contents of up to 10.94% (Waples & Cunningham
1985; Cunningham & Kroopnick, 1985). Marine
derived components make up about 30% of the
organic matter. These black shales are enriched
in Cu, Zn, Fe, V, Ni, and Ba. Further, carbon
isotopic values reported (Cunningham & Kroopnick 1985) show that $\delta^{13}C$ values in the late
Cenomanian–early Turonian black shales reach
values of +4.47‰ and +3.72‰. These are
significantly higher than values measured in
Middle Cenomanian chalks. Cunningham and
Kroopnick (1985) note that the $\delta^{13}C$ values for
the Cenomanian–Turonian black sediments are
similar to those reported by Scholle & Arthur
(1980) and they consider that the Goban Spur
$\delta^{13}C$ 'spike' is coeval with the worldwide Cenomanian–Turonian oceanic anoxic event. Waples
& Cunningham (1985) interpret these organic
carbon-rich sediments to have been deposited
within an oxygen-minimum layer at depths of 1
to 2 km during latest Cenomanian to earliest
Turonian time.

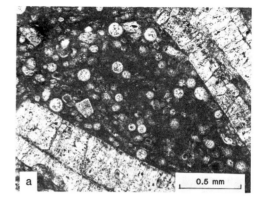

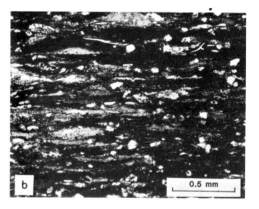

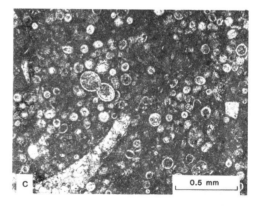

FIG. 6. Photomicrographs of thin-sections from the
South Ferriby Pit section: (a) Massive chalks above
the Black Band are rich in planktonic and benthonic
foraminifera and contain abundant fragments of
Inoceramus shells; (b) the Black Band itself is
characterized by undisturbed laminae marked by
wisps and stringers of black carbonaceous matter and
smectitic clay enclosing small foraminifera; (c) the
underlying, nodular chalks are intensely bioturbated
and contain an abundant fauna of both planktonic and
benthonic foraminifera.

Central North Sea (Locality 3, Fig. 4)

Burnhill and Ramsay (1981) in a study of North Sea wells delineate the Plenus Marl Formation as a dark brown to black, carbonaceous, pyritic, calcareous mudstone in a thick limestone section (Fig. 7). They consider that the Plenus Marl is early Turonian in age because the uppermost occurrence of *Rotalipora sp.* lies in the uppermost few metres of the underlying Hidra Formation. The authors point out that the Plenus Marl in the North Sea was deposited during the peak transgression of the early Turonian and that these sapropelic mudstones are rich in planktonic foraminifera and radiolarians but contain only a sparse benthonic fauna. They consider the Plenus Marl to have been deposited in an oxygen-minimum layer in an open continental shelf setting.

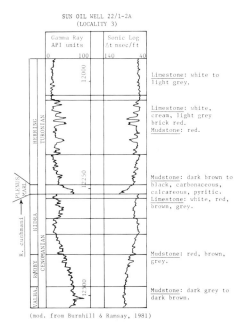

(mod. from Burnhill & Ramsay, 1981)

FIG. 7. Log of Sun Oil Well no. 22/1–2A in the North Sea. At the top of the *R. cushmani* zone dark brown to black, carbonaceous, pyritic sediments of the Plenus Marl horizon are characterized by a gamma ray kick and a low sonic velocity. We interpret the log as indicating the presence of a North Sea equivalent of the Black Band which in this well is probably less than 3–4 metres thick, based on the span of the gamma ray kick. According to Burnhill and Ramsay (1981) the Plenus Marl Formation, which is present in a number of wells in the North Sea, was deposited at the peak of the transgressive phase in early Turonian time and is characterized by a rich planktonic foraminiferal and radiolarian fauna and a sparse benthonic foraminiferal fauna.

Danish Central Graben (Locality 4, Fig. 4)

A number of exploratory wells have been drilled in the Danish Central Graben (Michelsen 1982; Nygaard et al. 1983). These wells have revealed the presence of a 1500 m thick chalk section of late Cenomanian through Danian age; 6 chalk units have been delineated and correlated with the formations established by Deegan & Scull (1977) for the Northern and Central North Sea area. Chalk Unit 1 of Cenomanian age correlates with the Hidra Formation. Chalk Unit 2 is Turonian to Coniacian and Santonian in age and contains at its base beds equivalent to the Plenus Marl Formation. In the Danish Central Graben the massive light-coloured Cenomanian chalk of Unit 1 is separated from the overlying Turonian of Chalk Unit 2 by a section of several metres thickness marked by black to dark grey shales (see Fig. 8). These 'Turonian shales' of Nygaard et al. (1983) and Michelsen (1982) are taken to be the base of the Turonian section and to be within the Plenus Marl Formation. The log characteristics of the shales are identical to the log character of the Plenus Marl section seen in the Sun Oil well 22/1–2A (Fig. 7). It is important to note that both above and below these black shales normal light-coloured chalks occur for at least tens of metres; these pure chalks were deposited under open marine conditions. In the cores from well B0–1 made available to us by E. Nygaard of the Danish Geological Survey approximately 16 black or dark grey, clay-rich bands can be seen in 6 metres of section; core recovery was virtually 100%. The chalks immediately above and below are typical of the whole of both Chalk Units 1 and 2. A typical sandwich of shale between interbedded chalk consists of perhaps 10 cm of black or dark grey, finely to irregularly laminated claystone with internal thin bands rich in *Chondrites* burrows and pyrite. The association of *Chondrites*, pyrite, and laminated dark shales indicates deposition in an oxygen-poor environment (Bromley & Ekdale 1984). Some shale–chalk contacts are sharp whereas others show transitional features where burrowing organisms have brought black clay down into the underlying chalk, producing black, flattened burrow traces. Upper contacts are also commonly gradational with lighter grey, marly, burrowed chalks lying between the black shale and the very pale, orange, pure chalk.

Heligoland (Locality 5, Fig. 4)

Schmid and Spaeth (1980) have reported on a newly discovered black shale occurrence in Lower Turonian strata of Heligoland. They describe

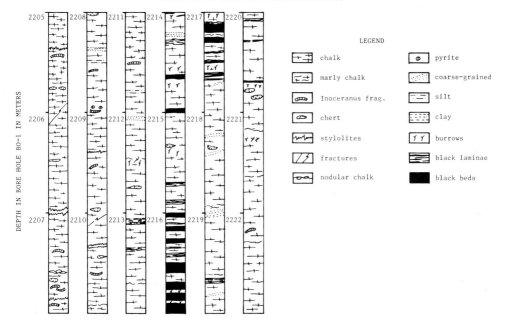

FIG. 8. Stratigraphic section measured in cores taken from borehole B0–1 in the Danish Central Graben in the North Sea. The age of the strata is basal Turonian (Michelsen 1982; Nygaard *et al.* 1983) and is considered equivalent to the Plenus Marl Formation found in other wells in the North Sea. Approximately 16 black to dark grey, laminated to irregularly banded clay units are seen in a cherty, pale orange to light grey chalk section; the dark clay beds are restricted to approximately 6 metres of the total section.

greyish-black, thin-layered and flat boulders of 'sapropelitic' marlstone associated with inoceramids of the *labiatus* group and relate these sapropels to the occurrences of the Northwest German Upper Cenomanian–Lower Turonian black shale facies discussed below.

Wünstorf-Salzgitter Anticline (Localities 6 and 7, Fig. 4)

Ernst, *et al.* (1979) in an extensive review of the stratigraphy of the Cretaceous chalks in the Hannover–Braunschweig region of north Germany describe as an unusual facies of black, bituminous, sapropelic marls in an otherwise normal chalk section exposed in quarries at Wünstorf (Fig. 9) and Misburg, east of Hannover. The lack of these black marls in coeval sections such as are exposed in the Salzgitter Anticline, where reddish limestones—the Rotpläner beds—occupy the horizon of the Wünstorf and Misburg black marls (Fig. 10), led Ernst *et al.* (1979) to postulate that the black marls were deposited in local 'fore deeps' in a Cretaceous palaeoterrain characterized by basin and swell submarine

topography; the Rotpläner beds having been deposited on swells. The following discussion is based on Ernst *et al.* (1979), stratigraphic data from the Mid-Cretaceous Events Working Group, 'Germany-North' made available to us by G. Ernst and F. Schmid, and our own field work in the area. In the Nordcement-AG quarry at Wünstorf (Locality 6, Fig. 4), 25 to 30 metres of chalk are well exposed; within this interval 21 distinct, dark grey, olive-black and clay-rich units stand out (Fig. 9). These dark clays are distributed in the section from near the base of the *A. plenus–M. geslinianum* Zone of middle late Cenomanian age through the *M. mytyloides* Zone (*I. labiatus*) of the lowermost Turonian. The thickest black clays and those that show millimetre-scale laminations due to a lack of bioturbation except for local concentrations of *Chondrites*, abundant fish debris, and pyrite are concentrated in the section from 5 to 12 metres, i.e., in the uppermost Cenomanian to lowermost Turonian strata.

The stratigraphy and geochemistry of Cenomanian-Turonian chalk sections in northern Germany are being investigated by a number of workers and more detailed studies will be forth-

NORDCEMENT-AG QUARRY, WÜNSTORF, GERMANY

(LOCALITY 6)

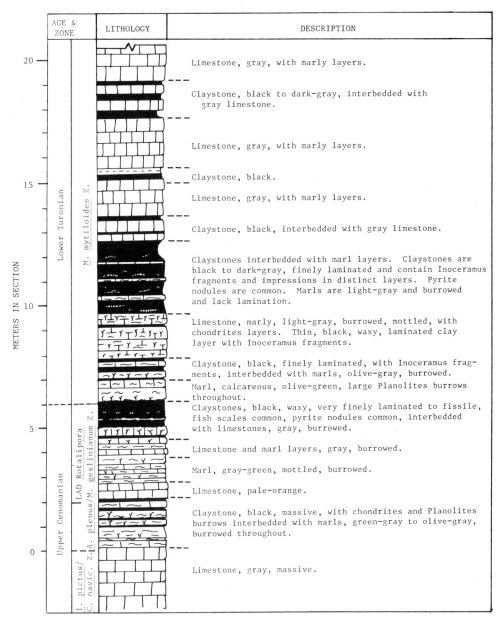

FIG. 9. Chalk section across the Cenomanian–Turonian boundary exposed in the Nordcement-AG quarry at Wünstorf, near Hannover, Germany. The fossil zonations are from data supplied by G. Ernst, E. Seibertz and F. Schmid of the Mid-Cretaceous Events Working Group 'Germany-North'.

coming. A set of 49 samples taken by us at Wünstorf shows that high orgC contents and $\delta^{13}C$ values are associated with the Cenomanian–Turonian boundary beds. From the 0 metre level shown on Fig. 9, to 11 metres below that level the grey, massive limestone yielded $\delta^{13}C$ values of from $+2.68$ to $+2.98‰$; orgC values in this part of the section are very low, ranging from virtually 0.0% to 0.17%. Between 0 and 1.85 metres $\delta^{13}C$ values of $+3.04$ to $+3.28‰$ were found. The

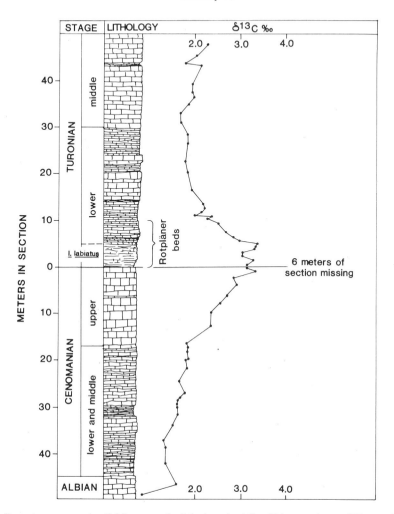

FIG. 10. Chalk section measured at Othfresen on the Salzgitter Anticline 90 km southeast of Wünstorf. At this locality carbonaceous shales such as those seen at Wünstorf are lacking; the 'Rotpläner' beds are present. A strong δ^{13}C 'spike' marks the Cenomanian–Turonian boundary as is seen in other sections in Europe.

δ^{13}C 'spike' appears to occur between 1.85 and 4.58 metres where values of $+3.95$ to $+4.26\%_0$ were obtained. From the 4.58 metre to the 10.4 metre level δ^{13}C values range from $+3.31$ to $+3.78\%_0$. From 0 to 10.4 metres orgC values are generally less than 0.2% in the grey marls and limestones whereas the black, laminated claystones contain from 1.2 to 2.8% orgC.

The highly burrowed character of the chalks and lighter coloured marls interbedded with the black laminated claystones argues for the idea that the section represents alternating conditions of normally oxygenated waters and dysaerobic or anoxic waters in the basin of deposition.

It should be pointed out here that the 21 black clay units at Wünstorf occupy 20 m of section. In the Danish Central Graben 16 black 'shale' units are present in 6 m of section. The Bridge Creek Limestone, which spans the Cenomanian–Turonian boundary in the United States Western Interior Basin (see discussion below) is described as containing similar cycles of laminated, organic carbon-rich shales, and burrowed micrites due to deposition under alternating states of aerobic and anaerobic bottom waters (Pratt 1982); 30 such cycles are present in the Bridge Creek Limestone (Fischer 1980) and de Boer (1982) has pointed out the presence of 28 ± 5 cycles in the Bonarelli horizon in Italy (see below). The implications of these cycles are discussed in Arthur *et al.* in this volume.

Near Othfresen, chalks of Cenomanian–Turonian age are exposed in the Salzgitter Anticline (Locality 7, Fig. 4). At this section (Fig. 10) approximately 6 metres of section are missing, due to minor faulting, from the upper *A. plenus* and lowermost *I. labiatus* Zones. Therefore the actual Cenomanian–Turonian boundary is missing. We conducted a detailed sampling and δ^{13}C

analytical programme for this section as shown on Fig. 10. The increase in δ^{13}C values begins in late Cenomanian time, rises to a peak by very early Turonian time, and δ^{13}C values sharply decrease by the end of Rotpläner deposition in early Turonian time. The δ^{13}C peak coincides with the most intense period of laminated, black clay deposition in the Wünstorf area 90 km to the northwest. The Cenomanian–Turonian boundary would fall in the middle of the δ^{13}C excursion.

The Wünstorf and Salzgitter Anticline sections vividly demonstrate the two depositional realms of the basin and swell palaeobathymetry of the north German Cretaceous shelf sea as described by Ernst *et al.* (1979).

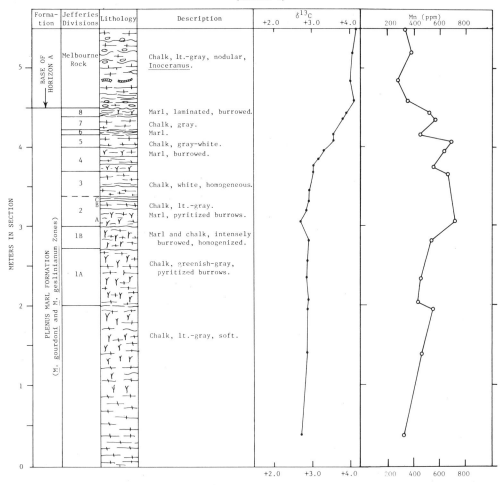

FIG. 11. Chalk section at Shakespeare Cliffs, Dover, England. Stratigraphic zonations are from Jefferies (1963) and Kennedy & Garrison (1975). The δ^{13}C and Mn profiles parallel those seen at the Cap d'Antifer section shown on Fig. 12. Acid-soluble Mn determined by atomic absorption flame photometry.

Dover, England (Locality 8, Fig. 4)

Well-exposed sections at Shakespeare Cliffs just south of Dover allowed detailed sampling of Upper Cenomanian chalks and correlation of $\delta^{13}C$ values with Jefferies (1963) stratal divisions. As shown on Fig. 11, $\delta^{13}C$ values rise from less than $+3\%$ to over $+4\%$ from Jefferies bed 3 through the base of the Melbourne Rock beds. The base of the Melbourne Rock level is taken as equivalent to the base of Horizon A (Kennedy & Garrison 1975) which represents the uppermost Cenomanian strata. The *I. labiatus* Zone lies higher in the Melbourne Rock unit and was not sampled by us. However, the base of the $\delta^{13}C$ spike at Dover is correlative with the base of the $\delta^{13}C$ spike at Cap d'Antifer which lies in Horizon A (see below) and the onset of the $\delta^{13}C$ spike at Othfresen on the Salzgitter Anticline (Locality 7).

Northern France (Locality 9, Fig. 4)

In order to trace further the relationships between the occurrence of actual carbonaceous black beds and the stratigraphic location of the $\delta^{13}C$ 'spike' in light-coloured chalks and limestones, postulated to mark the Cenomanian–Turonian OAE by Scholle and Arthur (1980), we measured and sampled a section at Cap d'Antifer, near Etretat on the French channel coast (Fig. 12). Our carbon isotope analyses reveal the presence of a strong, marked $\delta^{13}C$ spike at the top of Horizon A taken as the Cenomanian–Turonian boundary; a brown-red clay-rich layer marks the boundary and can be interpreted as a secondarily oxidized equivalent of the Black Band in the South Ferriby pit (Locality 1, Fig. 4). In the area around Mons, Belgium and adjacent northern France, green pyritic clays (the Dièves) characterize the Cenomanian–Turonian boundary (Leplet & Robaszynski, 1971; Robaszynski, 1971a, b). The coarse texture and varied macro- and micro-fossil content of the Etretat chalks indicate that they were probably deposited on a shallow shelf.

Investigations of carbon isotope ratios in three pelagic chalk sequences across North France by Letolle and Pomerol (1980) show strong $\delta^{13}C$ spikes associated with the *A. plenus* level. We consider these spikes as being correlative with the $\delta^{13}C$ peaks seen at Cap d'Antifer and the South Ferriby pit, among others.

At both the Shakespeare Cliffs and Cap d'Antifer sections, increases in the Mn content of the chalks are associated with the $\delta^{13}C$ 'spike'. These data agree with that published by Pomerol (1983) who pointed out the correlation of Mn and $\delta^{13}C$ values in the Pays de Caux, Pays de Bray and Champagne district of northern France.

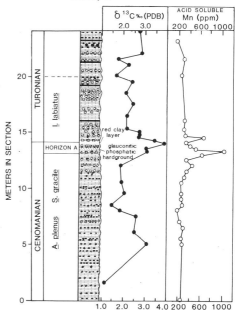

FIG. 12. Chalk section at Cap d'Antifer, France. Stratigraphic column is taken after Kennedy and Juignet (1974) for the Etretat area. The strong $\delta^{13}C$ 'spike' revealed here correlates with that seen at the South Ferriby pit, the Salzgitter Anticline, and Shakespeare Cliffs. The Mn content profile parallels the Mn profile shown by Pomerol (1983) for other northern France localities. A thin red-brown clay layer seen here at the top of Horizon A is taken to be correlative with the Black Band.

Force *et al.* (1983) and Cannon & Force (1983) argue that the stratigraphic correlation between sedimentary manganese deposits and oceanic anoxic events is due to the high solubility of manganese in anoxic waters which leads to the formation of Mn reservoirs in intensified oxygen-minimum zones. Mn is then precipitated in oxygenated waters above the oxygen-minimum zone on shallow shelves. We agree basically with the arguments of Force *et al.* (1983) and Cannon & Force (1983) that oceanic anoxic events may be a controlling factor in the formation of Mn deposits during transgression over shallow shelf areas.

The data for northern Europe are summarized and interpreted on a schematic palaeobathymetric reconstruction of the region during latest Cenomanian to earliest Turonian time (Fig. 13). We postulate that the shallow shelf chalks without marked, black, organic carbon-rich beds, but that do show marked $\delta^{13}C$ spikes, were deposited on

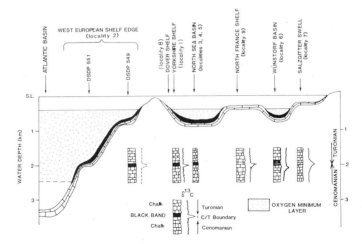

FIG. 13. Schematic diagram of the palaeobathymetric setting of north European basins during deposition of carbon-rich sediments and coeval limestones within a strongly developed oxygen-minimum zone (stippled) during the Cenomanian–Turonian Oceanic Anoxic Event. The generalized stratigraphic sections shown for the various localities are discussed in the text. Those sections of chalk that exhibit strong δ^{13}C 'spikes' with locally developed red limestones at the Cenomanian–Turonian boundary are interpreted as having been deposited in oxygenated waters above the oxygen minimum layer. In deeper embayments and shelf areas organic carbon-rich sediments formed where the oxygen deficient waters encroached into these palaeobathymetric lows. The development of oxygen deficiencies in these lows correlates with the sharp transgressive peak that marks the basal Turonian on a global basis. The Wünstorf–Salzgitter Anticline black shale–Rötplaner relationships have been interpreted by Ernst et al. (1979) as a reflection of basin and swell topography characterizing the north German area at the time. The Goban Spur area is interpreted after Waples & Cunningham (1985) and Cunningham & Kroopnick (1985) who argue, based on the presence of a δ^{13}C spike associated with organic carbon-rich sediments, that a strong oxygen minimum layer existed in the Goban Spur area during latest Cenomanian to earliest Turonian time. The general model is that of Schlanger and Jenkyns (1976).

relative highs above the upper boundary of the oxygen-minimum zone in aerated, mixed waters; where, however, the sediment-water interface lay within the oxygen-minimum zone organic carbon could accumulate. The thickness of the black sediments and the tenor of organic-carbon values appear to be related to the position of the interface in the oxygen-minimum zone. On the Goban Spur thicker beds rich in organic carbon accumulated while on shallower shelf areas only a thin (<1 m thick) band of slightly carbonaceous character developed, exemplified by the South Ferriby Pit section in Humberside (Locality 1).

Central Italy (Locality 10, Fig. 4)

The Bonarelli Horizon exposed at Gubbio in the Umbrian Apennines was considered to be one of the 'type localities' of the Cenomanian–Turonian OAE by Schlanger and Jenkyns (1976). Recently Arthur and Premoli-Silva (1982) have studied this unit and its correlatives and have presented a great deal of new data and a detailed review of older data. In this paper we simply list those features of the Bonarelli Bed germane to our

argument; readers are referred to Arthur and Premoli-Silva for full details. The Bonarelli Horizon in the Umbria region consists of 0.65 to 1.1 m of finely interbedded, dark brown to black and olive black fissile shale and mudstone and brown radiolarian sand layers 1 to 2 cm thick. This thin unit lies within a sharply contrasting sequence of light grey to cream-coloured dense, fine-grained, cherty, pelagic limestones. The upper and lower contacts between the Bonarelli Horizon and the enclosing limestone are very sharp. Organic carbon values in the unbioturbated, finely laminated black mudstones that make up the central part of the Horizon range from 11.8 to 23%. The organic matter is in the form of thin wisps and laminae interlayered with laminae of phosphate material. Fish scales and vertebrae are abundant on laminae surfaces. The organic matter is largely amorphous and of marine origin as indicated by high hydrogen and low oxygen indices revealed by pyrolysis. Detailed pyrolysis analyses of various levels in the Bonarelli Horizon by van Graas and others (1983) show that organic carbon-rich levels, where TOC values of 13.3 to 16.5% are recorded, have had a major marine input; they interpret their results as showing that the Bonarelli sediments were deposited under conditions of severe anoxia. The Bonarelli Horizon lies within the *W. archeocretacea* Zone; not only is it correlative with the Black Band in England but in its physical and chemical character it appears to be simply an expanded version of it. A positive δ^{13}C excursion was reported near the Cenomanian–Turonian boundary in the Gubbio section by Scholle and Arthur (1980). However within the Bonarelli Horizon itself there is relatively little carbonate and δ^{13}C values have been diagenetically altered to values as light as $-3\%_0$. Arthur and Premoli-Silva (1982) deduce, from sedimentation rate arguments, that the entire Bonarelli Horizon was deposited in 350,000–700,000 years; a similar figure was suggested by de Boer (1982). Arthur and Premoli-Silva (1982) interpret the Bonarelli Horizon as having been deposited in an oxygen minimum layer under anoxic conditions in a water depth of approximately 1 km on a continental margin. Their interpretation is similar to that proposed for the Goban Spur situation as interpreted by Waples and Cunningham (1985).

Beds identical to the Bonarelli both in age and lithology are exposed at Covelo and Massenza in the Trento region, and at Cinto Euganio in the Colli Euganei near Padua (Locality 11, Fig. 4). These have been described by Bosellini *et al.* (1978) and Arthur and Premoli-Silva (1982) and interpreted by them as having been formed on the edge of a topographic high (the Trento Plateau) within the oxygen-minimum zone (see Jenkyns 1980, for review).

Bürgenstock, Switzerland (Locality 12, Fig. 4)

On the Bürgenstock, in the Helvetic Zone of the Swiss Alps, some 8 km southeast of Luzern, the Cenomanian–Turonian passage beds are exposed in a folded limestone terrane (Bolli 1944). A positive δ^{13}C excursion can be seen in the passage beds (Fig. 15). According to Bolli (1944) the first appearance of *P. helvetica*, which marks the top of the *W. archeocretacea* Zone, lies 1 metre below a 70 cm thick reddish limestone in the section (Fig. 14). We propose that the reddish limestone at Bürgenstock is equivalent to the Rotpläner beds at the Salzgitter Anticline and that the drop in δ^{13}C values above the reddish limestone at Bürgenstock correlates with the drop in δ^{13}C values seen in the upper Rotpläner beds at the Salzgitter Anticline (Fig. 10).

Spain (Locality 13, Fig. 4)

A thin bituminous bed of Cenomanian–Turonian age, which lies in a sequence of normal pelagic limestones and is rich in planktonic foraminifera and radiolarians, crops out in the Subbetic geological province of Spain (Dürr 1967). Hernandez-Pacheco (1936) describes and figures the abundant, large and well-preserved fossil fish

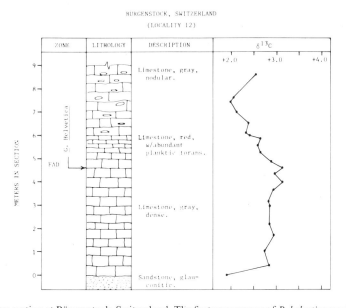

FIG. 14. Limestone section at Bürgenstock, Switzerland. The first appearance of *P. helvetica* marks the top of the *W. archeocretacea* Zone. Stratigraphic data after Bolli (1944).

skeletons and debris in these thin-bedded black shales in the Ronda area where the carbonaceous unit has been mapped.

Poland

In the Pieniny Klippen Belt, Polish Carpathians there is locally developed a bed of black and green radiolarian shales (Altana Shales or middle sub-unit of the Magierowa Member; Birkenmayer 1977; Birkenmayer & Jednorowska 1984). The lowest sub-unit of the Magierowa Member is constituted by grey-green and green marly shales with planktonic foraminifera alternating with black and brown radiolarian shales; they pertain to the *R. cushmani* Zone of the Cenomanian. The uppermost sub-unit of green and grey-green marly limestones and marls containing planktonic foraminifera and/or radiolarians belongs to the *P. helvetica* Zone of early Turonian age. It is thus very likely that the middle unit, consisting entirely of black to green radiolarian shales, spans the Cenomanian–Turonian boundary and falls within the *W. archeocretacea* Zone. We interpret these as organic-rich facies.

Crimea

Naidin (1981) reviewed the Albian to Coniacian strata of the Russian Platform and the Crimea and pointed out that the sections of the Crimea reflect anoxic events. He presented a figure showing a thin interlayer of black marl, that lies

1 or 2 metres below the Cenomanian–Turonian boundary in the Crimea, in a thick succession of marl and limestones, and ascribed this thin black marl to an anoxic event.

Yugoslavia

Polšak *et al.* (1982) describe and interpret a 2000 m thick sequence of shallow-water platform carbonates of Albian to Maastrichtian age in the External Dinarides of the Herzogovina area. The section is characterized by rudist 'bioherms' with interbeds of a pelagic nature and cherts. In this section are noted black, bituminous limestones containing well-preserved fish remains. These bituminous limestones, which Polšak *et al.* (1982) consider to have been deposited in oxygen-deficient, reducing environments, are stratigraphically restricted to beds of middle to late Cenomanian age.

North America

US and Canada Western Interior Basin (Fig. 15)

Frush and Eicher (1975) conducted detailed studies of the foraminiferal fauna of Cenomanian and Turonian age from the Big Bend regions of Texas and Mexico. They discovered that these faunas are characterized by a foraminiferal assemblage dominated by a diverse planktonic suite. Frush and Eicher (1975) considered the

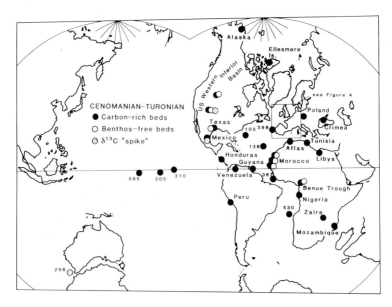

FIG. 15. Map of the world at 90 mybp showing locations of Cenomanian–Turonian sections (other than those in Europe) discussed in the text. Deep Sea Drilling Project Sites are designated by number.

Greenhorn Sea to have been occupied by an oxygen-minimum layer similar to that which exists in the modern Arabian Sea and came to the conclusion that 'The late Cenomanian lower planktonic zone and the early Turonian upper planktonic zone, with assemblages characterized by a dearth of benthonic foraminiferal specimens, may reflect the influence of such oxygen-depleted waters'. They reinforced their argument for the existence of an oxygen-minimum layer by stressing that planktonic tests were abundant and well-preserved in the Big Bend sections thus ruling out dissolution on the sea floor or the outcrop as a mechanism for the elimination of benthonic elements. Their model is in most respects similar to the model used by Schlanger and Jenkyns (1976) in their explanation of the formation of carbon-rich sediments in Cenomanian–Turonian time. Kauffman (1977) pointed out the scarcity or lack of benthonic foraminifera and ostracods in Gulf Coast and Western Interior Basin sediments that are rich in organic content of marine origin, rarely bioturbated and pyritiferous. Davis (1958) describes the Pepper Shale in south Texas as dense, black, pyritic, fissile shale; phosphate nodules and siderite are also present. The only fossil remains are casts of bivalves. Davis interprets the environment of deposition to have been in shallow, 'reducing' water. The Pepper Shale underlies the Woodbine Sand and is probably of Cenomanian–Turonian age. The northern extent of the oxygen-minimum zone in the cratonic interior basin of North America can be traced to Manitoba (McNeill & Caldwell 1981). These authors point out that 'the base of the *Hedbergella loettereli* Zone marks a complete shift of the foraminiferal spectrum from arenaceous walled benthonic foraminifera of the underlying zones to calcareous-walled planktonic foraminifers . . .'. This zone is in the Favel Formation in Manitoba which is made up of an upper Assiniboine member and a lower Keld member. The lowermost beds of the Keld member are taken to be uppermost Cenomanian; the upper Keld beds and the Assiniboine member are early Turonian. McNeill and Caldwell (1981) also point out that '. . . the *H. loetterelei* fauna is the only one in the entire foraminiferal sequence that is wholly pelagic'. They liken this benthonic-free zone to those zones in the US Western Interior described by Frush and Eicher (1975). While ascribing to the idea that oxygen-deficient waters were the control on the faunas, they point out that bivalves inhabited the somewhat restricted Greenhorn Sea and they subscribe to the interpretation of Kauffman (1977) that the oxygen-poor waters lay at, or slightly above the sediment/water interface. Simpson (1975), in a discussion of marine lithofacies and biofacies of Cretaceous strata in Saskatchewan, points out that the Second White Speckled Shale of basal Turonian age there contains abundant coccolith aggregates, which form carbonate layers, interbedded with bituminous mudstones. He compares these strata to Holocene sediments of the Black Sea and argues that these strata were deposited under lethal-isostrate conditions as defined by Schäfer (1972).

Alaska

In northern Alaska (Fig. 15) the widespread Seabee Formation has been divided into an upper Ayiyak member and a lower Shale Wall member (see Lanphere & Tailleur 1983, for review). The Shale Wall member is dated on a fossil basis as latest Cenomanian (?) and earliest Turonian age; the member unconformably overlies the Ninuluk Formation of Cenomanian age. The lower part of the Shale Wall member is generally made up of black, ferriferous, paper shale which is a low grade oil shale. Lanphere and Tailleur (1983) dated 5 biotites by the K-Ar method and 1 biotite by the ^{40}Ar/^{39}Ar method from bentonites in the Shale Wall member; the dates lie between 91.5 ± 0.9 m and 93.6 ± 1.2 myBP. Their data argue for the presence of oxygen-deficient conditions in northern Alaska during latest Cenomanian to earliest Turonian time.

Canadian Arctic Islands

Wall (1983) describes the Lower Kanguk shales on Ellesmere Island (Fig. 15) as a black, papery unit which contains bentonite seams. Further noted was a concentration of algal (?) cysts in a 6 m thick interval in the basal Kanguk in most of the sections studied. There, basal strata of the Kanguk are considered to be of late Cenomanian to early Turonian or early Turonian age. We suggest here, based on lithologic similarity and stratigraphic data, that the Lower Kanguk shale is equivalent to the Shale Wall member of the Seabee Formation described by Lanphere and Tailleur (1983) and that the Lower Kanguk was deposited under oxygen-deficient conditions.

In our own work in the US Western Interior basin we have studied strata from the Cenomanian–Turonian boundary following the age assignments as shown on Fig. 7. The Cenomanian–Turonian boundary was taken to be 3 m above the base of the Bridge Creek Limestone. Whole rock (limestone) δ^{13}C values rise sharply (Fig. 16) from a δ^{13}C of 0‰ just below the boundary to a δ^{13}C of $+3.2$ at the boundary. Within a few metres upwards in the section the δ^{13}C values

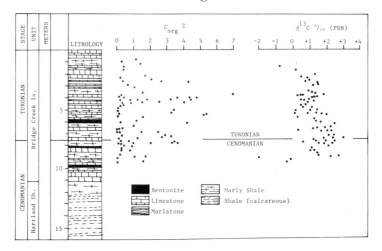

FIG. 16. Organic carbon values and $\delta^{13}C$ values across the Cenomanian–Turonian boundary at Pueblo, Colorado in the US Western Interior Basin. Stratigraphy after Pratt (1984).

drop back to 0‰. Organic-carbon content increases at the boundary with a peak value of 7% slightly above the $\delta^{13}C$ spike. Early diagenesis in the organic carbon-rich intervals of the Bridge Creek Limestone and the Hartland Shale may have modified the original whole rock $\delta^{13}C$ values, shifting them to more negative values. However, $\delta^{13}C$ values from isolated *Inoceramus* shells through Middle Cenomanian and Middle Turonian strata also show a $\delta^{13}C$ spike in the time envelope containing late Cenomanian through early Middle Turonian strata. A sharp positive $\delta^{13}C$ excursion of $+3$‰ occurs at the base of the Bridge Creek Limestone correlative with other peaks in late Cenomanian and early Turonian strata described above. We propose that the basal Bridge Creek spike represents the peak phase of the Cenomanian–Turonian OAE. In their regional study of the mid-Cretaceous of the Western Interior, Pratt and Threlkeld (1984) record a 2.5–3.5‰ positive shift in the $\delta^{13}C$ of organic carbon from the black shales at the base of the Bridge Creek Limestone and other coeval formations.

Mexico

In a study of carbon isotope fluctuations in Cretaceous limestones, Scholle and Arthur (1980) included the pelagic limestone section of the Taumalipas–La Luna Formations in Peregrina Canyon in Mexico. As shown on Fig. 2, in addition to a broad $\delta^{13}C$ peak in Aptian–Albian sediments there is a sharp peak in $\delta^{13}C$ values in strata dated as basal Turonian. Coeval with this $\delta^{13}C$ spike is a sharp increase in organic carbon

content of the strata. Early to Middle Cenomanian beds contain 0.2 to 0.3% by weight organic carbon; at the levels of the uppermost Cenomanian carbon tenor rises and peaks in basal Turonian strata at 2.7% organic carbon which is of marine origin as shown by pyrolysis analyses. Through early Middle Turonian beds the carbon content drops back to the 0.2–0.3% level. The elevated carbon levels are correlative with the $\delta^{13}C$ peak.

The stratigraphic restriction of the carbon content peak and the $\delta^{13}C$ peak in the Mexican section is of interest with relation to the broad stratigraphic range of the La Luna Formation in Venezuela as discussed below. We propose that the Peregrina Canyon section displays the true stratigraphic extent of the global Cenomanian–Turonian OAE as compared to the broad (Turonian–Coniacian) stratigraphic range of the La Luna Formation in Venezuela and Colombia which may have been deposited in a persistent upwelling region.

South and Central America

Venezuela and Colombia

The following summary is taken from Renz (1981). The La Luna Formation is considered to be the most important source rock for the prolific Venezuelan oil fields. On the Maracaibo Platform the La Luna of basal Turonian through Coniacian age directly and abruptly overlies the Cogollon orbitolinid limestone. The La Luna Formation is made up of bituminous, thin-bedded, black micritic limestones interbedded with black, platy, argillaceous limestones. Students of the region consider the La Luna to have been deposited in a euxinic environment. Also of interest in Venezuela is the Seboruco Shale, which is considered to be of Cenomanian to early Turonian age, described as uniform, massive, black, micaceous silty shale without age-indicative fossils. We propose that the persistence of carbon-rich sedimentation in the Venezuela area from basal Cenomanian through Coniacian time may have been due to persistent upwelling in the area as discussed by Barron and Washington (1983). Such an upwelling intensification would also apply to the North African occurrences of carbon-rich sediments discussed elsewhere. The La Luna Formation of central Colombia (Reyment 1981) also is made up of dark, finely bedded shales of Turonian to Coniacian age.

Honduras

According to Finch (1981) the Guare Member of the Jaitique Formation in central Honduras is a thin bedded, petroliferous, black limestone interbedded with black shale containing fine internal laminations. This unit is generally not fossiliferous except locally where it contains primarily remains of pelagic organisms. We view this bed, several metres thick, of late Cenomanian to early Turonian age, as having been deposited as a benthonic-free unit under anoxic conditions. Like the La Luna Shale in Venezuela, the Guare rests abruptly on a shallow-water limestone which contains reefoid facies.

In both Venezuela and Honduras, then, we see the deposition of anoxic sediments over normal marine limestone beginning in late Cenomanian or early Turonian time coincident with the marine transgression. In Venezuela the carbon-rich La Luna deposition persisted into Coniacian time.

Guyana

In the offshore Guyana Basin, the organic-rich Canje Formation of late Cenomanian age provides the principal source rock in a typical passive-margin sequence (Lawrence & Coster 1985). Organic-carbon values rise to 7%. The authors note a correlation of organic-rich shale deposition with an Oceanic Anoxic Event.

Africa

The major Cretaceous transgression left its mark on the relatively stable continent of Africa in the form of sediments laid down in a large number of coastal embayments and shallow marginal and interior seas. In recent years petroleum explora-

tion in Africa has resulted in a voluminous literature on these basins. The following section is a brief summary taken from that literature. (See Fig. 16 for localities.)

Libya

Clifford *et al.* (1980) have described the Messla field in the eastern part of the Sirte Basin in Libya. This is a new giant field in which the Sarir Sandstone reservoir, of early Cretaceous age, is separated by an unconformity from the overlying late Cretaceous sequence. They state that 'The surface of the unconformity reflects cessation of the lower Cretaceous non-marine conditions, and the influx of a late Cretaceous sea in Cenomanian–Turonian time'. They point out that the marine shale deposited during the transgression is '. . . both the seal and source for the oil'. Their analyses show that the crude oils derived from both Upper and Lower Cretaceous shales which contain up to 4% organic carbon. They further note, and this is germane to our discussion of the Cenomanian–Turonian OAE, that the low wax crude is derived from the Upper Cretaceous section and the high wax crude is possibly a result of a mixture of both Upper and Lower Cretaceous sources. If we take the wax content of these crudes to be indicative of the relative contributions of terrestrial plant debris and marine algal carbon to the original source material we can argue that the low wax content of the Upper Cretaceous source shows that marine algal contributions were high. These Upper Cretaceous sediments, then, laid down in the transgressing Cenomanian–Turonian sea, would reflect the high burial rate of marine algal organic carbon characteristic of sediments deposited during the Cenomanian–Turonian OAE.

Tunisia

In the Cretaceous sequences in Tunisia two periods of deposition of black, bituminous limestones are noted (Bismuth *et al.* 1982): one in late Albian and a second during late Cenomanian through early Turonian during which the Bahloul beds were deposited in a pelagic setting north of a shallow limestone facies—the Hippuritid Limestone. The deposition of the Bahloul Formation took place during the major Cenomanian–Turonian transgression which resulted in the linking of the Tunisian shelf with the Gulf of Guinea by way of Nigeria. According to Salaj (1976, 1978) who follows Burollet's (1956) stratigraphic assignments, the Bahloul Formation is of late Cenomanian through basal Turonian age; it is overlain by the Annaba Formation of early Turonian age in central Tunisia (Burollet 1956). Burollet (1975) recognized the unusual nature of the Bahloul Formation and described it as being of euxinic origin. At Oued Bahloul, 16 km southeast of Maktar, 30 metres of the Bahloul Formation is well-exposed (Fig. 17); we measured and sampled a section there. The most striking feature of these beds is the alternation of extremely fissile, perfectly laminated, dark-grey to black, bituminous shales and beds of bioturbated shales. At a

number of levels millimetre-scale laminae can be traced for 2 to 3 metres along the strike of the outcrop; no bioturbation of any kind is seen at these levels. These laminated units contain locally abundant fish scales and skeletal debris; flat pyrite nodules up to 6 cm in diameter are common in several horizons. A strong petroliferous odour is present on fresh fractures in several of the black, laminated units. Contacts between the black, laminated beds and interbedded lighter

OUED BAHLOUL, TUNISIA

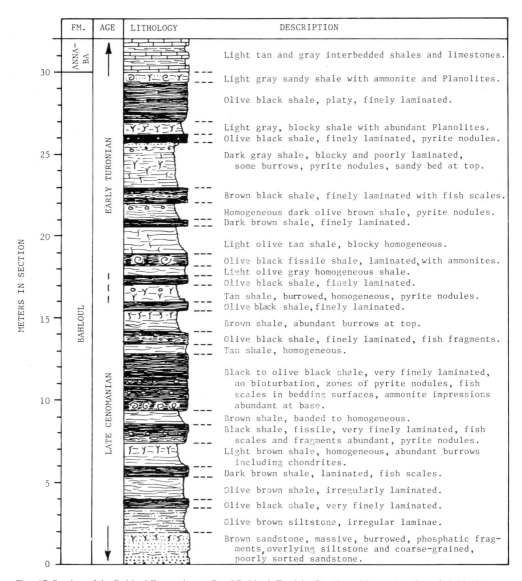

FIG. 17. Section of the Bahloul Formation at Oued Bahloul, Tunisia. Stratigraphic age data from Salaj (1976, 1978) and M. McDonald of Houston Oil and Minerals Co. of Tunisia.

coloured, burrowed limestone beds are sharp to gradational. Ammonite impressions are common, especially towards the top of the Bahloul, in association with heavily burrowed calcareous strata. The Bahloul is overlain by tan shales and sandy limestones of the Annaba Formation.

The perfect lamination, the lack of burrows, the abundance of fish debris and the general carbonaceous character of a number of beds in the Bahloul are considered by us to be the results of deposition under dysaerobic to anaerobic conditions. Intermittently, oxygenation took place and benthonic organisms reoccupied the sea floor. The number and spacing of the alternating black, laminated and lighter coloured, burrowed units at Oued Bahloul is similar to the configuration of the alternating black clays and chalks at Wünstorf and the alternations of darker and lighter units in the Danish Central Graben and in the Bridge Creek Limestone in the United States. The implications of these short term cycles are discussed in Part II of this paper (Arthur *et al.*, this volume).

Morocco and the Atlas Region

Thurow *et al.* (1982) made a detailed investigation of the deposition of organic-carbon rich sediments in Morocco. They point out that 'during Late Cenomanian to Turonian time a peculiar bituminous, biosiliceous type of sediment ("Pthanites" of French authors) interrupts the background sedimentation'. They compare these 'peculiar bituminous, siliceous . . .' sediments to the Bonarelli horizon in the Italian Apennines and other west African basins. These authors stress the high radiolarian content of these carbon-rich beds and propose, based on planktonic foraminifera zonations, that the onset of the 'pthanite-events' in the Moroccan Riff was in the late Cenomanian and was ended by late Turonian. According to their Figure 3 it appears that, at all but one of the six sections described, pthanite deposition ceased by the end of Middle Turonian (*P. helvetica* Zone) time. These authors reject the Schlanger and Jenkyns (1976) oxygen-minimum layer model and proposed Cenomanian–Turonian Oceanic Anoxic Event in favour of their own *ad hoc* coastal upwelling model for the late Cenomanian–Middle Turonian 'pthanite event' (see also Einsele & Wiedmann 1982).

Butt (1982) used benthonic foraminiferal assemblages to analyse the Cretaceous palaeobathymetry and palaeoenvironments of western Morocco. In the Agadir and Essaouira Basins of coastal Morocco the upper Cenomanian sediments were deposited in outer littoral to inner shelf depths under oxygenated conditions. In contrast the Turonian facies contain fish bone beds, and bituminous and phosphatic layers. These sediments contain a low diversity assemblage of planktonic foraminifera but lack benthonic assemblages. The disappearance of benthonic foraminifera in the sections correlates with the sharp early Turonian transgression. According to Butt (1982) the Turonian facies (phosphate, chert and non-keeled planktonic foraminifera) indicate an upwelling of cool water masses as well as an expanded oxygen-minimum zone along the NW African continental slope, which eliminated benthonic faunas. The striking similarity between these data and interpretations and the data and interpretations of Frush and Eicher (1975) concerning the benthonic foraminifera-free zones in the Cenomanian–Turonian of the US Western Interior Basin (see section on North America) and the European data cited above argues strongly, we believe, for the global nature of the encroachment of oxygen-deficient waters into shallow embayments and shelf and epicontinental seas during the Cenomanian–Turonian transgression. Stamm and Thein (1982), based on their analysis of Turonian sedimentation in the Atlas Gulf (their Figure 10), present a model wherein during the early Turonian transgression '. . . wide areas of the Atlas Gulf are influenced by anaerobic to dysaerobic bottom water conditions, overlain by an oxygen-rich water sheet in the photic zone . . .' they appeal to geochemical evidence such as the enrichment of basal Turonian beds in phosphate, silica, and the fixation of iron as pyrite in the Lower Turonian euxinic facies in their interpretation.

Nigeria

The work of Petters and Ekweozor (1982a, b) shows that the Benue Trough in Nigeria was the site of deposition of carbon-rich shales from late Cenomanian to early Santonian time. Although TOC values of 0.5% characterize most of the Albian to Eocene marine shales in the Benue Trough and the Turonian shales in the southern Chad Basin, the Turonian strata of the Nkalagu Formation contain up to 7.4% TOC. The highest values of TOC (7.4%, 3.8%, 4.8%) are in the Nkalagu Formation 'where abundant planktonic foraminifera and sparse to total absence of benthonic fossils suggest anaerobic bottom conditions'. They further point out that the finely laminated, flaggy, fissile, black shales of the Cenomanian–Santonian strata in the Benue Trough are largely devoid of a macrobenthos except for impressions of *Inoceramus*. Even in the intercalated limestones in these black shales the benthonic foraminifera are dwarfed and low in diversity. They compare the Benue Trough faunas to those described by Frush and Eicher (1975) from the US Western Interior Basin both in composition and in terms of deposition in oxygen-deficient waters.

Mozambique

The Domo Formation known from the subsurface of the southern Mozambique Basin has been described and interpreted by Flores (1973). The Domo is made up of dark grey to black, thin bedded, marly shales with some sandy layers. It ranges in age from Aptian–Albian and Albian–Cenomanian in the south to Cenomanian–Turonian in the north, reaching into the *G. helvetica* Zone. Uplifting of the basin borders, which started in Cenomanian time continued into the Turonian. Uninterrupted Cenomanian–Turonian deposition is known only from the basin described above where these dark shales formed in a reducing anoxic palaeoenvironment (Nairn 1978). The stratigraphic range of the Domo and its setting leads to comparisons with Atlantic Basin sections where organic carbon-rich shales were deposited from Aptian through late Cretaceous time (Summerhayes 1981; Graciansky *et al.* 1982). However, the coincidence of Cenomanian–Turonian euxinic sedimentation in the Mozambique Basin and the period of general stagnation postulated by Graciansky *et al.* (1982) to have taken place in the entire north Atlantic in late Cenomanian through early Turonian time is we believe a reflection of the Cenomanian–Turonian oceanic anoxic event.

Zaire

The Kwango Series of the Congo (Zaire) has been described and discussed by Cahen (1954) and Nairn (1978). The Series contains the only marine horizon in the area, the Inzia stage sediments, of Cretaceous age which are characterized by a marine fauna containing fish remains of Cenomanian–Turonian age. Also described from beds of the Inzia stage are the black, fossiliferous shales of Kipala. Bituminous beds are described from these horizons. The presence of this marine horizon in Zaire was taken by Cahen to indicate a marine connection between the Atlantic through the Gulf of Benue and the Cenomanian–Turonian marine fauna of the Inzia stage. We believe that this central African area was similarly influenced by the OAE.

We argue here that the circum-Africa persistence of beds of Cenomanian–Turonian age, interpreted as having been deposited in oxygen-deficient waters from Libya through Tunisia and the Atlas, along the west coast through Morocco and the Benue Trough—indeed into central Africa in Zaire—and along southeast Africa in Mozambique, are not simply the result of a coincidence of tectonic evolution and local upwelling conditions. We regard the deposition of organic carbon-rich beds all around Africa in synchronization with the Cenomanian–Turonian transgression as compelling evidence for the correlation of this transgression with the Cenomanian–Turonian OAE as postulated by Schlanger and Jenkyns (1976). We further propose that the African data support the argument that the Cenomanian–Turonian OAE was a global occurrence.

Pacific Basin and Indian Ocean

In the Pacific Basin three DSDP drill holes have recovered organic carbon-rich strata of Cenomanian–Turonian age relevant to this paper. In two of these, Sites 305 on the Shatsky Rise and 310 on the Hess Rise, poor core recovery makes precise dating difficult. At Site 585 in the Mariana Basin precise dating of the Cenomanian–Turonian section was possible. At Site 171 on Horizon Guyot TOC values of 2.3 and 2.8% were reported in volcaniclastic sediments of Turonian age. However, these values are probably due to the presence of terrestrial plant debris (Winterer *et al.* 1973); this site is not considered further here.

Shatsky Rise, DSDP Site 305 (see Larson & Moberly 1975)

This site was drilled on top of Shatsky Rise, a large plateau that rises from the deep Pacific floor. Core recovery was poor in the Upper Cretaceous section; only rock fragments were recovered as core catcher samples in the Santonian through late Albian section between 290 and 456 m sub-bottom depths. The section is made up entirely of cherty, foraminiferal-nannofossil chalk. In Core 37 a piece of carbonaceous, fissile zeolitic shale with a TOC of 9.3% was recovered. The age of this carbonaceous shale could be as old as early Cenomanian or as young as early Turonian. It is of interest to note here that the foraminiferal fauna in Core 37 is entirely planktonic; no benthonic types are listed.

Hess Rise, DSDP Site 310 (see Larson & Moberly 1975)

On Hess Rise, in a geological setting similar to that of the Shatsky Rise another fragment of black, carbonaceous shale was recovered in a

Cretaceous section of cherty chalk. The rock is described as a fissile, laminated, bituminous, pelagic shale containing thin laminae of pyrite and some siderite; the rock burned when heated (no TOC values are available). Core 17A was taken at a depth interval of 325 to 334 m sub-bottom. It should be noted here that the black, pyritic, laminated shale in Core 17A was barren of foraminifera and so the shale itself could not be assigned an age. Tan shales in Core 17A found as lumps with the fragments of black shale were dated as being within the *R. appenninica* Zone of latest Albian to basal Cenomanian age. Of further interest is that Core 16A taken at a sub-bottom depth of 306 to 315 m, was in the *G. helvetica* Zone of definite Turonian age. Thus the drill must have penetrated, in going from 306 to 334 m in depth, Turonian to late Albian strata; the black shale is probably older than the *G. helvetica* determined Turonian age (above the Cenomanian–Turonian boundary) and could be younger than the tan shales of latest Albian to Cenomanian age and hence could straddle the Cenomanian–Turonian boundary.

Mariana Basin, Site 585

Drilling operations in the Mariana Basin recovered a section of Cenomanian–Turonian radiolarian and zeolite-rich siltstones, claystones and nannofossil chalks. In hole 585 a thin (2 cm) band of radiolarian-rich, black, pyritic, carbonaceous sediment, was found in strata assigned to the *W. archeocretacea* Zone (Leg 89 staff 1983; DSDP Scientific Staff 1983; Premoli Silva & Sliter *pers. comm.*). Analyses by R. Schaefer and P. Mukhopadadhyay made at the Institute for Petroleum and Geochemistry, Julich, Germany show this band to contain 9.9% total carbon with a hydrogen index of 383; the organic carbon is largely of marine planktonic origin. We take this occurrence of carbonaceous sediment to be a manifestation of the Cenomanian–Turonian OAE. However, in contrast to other occurrences of carbonaceous sediments deposited in the Cenomanian–Turonian time envelope, as described above, which were discovered atop oceanic plateaus and rises, the Mariana Basin carbonaceous sediments were deposited in a palaeodepth of from 4 to 5 km. However, the organic carbon-rich sediments may originally have been deposited in much shallower water. The geological history recorded at the site (Leg 89 staff 1983; DSDP Scientific Staff 1983) shows that during Aptian–Albian time large seamounts formed atop the 160 my old Pacific Plate. These seamounts reached sea level by Aptian–Albian time as shown by the large amounts of shallow-water fossil debris and ooids in the volcanogenic section.

The carbonaceous sediment of Cenomanian–Turonian boundary age (*W. archeocretacea* Zone) is in a turbidite section and therefore may be interpreted as a turbidite in itself. It is possible, therefore, that organic carbon-rich sediments were accumulating on the relatively shallow flanks of major seamounts that were, during Cenomanian–Turonian time, projecting upwards from the 4–5 km deep-sea floor into an oxygen-minimum zone the bottom of which was between 1 and 2 km below sea level. The position of this western Pacific occurrence in the *W. archeocretacea* Zone and the occurrence of the Black Band in England and the Bonarelli Horizon in Italy—both in the *W. archeocretacea* Zone—argues for the global nature of the oceanic anoxic event. We point out here that the entire *W. archeocretacea* Zone at Site 585 occupied only 1.5 m or less in Core 32 which also contained sediments, below the black bed, of definite Cenomanian age and sediments, above the black bed, of definite Turonian age. Therefore the occurrence of similar organic carbon-rich shales as fragments in core catcher samples at Sites 305 and 310 is not surprising. The difficulty in precisely dating the Site 305 and 310 black shales allows that they could both be latest Cenomanian to early Turonian in age. We interpret the Shatsky Rise and Hess Rise carbonaceous sediments as being in the form of very thin bands which could both be correlative with the carbonaceous stratum in the Mariana Basin.

Naturaliste Plateau, DSDP Site 258

DSDP Site 258 was drilled on top of the Naturaliste Plateau off the southwest tip of Australia (Davies *et al.* 1974). A coccolith chalk section of Coniacian to late (?) Cenomanian age was cored between a sub-bottom depth of 234.5 m (top of core 12) and 272.5 m (in core 14). The results of isotopic analyses of these chalks is shown on Fig. 18. The $\delta^{13}C$ values of $\sim +2.5\%$ to $+2.6\%$ in the Coniacian–Turonian interval in Core 12 are well within the range of $\delta^{13}C$ values seen in post-Cenomanian–Turonian boundary beds in other regions of the world as discussed above. The higher values, reaching a $\delta^{13}C$ of $+3.77\%$ in the basal Turonian of Core 13 are equivalent to the higher values seen in the $\delta^{13}C$ spikes from other regions. We believe that the $\delta^{13}C$ values obtained from DSDP Site 258 show that the oceanographic effects of the Cenomanian–Turonian OAE were recorded at high latitudes in the Indian Ocean.

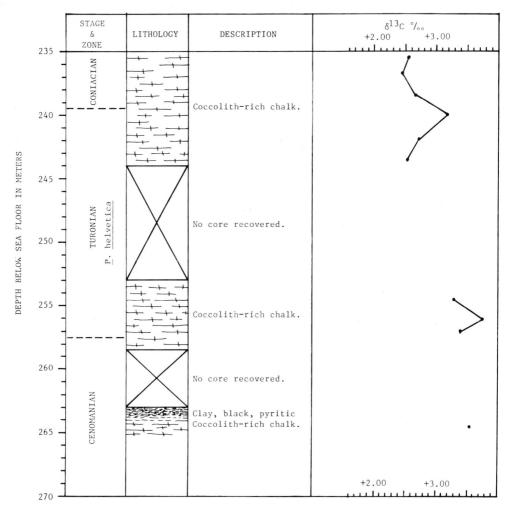

FIG. 18. Stratigraphy and $\delta^{13}C$ analyses of Cenomanian to Coniacian chalks from DSDP Site 258, Naturaliste Plateau, Indian Ocean.

Discussion

With regard to the geographical distribution of laminated, carbon-rich facies and benthonic foraminifera-free sediments that reflect deposition under oxygen-deficient conditions or bear the coeval $\delta^{13}C$ signal, we have attempted to point out that such sediments of Cenomanian–Turonian age are found in a wide variety of basinal settings: circum-African marginal embayments, the US Western Interior Basin, the open pelagic Pacific Basin, and the north European shelf as well as the continental margins of the Tethys. Sediments deposited in appropriate

basinal settings during the Cenomanian–Turonian OAE exhibit some, or in well-developed sections almost all, of the following characteristics:

(1) they are found within sequences of light-coloured pelagic or shelf chalk and limestone;

(2) the shales themselves are fissile (where indurated), laminated rather than bioturbated although the enclosing carbonates are highly bioturbated;

(3) organic carbon values range from 1.0 to 27%; marine-derived organic matter makes up a significant percentage of the total organic carbon;

(4) abundant planktonic foraminiferal assemblages of low diversity may be present but benthonic foraminiferal faunas are absent to sparse or composed of agglutinate types;
(5) fish remains are common.

The black sediments are generally pyritic and relatively rich in phosphate. High silica contents are due to abundant radiolarian tests deposited with the black shales. We argue for the existence of an oxygen-deficient mid-water layer that was developed over much of the world ocean concomitant with the Cenomanian–Turonian transgression. The stratigraphic sections studied show that shallow-water sediments, i.e. those deposited in less than 100–200 metres, do not contain a marked organic carbon-rich layer; the red limestones of the Bürgenstock section in Switzerland and the Salzgitter anticline section in Germany are interpreted as having been deposited above the oxygen-minimum layer in well-oxygenated waters. These shallow-water sediments do, however, display strong $\delta^{13}C$ spikes. The depth of the base of the oxygen-minimum layer is more difficult to determine. Palaeodepth analysis of the Bonarelli Horizon and the Goban Spur and the Mariana Basin occurrences of carbon-rich sediments indicates a depth of 1 to 2 km for the bottom of the oxygen-minimum layer and would account for these. In the stratigraphic sections discussed in this paper the $\delta^{13}C$ spike described at the Cenomanian–Turonian boundary is taken to indicate that large amounts of ^{12}C were being preserved in marine sediments leaving the oceanic reservoir relatively enriched in ^{13}C as reflected in the high $\delta^{13}C$ of both pelagic and shelf limestones deposited during late Cenomanian through early Turonian time. Assuming that the ^{12}C sequestering argument is valid, what is relevant to this discussion of the Cenomanian–Turonian OAE is the global stratigraphical distribution of the $\delta^{13}C$ spike and carbon-rich sediments and the striking coeval character of these sedimentary attributes, within the limits of current palaeontological resolution.

With regard then to the timing of the Cenomanian–Turonian OAE we refer to the original paper of Schlanger and Jenkyns (1976) in which Oceanic Anoxic Events were first described and defined. It was pointed out that the concept of a Cenomanian–Turonian 'Oceanic Anoxic Event' did not '. . . imply that during the *whole* of Cenomanian–Turonian time the entire world ocean was undergoing a *single, continuous* OAE' (emphasis and correction of typographical errors in original publication added in this paper). It was further pointed out that the time boundaries of an Oceanic Anoxic Event as originally defined '. . . should be thought of as enclosing a period of time during which Oceanic Anoxic Events were frequent and prolonged'. With these points in mind we have attempted to show in this present paper that the time period when oceanic oxygen deficiency was most marked was at or close to the Cenomanian–Turonian boundary. This is not intended to imply that the entire, global oceanic water column was entirely anoxic at any one moment in time. The strength, global distribution, and stratigraphic restriction of the $\delta^{13}C$ signal discussed and illustrated above is taken as strong evidence for the existence of a short, sharply defined period during which organic carbon was withdrawn from the oceanic reservoir. Carbon-rich sediments obviously are not found at every known Cenomanian–Turonian contact; due to the vertically restricted depth range of the extant oxygen-minimum zone during this time, much of the sea floor was in oxygenated waters.

Some workers involved in studies of mid-Cretaceous palaeoceanography have called into question the efficacy of the 'Oceanic Anoxic Event' model in explaining the geographical and stratigraphical distribution of the carbonaceous sediments discussed in this paper. They argue (e.g. Parrish 1982; Wiedmann *et al.* 1982; Thiede *et al.* 1982; Einsele & Wiedmann 1982) that local upwelling conditions were the major factor in the accumulation of the anomalously high organic-carbon content of mid-Cretaceous sediments, that there were no discrete, global oceanic anoxic events, and that carbonaceous sediments are actually stratigraphically scattered throughout the rock record during the whole of Cenomanian and Turonian time. Parrish and Curtis (1982), however, do find that many organic carbon-rich strata of these ages cannot be accounted for in their upwelling models and therefore suggest that oceanic anoxic events and transgressions may also have played an important role in deposition of these carbonaceous sediments.

We acknowledge, and indeed have pointed out, that organic carbon-rich beds are found in early to middle Cenomanian and middle Turonian sections—in some areas such as North Africa these bituminous shales extend in time into what has been termed the Coniacian–Santonian Oceanic Anoxic Event by Jenkyns (1980). Indeed, off Northwest Africa, organic carbon enrichment occurred at times throughout the lower through middle Cretaceous interval, and persistent upwelling is the preferred explanation for this (Tissot *et al.* 1980; Arthur & Natland 1979; Summerhayes 1981, etc.). In these areas, local upwelling may have intensified and prolonged the Oceanic Anoxic Event. These early to middle Cenomanian occurrences could be temporal predecessors formed by upwelling conditions in an already poorly oxygenated ocean. In the US Western Interior Basin, the two benthonic-free zones described by Frush and Eicher (1975) in both late Cenomanian and early Turonian time may indicate that more than one intensification of the oxygen-minimum zone occurred close to the Cenomanian–Turonian boundary. We argue that local upwelling conditions do not account for many of the widespread occurrences of sediments deposited under oxygen-deficient conditions (see part II, Arthur *et al.* this volume, for a detailed discussion of palaeoceanographic arguments relative to upwelling as a factor).

It has been suggested that volcanism plays an important role in the development of carbon-rich sediments because the addition of volcanic sediment to the background sedimentation produces high sedimentation rates that tend to bury organic carbon and thus preserve it from recycling. The smectite content of the Black Band in England and the Bonarelli Horizon in Italy, the increase in manganese at the $\delta^{13}C$ spike in French sections (Pomerol 1983), the bentonites in the Hartland Shale–Bridge Creek Limestone section of the US Western Interior Basin, and the obvious volcanic context of the Pacific Basin occurrences can be taken as evidence of volcanic activity at the Cenomanian–Turonian boundary. However, we point out that Cretaceous time from 115 to 70 myBP was a period of intense and widespread volcanic activity (Schlanger *et al.* 1981; Axelrod 1981). It is well known that the tenor of organic carbon in sediments is, in part, a function of sedimentation rate. However, this is true in general for clastic sequences that lack volcanic contributions (Müller & Suess 1979) and for pure carbonate sequences in pelagic settings (Pedersen 1983). That there is a correlation between the intensity of volcanism in the mid-Cretaceous and the occurrence of carbonaceous sediments cannot be denied. However, a causal link is difficult to establish unless, as it has already

been argued, transgressions which are linked to Oceanic Anoxic Events are the result of increased volcanic activity in the ocean basins (Hays & Pitman 1973; Schlanger *et al.* 1981); however, the geochemical implications of such intense volcanism should be explored.

The association of Mn deposition and oceanic anoxic events is, we believe, an indicator that other metals may show similar patterns of association.

We propose, based on the stratigraphic evidence presented, that the world ocean in Cenomanian–Turonian time displayed a tendency towards oxygen deficiency. This oxygen-deficient tendency was intensified during the sharp transgression that marked late Cenomanian–early Turonian time. The Cenomanian–Turonian boundary passage beds therefore bear the strong imprint of a globally distributed oxygen-minimum zone that impinged on marine sedimentary environments throughout the world during a short period of less than 1 my; this period of widespread oxygen deficiency has been termed the Cenomanian–Turonian Oceanic Anoxic Event by Schlanger and Jenkyns (1976).

ACKNOWLEDGEMENTS: This work was supported by Grant no. EAR-8207387 from the US National Science Foundation to the University of Hawaii and to Northwestern University. We wish to thank E. Nygaard of the Geological Survey of Denmark for his help in examining cores from the Danish Central Graben. G. Ernst, of the Free University of Berlin, F. Schmid, and P. Cepek of the Geological Survey of Germany (BGR) were of great help in our studies of the Wünstorf-Salzgitter Anticline area. Prof. H. Bolli (ETH, Zürich) helped us to find localities in the Swiss Alps. M. McDonald of Houston Oil and Minerals Co. of Tunisia and A. bel Haiza of ETAP guided us in the field and made available to us data on the Bahloul Formation. I. Premoli-Silva of the University of Milan introduced some of us to the peculiarities of Cretaceous sediments in Italy and with W. Sliter of the US Geological Survey contributed discussions on the foraminiferal zonation of mid-Cretaceous strata.

References

ARTHUR, M. A. & NATLAND, J. H. 1979. Carbonaceous sediments in North and South Atlantic: the role of salinity in stable stratification of early Cretaceous basins. *In:* TALWANI, M., HAY, W. W. & RYAN, W. B. F. (eds), *Deep Drilling Results in the Atlantic Ocean: Continental Margins and Paleoenvironment.* Washington, American Geophysical Union, M. Ewing Series, **3**, 297–344.

—— & PREMOLI-SILVA, I. 1982. Development of widespread organic carbon-rich strata in the Mediterranean Tethys. *In:* SCHLANGER, S. O. & CITA, M. B. (eds), *Nature and Origin of Cretaceous Carbon-Rich Facies.* Academic Press, London, 7–54.

—— & SCHLANGER, S. O. 1979. Cretaceous 'oceanic

anoxic events' as causal factors in development of reef-reservoired giant oil fields. *Bull. Am. Ass. Petrol. Geol.,* **63**, 870–885.

——, —— & JENKYNS, H. C. 1986. The Cenomanian–Turonian oceanic anoxic event, II. Paleoceanographic controls on organic matter production and preservation, this volume.

AXELROD, D. I. 1981. Role of volcanism in climate and evolution. *Spec. Pap. Geol. Soc. Am.,* **185**, 1–59.

BARRON, E. J. & WASHINGTON, W. M. 1983. Numerical climate modeling: An exploration frontier in petroleum source rock prediction. *Bull. Am. Ass. Petrol. Geol.,* **67**, 419.

BERGER, W. & VON RAD, V. 1972. Cretaceous and

Cenozoic sediments from the Atlantic Ocean. *In:* HAYS, D. E., PIMM, A. C. *et al. Initial Reports Deep Sea Drilling Project*, **14**, U.S. Government Printing Office, Washington D.C., 784–954.

BIRKENMAYER, K. 1977. Jurassic and Cretaceous lithostratigraphic units of the Pieniny Klippen Belt, Carpathians, Poland. *Studia Geol. Pol.*, **45**, 1–58.

BIRKENMAYER, K. & JEDNOROWSKA, A. 1984. Upper Cretaceous stratigraphy in the Pieniny Nappe at Sromowce Nizne, Pieniny Klippen Belt (Carpathians, Poland). *Studia Geol. Pol.*, **83**, 25–50.

BISMUTH, H., BOLTENHAGEN, C., DONZE, P., FÈVRE, J. & SAINT-MARC, P. 1982. Etude sédimentologique et biostratigraphique du Crétacé moyen et supérieur du Djebel Semmama (Tunisie du Centre Nord). *Cretaceous Res.*, **3**, 171–185.

BOER, P. L. DE, 1982. Cyclicity and the storage of organic matter in middle Cretaceous pelagic sediments. *In:* EINSELE, G. & SEILACHER, A. (eds). *Cyclic and Event Stratification.* Springer-Verlag, Berlin, 456–475.

BOLLI, H. 1944. Zur stratigraphie der oberen Kreide in den höheren helvetischen decken. *Eclog. Geol. Helv.*, **37**, 217–329.

BOSELLINI, A., LORIGA, C. & BUSETTO, C. 1978. I bacini cretacei del Trentino. *Riv. Ital. Paleont.*, **84**, 897–946.

BROMLEY, R. G. & EKDALE, A. A. 1984. *Chondrites:* A trace fossil indicator of anoxia in sediments. *Science*, **224**, 872–874.

BURNHILL, T. J. & RAMSAY, W. V. 1981. Mid-Cretaceous paleontology and stratigraphy, Central North Sea. *In:* ILLING, L. V. & HOBSON, G. D. (eds). *Petroleum Geology of the Continental Shelf of North-West Europe*, Institute of Petroleum, London, 245–254.

BUROLLET, P. F. 1956. Contribution à l'étude stratigraphique de la Tunisie centrale. *Ann. Mines Geol., Tunis*, **18**, 1–350.

—— 1975. Géologie et sédimentologie de la Tunisie. Exc. **15**, IX Cong. Int. Sed., Nice, France, 172 pp.

BUTT, A. 1982. Micropaleontological bathymetry of the Cretaceous of western Morocco. *Paleogeogr., Paleoclimatol., Paleoecol.*, **37**, 235–275.

CAHEN, L. 1954. *Géologie du Congo Belge.* H. Vaillant-Carmanne, S. A., Liege, 547 pp.

CANNON, W. F. & FORCE, E. R. 1983. Potential for high-grade shallow marine manganese deposits in North America. *In:* SHANKS, W. P. (ed.), *Cameron Volume on Unconventional Mineral Deposits*, American Inst. of Mining, Metallurgical, and Petroleum Engineers, Inc., New York, 175–189.

CLIFFORD, H. J., ROGERS, G. & MUSRATI, H. 1980. Geology of a stratigraphic giant: Messla field, Libya. *In:* HALBOUTY, M. (ed.). *Giant Oil Fields of the Decade 1968–1978*, Mem. Am. Ass. Petrol. Geol., **30**, 507–524.

CUNNINGHAM, R. & KROOPNICK, P. M. 1985. Inorganic and isotopic geochemistry of sediments from DSDP Sites 549–551, northern North Atlantic. *In:* POAG, W., DE GRACIANSKY, P. C. *et al. Initial Reports Deep Sea Drilling Project*, **80**, U.S. Government Printing Office, Washington, D.C., 1073–1079.

DAVIES, T. A., LUYENDYK, B. P. *et al.* 1974. *Initial Reports of the Deep Sea Drilling Project*, **26**, U.S.

Government Printing Office, Washington, D.C., 1129 p.

DAVIS, A. E. 1958. The Pepper shale. *Guide to the mid-Cretaceous geology of Central Texas. Baylor Geol. Soc.*, 67–69.

DEEGAN, C. E. & SCULL, B. J. 1977. A proposed standard lithostratigraphic nomenclature for the Central and Northern North Sea. *Rep. Inst. Geol. Sci., No. 77/25*, 36 pp.

DEMAISON, G. J. & MOORE, G. T. 1980. Anoxic environments and oil source bed genesis. *Bull. Am. Ass. Petrol. Geol.*, **64**, 1179–1209.

DSDP SCIENTIFIC STAFF 1982. Goban Spur Transect is drilled. *Geotimes*, **27/5**, 23–24.

—— 1983. Leg 89 drills Cretaceous volcanics. *Geotimes*, **28/4**, 17–20.

DÜRR, ST. H. 1967. Geologie de Serrañia de Ronda und ihrer sudwestlicher Ausläüfer (Andalusien). *Geol. Romana*, **6**, 1–73.

EINSELE, G. & WIEDMANN, J. 1982. Turonian black shales in the Moroccan coastal basins: first upwelling in the Atlantic Ocean? *In:* VON RAD, U., HINZ, K., SARNTHEIN, M. & SEIBOLD, E. (eds). *Geology of the Northwest African Margin.* Springer-Verlag, New York, 396–414.

ERNST, G., SCHMID, F. & KLISCHIES, G. 1979. Multistratigraphische Untersuchungen in der Oberkreide des Raums Braunschweig-Hannover. *In:* WIEDMANN, J. (ed.). *Aspeckte der Kreide Europas.* Int. Union Geol. Sciences, Series A, No. **6**, 11–46.

FINCH, R. C. 1981. Mesozoic stratigraphy of central Honduras. *Bull. Am. Ass. Petrol. Geol.*, **65**, 1320–1333.

FISCHER, A. G. 1980. Gilbert-bedding rhythms and geochronology. *Spec. Pap. geol. Soc. Am.*, **183**, 93–104.

—— & ARTHUR, M. A. 1977. Secular variations in the pelagic realm. *Spec. Publ. Soc. econ. Paleont. Miner.* **25**, 19–50.

FLORES, G. 1973. The Cretaceous and Tertiary sedimentary basins on Mozambique and Zululand. *In:* BLANT, G. (ed.). *Basins Sedimentaires du Littoral Africain.* Assoc. Serv. Geol. Africains, Paris, 81–111.

FORCE, E. R., CANNON, W. F., KOSKI, R. A., PASSMORE, K. T. & DOE, B. R. 1983. Influences of ocean anoxic events on manganese deposition and ophiolite-hosted sulphide preservation. *Paleoclimate and Mineral Deposits*, U.S. Geological Survey Circular **822**, 26–29.

FRUSH, M. P. & EICHER, D. L. 1975. Cenomanian and Turonian foraminifera and paleoenvironments in the Big Bend region of Texas and Mexico. *Spec. Pap. geol. Ass. Canada*, **13**, 277–301.

GRACIANSKY, P. C. DE, BROSSE, E., *et al.* 1982. Les formations d'âge crétacé de l'Atlantique Nord et leur matière organique: paléogéographie et milieux de dépôt. *Revue de L'Institut Français du Petrole*, **37**, 275–336.

GRAAS, G. VAN, VIETS, T. C., DE LEEUW, J. W. & SCHENCK, P. S. 1983. A study of the soluble and insoluble organic matter from the Livello Bonarelli, a Cretaceous black shale deposit in the Central Apennines, Italy. *Geochim. cosmochim. Acta*, **47**, 1051–1059.

GROUPE DE TRAVAIL EUROPÉEN DES FORAMINIFÈRES PLANCTONIQUES 1979. Atlas de foraminifères planctoniques du Crétacé Moyen (Mer Boréale et Téthys). *Cahiers de Micropaleont.*, **1**, 30 p.

HALLAM, A. & SELLWOOD, B. W. 1968. Origin of Fuller's earth in the Mesozoic of southern England. *Nature*, **220**, 1193–1195.

HARLAND, W. B., COX, A. U., LLEWELLYN, P. G., PICKTON, C. A. G., SMITH, A. G. & WALTERS, R. 1982. *A Geologic Time Scale.* Cambridge University Press, Cambridge, 131 pp.

HART, M. B. 1985. Oceanic anoxic event 2 on-shore and off-shore S.W. England. *Proc. Ussher Soc.*, **6**, 183–190.

—— & BIGG, P. J. 1981. Anoxic events in the chalk seas of north-west Europe. *In:* NEALE, J. W. & BRASIER, M. D. (eds). *Microfossils from Recent and Fossil Seas.* The British Micropalaeont. Soc., 177–185.

HAYS, J. D. & PITMAN, W. C. 1973. Lithospheric plate motion, sea level changes and climatic and ecological consequences. *Nature*, **246**, 18–22.

HERNANDEZ-PACHECO, F. 1936. Los materiales bituminosos de la Serranía de Ronda (Málaga). *Bolet. Soc. Española Nat. Hist.*, **36**, 245–275.

HINTE, J. E. VAN. 1976. A Cretaceous time scale. *Bull. Am. Ass. Petrol. Geol.*, **60**, 498–516.

IRVING, E., NORTH, T. K. & COUILLARD, R. 1974. Oil, climate and tectonics. *Can. J. Earth Sci.*, **11**, 1–15.

JEFFERIES, R. P. S. 1963. The stratigraphy of the *Actinocamax plenus* subzone (Turonian) in the Anglo-Paris Basin. *Proc. geol. Soc. London*, **74**, 1–31.

JENKYNS, H. C. 1980. Cretaceous anoxic events: from continents to oceans. *J. geol. Soc. London*, **137**, 171–188.

KAUFFMAN, E. G. 1977. Geological and biological overview: western interior Cretaceous basin. *Mountain Geologist*, **14**, 75–99.

KENNEDY, W. J. & GARRISON, R. E. 1975. Morphology and genesis of nodular chalks and hard grounds in the upper Cretaceous of southern England. *Sedimentology*, **22**, 311–386.

—— & JUIGNET, P. 1974. Carbonate banks and slump beds in the upper Cretaceous (upper Turonian–Santonian) of Haute Normandie, France. *Sedimentology*, **21**, 1–42.

——, WRIGHT, C. W. & HANCOCK, J. M. 1981. Ammonite zonation and correlation of the uppermost Cenomanian and Turonian of southern England, Sarthe, and Touraine. *In:* Groupe Français de Crétacé, *Colloque sur le Turonien,* Mem. Mus. Nat. His. Naturelle, Paris, 175–183.

LANPHERE, M. A. & TAILLEUR, I. L. 1983. K-Ar ages of bentonites in the Seabee Formation, northern Alaska: a Late Cretaceous (Turonian) time-scale point, *Cretaceous Res.*, **4**, 361–370.

LARSON, R. L., MOBERLY, R. *et al.* 1975. *Initial Reports of the Deep Sea Drilling Project,* **32**, U.S. Government Printing Office, Washington, D.C., 973 pp.

LAWRENCE, S. & COSTER, P. 1985. Petroleum potential of offshore Guyana. *Oil & Gas Jl.*, **83** (Dec. 9th), 67–74.

LEG 89 STAFF 1983. The Mesozoic superocean. *Nature*, **302**, 381.

LEPLAT, J. & ROBASZYNSKI, F. 1971. Une couche á rotalipores dans les "Dièves" (Crétacé supérieur) dans un sondage à Trith (Nord). *Ann. Soc. géol. Nord*, **91**, 199–202.

LETOLLE, R. & POMEROL, B. 1980. Mise en évidence dans les craies du Bassin de Paris d'un accident dans le répartition du $\delta^{13}C$ d'âge Cénomanian terminal. *C.R. Acad. Sc. Paris*, **291**, Serie D, 133–136.

MCNEIL, D. H. & CALDWELL, W. G. E. 1981. Cretaceous rocks and their foraminifera in the Manitoba escarpment. *Spec. Pap. Geol. Ass. Canada*, **21**, 1–439.

MICHELSEN, O. (ed.) 1982. *Geology of the Danish Central Graben.* Geol. Survey Denmark, Series B, **8**, 132 pp.

MÜLLER, P. J. & SUESS, E. 1979. Productivity, sedimentation rate, and sedimentary organic matter in the oceans—I. Organic carbon preservation. *Deep-Sea Res.*, **26A**, 1347–1362.

NAIDIN, D. P. 1981. The Russian platform and the Crimea. *In:* REYMENT, R. A. & BENGTSON, P. (eds). *Aspects of Mid-Cretaceous Geology.* Academic Press, New York, 29–68.

NAIRN, A. E. M. 1978. Northern and eastern Africa. *In:* MOULLADE, M. & NAIRN, A. E. M. (eds). *The Phanerozoic Geology of the World II: The Mesozoic, A.* Elsevier Sci. Pub. Co., New York, 329–370.

NORTH, T. K. 1979. Episodes of source-sediment deposition. *J. Petrol. Geol.*, **2**, 199–218.

NYGAARD, E., LIEBERKIND, K., FRYEMAN, P. 1983. Sedimentology and reservoir parameters of the Chalk Group in the Danish Central Graben. *In:* KAASSCHIETER, J. P. H. & REIJERS, T. J. A. (eds). *Petroleum Geology of the Southeastern North Sea and the Adjacent Onshore Areas.* Geol. N Mijnbouw, **62**, 177–190.

PARRISH, J. T. 1982. Upwelling and petroleum source beds, with reference to Paleozoic. *Bull. Am. Ass. Petrol. Geol.*, **66**, 750–774.

—— & CURTIS, R. L. 1982. Atmospheric circulation, upwelling, and organic rich rocks in the Mesozoic and Cenozoic eras. *Paleogeogr., Paleoclimatol., Paleoecol.*, **40**, 31–66.

PEDERSEN, T. F. 1983. Increased productivity in the eastern equatorial Pacific during the last glacial maximum (19,000 to 14,000 yr B.P.). *Geology*, **11**, 16–19.

PETTERS, S. W. & EKWEOZOR, C. M. 1982a. Origin of mid-Cretaceous black shale in the Benue Trough, Nigeria. *Paleogeogr., Paleoclimatol., Paleoecol.*, **40**, 311–319.

—— & —— 1982b. Petroleum geology of Benue Trough and southeastern Chad Basin, Nigeria. *Bull. Am. Ass. Petrol. Geol.*, **66**, 1141–1149.

POLŠAK, A., BAUER, V. G. & SLIŠKOVIĆ, T. 1982. Stratigraphie du Crétacé Supérieur de la plateforme carbonatée dans les Dinarides Externes, *Cretaceous Res.*, **3**, 125–133.

POMEROL, B. 1983. Geochemistry of the late Cenomanian–early Turonian chalks of the Paris basin: manganese and carbon isotopes in carbonates as paleoceanographic indicators. *Cretaceous Res.*, **4**, 85–93.

PRATT, L. 1982. Rhythmic sedimentation documented in a Late Cretaceous core (abstract). *In:* EINSELE, G. & SEILACHER, A. (eds). *Cyclic and Event Stratification.* Springer-Verlag, Berlin, p. 96.

—— 1984. Influence of paleoenvironmental factors on preservation of organic matter in Middle Cretaceous Greenhorn Formation, Pueblo, Colorado. *Bull. Am. Assoc. Petrol. Geol.,* **68**, 1146–1159.

—— & THREKELD, C. N. 1984. Stratigraphic significance of $^{13}C/^{12}C$ ratios in mid-Cretaceous rocks of the Western Interior, USA. *In:* STOTT, D. F. & GLASS, D. J. (eds) *The Mesozoic of middle North America.* Mem. Can. Petrol. Geol., **9**, 305–312.

RENZ, O. 1981. Venezuela. *In:* REYMENT, R. A. & BENGTSON, P. (eds). *Aspects of Mid-Cretaceous Regional Geology.* Academic Press, New York, 197–220.

REYMENT, R. A. 1981. Colombia. *In:* REYMENT, R. A. & BENGTSON, P. (eds). *Aspects of Mid-Cretaceous Regional Geology.* Academic Press, New York, 175–196.

ROBASZYNSKI, F. 1971a. Les foraminifères pélagiques des "Dièves" crétacées aux abords du golfe de Mons (Belgique). *Ann. Soc. géol. Nord,* **91**, 31–38.

ROBASZYNSKI, F. 1971b. Les "Dièves" de Mauberge (Nord) et leurs deux Tourtias (Crétacé supérieur). *Ann. Soc. géol. Nord,* **91**, 193–197.

RYAN, W. B. F. & CITA, M. B. 1977. Ignorance concerning episodes of ocean-wide stagnation. *Marine Geol.,* **23**, 197–215.

SALAJ, J. 1976. Contribution a la microstratigraphie du Mesozoique et du Tertiare de Tunisie septentrionale. *Notes du Service Geol. de Tunisie,* **42**, 29–69.

—— 1978. The geology of the Pelagian Block: the Eastern Tunisian platform. *In:* NAIRN, A. E. M. & KANES, W. H. (eds). *The Ocean Basins and Margins.* Vol. 4B, The Western Mediterranean, 361–416.

SCHÄFER, W. 1972. *Ecology and Paleoecology of Marine Environments.* Oliver and Boyd, Edinburgh, 538 pp.

SCHLANGER, S. O. & CITA, M. B. (eds) 1982. *Nature and Origin of Cretaceous Carbon-rich Facies.* Academic Press, New York, 229 pp.

—— & JENKYNS, H. C. 1976. Cretaceous oceanic anoxic events: causes and consequences. *Geol. Mijnbouw,* **55**, 179–184.

——, —— & PREMOLI-SILVA, I. 1981. Volcanism and vertical tectonics in the Pacific basin related to global Cretaceous transgressions. *Earth Planet. Sci. Lett.,* **52**, 435–449.

SCHMID, F. VON & SPAETH, C. 1980. Erster Nachweis von Schwarzschiefern im Unter-Turon Helgolands (Nordsee, NW-Deutschland). *N. Jb. Geol. Pälaont. Mh., H.* **11**, 703–706.

SCHOLLE, P. A. & ARTHUR, M. A. 1980. Carbon isotope fluctuations in Cretaceous pelagic limestones: potential stratigraphic and petroleum exploration tool. *Bull. Am. Ass. Petrol. Geol.,* **64**, 67–87.

SIMPSON, T. 1975. Marine lithofacies and biofacies of the Colorado Group (middle Albian to Santonian). *In:* Saskatchewan. *Spec. Pap. Geol. Ass. Canada,* **13**, 553–587.

STAMM, R. & THEIN, J. 1982. Sedimentation in the Atlas Gulf, III: Turonian carbonates. *In:* VON RAD, U., HINZ, K., SARNTHEIN, M. & SEIBOLD, E. (eds). *Geology of the Northwest African Margin,* Springer-Verlag, New York, 459–474.

SUMMERHAYES, C. P. 1981. Organic facies of middle Cretaceous black shales in deep North Atlantic. *Bull. Am. Ass. Petrol. Geol.,* **65**, 2364–2380.

THIEDE J. & VAN ANDEL, T. H. 1977. The paleoenvironment of anaerobic sediments in the late Mesozoic South Atlantic Ocean. *Earth Planet. Science Lett.,* **33**, 301–309.

——, DEAN, W. E. & CLAYPOOL, G. E. 1982. Oxygen deficient paleoenvironments in the mid-Cretaceous tropical and subtropical Pacific Ocean. *In:* SCHLANGER, S. O. & CITA, M. B. (eds). *Nature and Origin of Cretaceous Carbon-rich Facies.* Academic Press, London, 79–100.

THUROW, J., KUHNT, W. & WIEDMANN, J. 1982. Zeitlicher and paläogeographisher Rahmen der Pthanit-und Black Shale Sedimentation in Marokko. *N. Jb. Geol. Paläont. Abh.,* **165**, 147–176.

TISSOT, B. 1979. Effects on prolific petroleum source rocks and major coal deposits caused by sea level changes. *Nature,* **277**, 463–465.

——, DEMAISON, G., MASSON, P., DELTEIL, J. R. & COMBAZ, A. 1980. Paleoenvironment and petroleum potential of middle Cretaceous black shales in Atlantic basins. *Bull. Am. Ass. Petrol. Geol.,* **64**, 2051–2063.

VALENTINE, P. C. 1982. Upper Cretaceous subsurface stratigraphy and structure of coastal Georgia and South Carolina. *Prof. Pap. U.S. Geol. Surv.* **1222**, 1–33.

WALL, J. H. 1983. Jurassic and Cretaceous foraminiferal biostratigraphy in the eastern Sverdrup Basin, Canadian Arctic Archipelago, *Bull. Can. Petroleum Geology,* **31**, 246–281.

WAPLES, D. W. & CUNNINGHAM, R. 1985. Shipboard organic geochemistry, Leg 80, Deep Sea Drilling Project. *In:* POAG, W., DE GRACIANSKY, P. C. *et al. Initial Reports Deep Sea Drilling Project,* **80**, US Government Printing Office, Washington, D.C., 949–968.

WIEDMANN, J., BUTT, A. & EINSELE, G. 1982. Cretaceous stratigraphy, environment and subsidence history at the Moroccan continental margin. *In:* VON RAD, U., HINZ, K., SARNTHEIM, M. & SEIBOLD, E. (eds), *Geology of the Northwest African Margin.* Springer-Verlag, New York, 366–395.

WINTERER, E. L., EWING, J. I. *et al.* 1973. *Initial Reports of the Deep Sea Drilling Project,* **17**. US Government Printing Office, Washington, D.C. 927 pp.

S. O. SCHLANGER, Department of Geological Sciences, Northwestern University, Evanston, IL 60201, USA.

M. A. ARTHUR, Graduate School of Oceanography, University of Rhode Island, Narragansett, RI 02882, USA.

H. C. JENKYNS, Department of Earth Sciences, Oxford University, Parks Road, Oxford OX1 3PR, UK.

P. A. SCHOLLE, Southern Methodist University, Dallas, TX 75275, USA.

The Cenomanian–Turonian Oceanic Anoxic Event, II. Palaeoceanographic controls on organic-matter production and preservation

M. A. Arthur, S. O. Schlanger & H. C. Jenkyns

S U M M A R Y : Correlation of the $\delta^{13}C$ spike with the well dated occurrences of strata rich in organic carbon detailed in Schlanger *et al.* (this volume), indicates that a global episode of intense organic carbon (*org*C) burial took place during the latest Cenomanian–earliest Turonian 'Oceanic Anoxic Event' (OAE) (*A. plenus* through *I. labiatus* macrofossil zones and upper *R. cushmani* TRZ through *W. archecretacea* PRZ foraminiferal zones) over a period of no more than 1 million years (m.y.). The shape of the $\delta^{13}C$ curve indicates that rates of *org*C burial gradually increased in the early part of the late Cenomanian, increased more rapidly in the later Cenomanian, and levelled off at peak values in latest Cenomanian–early Turonian time during the maximum rate of *org*C burial. The $\delta^{13}C$ values decreased nearly to pre-late Cenomanian levels in the early to middle Turonian. The decrease in $\delta^{13}C$ reflects decreasing rates of *org*C burial following the Cenomanian–Turonian 'oceanic anoxic event' as well as the probable oxidation and return of significant amounts of *org*C to the oceans following regression and re-oxygenation of much of the deeper water masses in contact with the seafloor.

The Cenomanian–Turonian OAE coincided with a maximum sea level highstand. We suggest that sea level, which may be responding to some volcano-tectonic event, is the common link and ultimately the driving force for *org*C deposition in globally distributed basins under different climatic and ocean circulation regimes. The rate of production of warm, saline deep water may have been proportional to the area of shelf flooding such that the maximum occurred near the Cenomanian-Turonian boundary. As rates of deep-water formation increased, rates of upwelling of deeper oceanic water masses must also have increased thereby increasing sea-surface fertility and productivity. In somewhat restricted higher latitude basins, such as the Cretaceous Interior Seaway of North America, periodic high rates of freshwater runoff coupled with deepening seas during the transgression created periodic salinity stratification, oxygen depletion in bottom waters, and resultant enhanced *org*C preservation.

The disappearance of some types of keeled planktonic foraminifers and ammonites at the Cenomanian–Turonian boundary is probably due to the rather sudden but short-term disappearance of suitable shallow midwater habitats because of widespread severe oxygen depletion in these levels. This interpretation is strengthened by the occurrence of benthic-free zones or depauperate benthic faunas near the Cenomanian–Turonian boundary in many localities.

Introduction

In a companion paper in this volume (Schlanger *et al.*, 1987), we have presented lithological, biostratigraphical, and geochemical data from five continents and several major ocean basins which demonstrate that a significant short-term, global, marine organic carbon (*org*C) burial event occurred during the Middle Cretaceous (Fig. 1). This episode of enhanced *org*C burial took place in conjunction with a major but relatively brief global sea level rise during late Cenomanian–early Turonian time, but the main interval of increased *org*C burial rates on continental margins and in epicontinental seas probably occurred over a period of less than 1 m.y. during maximum transgression in latest Cenomanian–earliest Turonian time. This episode of deposition of carbonaceous strata was termed the Cenomanian–Turonian 'Oceanic Anoxic Event' (OAE) by Schlanger and Jenkyns (1976).

The term 'OAE', which has now become ensconced in the literature, was not meant to imply that anoxic conditions existed throughout the global oceanic water column or even that organic carbon burial took place in every marine section during the event. We consider the term OAE as a useful way of referring to time-bounded envelopes of particularly, perhaps more globally, widespread deposition of *org*C-rich sediment (black shale) in marine environments.

Our aim in this paper is to present a model for the origin of the Cenomanian–Turonian 'OAE' which integrates regional and palaeodepth variations in the amounts and types of *org*C preserved in Cenomanian–Turonian marine strata with

From: BROOKS, J. & FLEET, A. J. (eds) 1987, *Marine Petroleum Source Rocks*
Geological Society Special Publication No. 26 pp. 401–420.

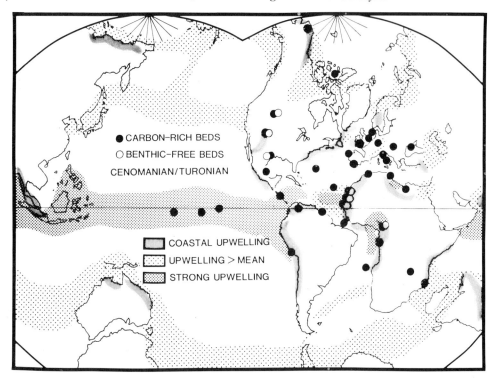

Fig. 1. Predicted areas of upwelling for the mid-Cretaceous (from E. J. Barron, *pers. comm.*; based on results of modelling using the NCAR Community Climate Model) plotted on a Cenomanian–Turonian palaeocontinental reconstruction (see Schlanger *et al.*, 1987). Different shadings represent types or intensity of upwelling. Black dots are known organic carbon-rich Cenomanian–Turonian localities (from Schlanger *et al.*, 1987) with the inclusion of additional North Atlantic Deep Sea Drilling Project Sites (see Fig. 2).

related changes in sea level, climate and palae-oceanography. The model involves feedback between volcano-tectonic events, sea level, climate, and consequent changes in the development of oceanic surface- and deep-water masses. The changing density stratification and rates of deep-water production are probably responsible for an increase in the nutrient supply and concommitant surface biological productivity in some regions while promoting intensification of the midwater oxygen-minimum zone and enhanced preservation of *org*C as well. In some regions, characterized by humid climates and high rates of fresh-water runoff, rising sea level apparently led to the episodic development of salinity-stratified water masses with consequent oxygen-depletion in the lower part of the water column. *Org*C preservation could thus be enhanced with or without increases in surface productivity in such circumstances.

The recognition, understanding, and modelling of OAEs is important both for the understanding of the relationship between tectonic events, sea level, ocean circulation and chemistry, and for

hydrocarbon exploration. Prediction of the stratigraphic distribution and organic richness of hydrocarbon source beds in sedimentary basins is a fundamental goal of such modelling. Obviously, Cretaceous sequences are a major potential and actual hydrocarbon source-bed interval (Irving *et al.* 1974; Moody 1975; Arthur & Schlanger 1979; Tissot 1979; North 1979; Bois *et al.* 1980) and are therefore of prime interest to explorationists and researchers alike.

Timing of Cenomanian–Turonian events and the duration of the primary organic-carbon burial episode

Schlanger *et al.* (1987) presented evidence for the biostratigraphic correlation of 'black shale' beds or *org*C-rich strata and additional evidence for the important carbon isotope excursion (Scholle & Arthur 1980) in marine sediments of Cenomanian–Turonian age in a large part of the world. It appears that the important *org*C burial event and the maximum of the correlative positive δ^{13}C 'spike' occurred in most intermediate and shallow water depositional sites within the *Whiteinella archeocretacea* PRZ at the Cenomanian–Turonian boundary transition, although the trend towards more positive δ^{13}C values probably began some time in the late Cenomanian. Nearly all *org*C-rich beds in NW Europe are confined to the interval *Actinocamax plenus* through *Inoceramus labiatus* (latest Cenomanian through earliest Turonian) and mainly within the *W. archeocretacea* PRZ on a global basis.

The planktonic foraminiferal *Whiteinella archeocretacea* PRZ probably represents less than 1 m.y. in absolute time (see Fig. 3, Schlanger *et al.* 1986); most of the *org*C-rich layers, which are generally calcareous shales or marlstones and commonly, but not always, contain significant amounts of radiolarian tests, occupy less than half of that interval. The peak organic-carbon burial event, as indicated by *org*C and δ^{13}C

patterns, therefore occurred in less than 1 m.y. However, there may be some age pattern to the partitioning of *org*C preservation in deep *vs.* shallow water sites (Fig. 2) which suggests a slightly longer-term overall OAE, provides constraints on models for the origin of the OAE, and may help to explain the pattern of global δ^{13}C variations during the mid-Cretaceous.

Because the lithology of the Cenomanian–Turonian organic-carbon rich strata commonly differs from enclosing sedimentary rocks, it is important to gauge the relative rates of accumulation of the *org*C-rich interval, particularly because *org*C preservation may be, in part, a function of sedimentation rate (e.g. Müller & Suess 1979). Some independent estimates of the duration of the *org*C-rich episode are available from a few sequences. In the Umbrian Apennines, central Italy, the so-called Bonarelli horizon is a particularly *org*C- and radiolarian-rich black shale bed (up to 23% *org*C) with a maximum thickness of 1 metre. Arthur (1979a) and Arthur and Premoli Silva (1982) estimated a possible

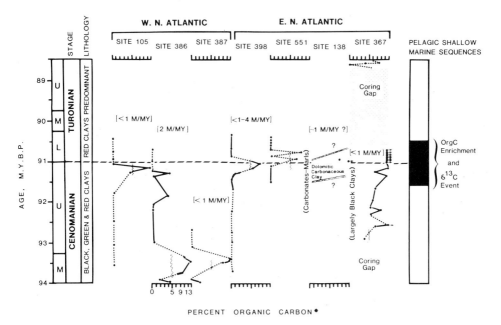

PERCENT ORGANIC CARBON *

* NOTE: scale change above 5%
[< 1 M/MY] average sedimentation rates
•– OrgC >15%

FIG. 2. North Atlantic DSDP Sites which recovered known Cenomanian–Turonian age sediments. Stratigraphy revised by de Graciansky *et al.* (1982). Organic carbon data from relevant DSDP Initial Reports and other sources; note scale change above 5% *org*C. Sample locations approximate in time framework on basis of interpolation of average sedimentation rates (shown in brackets). Turonian data are usually lacking because sediments are slowly deposited red clays. Note age comparison with black, *org*C-rich beds in pelagic shallow-marine sequences.

duration of 200,000 y to 600,000 y for the deposition of the Bonarelli bed, using the van Hinte (1976) timescale, on the basis of varve thickness and on the assumption that Al and Ti accumulation rates did not change from those in adjacent pelagic limestones stratigraphically above and below. Sliter and Premoli Silva (*pers. comm.*), have reinvestigated the planktonic foraminiferal biostratigraphy of the Gubbio sequence near the Cenomanian–Turonian boundary and suggest that the *W. archeocretacea* PRZ (perhaps 1 m.y. duration) is about 8 m thick there; the Bonarelli horizon falls in the middle of that interval. On the basis of that conclusion, a duration of enhanced *org*C preservation from 150–500 thousand years is possible.

Relatively high *org*C contents also occur within the Cenomanian–Turonian Bridge Creek Limestone member of the Greenhorn Formation in the Western Interior of the U.S. (see Pratt, 1984; Schlanger *et al.* 1987, Fig. 16). The highest values, up to 7% *org*C, occur in somewhat bioturbated to laminated dark marlstone intervals (tens of cm thick) which are interbedded with highly bioturbated, light-coloured pelagic limestone beds having *org*C contents of generally less than 0.5 wt. %. Fischer (1980) has argued on the basis of a variety of evidence that individual marlstone-limestone couplets represent about 40,000 y (using an adaptation of the Obradovich and Cobban (1975) timescale for the Western Interior U.S. modified by Kauffman, 1977; see also Barron *et al.* 1985). There are about 16 such couplets within the *org*C maximum of the Bridge Creek Limestone; therefore, it appears that the duration of the Cenomanian–Turonian OAE in the Western Interior U.S. was on the order of 600,000–700,000 y. Similar conclusions can be made for the Danish North Sea section where about 16 thin black shale horizons occur over 4 m of section, at the Wünstorf (Germany) locality where as many as 23 black, relatively *org*C-rich beds occur in a 20 m section, and at the Oued Bahloul section in Tunisia which has a similar number of laminated, *org*C-rich intervals within a 20 m interval at the Cenomanian–Turonian boundary (see sections in Schlanger *et al.*, 1987). In each case, the number of layers and duration of the deposition inferred from average sedimentation rates are nearly the same. De Boer (1982) has even suggested that as many as 28 depositional cycles (black shale-radiolarite couplets representing 20,000 y cycles) may be distinguished within the Bonarelli horizon at Moria, Italy, although the origin of these cycles is not clear. The 'Black Band' of Yorkshire is very thin and exhibits no obvious cyclic development, but because it occurs in a generally condensed interval in the chalk

sequence (C. Wood, *pers. comm.*) multiple *org*C preservation events may be condensed into one horizon (see discussion in Schlanger *et al.* 1987). Some of the implications of this periodic development of *org*C-rich layers in many sequences near the Cenomanian–Turonian boundary are discussed below.

We conclude from the above arguments that the maximum development of the OAE took place during an interval of about 500,000 y in shallow epicontinental seas and along somewhat deeper continental slopes and margins (*i.e.*, Gubbio estimated palaeodepth is 1–2 km; Arthur & Premoli Silva 1982). However, in coastal upwelling zones, such a development might appear more prolonged because of relatively higher pre-existing productivity and probably well developed midwater oxygen-minimum zones in those areas. Some predicted areas of wind-driven upwelling for the mid-Cretaceous are shown in Figure 1 (from information supplied by E. J. Barron, *pers. comm.*, using the Community Climate Model at NCAR as described in Barron & Washington 1983). A substantial number of the known *org*C-rich beds do occur in areas of predicted upwelling as suggested by Parrish and Curtis (1982). In the shallowest palaeoenvironments, the maximum development of the OAE was synchronous with the apparent maximum of the Cenomanian–Turonian transgression (Figs. 3 and 4). However, in the deep North Atlantic, the OAE appears to have begun somewhat earlier (Fig. 2), perhaps beginning in early Late Cenomanian time (data of de Graciansky *et al.* 1982).

The precise dating of the Mid-Cretaceous portion of many of the deeper North Atlantic DSDP sites is difficult because of a shallow carbonate compensation depth (CCD) (e.g. Thierstein, 1979; Tucholke and Vogt, 1979); calcareous faunal and floral elements which provide the best stratigraphic resolution are generally absent. In a synthesis of DSDP North Atlantic Cretaceous litho- and biostratigraphy, de Graciansky *et al.* (1982) have shown that by middle Cenomanian time, sedimentation rates were reduced at most sites to less than 1 m/m.y. At many DSDP sites, the upper Cenomanian and later section is either missing in a major hiatus (due to nondeposition or to later erosion) or extremely condensed (see also Hart 1980). A few of the deeper DSDP sites (105, 138, 367, 386, 387, 398) recovered red and green clays of middle and late Cenomanian–possibly early Turonian age. Enrichment in *org*C occurs in these sites near the base of this unit, probably in the mid- to late Cenomanian. The organic carbon occurs in thin (< 10 cm) beds (of which there may be from one to several) in these sites, with *org*C values of up

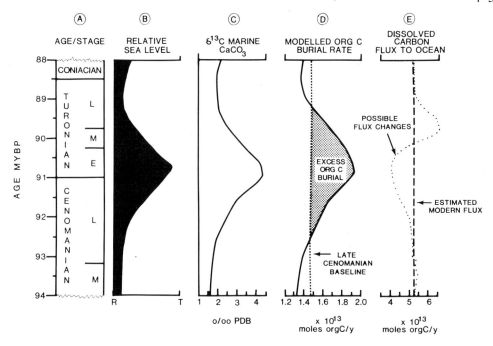

FIG. 3. Comparison of relative ages of t̲ɔ̲ Cenomanian–Turonian transgression (B), δ^{13}C of pelagic marine carbonates (C) (see Scholle & Arthur 1980; Schlanger *et al.* 1987), and (D) a model for *org*C depositional rate based on (C) and the methods outlined in text; (E) is a speculative curve illustrating possible variations in dissolved carbon input to the oceans as the result of changes in shelf area. Absolute values are for reference; only extent of relative changes are implied.

to 14% in the Western Atlantic basin, 22% in the Eastern basin and 8% at Site 398 in the northern North Atlantic (see Fig. 1 for locations). We suggest that all of the supposed mid-to-late Cenomanian *org*C enrichments at North Atlantic DSDP Sites shown in Figure 2 may be coeval and are possibly of latest Cenomanian age. Accumulation rates and values of *org*C in W. North Atlantic DSDP sites are higher over a brief interval of the late Cenomanian than those for some 5–10 m.y. before and for 30–40 m.y. after this period (e.g. Summerhayes & Masran 1983; Arthur & Dean 1986). DSDP Site 530 in the South Atlantic (Angola Basin) also exhibits a pattern of *org*C enrichment which suggests a maximum near the Cenomanian–Turonian boundary within a predominantly red clay section (Dean *et al.* 1984). Schlanger *et al.* (1986) have already discussed the timing of *org*C-rich layers in three mid-Pacific DSDP sites (late Cenomanian–earliest Turonian). The possible slightly greater age of *org*C-rich layers in deeper N. Atlantic sites, as opposed to a probable early Turonian age at shallower sites, is, however, not contradictory to our suggested model, as we discuss later.

The carbon-isotope record and patterns of marine organic-carbon burial

A positive excursion in δ^{13}C of pelagic carbonates and calcareous fossils across the Cenomanian–Turonian boundary was first reported by Scholle and Arthur (1980). The increase in δ^{13}C was proposed to reflect directly changes in the δ^{13}C of oceanic total dissolved carbon (TDC) because of an increase in the burial ratio of *org*C to $CaCO_3$ in marine sequences during the Cenomanian–Turonian OAE. Our subsequent studies have documented both the global nature of the Cenomanian–Turonian δ^{13}C excursion and the occurrence of *org*-rich horizons in many pelagic chalk and limestone sequences (Schlanger *et al.* 1987). Because of the difficulty in calculating global *org*C burial rates using actual *org*C concentrations from the studied sequences, we will here use the δ^{13}C record as a proxy indicator of changes in rates of *org*C burial and input of carbon to the oceans in conjunction with observations of patterns in *org*C contents of selected marine sequences.

The basic elements of modelling variations in $\delta^{13}C$ as changes in rates of *org*C burial in marine sequences and the assumptions therein have been outlined by a number of workers, including Schidlowski *et al.* (1977), Garrels & Lerman (1981), and Berner & Raiswell (1983). In most simple models, it is assumed that the mass and isotopic composition of the flux of dissolved carbon to the oceans from rivers is constant through time and that the fluctuations in $\delta^{13}C$ of oceanic TDC inferred from the $\delta^{13}C$ $CaCO_3$ record are due entirely to changes in the proportion of carbon buried as *org*C and as $CaCO_3$ (transfer of carbon from $CaCO_3$ to *org*C reservoir). In such models, the total amount of carbon extracted from the oceanic reservoir and buried cannot exceed the input from external sources such that the mass of oceanic TDC does not vary. In our modelling, we maintain constancy of the mass of oceanic TDC, although this may be a somewhat unrealistic assumption. We also assume constant mass and carbon-isotopic composition of the riverine (and atmospheric exchange) flux of dissolved carbon to the oceans during the Cenomanian–Turonian as a further constraint on the model. As we suggest later, however, the latter assumption is probably not valid because variations in the dissolved carbon flux to the oceans occur as the result of changes in climate, sea level, and continental area (e.g. Berner *et al.*, 1983). Nonetheless, the modelling provides some insights into changing rates of total *org*C burial across the Cenomanian–Turonian boundary.

The equations used are of the form:

$$C_1 \frac{d\delta_1}{dt} = \delta_4 C_{41} - (\delta_3 - \alpha)C_{12} - \delta_3 C_{13}$$

and $C_{41} = C_{12} + C_{13}$

Where:

C_1 and δ_1 are the mass and $\delta^{13}C$ of the oceanic TDC reservoir,

C_{41} and δ_4 are the mass and $\delta^{13}C$ of the riverine TDC flux to the oceans per unit time,

C_{12} is the flux of *org*C from the ocean reservoir per unit time,

$\alpha = 23\%_0$ is the mean difference in $\delta^{13}C$ between marine *org*C and $CaCO_3$,

and C_{13} and δ_3 are the flux rate and $\delta^{13}C$ of carbon leaving the ocean reservoir per unit time.

Estimates for the relevant masses and isotopic compositions of carbon in various reservoirs and fluxes for the present-day carbon cycle used in our modelling (compiled from many sources as shown) are given in Table 1. The idealized $\delta^{13}C$ curve, compiled from available data given in Schlanger *et al.* (1987) is shown in Figure 3. Estimates of the present *org*C burial rate in marine strata are quite variable. For the purposes of our calculations we have adopted the approximate value of Berner (1982) which is about a factor of 3 larger than that adopted by Garrels and Lerman (1981) and that accepted by Berner *et al.* (1983).

The $\delta^{13}C$ $_{CaCO_3}$ values initially appear to rise slowly in the late Cenomanian from a base level of about $+2\%_0$ within the early-to middle-late Cenomanian (ca. 92.5 m.y. B.P. according to the timescale adopted in Schlanger *et al.* 1986). The average rate of rise during that time is about $1\%_0/$ m.y. The $\delta^{13}C$ rise probably represents an increase in the rate of burial of *org*C of about 0.25×10^{13} moles of *org*C/y or an estimated 20% increase over today's steady-state *org*C burial rate (Table 1). The peak rate of $\delta^{13}C$ rise during latest Cenomanian–early Turonian time was at least $2\%_0/$m.y. (increasing over $1\%_0$ from 91.5–91 m.y. BP). The peak $\delta^{13}C$ value represents an *org*C burial rate of about 1.93×10^{14} moles *org*C/y or about 40% higher than today's rate. The $\delta^{13}C$ rise apparently levels off between 91 and 90.5 m.y. during earliest Turonian time. This suggests that *org*C burial rates remained nearly constant at peak rates during the peak of the 'anoxic event'. Integrating the estimated excess *org*C deposited over the approximately 2 m.y. period gives us a total of 9×10^{18} moles of excess *org*C (over the Cretaceous average or late Cenomanian 'background') buried as the result of the Cenomanian–Turonian OAE.

TABLE 1. *Masses and fluxes of carbon in the modern marine system**

Flux or reservoir	Mass or rate	Average $\delta^{13}C$ $\%_0$
Ocean total dissolved carbon	350×10^{17} g	0
Organic carbon burial	1.57×10^{14} g/y	-21
(corrected for diagenetic loss)	1.26×10^{14} g/y	
Marine carbonate burial	5.04×10^{14} g/y	$+0.5$
(estimated ca. $4 \times org$C burial)		
Dissolved carbon flux to oceans	6.30×10^{14} g/y	-3.7

* Data sources in text.

The record of *org*C burial, inferred from secular changes in carbonate δ^{13}C, agrees well with the stratigraphic distribution of *org*C in marine sequences. The majority of shallow shelf sea sections studies have *org*C contents less than 0.5% during most of the Cenomanian. Higher *org*C contents in shelf 'black shale' facies occur in the uppermost Cenomanian–lower Turonian (see Schlanger *et al.* 1987, for details) at the time of peak δ^{13}C values. The relatively slow late Cenomanian δ^{13}C increase may have been caused by increased rates of *org*C accumulation in deeper water environments, as seen, for example, in many North Atlantic DSDP sites. At the peak of the *org*C burial event, rates of *org*C accumulation (see Table 2) are estimated to have been 0.53×10^{-5} moles *org*C/cm^2/y at Gubbio in the Bonarelli horizon, 0.30×10^{-5} moles *org*C/cm^2/y in the Western Interior Seaway of North America, 3.3×10^{-5} moles *org*C/cm^2/y in the Bahloul Formation of Tunisia, and 0.52×10^{-5} moles *org*C/cm^2/y in the black shale facies of Northern Germany. Adopting a value of 1.0×10^{-5} moles *org*C/cm^2/y for the mean *org*C accumulation rate in Cenomanian–Turonian pelagic shelf sequences and extrapolating over about 50% of the approximate area of shelf seas for the early Turonian (Fig. 4), the calculated *org*C burial rate is 0.14×10^{13} moles/y. Available data from many sequences also suggest that the majority of the *org*C preserved in pelagic sequences during the Cenomanian–Turonian OAE consisted of amorphous marine organic matter (e.g. Summerhayes 1981; de Graciansky *et al.* 1982; Arthur & Premoli Silva 1982; Van Graas *et al.* 1983; Moberly, Schlanger *et al.* 1983; Schlanger *et al.* 1987). The estimate of the increase in *org*C burial rate at the Cenomanian–Turonian boundary in pelagic shelf sequences from analysis of selected sequences discussed above is greater than 25% of the total increase in the *org*C burial rate estimated from modelling of the δ^{13}C excursion. This result is of interest because the remainder of the *org*C burial rate increase can easily be accounted for by increases in the rate of *org*C burial in slope

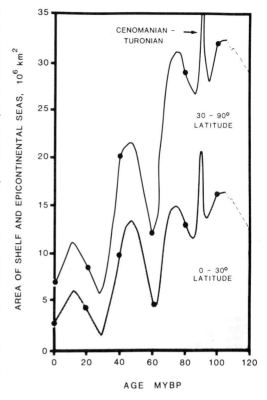

FIG. 4. Changes in shelf and epicontinental sea area for low latitude (0–40° N and S) and high latitude (40–90° N and S) regions during the Cretaceous and Cenozoic. The basis for this figure is the planimetered areas of flooding (Brass *et al.*, 1982; dots) from the palaeoreconstructions of Barron *et al.* (1981) with added interpolation from relative sea level changes.

and deep-sea environments (e.g. Arthur 1982; Arthur & Dean 1986; see Table 2). The calculated pelagic-carbonate shelf *org*C burial rate at the Cenomanian–Turonian boundary is nearly equivalent to the estimated total *org*C burial rate for today's deep-sea and shelf areas (not influenced by rivers) combined, which together encompass

TABLE 2. *Calculated* orgC *accumulation rates at the Cenomanian–Turonian boundary**

Locality	Average *org*C	Density	Thickness	Duration	*org*C Accum. rate
	%	g/cc	cm	ky	moles/cm^2/y
Gubbio, Italy	12	2.1	100	400	5.3×10^{-6}
Bahloul, Tunisia	4	2.3	2600	600	33.0×10^{-6}
Wünstorf, Germany	1	2.1	1800	600	5.2×10^{-6}
Pueblo, Colorado	1	2.1	1000	600	3.0×10^{-6}

*Data from Schlanger *et al.* (1987) and unpublished data.

an area at least 15 times as large (cf. Berner 1982) than that used in the calculation of Cretaceous rates. We assume for the purposes of this paper that the rate of *org*C burial in deltaic-shelf environments at the Cenomanian–Turonian boundary was equivalent to that estimated for these regions today, although it is possible that rates were even higher.

As described above, the maximum rate of *org*C burial and the peak of $\delta^{13}C$ values apparently coincide with maxima in sea level and shelf-sea area in the early Turonian. By the late Turonian, the area of shelf seas had declined to a minimum (Fig. 4) as the result of an apparent rapid regression which began in the late-early Turonian. Evidence from most pelagic sequences in all major ocean basins suggests that enhanced *org*C deposition ceased in the early Turonian. Red clay deposition or hiatuses in the post-late Cenomanian interval occur in the deepest North and South Atlantic sequences penetrated in DSDP sites (e.g. Arthur 1979b; Arthur & Natland 1979; de Graciansky *et al.* 1982) and oxidized bioturbated chalk or marl sequences are typical of post-earliest Turonian shallow to intermediate depth pelagic environments (e.g. Hancock 1975). The $\delta^{13}C$ curve shows a rapid return to $\delta^{13}C$ values of about +2 parts per thousand within about 0.5–1.5 m.y. following the maximum in the early Turonian. The rapid rate of $\delta^{13}C$ decrease (1 to 2‰ per m.y.) could have resulted from two possible effects:

(1) a pronounced decrease in the rate of *org*C burial; and

(2) an increase in the rate of supply of isotopically light carbon to the ocean.

Mechanism (1) above is plausible, but the rate of decline of $\delta^{13}C$ is very rapid and requires a nearly 30% reduction in the *org*C burial rate. A more plausible explanation of the very fast $\delta^{13}C$ decrease is that the *org*C burial rate decreased while an increase in the flux of isotopically light carbon to the oceans occurred. A drop in sea level, re-exposure of shallow water depositional sites, and better oxygenation of former poorly oxygenated depositional environments would have led to erosion and/or oxidation and a return to the ocean reservoir of some *org*C initially preserved during the Cenomanian–Turonian OAE. This sequence of events is shown schematically in Figure 5.

Therefore, there is a form of feedback mechanism which allows fairly rapid recycling of some proportion of nutrients and carbon sequestered during a short-term OAE. Overall oceanic fertility must have declined following the rapid *org*C burial event because of the concomitant extraction of nutrients. However, increased rates of

oxidation and erosion of *org*C and associated nutrient elements during the subsequent lowstand of sea level may have allowed a reasonably rapid return of nutrients to the sea.

In this section, we have considered only a more or less direct interpretation of the *org*C burial record associated with the Cenomanian–Turonian OAE. A model which attempts to explain the global nature of the event is presented below.

Sea level, climate and palaeocirculation

An open ocean model

Brass *et al.* (1982) have suggested that during globally warm, equable climatic episodes, such as existed during much of Mesozoic–early Paleogene time, the mode of oceanic bottom water formation may have been quite different from that of today. They propose that in the absence of formation of cold polar deep-water masses, warm saline water may have become the major bottom water source. Such warm, saline bottom water (WSBW) is suggested to have formed on low-latitude shelves or in more isolated Mediterranean seas characterized by a negative water balance (evaporation > precipitation + inflow). A variation of this idea was originally proposed by Chamberlain (1906) and later discussed by Roth (1978), Thierstein & Berger (1978), and Arthur & Natland (1979).

The important constraint provided by the WSBW model proposed by Brass *et al.* (1982) is that although very dense water may be produced locally, the 'buoyancy flux' (the volume produced times the density difference between the sinking plume and ambient interior water masses) determines what will actually become the major deep-water mass in the oceans. The model incorporates a plume of sinking water which is allowed to mix at turbulent boundaries with ambient water masses, thereby modifying original characteristics of the plume. Therefore, only larger volume plumes of greater density contrast will maintain their integrity and sink to become a distinct bottom water mass. Brass *et al.* (1982) suggest that rates of bottom water production may be modulated by a low-latitude shelf area which is determined by sea level and continental hypsometry. The buoyancy flux of warm, saline low-latitude surface waters sinking to become deep-water masses would effectively increase during transgressions. In essence, the rates of bottom water production and overturn of deep-water masses during such periods of high sea level could

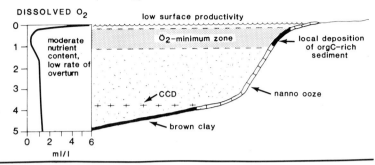

(A) MID CENOMANIAN ($\delta^{13}C_{CaCO_3} \approx$ +2 o/oo)

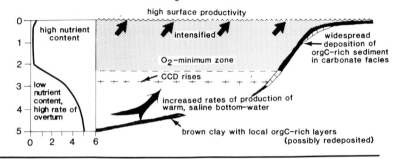

(B) CENOMANIAN/TURONIAN ($\delta^{13}C_{CaCO_3} \approx$ +4 o/oo)

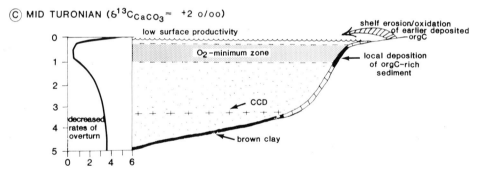

(C) MID TURONIAN ($\delta^{13}C_{CaCO_3} \approx$ +2 o/oo)

FIG. 5. Diagrammatic history of deep-water circulation and productivity for (A) the mid Cenomanian; (B) the Cenomanian–Turonian boundary; and (C) the mid Turonian. See text for details.

be equivalent to or more rapid than those of today according to Brass *et al.* (1982) and Southam *et al.* (1982). Wilde and Berry (1982) have also proposed a model of warm, saline deep-water mass formation to account for apparent intensification of midwater oxygen-minimum zones at times during the Mesozoic, but their model differs in some details from that of Brass *et al.* (1982) in that it incorporates sinking of intermediate to deep-water masses from net evaporation, low-latitude, open-ocean environments (as suggested by Chamberlain, 1906). Brass *et al.* (1982), Southam *et al.* (1982), and Wilde and Berry

(1982), among many others (e.g. Fischer & Arthur 1977; Berger 1979; Arthur *et al.* 1984a), have argued that because the solubility of oxygen (and other gases) decreases with increasing temperature and salinity, warm, saline water masses, even if sinking at rates equivalent to deep-water formation today, would advect less dissolved oxygen to oceanic deep-water masses. Southam *et al.* (1982; 1984) have shown in a simple one-dimensional model that if WSBW was formed, oceanic deep-water oxygen deficits would intensify first at intermediate depths to form a distinct oxygen-minimum zone. The thickness and intensity of oxygen deficits in the oxygen-minimum zone would depend on the average nutrient content of upwelling deep-water masses (and surface production of *org*C) which are displaced surfaceward by sinking deep-water masses, on the initial dissolved-oxygen content of WSBW and on the rate of WSBW formation.

One could even envisage a multilayer deep-water mass system (e.g. Berger 1979; Wilde & Berry 1982) for the Cretaceous oceans with multiple sources and source strengths. Short- or longer-term temporal variations in shelf area and rates of evaporation, connection of open-ocean basins with isolated but potentially large sources of saline water such as evaporite basins (e.g. Thierstein & Berger 1978; Arthur & Natland 1979), or competition for exportation of deep water between potential high- or low-latitude (or even different low-latitude evaporative shelves) sources could all complicate the more straightforward models of WSBW discussed above. We suggest that such complications did exist and have incorporated them in our model for the origin of the global Cenomanian–Turonian OAE below.

Many workers have pointed to an apparent correlation between OAEs and sea level highstands (Schlanger & Jenkyns 1976; Fischer & Arthur 1977; Jenkyns 1980). Figure 4 illustrates approximate changes in the area of shelf and epicontinental seas from about Aptian through the Holocene summarized for two latitudinal bands, 0–40° and 40–90° North and South. The dots superimposed on the curves are data from time slice palaeogeographic maps (Barron *et al.* 1981) which were planimetered and presented by Brass *et al.* (1982). The curves represent interpolated areas of shelf and epicontinental seas from analysis of relative sea level curves (e.g. Hancock 1975; Vail *et al.* 1977; Hart & Bailey 1979; Hancock & Kauffman 1980). Increased area of low-latitude shallow seas is apparent during much of the mid-Cretaceous in comparison with the Cenozoic. In particular, we note a brief transgressive episode in the late Cenomanian–early Turonian which substantially increased the area of shallow seas relative to the preceding late Albian to middle Cenomanian and succeeding mid-Turonian–early Coniacian intervals. This extensive late Cenomanian–early Turonian transgression has been well documented in the Western Interior Seaway of North America (e.g. Kauffman 1977), Northwest Europe (Hancock 1975; Cooper 1977), and Africa (Van Houten 1980; Reyment & Mörner 1977; Matsumoto 1977; Einsele & Wiedmann 1982; Petters & Ekweozor 1982) for example.

We believe that the correlation between the sharp Cenomanian–Turonian transgressive episode, regardless of its origin, and the widespread *org*C burial event (OAE) documented here is not fortuitous. We postulate that oceanic deep-water circulation and surface water biological productivity responded to the rapid and pronounced sea level/shelf area change. The basic elements of our model are shown in Figure 5:

(A) Early to mid-Cenomanian

During this period low-latitude shelf sea area was relatively small (Fig. 4) and the salinity-buoyancy flux drive for oceanic deep-water circulation sluggish. Oceanic surface water productivity was also low, except in regions of wind-driven upwelling, because net rates of oceanic overturn were low as the result of the relatively slow rates of deep-water circulation. Certain shelf areas or the relatively isolated northern South Atlantic basin may have exported WSBW, but we suggest that the buoyancy fluxes were sufficiently small that individual sources were in competition and that the rates of WSBW formation were insufficient to oxygenate effectively many semi-restricted ocean basins. Intermediate water mass formation could, however, have been quite rapid due to mixing of water masses with sufficient density and buoyancy flux to occupy deep but not the deepest levels in the ocean. Therefore, bottom-water and intermediate-water circulation could even have been decoupled. This would have allowed sufficient turnover to stimulate surface water productivity while allowing bottom waters a longer residence time to develop anoxia or low-oxygen conditions. Nutrients were allowed to build-up in deeper water masses, particularly in somewhat isolated basins, such as the North Atlantic which may also have had a partly estuarine-like circulation (e.g. Berger, 1979) with nutrients supplied in deep-water inflow from other basins. At the same time oxygen deficits developed or persisted (from Aptian–Albian time) in the bottom-water column allowing enhanced preservation of *org*C in some deep-water environments within laminated clays or nannofossil marls (Fig. 2). However, the *org*C contents and accumulation rates (e.g. Arthur & Dean 1986) were not exceptionally high, probably because of low surface water productivity. Only local upwelling regions along shelf edges or over slopes (i.e. NW Africa; Einsele & Wiedmann, 1982) were characterized by *org*C-rich strata. The midwater oxygen-minimum zone was probably best developed in such regions. The carbon-isotope curve indicates that *org*C burial rates were low relative to the succeeding Cenomanian–Turonian OAE.

(B) Late Cenomanian–early Turonian

With the transgression of this period rates of WSBW formation may have increased drastically, leading to more rapid overturn of nutrient-enriched deep waters and stimulating surface productivity. With the initial burst in production of *org*C, perhaps in a situation where rates of intermediate water-mass formation were initially higher than bottom-water circulation rates, preservation of *org*C may have been enhanced in initially deoxygenated deep-water environments. Such an explanation would account for the somewhat earlier timing of the *org*C spike in deep North Atlantic DSDP sites (Fig. 2) than in slope or shelf settings. At maximum transgression, rates of WSBW formation were highest as a function of the great expanse of shallow seas in highly evaporative settings, surface water productivity was high in many regions, and the midwater oxygen-minimum zone was expanded and intensified. Deep-water environments may have been fully oxygenated in most ocean basins, with the exception of areas under regions of highest primary productivity where the oxygen-minimum zone was most intense and impinged on a greater area of the seafloor (e.g. high rates of nutrient supply along oceanic divergences or coastal upwelling zones). Figure 1 shows predicted upwelling regions for the mid-Cretaceous. Note that many of the *org*C-rich. Cenomanian–Turonian beds occur within predicted areas of upwelling; however, most of the same areas that were marine before and after the Cenomanian–Turonian transgression were not characterized by significant *org*C-rich intervals other than during the OAE. Slow accumulation of red clays occurred at many of the deepest sites in the ocean (see de Graciansky *et al.* 1982; Arthur *et al.* 1984b for summary) under an elevated carbonate compensation depth (CCD) (e.g. Thierstein 1979) during the late Cenomanian–early Turonian. The shallow CCD may have been a response to higher rates of accumulation of pelagic chalks over a greater expanse of shelf seas during the overall transgressive episode (e.g. Berger & Winterer 1974).

Several DSDP sites drilled on old crust, and presumably very deep-water sites during the mid-Cretaceous, recovered exceptionally *org*C-rich intervals at the Cenomanian–Turonian boundary. Sites 367 in the Eastern North Atlantic and 530 in the Cape Basin (Figs 1 and 2) are good examples. *Org*C-rich beds, characterized by marine amorphous organic matter, occur at the Cenomanian–Turonian boundary in both sites (de Graciansky *et al.* 1982; Dean *et al.* 1984 for details) and were deposited in at least 4 km of

water. Both sites are adjacent to predicted areas of upwelling and high productivity (Fig. 1), but there is insufficient evidence to argue that the deep-water masses were anoxic. Dean *et al.* (1984) and Arthur *et al.* (1984b) have suggested that much of the organic matter at those sites may have been redeposited from shallower-water regions of enhanced preservation.

During the Cenomanian–Turonian transgression the high productivity regions and the top of the oxygen-minimum zone were carried into shelf and epicontinental seas in continental interiors; this led to periodic development of *org*C-rich beds in pelagic-hemipelagic environments in these shallow seas (see Fig. 1 and Schlanger *et al.* 1987).

(C) Mid-Turonian regression

During this rapid regression the rates of deep-water formation declined as shelf area decreased. Surface water biological productivity was relatively low in most areas because of increased deep-water residence time and overall low oceanic fertility as the result of extraction and burial of nutrients with *org*C during the preceding OAE. Therefore, rates of marine *org*C burial (and δ^{13}C) decreased rapidly in the mid- to late Turonian. Erosion and oxidation of previously deposited marine strata during the Turonian regression may have allowed gradual return of nutrients and dissolved carbon to the oceans.

Restricted basins with positive water balance

At first glance, it seems difficult to envisage why certain 'black shale' horizons have global distribution, particularly because of the widely varying palaeoclimatic-palaeoceanographic settings. As we have already argued, the major rapid transgression at the Cenomanian–Turonian boundary seems to be the common link between the occurrences of *org*C-rich intervals in different basins. It is unlikely, however, that the postulated link between low-latitude shelf area, production of saline deep water, and sea surface fertility and the widespread intensification of midwater oxygen deficits can explain the better preservation of marine autochthonous organic matter in shallow epicontinental seas of all midcontinent regions at relatively high palaeolatitudes, such as the Cretaceous Western Interior Seaway of North America.

The stratigraphy of the Cretaceous Western Interior Seaway of the U.S. has been summarized in Kauffman (1977). The Bridge Creek Limestone member of the Greenhorn Formation comprises strata deposited at maximum transgression near the Cenomanian–Turonian boundary. These deposits are markedly cyclic (Fischer 1980; Arthur et al. 1984a; Pratt 1984; Barron et al. 1985) consisting of alternations of dark, relatively orgC-rich laminated to burrowed marlstones and light-coloured, highly bioturbated pelagic limestones. Organic carbon and carbon isotope data for the Bridge Creek Limestone unit are given in Schlanger et al. (1986). The orgC values within the laminated to partly laminated marlstone beds reach a maximum in the lower Turonian, but the cyclic nature of the lithology and orgC contents suggests periodic changes in environmental conditions. Such cycles are not seen in immediately underlying or overlying strata. Mineralogical, oxygen isotope and other geochemical data reported elsewhere (Arthur et al. 1984a; Barron et al. 1985) suggest that major salinity changes in surface waters played a role in development of oxygen-deficient bottom-waters and enhanced organic matter preservation during deposition of the Bridge Creek Limestone.

The basic model is one of periodic stable water mass stratification in a relatively shallow sea with or without major changes in surface-water productivity. The relatively high latitude and somewhat restricted long, broad seaway probably received large amounts of fresh water runoff, particularly from uplands to the west (Kauffman 1977). Numerical climatic models of Barron and Washington (1982a, b) and the qualitative models of Parrish et al. (1982) suggest the possibility of localized high rainfall along part of the Western Interior Seaway. In fact, enhanced rates of evaporation at low latitudes and latent heat transport with water vapour to higher latitudes may have been one way to maintain the warm, equable climate of the Cretaceous. High runoff provides the potential for salinity stratification, but in seas less shallow than 200 m, low salinity surface layers may be short lived because of effective wind and wave mixing. Estimates for the depth of most of the seaway vary, but much evidence suggests a maximum of 600 m (Kauffman 1977). However, much of the seaway may have been as shallow as 100 m during sea-level lowstands. We suggest that the Cenomanian–Turonian transgression increased the possibility of establishing longer-term salinity stratification because greater water depths (e.g. >200 m) would allow a multiple layer density stratification. Such a scheme is illustrated in Figure 6.

During times of higher freshwater runoff, a lower salinity lid would have formed and the bottom-water mass would have been isolated from gaseous exchange with the atmosphere. Oxygen could therefore have been gradually drawn down during oxidation of orgC falling from surface waters, and given a long enough residence time, the bottom waters may have become dysaerobic or anoxic. The gradual elimination of a burrowing bottom fauna would decrease the rate of consumption of orgC and allow for a lower residence time of orgC at the sediment/water interface. Low surface-water productivity requires longer isolation of the bottom water before oxygen is depleted, depending on initial O_2 concentrations and thickness of the water column. At present, there is no way to ascertain whether productivity changes accompanied the palaeoenvironmental changes, but outflow of fresh water from fluvial sources may have been accompanied by increased nutrient levels. The marlstone-limestone cycles have an estimated periodicity of 20–40,000y (Fischer 1980) which would have allowed sufficient time (half a cycle) in which to have developed anoxia. It is likely that the cyclic stratification represents periodic alternation of humid and arid climate episodes, perhaps driven by insolation changes and accompanying orbital variations (Milankovitch-like cycles; e.g. Fischer 1980; Arthur et al. 1984a; Barron et al. 1985). The flooding and deepening of the seaway during the Cenomanian–Turonian transgression may have had the combined effect of intensifying rainfall in the region (e.g. Barron & Washington 1982a) and allowing stable density stratification to occur. In addition, the transgression may also have raised the upper part of a midwater oxygen-minimum zone onto the shelf as proposed by Schlanger and Jenkyns (1976) and Fischer and Arthur (1977), thereby aiding in the development of more widespread oxygen-deficiency in the basin.

The model proposed here to explain the occurrence of multiple laminated 'black shale' layers in a basin having a positive water balance (e.g. Grasshoff 1975) is a refinement of a similar model for Cretaceous black shale deposition discussed by Ryan and Cita (1977) by analogy to explanations for the origin of Pleistocene sapropels in the Mediterranean elaborated upon by Rossignol-Strick et al. (1982) among others. Petters and Ekweozor (1982) also have suggested that development of brackish surface water lids aided in creating anoxic conditions and enhanced preservation of orgC in the mid-Cretaceous Benue Trough of west Africa.

Again, we emphasize that major positive eustatic sea level changes were probably the driving force for and common link in the origin

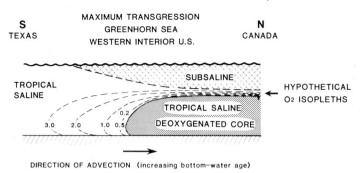

FIG. 6(A). Model for a mid-to-high latitude epicontinental sea during the Cenomanian–Turonian transgression. High rainfall and runoff led periodically to subsaline surface water masses in the somewhat restricted seaway. Bottom-waters in the basin are tropical-saline surface waters with low initial dissolved oxygen. O_2 isopleths are schematic (see text for details).

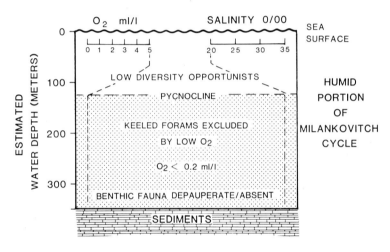

FIG. 6(B). Estimated salinity/oxygen gradients in the U.S. Western Interior Seaway water column during deposition of *org*C-rich layers (see text).

of time-equivalent *org*C-rich units within basins of very different palaeoceanographic-palaeoclimatic character.

Faunal changes associated with the Cenomanian–Turonian event

Although the faunal turnover at the Cenomanian–Turonian boundary is not drastic, some interesting marine faunal events do occur. These are:

(1) the common occurrence of benthic-free zones or depauperate benthic faunas in marine sequences from environments with inferred palaeodepths of more than 100–200 m (e.g. see Schlanger *et al.* 1987 for review),

(2) disappearance of many species of keeled planktonic foraminifera and some cephalopod genera and species at the boundary, and

(3) a peak in abundance of radiolarians and/or calcispheres (e.g. *Pithonella ovalis*) near the Cenomanian–Turonian boundary in many pelagic sequences. These faunal events can be interpreted within the framework of our palaeoceanographic model for the Cenomanian–Turonian OAE.

The occurrences of benthic-free zones, or intervals characterized by depauperate benthic foraminiferal assemblages where the planktonic/benthic ratio commonly increases at or near the Cenomanian–Turonian boundary, have been discussed in Schlanger *et al.* (1987). In general, the lithological and geochemical evidence from many sections, particularly finely laminated to sparsely bioturbated relatively orgC-rich strata, suggests that benthic faunas are absent or sparse because of poorly oxygenated conditions at the seafloor during the period of expanded and intensified oxygen deficits mainly within intermediate to shallow intermediate water masses. However, in some sequences (e.g. the dark relatively orgC-rich marls of the Bridge Creek Limestone near Pueblo, Colorado), a low-diversity benthic foraminiferal assemblage characterizes somewhat laminated, orgC-rich layers and *Chondrites*-type burrow systems are found within the lower and upper parts of many otherwise laminated units. Very thin inoceramid shells are also found lying parallel to bedding in certain finely laminated dark-coloured intervals. We have also found crushed, thin-shelled inoceramids and *Chondrites* burrows in some but not all of the more-or-less finely laminated black marl or clay layers at the Wünstorf (Germany) locality. We interpret the inoceramid and benthic foraminifera occurrences as indicating extremely low-oxygen concentrations but not anoxic conditions at the sediment water interface. The benthic foraminifera are morphologically similar to modern bolivinids or buliminids, which today are characteristic of benthic environments within well-developed oxygen-minimum zones (e.g. Phleger & Soutar 1973; Ingle 1981). Certain inoceramids may also be extremely tolerant of low-dissolved oxygen concentrations and are found in orgC-rich strata having no other benthic faunas or signs of bioturbation (for example, in parts of the Greenhorn and Niobrara Formations of the Cretaceous Western Interior U.S., e.g. Kauffman, *pers. comm.*, 1982). Thus, it is likely that some laminated intervals represent very low oxygen concentrations at the sediment/water interface (perhaps <0.2 ml/l) which would exclude most benthic infaunal organisms, but allow a few tolerant epifaunal organisms to survive. Also, it is possible that brief periods of slightly better oxygenation occur within dominantly anoxic episodes such that colonization of the seafloor by certain opportunistic organisms, such as inoceramids, might take place. The relatively small size and thin shells of these inoceramids may attest to the short-lived nature of such oxygenation events. *Chondrites* generally appear as the last (or only) trace fossil in many Cretaceous black shales (e.g. Bromley & Ekdale 1984) and is probably also very tolerant of low dissolved oxygen concentrations and even of dissolved sulphide below the sediment/water interface. Many of the *Chondrites* burrows in orgC-rich layers may occur following reoxygenation of the seafloor. Total anoxia, therefore, is not a necessary condition for the preservation of fine

lamination and of orgC, and some epifaunal benthic faunal elements may be found in orgC-rich strata. However, the exclusion of a benthic infauna aids in orgC preservation because bioturbation tends to increase the residence time of orgC particles in the oxygenated zone and benthic macrofaunal consumption of orgC may be great in comparison to that accomplished by bacterial populations (e.g. Brooks 1978; Müller & Suess 1979; Demaison & Moore 1980). Many of the pelagic sequences from the Cenomanian–Turonian that we have studied are marked by cyclic or periodic interbedding of laminated to slightly bioturbated, relatively orgC-rich and $CaCO_3$-rich intervals. These cycles apparently represent periodic oxygenation-deoxygenation events at the seafloor, and therefore, benthic faunal abundance may also fluctuate.

The disappearance of some keeled planktonic foraminifers and the extinction of certain ammonites (Sepkoski 1982; Raup & Sepkoski 1982) over a brief interval of latest Cenomanian–early Turonian time is perhaps the most intriguing of the biotic events associated with this boundary. Planktonic foraminifera (and probably ammonites as well) are specifically adapted to a given water mass. Any disturbance of the salinity/temperature characteristics of that water mass and/or a change in its nutrient and oxygen content might result in the disappearance of the foraminifera that typically inhabits that water mass (e.g. Bé 1977; Hart & Bailey 1979; Haig 1979). Because dissolved-oxygen levels in shallow-intermediate water masses probably decreased rapidly during the latest Cenomanian and changes in the distribution of salinity and temperature with depth may have occurred in response to changes in production of deeper water masses concomitant with a sharp sea-level rise, we suggest that the deterioration of this habitat and increasing stress levels led to the extinction of keeled foraminifers (Wonders 1980; Caron & Homewood 1983) and of certain cephalopods (see Sepkoski 1982). In this regard, it is interesting to note that new keeled planktonic foraminifer species evolved shortly after the beginning of the Turonian (e.g. *P. helvetica*). The *Whiteinella archeocretacea* PRZ zone spans the interval during which few keeled forms existed (Hart & Bailey 1979; Haig 1979). The planktonic foraminiferal population was, for a brief interval, dominated by a low diversity generalized fauna during the peak transgression.

Finally, the abundance of calcispheres and radiolaria increases in pelagic marine sequences across the Cenomanian–Turonian boundary at many localities. In part, the increased abundance of these more resistant forms may be a preservational phenomenon because of possibly increased rates of carbonate dissolution associated with high organic productivity in surface waters and low dissolved-oxygen contents and high CO_2 input to intermediate waters because of increased rates of *org*C degradation. Berger and Winterer (1974) among others have discussed the increased rates of carbonate dissolution along highly productive continental margin regions (see also Berger & Soutar 1970). We have noted (Schlanger *et al.* 1987) that many Cenomanian–Turonian sequences are marked by transitions from highly calcareous Upper Cenomanian chalks to more marly and/or condensed units at the Cenomanian–Turonian boundary, followed again by resumed pure chalk deposition in the mid-Turonian. De Graciansky *et al.* (1982) and Arthur and Dean (1986) have suggested a possible CCD rise in the late Cenomanian–Turonian. Therefore, sequences in deep-sea settings representing that time period are highly condensed or marked by a hiatus. The postulated CCD rise is probably due to a combination of increased rates of carbonate dissolution in midwater masses associated with intensified *org*C degradation there and to the much larger shelf area and increased shallow-water carbonate deposition at maximum transgression. The radiolarian and calcisphere relative abundance patterns probably also indicate increasing surface water instability, fertility, and productivity. The abundance and accumulation rate of siliceous microfossils in pelagic sediments is probably proportional to rates of production (e.g. Berger 1976). Calcispheres, on the other hand, are generally assumed to indicate neritic conditions (Masters & Scott 1978; Caron & Homewood 1983); however, as such, they probably inhabit surface waters where nutrient supply is episodic and/or conditions are inimical to normal pelagic calcareous plankton production. The calcispheres have been termed 'opportunistic' species (e.g. Fischer & Arthur 1977) and may be resting cysts of dinoflagellates or calcareous nannoplankton (Keupp 1979), as are thoracospheres today. Their abundance at the Cenomanian–Turonian boundary in offshore and in onshore regions may be in response to instability and intermittent upwelling during the Cenomanian–Turonian OAE.

Other geochemical implications of the Cenomanian–Turonian event

The increased burial rates of marine *org*C under widespread anoxic mid-water masses during the late Cenomanian–early Turonian OAE also must have had an impact on the geochemical cycles of redox sensitive metals, phosphate, and sulphur. Important mineral deposits may have formed in conjunction with the OAE and the events may also have led to significant perturbations of the ocean chemical cycles of some elements.

The Cenomanian–Turonian $\delta^{13}C$ excursion occurs in conjunction with an apparent positive $\delta^{34}S$ excursion (Claypool *et al.* 1980). This implies that significant amounts of reduced sulphur were buried along with the organic carbon (e.g. see Veizer *et al.* 1980; Garrels & Lerman 1981; Berner & Raiswell 1983 for discussion of overall relationship between C and S and their isotopic curves), perhaps in excess of normal rates.

Arthur and Jenkyns (1981) discussed the relative paucity of major economic phosphorite deposits associated with Cretaceous OAEs. The lack of such widespread sedimentary mineralization could indicate that the oceans were relatively phosphate-poor and/or that the phosphate was fixed rapidly in organic carbon in such a short a time period over widespread regions of the ocean that it was not mobilized to form significant deposits.

Force *et al.* (1983), Cannon and Force (1983), and Frakes and Bolton (1984) have made the intriguing suggestion that OAEs may correspond to times of widespread marine manganese mineralization. Pomerol (1983) and Renard and Letolle (1983) have also drawn attention to Mn enrichments in pelagic carbonate strata of Cenomanian–Turonian age (see Schlanger *et al.* 1987 for correlations of Mn and $\delta^{13}C$). Pomerol (1983) appealed to volcanism as the cause, but we agree with Force *et al.* (1983) that economic Mn deposits of Cenomanian–Turonian age probably resulted from major mobilization of reduced Mn via an increase in the volume of anoxic intermediate waters and in the interiors of epicontinental seas. The same reasoning may apply to sedimentary iron ore deposits such as the Cenomanian–Turonian chamositic ooids of Egypt (Van Houten & Bhattycharyya 1982). Further search for mineral deposits of Cenomanian–Turonian age may be fruitful.

Conclusions

The correlation of the $\delta^{13}C$ spike and the well-dated occurrences of layers rich in organic carbon detailed in Schlanger *et al.* (1987) indicate that the global episode of intense *org*C burial took place during the latest Cenomanian–earliest Turonian OAE (upper *R. cushmani* TRZ through

W. archeocretacea PRZ planktonic foraminiferal zones) over a period of no more than 1 m.y. The positive $\delta^{13}C$ excursion from pelagic carbonate sediments and fossils records *org*C burial and the effect of this burial on the $\delta^{13}C$ of oceanic total dissolved carbon. Peak rates of *org*C burial were probably as much as one and a half times as high as those in the mid-Cenomanian or mid-Turonian, as indicated by the more than 2 parts per thousand $\delta^{13}C$ excursion. The shape of the $\delta^{13}C$ curve suggests that rates of *org*C burial gradually increased in the lower part of the late Cenomanian, increased more rapidly in the uppermost Cenomanian, and levelled off at peak values in the latest Cenomanian–early Turonian during the maximum *org*C burial interval. The $\delta^{13}C$ values decreased nearly to pre-late Cenomanian levels in the early to middle Turonian. The decrease in $\delta^{13}C$ reflects decreasing rates of *org*C burial following the Cenomanian–Turonian 'oceanic anoxic event' as well as the probable oxidation and return of significant amounts of *org*C to the oceans following reoxygenation of much of the deeper water masses in contact with the seafloor.

The Cenomanian–Turonian OAE coincided with a maximum sea level highstand. We suggest that sea level is the common link and ultimately the driving force for *org*C deposition in globally widespread basins under different climatic and ocean circulation regimes. The Cenomanian–Turonian transgression flooded arid low-latitude shelves and this led to increased rates of production of warm, saline water which sank to become various intermediate to deep-water masses depending on density contrasts and production volumes (Brass *et al.* 1982). The rate of deep-water production may have been proportional to the area of shelf flooding such that the maximum occurred near the Cenomanian–Turonian boundary. As rates of deep-water formation increased, rates of upwelling of deeper oceanic water masses must also have increased thereby increasing sea surface fertility and productivity, particularly along continental margins. This, in turn, probably caused short-term expansion and intensification of a midwater oxygen-minimum zone. The post-early Turonian regression caused a decrease in deep-water production, upwelling, and productivity; *org*C burial rates decreased as a result. In somewhat restricted higher latitude basins, such as the Cretaceous Interior Seaway of North America periodic high rates of freshwater runoff coupled with deepening seas during the transgression created a periodic salinity stratification, oxygen depletion in bottom water, and resultant enhanced *org*C preservation. Climate and water mass stratification were probably directly related to the sea level change; oxygen depletion and enhanced *org*C preservation were periodic rather than continuous, suggesting short period (e.g. 20–40,000 y) climatic pulses superimposed on the overall pattern of transgression and *org*C burial. We noted such cycles in the U.S. Western Interior, Danish North Sea, German (Wünstorf) and Tunisian localities, whereas they are not so obviously developed in the Gubbio section (Schlanger *et al.* 1987).

The disappearance of some types of keeled planktonic foraminifers and ammonites at the Cenomanian–Turonian boundary is probably due to the rather sudden but short-term disappearance of suitable shallow midwater habitats because of widespread severe oxygen depletion in these levels. This interpretation is strengthened by the occurrence of benthic-free zones or depauperate benthic faunas near the Cenomanian–Turonian boundary in many localities (Schlanger *et al.* 1987 for review). Blooms of radiolaria in many localities near the Cenomanian–Turonian boundary and the peak in abundance of calcispheres (e.g. *Pithonella*) which mark the boundary transition in many places probably indicate the highly fertile but unstable ecological conditions at that time.

We have provided an integrated model for Cenomanian–Turonian events which links events seen on a global scale to change in sea level and continental area. Palaeoceanographic events at the Cenomanian–Turonian boundary may have been ultimately influenced by some as yet undocumented volcano-tectonic event. Nonetheless, we suggest that understanding the interaction between sea level changes, climate, and ocean circulation is fundamental to the explanation of such significant relatively short-term palaeoceanographic events as the Cenomanian–Turonian OAE and that stratigraphical, lithological, geochemical, and palaeontological data are all necessary in order to provide satisfactory comprehensive palaeoceanographic models.

ACKNOWLEDGEMENTS: We thank Eric Barron, Gary Brass, Walter Dean, Erle Kauffman, Abe Lerman, Lisa Pratt, Peter Scholle and Colin Summerhayes for discussion of various aspects of this work, and Chuck Threlkeld, Jane Murphy and George Claypool for some of the analytical support. The work was done under the auspices of National Science Foundation Grants OCE 82–14931 to The University of South Carolina and EAR 82–07387 to Northwestern University. We thank Malcomb Hart and an anonymous reviewer for their comments and Andy Fleet and Jim Brooks for inviting us to contribute this paper to their symposium.

References

ARTHUR, M. A. 1979a. *Sedimentologic and geochemical studies of Cretaceous and Paleogene pelagic sedimentary rocks: the Gubbio sequence*, Part I: Unpubl. PhD Dissertation, Princeton University, 171 p.

—— 1979b. North Atlantic Cretaceous black shales: the record at Site 398 and a brief comparison with other occurrences. *In:* SIBUET, J.-C., RYAN, W. B. F. *et al.* (eds) *Initial Reports of the Deep Sea Drilling Project*, **47**, part 2; Washington (U.S. Government Printing Office), p. 719–751.

—— 1982. The Carbon cycle controls on atmospheric CO_2 and climate in the geologic past. *In:* BERGER, W. H. & CROWELL, J. C. (eds), *Climate in Earth History.* Nat. Acad. Press, Washington. p. 55–67.

—— & DEAN, W. E. 1986. Cretaceous paleoceanography. *In:* TUCHOLKE, B. E., & VOGT, P. R. (eds), *Decade of North American Geology, Western North Atlantic Basin Synthesis*, Geol. Soc. Amer., in press.

——, DEAN, W. E., BOTTJER, D. & SCHOLLE, P. A. 1984a. Rhythmic bedding in Mesozoic-Cenozoic pelagic carbonate sequences: the primary and diagenetic origin of Milankovitch-like cycles. *In:* BERGER, A., IMBRIE, J., HAYS, J., KUKLA, G. & SALTZMAN, B. (eds), *Milankovitch and Climate.* Riedel Publ. Co., Holland; 191–222.

——, & STOW, D. A. V. 1984b. Models for the deposition of Mesozoic-Cenozoic fine-grained organic-carbon-rich sediment in the deep sea. *In:* STOW, D. A. V. & PIPER, D. (eds) *Fine-Grained Sediments: Processes and Products*, Geol. Soc. Spec. Publ. No. 15, 527–560. Blackwell Scientific Publications, Oxford.

—— & JENKYNS, H. C. 1981. Phosphorites and paleoceanography. *In:* BERGER, W. (ed.), *Geology of Oceans*, Proc. 26th int. Geol. Congr., Paris: Oceanologica Acta Spec. Iss., p. 83–96.

—— & NATLAND, J. H. 1979. Carbonaceous sediments in North and South Atlantic: the role of salinity in stable stratification of early Cretaceous basins. *In:* TALWANI, M., HAY, W. W. & RYAN, W. B. F. (eds), *Deep Drilling Results in the Atlantic Ocean: Continental Margins and Paleoenvironment.* American Geophysical Union, Washington. Maurice Ewing Series, v. 3, p. 297–344.

—— & PREMOLI SILVA, I., 1982, Development of widespread organic carbon-rich strata in the Mediterranean Tethys. *In:* SCHLANGER, S. O. & CITA, M. B. (eds), *Nature of Cretaceous carbon-rich Facies.* Academic Press, London, p. 7–54.

—— & SCHLANGER, S. O., 1979. Cretaceous 'oceanic anoxic events' as causal factors in development of reef-reservoired giant oilfields. *Bull. Amer. Assoc. Petrol. Geologists* **63**, 870–885.

BARRON, E. J., ARTHUR, M. A., & KAUFFMAN, E. G. 1985, Cretaceous rhythmic bedding sequences: a plausible link between orbital variations and climate. *Earth and Planetary Science Letters*, **72**, 327–340.

——, HARRISON, C. G. A., SLOAN, J. L. & HAY, W. W. 1981. Paleogeography, 180 million years ago to the present. *Ecologae Geologicae Helv.*, **74**, 443–469.

BARRON, E. J. & WASHINGTON, W. M. 1982a. Atmos-

pheric circulation during warm geologic periods: is the equator-to-pole surface-temperature gradient the controlling factor? *Geology*, **10**, 633–636.

—— & —— 1982b. Cretaceous climate: a comparison of atmospheric simulations with the geologic record. *Palaeogeography, Palaeoclimatology, Palaeoecology*, **40**, 103–133.

—— & —— 1983. Numerical climate modeling: an exploration frontier in petroleum source rock prediction. *Bull. Amer. Assoc. Petrol. Geol.*, **67**, 419.

BÉ, A. W. H. 1977. An ecological, zoogeographic and taxonomic review of recent planktonic foraminifera. *In:* RAMSAY, A. T. S. (ed.) *Oceanic Micropaleontology.* Academic Press, London. 1–100.

BERGER, W. H., 1976, Biogenous deep-sea sediments: production, preservation and interpretation. *In:* RILEY, J. P. & CHESTER, R. (eds), *Chemical Oceanography*, v. 5, 2nd Edition: Academic Press, London, p. 265–388.

—— 1979. Impact of deep sea drilling on paleoceanography. *In:* TALWANI, M., HAY, W. W. & RYAN, W. B. F. (eds), *Deep Drilling Results in the Atlantic Ocean, v. 3:* Second Maurice Ewing Symposium, Amer. Geophys. Un., p. 297–314.

—— & SOUTAR, A. 1970. Preservation of plankton shells in an anaerobic basin off California. *Geol. Soc. Amer. Bull.*, **81**, 275–282.

—— & WINTERER, E. L. 1974. Plate stratigraphy and the fluctuating carbonate line. *In:* HSÜ, K. J. & JENKYNS, H. C. (eds), *Pelagic sediments: on land and under the sea.* Spec. Publ. Internat. Assoc. Sediment., **1**, 11–48.

BERNER, R. A. 1982. Burial of organic carbon and pyrite sulfur in the modern ocean: its geochemical and environmental significance. *Amer. Jour. Sci.*, **282**, 451–473.

——, LASAGA, A. C. & GARRELS, R. M. 1983. The carbonate-silicate geochemical cycle and its effect on atmospheric carbon dioxide over the past 100 million years. *Amer. Jour. Sci.*, **283**, 641–683.

—— & RAISWELL, R. 1983. Burial of organic carbon and pyrite sulfur in sediments over Phanerozoic time: a new theory. *Geochim. Cosmochim. Acta*, **47**, 855–862.

BOIS, C., BOUCHE, P. & PELET, R. 1980. Histoire géologique et repartition des reserves d'hydrocarbures dans le monde. *Rev. Inst. Français Pétrole*, **35**, 273–298.

BRASS, G. W., SOUTHAM, J. R. & PETERSON, W. H. 1982. Warm saline bottom water in the ancient ocean. *Nature*, **296**, 620–623.

BROMLEY, R. G. & EKDALE, A. A. 1984. *Chondrites*: a trace fossil indicator of anoxia in sediments. *Science*, **224**, 872–874.

BROOKS, J. 1978. Diagenesis of organic matter: some microbiological, chemical and geochemical studies on sedimentary organic matter. *In: Environmental Biogeochemistry and Geomicrobiology.* Ann Arbor Science, Ann Arbor, MI, v. 1, p. 287–308.

CANNON, W. F. & FORCE, E. R. 1983. Potential for high-grade shallow-marine manganese deposits in North America. *In:* W. C. SHANKS (ed.), *Cameron*

Volume on Unconventional Mineral Deposits, Soc. Mining Engineers Publ., New York, p. 175–189.

CARON, M. & HOMEWOOD, P. 1983. Evolution of early planktic foraminifers. *Mar. Micropaleont.*, **7**, 453–262.

CHAMBERLAIN, T. C. 1906. On a possible reversal of deep-sea circulation and its influence on geologic climates. *J. Geol.*, **14**, 363–373.

CLAYPOOL, G. E., HOLSER, W. T., KAPLAN, I. R., SAKAI, H. & ZACH, I. 1980. The age curves of sulfur and oxygen isotopes in marine sulfate and their mutual interpretation. *Chem. Geol.*, **28**, 199–260.

COOPER, M. R. 1977. Eustacy during the Cretaceous: its implications and importance. *Palaeogeogr., Palaeoclimatol., Palaeoecol.*, **22**, 1–60.

DEAN, W. E., ARTHUR, M. A. & STOW, D. A. V. 1984. Origin and geochemistry of Cretaceous deep-sea black shales and multicolored claystones, with emphasis on Deep Sea Drilling Project Site 530, Southern Angola Basin. *In*: HAY, W. W., SIBUET, J.-C. *et al. Initial Reports of the Deep Sea Drilling Project*, 75: Washington D.C. (U.S. Government Printing Office), 819–844.

DE BOER, P. L. 1982. Cyclicity and the storage of organic matter in middle Cretaceous pelagic sediments. *In*: EINSELE, G. & SEILACHER, A. (eds) *Cyclic and Event Stratification*. Springer-Verlag, Berlin, p. 456–475.

DEMAISON, G. J. & MOORE, G. T. 1980. Anoxic environments and oil source bed genesis. *Organic Geochem.*, **2**, 9–31.

EINSELE, G. & WIEDMANN, J. 1982. Turonian black shales in the Moroccan coastal basins: first upwelling in the Atlantic Ocean? *In*: VON RAD, U., HINZ, K., SARNTHEIN, M. & SEIBOLD, E. (eds), *Geology of the Northwest African Margin*. Springer-Verlag, New York, p. 396–414.

FISCHER, A. G., 1980. Gilbert-bedding rhythms and geochronology. *In*: YOCHELSON, E. I. (ed.) *The Scientific Ideas of G. K. Gilbert*, Geol. Soc. Amer. Spec. Pap. **183**, 93–104.

—— & ARTHUR, M. A. 1977. Secular variations in the pelagic realm. *In*: COOK, H. E. & ENOS, P. (eds) *Deep Water Carbonate Environments*. Soc. Econ. Paleont. Mineral. Spec. Publ., **25**, p. 19–50.

FORCE, E. R., CANNON, W. F., KOSKI, R. A., PASSMORE, K. T. & DOE, B. R. 1983. Influences of ocean anoxic events on manganese deposition and ophiolite-hosted sulfide preservation. *In*: *Paleoclimate and Mineral Deposits*, United States Geological Survey Circular **822**, 26–29.

FRAKES, L. A. & BOLTON, B. R. 1984. Origin of manganese giants: sea-level change and anoxic-oxic history. *Geology*, **12**, 83–86.

GARRELS, R. M. & LERMAN, A. 1981. Phanerozoic cycles of sedimentary carbon and sulfur. *Proc. Natl. Acad. Sci.*, **78**, 4652–4656.

DE GRACIANSKY, P. C., BROSSE, E. *et al.* 1982. Les formations d'âge Crétacé de l'Atlantique Nord et leur metiere organique: paleogéographie et milieux de depot: *Revue de l'Institut Français du Pétrole*, **37**, 275–337.

GRASSHOFF, K. 1975. The hydrochemistry of landlocked basins and fjords. *In*: RILEY, J. & CHESTER, R. (eds)

Chemical Oceanography, v. 2, 2nd Edition. Academic Press, New York, p. 456–597.

HAIG, D. W. 1979. Global distribution patterns for mid-Cretaceous foraminiferids. *J. Foram. Res.*, **9**, 29–40.

HANCOCK, J. M. 1975. The sequence of facies in the Upper Cretaceous of northern Europe compared with that in the Western Interior. *In*: CALDWELL, W. G. E. (ed.) *Cretaceous System in the Western Interior of North America*. Geol. Assoc. Canada Spec. Pap., **13**, 83–118.

—— & KAUFFMAN, E. G. 1979. The great transgressions of the Late Cretaceous. *J. Geol. Soc. London*, **136**, 175–186.

HART, M. B. 1980. The recognition of mid-Cretaceous sea-level changes by means of foraminifera. *Cretaceous Res.* **1**, 289–297.

—— & BAILEY, H. W. 1979. The distribution of planktonic foraminiferida in the mid-Cretaceous of N.W. Europe. *Aspekte der Kreide Europas*. I.U.G.S., Ser. A, **6**, 527–542.

INGLE, J. C. 1981. Origin of Neogene diatomites around the North Pacific rim. *In*: GARRISON, R. E., DOUGLAS, R. G., PISCIOTTO, K. E., ISAACS, C. M. & INGLE, J. C. (eds) *The Monterey Formation and related siliceous rocks of California*. Soc. of Econ. Paleon. and Mineral., Pacific Section, Special Publ., p. 159–180.

IRVING, E., NORTH, F. K. & COUILLARD, R. 1974. Oil, climate and tectonics. *Can. J. Earth Sci.*, **11**, 1–15.

JENKYNS, H. C. 1980. Cretaceous anoxic events: from continents to oceans. *J. Geol. Soc. London*, **137**, 171–188.

KAUFFMAN, E. G. 1977. Geological and biological overview: western interior Cretaceous basin. *Mountain Geologist*, **14**, 75–99.

KEUPP, H. 1979. Lower Cretaceous Calcisphaerulidae and their relationship to calcareous dinoflagellate cysts. *Bull. Centres Rech. Explor.-Prod. Elf-Aquitaine*, **3**, 2, 651–663.

MASTERS, B. A. & SCOTT, R. W. 1978. Microstructure, affinities and systematics of Cretaceous calcispheres. *Micropaleontology*, **24**, 210–221.

MATSUMOTO, T. 1980. Inter-regional correlation of transgressions and regressions in the Cretaceous period. *Cret. Res.*, **1**, 359–373.

MOBERLY, R. L., SCHLANGER, S. O. *et al.* 1983. The Mesozoic superocean. *Nature*, **302**, 381–382.

MOODY, J. D. 1975. Distribution and geological characteristics of giant oilfields. *In*: FISCHER, A. G. & JUDSON, S. (eds) *Petroleum and Global Tectonics*. Princeton Univ. Press, p. 307–320.

MÜLLER, P. S. & SUESS, E. 1979. Productivity, sedimentation rate, and sedimentary organic carbon content in the oceans. *Deep-Sea Research*, **26**, 1347–1362.

NORTH, T. K. 1979. Episodes of source-sediment deposition: *J. Petrol, Geol.*, **2**, 199–218.

OBRADOVICH, J. D. & COBBAN, W. A. 1975. A time scale for the Late Cretaceous of the Western Interior of North America. *In*: CALDWELL, W. G. E. (ed.) *The Cretaceous System in the Western Interior of North America*. Geol. Assoc. Can. Spec. Pap. **13**, 31–54.

PARRISH, J. T. & CURTIS, R. L. 1982. Atmospheric

circulation, upwelling, and organic-rich rocks in the Mesozoic and Cenozoic eras. *Palaeogeography, Palaeoclimatology, Palaeoecology*, **40**, 31–66.

——, ZIEGLER, A. M. & SCOTESE, C. R. 1982. Rainfall patterns and the distribution of coals and evaporites in the Mesozoic and Cenozoic. *Palaeogeography, Palaeoclimatology, Palaeoecology*, **40**, 67–101.

PETTERS, S. W. & EKWEOZOR, C. M. 1982. Origin of mid-Cretaceous black shale in the Benue Trough, Nigeria. *Palaeogeography, Palaeoclimatology, Palaeoecology*, **40**, 311–319.

PHLEGER, F. P. & SOUTAR, A. 1973. Production of benthic foraminifera in three east Pacific oxygen minima. *Micropaleontology*, **19**, 110–115.

POMEROL, B. 1983. Geochemistry of the late Cenomanian–early Turonian chalks of the Paris Basin: manganese and carbon isotopes in carbonates as paleoceanographic indicators. *Cretaceous Res.*, **4**, 85–93.

PRATT, L. M. 1984. Influence of paleoenvironmental factors on preservation of organic matter in middle Cretaceous Greenhorn Formation, Pueblo, Colorado. *Bull. Am. Assoc. Petrol. Geol.*, **68**, 1148–1159.

RAUP, D. M. & SEPKOSKI, J. J. 1982. Mass extinctions in the marine fossil record. *Science*, **215**, 1501–1503.

RENARD, M. & LETOLLE, R. 1983. Essai d'interpretation du rôle de la profonduer de dépôt dans la répartition des teneurs en manganèse et dans l'évolution du rapport isotopique du carbone des carbonates pélagiques: influence de l'oxygenation du milieu: *C. R. Acad. Sci. Paris*, t. **296**, Serie II, 1737–1740.

REYMENT, R. A. & MÖRNER, N. A. 1977. Cretaceous transgressions and regressions exemplified by the South Atlantic Mid-Cretaceous Events. *Paleontol. Soc. Japan, Spec. Pap.* **21**, 247–262.

ROSSIGNOL-STRICK, M., NESTEROFF, W., OLIVE, P. & VERGRAND-GRAZZINI, C. 1982. After the deluge: Mediterranean stagnation and sapropel formation. *Nature*, **295**, 105–110.

ROTH, P. H. 1978. Cretaceous nannoplankton biostratigraphy and oceanography of the northwestern Atlantic Ocean. *In*: BENSON, W. E., SHERIDAN, R. E. *et al.*, *Initial Reports of the Deep Sea Drilling Project*, **44**. Washington D.C. (U.S. Government Printing Office), p. 731–752.

RYAN, W. B. F. & CITA, M. B. 1977. Ignorance concerning episodes of ocean-wide stagnation. *Marine Geology*, **23**, 197–215.

SCHIDLOWSKI, M., JUNGE, C. E. & PIETRECK, H. 1977. Sulfur isotope variations in marine sulfate evaporites and the Phanerozoic oxygen budget. *J. Geophys. Res.*, **82**, 2557–2565.

SCHLANGER, S. O., ARTHUR, M. A., JENKYNS, H. C. & SCHOLLE, P. A. 1987. The Cenomanian-Turonian Oceanic Anoxic Event, I. Stratigraphy and distribution of organic carbon-rich beds and the marine $\delta^{13}C$ excursion. *This volume*, pp. 371–399.

—— & JENKYNS, H. C. 1976. Cretaceous oceanic anoxic events—causes and consequences. *Geologie en Mijnbouw*, **55**, 179–184.

SEPKOSKI, J. J. 1982. Mass extinctions in the Phanerozoic oceans: a review. *In*: SILVER, L. T. & SCHULTZ, P. H. (eds) *Geological implications of impacts of large*

asteroids and comets on the earth, Geol. Soc. Amer. Spec. Paper **190**, p. 282–290.

SCHOLLE, P. A. & ARTHUR, M. A. 1980. Carbon isotope fluctuations in Cretaceous pelagic limestones: potential stratigraphic and petroleum exploration tool. *Bull. Amer. Assoc. Petrol. Geol.* **64**, 67–87.

SOUTHAM, J. R., PETERSON, W. H. & BRASS, G. W. 1982. Dynamics of anoxia. *Palaeogeography, Palaeoclimatology, and Palaeoecology*, **40**, 183–198.

——, —— & —— 1984. A model of the coupled carbon, oxygen phosphorus system and anoxia in the deep sea. *Deep-Sea Res.*, in press.

SUMMERHAYES, C. P. 1981. Organic facies of middle Cretaceous black shales in deep North Atlantic. *Bull. Amer. Assoc. Petrol. Geol.*, **65**, 2364–2380.

—— & MASRAN, P. 1983. Organic facies of Cretaceous and Jurassic sediments from DSDP Site 534 in the Blake-Bahama Basin, Western North Atlantic. *In*: SHERIDAN, R. E., GRADSTEIN, F., *et al. Initial Reports of the Deep Sea Drilling Project*, **76**. Washington D.C. (U.S. Government Printing Office), 469–480.

THIERSTEIN, H. R. 1979. Paleoceanographic implications of organic carbon and carbonate distribution in Mesozoic deep sea sediments. *In*: TALWANI, M., HAY, W. W. & RYAN, W. B. F. (eds) *Deep Drilling Results in the Atlantic Ocean: Continental Margins and Paleoenvironment*. Washington, Amer. Geophysical Union, Maurice Ewing Series, **3**, 249–274.

—— & BERGER, W. H. 1979. Injection events in earth history. *Nature*, **276**, 461–466.

TISSOT, B. 1979. Effects on prolific petroleum source rocks and major coal deposits caused by sealevel changes. *Nature*, **277**, 463–465.

TUCHOLKE, B. E. & VOGT, P. R. 1979. Western North Atlantic: sedimentary evolution and aspects of tectonic history. *In*: TUCHOKE, B. E., VOGT, P. R. *et al. Initial Reports of the Deep Sea Drilling Project*, **23**, Washington (U.S. Government Printing Office), p. 791–825.

VAIL, P. R., MITCHUM, R. J. & THOMPSON, S. 1977. Seismic stratigraphy and global changes of sealevel, Part 4: Global cycles of relative change of sea level. *AAPG Mem.* **26**, 83–97.

VAN GRASS, G., VIETS, T. C., DE LEEUW, J. W. & SCHENCK, P. A. 1983. A study of the soluble and insoluble organic matter from the Livello Bonarelli, a Cretaceous black shale deposit in the Central Apennines, Italy. *Geochimica et Cosmochimica Acta*, **47**, 1051–1059.

VAN HINTE, J. E. 1976. A Cretaceous time scale. *Amer. Assoc. Petrol. Geol. Bull.*, **60**, 498–516.

VAN HOUTEN, F. B. 1980. Latest Jurassic–Early Cretaceous regressive facies, northeast Africa craton. *Amer. Assoc. Petrol Geol. Bull.*, **64**, 857–867.

—— & BHATTACHARYYA, D. P. 1982. Phanerozoic oolite ironstones—the geologic record and facies model: *Ann. Rev. Earth Planet, Sci.*, **10**, 441–457.

VEIZER, J., HOLSER, W. T. & WILGUS, C. K. 1980. $^{13}C/^{12}C$ and $^{34}S/^{32}S$ secular variations. *Geochim. Cosmochim. Acta*, **44**, 579–587.

WILDE, P. & BERRY, W. B. N. 1982. Progressive ventilation of the oceans—potential for return to anoxic conditions in the post-Paleozoic. *In*:

SCHLANGER, S. O. & CITA, M. B. (eds) *Nature and origin of Cretaceous carbon-rich facies.* Academic Press, New York, p. 209–224.

WONDERS, A. 1980. Middle and Late Cretaceous planktonic foraminifera of the Western Mediterranean area. *Utrecht Micropaleontol. Bull.*, **24**, 158 p.

M. A. ARTHUR, Graduate School of Oceanography, University of Rhode Island, Narragansett, RI 02882, USA.

S. O. SCHLANGER, Department of Earth Sciences, Northwestern University, Evanston, IL 60201, USA.

H. C. JENKYNS, Department of Earth Sciences, University of Oxford, Parks Road. Oxford OX1 3PR UK.

Anoxic non-events; alternative explanations

B. M. Funnell

The solubility of oxygen in ocean surface waters depends on the partial pressure of oxygen in the atmosphere, and on the temperature and salinity of those waters. At present-day partial pressures the oxygen content of sea-waters varies from slightly in excess of 8 ml l^{-1} in normal salinity water at 0°C to approximately 2 ml l^{-1} in halite-precipitating brines at 25–30°C. Oxygen is removed from subsurface ocean waters, out of contact with the atmosphere, by the oxidative (aerobic) decomposition of organic matter. Oxygen contents may be at least seasonally reduced to as little as 0.1 ml l^{-1} in oxygen minimum zones underlying some biologically highly productive surface waters associated with upwelling. (In these circumstances sedimenting organic matter creates a strong biological oxygen demand in the water column below the euphotic zone.) Under the low productivity conditions of more stably stratified ocean waters such as occur in the central ocean gyres, the oxygen content in the oxygen minimum zone typically only falls to around 3 ml l^{-1}. The oxygen content of subsurface ocean waters therefore depends mainly on the amount of biological production in overlying waters. It also depends on the length of time (inverse of rate of circulation) over which it satisfies the biological oxygen demand created by aerobic decomposition of organic matter generated by that production. Initial oxygenation levels of the surface waters is less significant. Surface and subsurface waters in the contemporary ocean are generally well oxygenated, but there are regional exceptions where either high primary surface productivity or sluggish subsurface water circulation leads to varying degrees of deoxygenation. This deoxygenation affects the biota and geochemistry of both the water column and the sediment-water interface.

In aerobic waters, containing more than 1 ml l^{-1} of oxygen, macro- and micro-organisms are generally both abundant and diverse, although there may already be some reduction in the diversity of calcareous macro-invertebrates at oxygen levels of less than 2 ml l^{-1}. Consequently most marine bottom sediments under these conditions are well-burrowed to a depth of at least 20–30 mm by deposit feeding and other burrowing macro-invertebrate infauna, even if the interstitial water in the underlying sediment is itself anoxic. Some deeper burrowing deposit feeders (e.g. holothurians) may indeed extend their operations well into any underlying anoxic sediment zone (e.g. to depths of 100 mm). However high the input of organic matter into such benthic ecosystems, as long as the water column remains aerobic, detritus feeding, burrowing and active aerobic microbial decomposition proceeds apace, and the incorporation of unutilized and unoxidized organic matter into the accumulating sediment underlying the burrowed zone is unlikely to exceed 0.5–2.0%.

In dysaerobic waters, containing 1–0.1 ml l^{-1} of oxygen (Tyson, this volume; Summerhayes, this volume, refers to waters containing 0.5–0.2 ml l^{-1} O_2 as suboxic) aerobic macro- and ultimately micro-organisms are progressively reduced. Near 1 ml l^{-1} of oxygen some calcareous macro-invertebrates (e.g. echinoderms) may still be abundant (down to 0.3 ml l^{-1} O_2), but faunal diversity is significantly reduced. Below 0.3 ml l^{-1} of oxygen the only macro-invertebrates are small (1–2 mm), soft-bodied, weakly burrowing forms. These, together with both planktonic (in the water column) and benthonic micro-organisms (e.g. foraminiferans) often thrive at oxygen concentrations down to 0.1 ml l^{-1}. In dysaerobic waters therefore benthic activity is sharply reduced, and although some sediment disturbance may occur even down to 0.1 ml l^{-1} it becomes inconspicuous and the throughput of organic matter into anoxic sediments beneath the sediment-water interface is much enhanced, leading to organic matter contents of more than 2%.

At oxygen levels of less than 0.1 ml l^{-1} organisms with aerobic metabolism give place to organisms with anaerobic metabolism (e.g. denitrifying bacteria), and between 0.1 ml l^{-1} and 0 ml l^{-1} O_2 marine waters may also be termed anaerobic (Tyson, this volume; Summerhayes, this volume, refers to all water containing less than 0.2 ml l^{-1} O_2 as anoxic). In the total absence of oxygen other anaerobic microbes (i.e. sulphate-reducing bacteria) operate, and the water can be strictly termed anoxic. Under anaerobic and anoxic conditions burrowing and other aerobic organisms are absent from the sediment surface. Therefore any primary lamination will be preserved, and a high proportion of incoming organic matter will be incorporated into the accumulating sediment.

In contemporary seas and oceans deoxygenated (dysaerobic, aerobic and anoxic) waters are

From: BROOKS, J. & FLEET, A. J. (eds) 1987, *Marine Petroleum Source Rocks* Geological Society Special Publication No. 26 pp. 421–422.

typically found in association with high, upwelling-enhanced biological production, which produces a strong underlying oxygen minimum zone, in places intersecting the bottom, and therefore allowing the accumulation of organic rich sediments, on the upper continental rise (e.g. Peru) or shelf (e.g. S.W. Africa). Alternatively salinity or temperature stratified waters may accumulate in silled basins (e.g. Black Sea, Cariaco Trench), leading to deoxygenation of the slowly ventilated bottom waters, even if primary biological production is very low. In some cases (e.g. the basins of the Californian continental borderland) these two mechanisms may to some extent be combined. Because of these present-day occurrences, in various marginal seas and on several continental margins the late Pleistocene and Holocene could well be regarded as a Quaternary anoxic event, but the contemporary oceans generally are in no sense poorly oxygenated. Today the deposition of organic rich sediments under dysaerobic to anoxic water columns is mainly an accident of the localization of upwelling current systems and the tectonic conditioning of the entrances to marginal seas. (The adjacent or surrounding terrestrial climatic conditions are in both cases also important controls.) Past (Phanerozoic) oceans may have been more prone to the development of dysaerobic to anoxic waters for two reasons. First, the opportunity for thermal-induction of stable density stratification in wide epeiric shelf seas would have been greater in periods of more widespread tropical marine temperatures (Tyson, this volume). Secondly, the existence of warmer saline bottom waters (Brass *et al.* 1982) with lower initial oxygen contents could (if surface biological production were sufficient, or bottom water circulation adequately slow) pass the dysaerobic threshold earlier than the modern, cold, well-oxygenated bottom waters would. In this context it is worth remembering that the transition from one thermohaline bottom water drive to another could have crucial effects, and be liable to lead to a period of near or total stagnation followed by almost total overturn (cf. recent events in the Dead Sea).

Recent authors (Waples 1983; Summerhayes, this volume) have given close and critical attention to the precise conditions in which the accumulation of organic rich muds under deoxygenated water columns occurred in Cretaceous seas. All of these occurrences, except perhaps one (the Cenomanian–Turonian event; see Arthur *et al.* and Schlanger *et al.* this volume) appear to be explicable in terms of processes operating at the present-day, and seem to be more geographically than temporally constrained. In this respect the temporal imperative of the 'oceanic anoxic event' concept is perhaps best relaxed and more attention given to the spatial (geographical, oceanographic and climatic) contexts in which such occurrences are found.

Finally, attention can be drawn to a few other possible circumstances favouring at least temporary preservation of organic matter in ocean bottom sediments. It is clear that prime source rocks are likely to be accumulated in dysaerobic to anoxic water conditions, when exclusion of a diverse, active macrobenthos inhibits bioturbation. Temporary exclusion of the macrobenthos may however occur for a number of reasons other than the deoxygenation of the bottom water.

Examples are: sudden sediment influxes (mass flows, turbidites, ash falls, meteoritic impact debris), introduction of hypersaline bottom waters, toxic plankton production. Each of these may be sufficient to eliminate the *in situ* macrobenthos for a time leading to ineffective organic matter recycling and the preservation of thin organic rich sediments that will be virtually indistinguishable from those deposited under dysaerobic to anoxic water columns.

References

ARTHUR, M. A., SCHLANGER, S. O. & JENKYNS, H. C. 1987. The Cenomanian–Turonian anoxic event, II. Palaeoceanographic controls on organ matter production and preservation. *This volume*, pp. 401–420.

BRASS, G. W., SOUTHAM, J. R. & PETERSON, W. H. 1982. Warm saline bottom water in the ancient ocean. *Nature* **296**, 620–623.

SCHLANGER, S. O., ARTHUR, M. A., JENKYNS, H. C. & SCHOLLE, P. A. 1987. The Cenomanian–Turonian oceanic anoxic event, I. Stratigraphy and distribution of organic carbon-rich beds and the marine ^{13}C excursion. *This volume*, pp. 371–400.

SUMMERHAYES, C. P. 1987. Organic rich Cretaceous sediments from the North Atlantic. *This volume*, pp. 301–316.

TYSON, R. V. 1987. Palynofacies and the Palaeoenvironment of Marine Source Rocks. *This volume*, pp. 47–68.

WAPLES, D. W. 1983. Reappraisal of Anoxia and Organic Richness, with Emphasis on Cretaceous of North Atlantic. *Am. Ass. Petrol. Geol. Bull.* **67**, 963–978.

B. M. FUNNELL, School of Environmental Sciences, University of East Anglia, Norwich NR4 7TJ, UK.

The carbon isotope record of the Cenozoic: history of organic carbon burial and of oxygen in the ocean and atmosphere

N. J. Shackleton

SUMMARY: Carbon isotope measurements in deep-sea sediments may be used to obtain the history of the mean ^{13}C content of CO_2 dissolved in the ocean, of ^{13}C gradients within the ocean, and of the globally averaged ^{13}C content of the carbonate accumulated on the sea floor. The last has some interest in relation to energy reserves, because it provides a means of monitoring the changing rate of accumulation of organic matter on the globe.

Data are shown for the ^{13}C composition of Cenozoic marine carbonates, based on a suite of sites from DSDP (Deep Sea Drilling Project) Leg 74 in the South Atlantic. If the published estimates of global accumulation rates for marine carbonate are recalculated on the basis of recent timescales for the Cenozoic it is found that changes were rather subtle, contrary to the conclusion of Davies and Worsley (1981), so that a model of constant carbon input may be used to estimate changes in organic carbon accumulation from the ^{13}C data. A cumulation of changes in the global organic carbon reservoir is also obtained and is used to infer changes in the amount of oxygen in the atmosphere, which was 20% higher than today during most of the Cenozoic. However, the solubility of oxygen in the warm early Cenozoic oceans was about 20% lower than today's value, so that the early Cenozoic ocean had a similar dissolved oxygen content to today's ocean.

Introduction

The chief process which gives rise to fractionation of the stable carbon isotopes at the earth's surface is photosynthesis (Craig 1953). Most plant material is isotopically depleted in ^{13}C with respect to the carbon dioxide from which it was photosynthesized by about -25 per mil (Craig 1953) while in a minority of species in which a different biochemical pathway is utilized in photosynthesis, a less depleted ^{13}C value around -18 per mil is observed (Bender 1968). The carbon of marine organic matter is only slightly less isotopically depleted than that in average terrestrial plants (Sackett et al. 1965). On the gross scale there is little fractionation associated with the passage of carbon down the food chain (DeNiro & Epstein 1978). For marine plankton, a temperature effect on the photosynthetic fractionation factor of about 0.35 per mil per °C has been demonstrated (Sackett et al. 1965; Fontugne & Duplessy 1981), although the latter workers found that some other factor intervenes in such a manner that the overall range of ^{13}C in marine plankton is smaller than this temperature factor would suggest should be the case. It is clear from accumulated data on the ^{13}C content of organic matter in the geological column that the fractionation factor involved in photosynthesis has been more or less constant since the origin of life (Craig 1953). Both globally in the lithosphere, and in average marine sediments accumulating today, approximately 20–25% of carbon is stored in organic matter and most of the remainder in

carbonate (Garrels & Perry 1974; Kempe 1977). Thus fluctuations in organic carbon storage on a geological timescale may be expected to leave an imprint in the carbon isotope record of the carbonate. In order to illustrate the potential value of the carbon isotope record, a brief summary of ^{13}C variability on shorter timescales will precede presentation of data that relates to changes in global carbon storage.

On an annual scale, seasonal changes in global biomass (which are dominated by the Northern Hemisphere growing season, because this hemisphere contains a disproportionate area of the continents) give rise to seasonal variations in the CO_2 content of the atmosphere (Keeling et al. 1976) and in the ^{13}C content of this CO_2 (Mook et al. 1981). This annual cycle is not damped out by exchange with the ocean because the time constant for equilibrating the atmospheric carbon dioxide with the surface ocean is long compared with the seasonal cycle. The mixing between the atmosphere and the deep ocean is so slow that the atmospheric carbon dioxide load resulting from man's fossil fuel combustion will equilibrate with the ocean only on a timescale of centuries (see, for example, papers in Andersen & Malahoff 1977).

On a longer timescale, glacial-interglacial changes in the continental biomass (particularly the tropical rainforests) must have left their imprint in the ^{13}C content of ocean CO_2 (Shackleton 1977). This is to be expected because the ocean ^{13}C content will only regain a steady-state equilibrium value with respect to incoming

From: BROOKS, J. & FLEET, A. J. (eds) 1987, *Marine Petroleum Source Rocks* Geological Society Special Publication No. 26 pp. 423–434.

river-borne carbon with a time constant of the order 3×10^5 years, so that changes on a 10^4 year scale can be recorded by the ocean. Broecker (1982) suggested that changes in the carbon stored on the continental shelves could also give rise to significant changes in ocean ^{13}C on this timescale.

The residence time of carbon in the ocean is about 3×10^5 years (Broecker 1974). On a timescale that is long compared with this residence time, a change in the global organic carbon reservoir, arising from a persistent change in the proportion of carbon that is stored as organic carbon rather than as carbonate, must give rise to a change in the global mean ^{13}C content of the carbonate that is being stored. On this timescale, the ^{13}C content of CO_2 dissolved in the ocean will change in response to variation in the partitioning of carbon; its ^{13}C content will float at whatever value enables carbonate to accumulate with the ^{13}C content appropriate for steady-state conservation of mass of ^{13}C and of total carbon. Thus if one were to hypothesize that a change in the average fractionation factor between dissolved CO_2 and coccolith carbonate occurred as a result of an evolutionary overturn among the coccoliths that make up the bulk of the carbonate accumulating in the deep sea, the immediate result would be an isotopic change in the carbonate sediment. However, within well under a million years the isotopic composition of CO_2 dissolved in the ocean would adjust until the ^{13}C content of the sediment returned to its steady state value.

Fischer and Arthur (1977) were the first to draw attention to a quasi-cyclic variation (with a timescale of the order 3×10^7 years) in ^{13}C values for Mesozoic carbonates, and their implications for carbon storage, while Arthur (1982) has given an elegant discussion of some of the topics discussed here. This is the timescale with which the present paper is chiefly concerned. It must be remembered, however, that in order to make deductions about carbon partitioning from ^{13}C data one must always bear in mind the scale and the time constant of the system in which one is working.

Data

Measurements of the ^{13}C content of foraminiferal tests through long sections of the Cenozoic have been made by several workers: Douglas & Savin (1971, 1973, 1976); Shackleton & Kennett (1975); Boersma & Shackleton (1977a, 1977b); Boersma et al. (1979); Shackleton et al. (1984). However, most of these studies are of limited value for

evaluating the global distribution of ^{13}C. On the one hand, in order to evaluate possible changes in the ^{13}C content of ocean water, one needs to know both the fractionation factor for the particular species analysed, and the position in the water column at which the species calcified, neither of which is known for the majority of extinct species. On the other hand, the data are not suitable for investigating global carbon budgeting, for which purpose we need to have an estimate of the ^{13}C content of all the carbonate stored rather than of a specially selected fraction. Shackleton et al. (1984) attempted to derive a record of the ^{13}C content of dissolved CO_2 in the deep water of the South Atlantic and, more tentatively, the surface water. For deep water this is a realistic aim since several species of benthic Foraminifera, which have evolutionarily long lifetimes of tens of million years, have been calibrated against present-day conditions (Graham et al. 1981; Duplessy et al. 1984). For surface water it is more problematic since it is not even certain which species inhabited the ocean surface and which calcified deeper in the water column. Indeed, stable isotope data provide some of the best evidence for the depth habitat of extinct species. Moreover although some of the species living in today's ocean deposit carbonate that is isotopically close to the ^{13}C content of the water they inhabit, others do not, while for many species there is a significant ontogenetic effect on isotopic composition (Berger et al. 1978).

Since deep-sea carbonate is a mixture of many different species of both foraminifers and coccoliths, its ^{13}C content is not related to the ^{13}C content of the ocean in a simple manner. Very little information has been obtained on the ^{13}C content of total carbonate sediment, and geochemists have generally assumed that the single value given by Craig (1953) for foraminiferans is a valid estimate of the mean ^{13}C content of deep-sea sediment. Recently a summary of the ^{13}C history of Phanerozoic sediments (Veizer et al. 1980) attempted to improve the situation by obtaining a mean of several hundred analyses taken from the literature; the mean value was stated to have 95% confidence limits of ± 0.05 per mil. This implies that the standard deviation of the original data set was over 1.0 per mil, which in turn would imply that 1.0 per mil is a valid estimate of the variability of the ^{13}C content of recent marine sediments. However, inspection of the sources of the data in Veizer et al. (1980) reveals that none of the sources contained ^{13}C data for total sediment; the variability reflects the heterogeneity of the components analysed, as the data are mainly from separate analyses of benthic and planktonic foraminifera.

Table 1 summarizes new analyses of the ^{13}C content of bulk sediment of recent and late Pleistocene age. These provide for the first time an estimate of the ^{13}C content of the total deep sea carbonate that is accumulating under present-day conditions. These data suggest that in fact the spatial variability in the ^{13}C content of normal marine sediment carbonate is quite small (standard deviation 0.3 per mil), so that a record from a single site should represent a reasonable approximation to a global average record (Cenozoic range about 3 per mil). Whether there exists a coherent spatial pattern in the ^{13}C content of deep-sea carbonate sediment remains to be seen.

Shackleton and Hall (1984) analysed bulk sediment from deep sea drilling sites 525, 527, 528 and 529 in the South Atlantic. Figure 1 shows these data (together with some new analyses) averaged in million year increments and plotted against estimated age (ages from Shackleton and members of the shipboard party, 1984). Data recently obtained from north Pacific DSDP site 577 (Shackleton *et al.* 1985) are remarkably similar to those obtained for DSDP Leg 74 sediments over the period of time analysed (the Paleocene and Lower Eocene). This also suggests that data from a single area, such as are displayed in Fig. 1, do indeed approximate a global record.

For several reasons, the effect of diagenesis on the data in Figure 1 may be neglected. First, as Scholle and Arthur (1980) have pointed out, even in a setting such as Cretaceous chalk exposure that has undergone extensive oxygen isotopic exchange with percolating groundwaters, it is only rarely that a sufficient mass of dissolved carbon of different isotopic composition can be brought in to obliterate the primary bulk ^{13}C signal in the rock. In deep sea sequences such as those investigated by Shackleton and Hall (1984) where there is no evidence of significant ^{18}O exchange, ^{13}C exchange is even less likely. Secondly, the main features of the ^{13}C record shown here were first demonstrated in unaltered foraminiferal tests (Shackleton & Kennett 1975). Thirdly, in the Cenozoic both the impressive ^{18}O events (for example, one very close to the Eocene–Oligocene boundary, and one in the later part of the Middle Miocene) and equally significant ^{13}C events (for example, one at the Cretaceous–Tertiary boundary and one near the Paleocene–Eocene boundary) occur at stratigraphically equivalent points in sequences that have experienced widely differing degrees of burial and lithification. This would not be the case if they were the result of diagenesis. Indeed, the impressive ^{13}C events at the boundaries of the Paleocene are preserved intact even in the completely lithified limestones of Gubbio, Italy (Letolle & Renard 1980; Shackleton & Backman unpublished data).

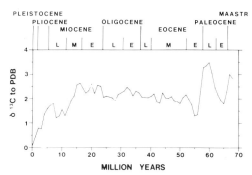

FIG. 1. Carbon isotope record of bulk sediment in DSDP Sites 525 and 528, per mil to the PDB standard, averaged in million year increments (data from Shackleton & Hall 1984 and unpublished).

TABLE 1. *Carbon isotope data for total carbonate in recent deep sea sediment. (All samples are from near core top in Holocene age sediment)*

Core	Latitude	Longitude	Water depth	$\delta^{13}C$
			m	
V29-179	44°00′N	24°32′W	3331	−0.08
V30-40	00°12′S	23°09′W	3706	0.53
V22-182	00°33′S	17°16′W	3614	0.66
V22-174	10°04′S	12°49′W	2630	0.38
RC8-18	24°04′S	15°07′W	3977	−0.05
RC15-94	42°59′S	20°51′W	3762	0.45
V22-108	43°11′S	03°15′W	4171	0.60
RC11-147	19°03′S	112°45′E	1953	0.83
RC11-120	43°31′S	79°52′E	3135	0.21
V28-238	01°01′N	160°29′E	3120	0.27
V28-203	00°57′N	179°25′W	3243	0.42
mean				0.38 ± 0.28 (std.dev.)

The global deep sea sediment budget

Davies *et al.* (1977), and a series of subsequent papers (Worsley & Davies 1979; Whitman & Davies 1979; Davies & Worsley 1981), summarized evidence for substantial, persistent changes in globally integrated deep-sea sedimentation rates during the Cenozoic. They argued, reasonably as it seemed, that although the picture that they obtained was subject to many uncertainties, the timescale used was not likely to be a major source of error. However, recalculation of their data using the new timescale obtained for the Palaeogene by Berggren *et al.* (1985a) and for the Neogene by Berggren *et al.* (1985b) shows that in reality much of the dramatic variability that Davies *et al.* (1977) found may have been an artefact of a timescale. These recent timescales are tied to the geomagnetic polarity record, which is calibrated using the assumption that the process of sea floor spreading is sufficiently uniform that a valid timescale for the polarity record can be derived from only a few calibration points. Although this can only produce a model timescale subject to revision when more appropriate control points are obtained, there are good reasons for regarding it as a useful step forward. For the past five million years an independent polarity timescale can be constructed that is based only on radiometric age determinations in lavas whose polarity is known. Distinctive portions of the polarity record are dated to beyond ten million years ago (Harrison *et al.* 1979). There is no evidence for changes in South Atlantic spreading rate over this interval. This means that even in the most recent part of the geological record, for which radiometric dating is most accurate, changes in sea-floor spreading rate at a zone-by-zone scale are not detectable. On the other hand changes in sediment accumulation rate of a factor of ten on a zone-by-zone basis can occur even in deep-sea sediments and must be commonplace in the shallow-water sediments of the European type localities where traditional timescales are based.

Extrapolating the late Neogene South Atlantic spreading rate back to the reversed interval between Anomaly 29 and Anomaly 30 produces an age estimate of about 75 million years (Heirtzler *et al.* 1968). The Cretaceous–Tertiary boundary is now known to lie within this reversed interval; the extrapolated age is only about 15% greater than the accepted figure of about 65 million years. Thus even over the scale of stages and series, the changes in sea-floor spreading rate that are required by radiometric age determinations are modest compared with changes in the rate of sediment accumulation at any particular

site. The version of the Cenozoic timescale used by Davies *et al.* (1977) incorporated elements of earlier versions in which biostratigraphic zones were assumed to be equal in length, and in which sediment was assumed to have accumulated uniformly in particular areas, both of which are weak assumptions on which to base a timescale which is to be used in order to depict changing global accumulation rates.

The recalculated record of changes in global oceanic sediment accumulation rates shown in Fig. 2 resembles the sediment survival record of Moore and Heath (1977). These workers examined the Deep Sea Drilling Project records in order to determine the chance of survival of deep sea sediment as a function of its geological age. They sought to formalize and explain the observation that the chance of recovering sediment of specified age in a deep-sea drilling site is systematically higher for younger sediment and falls off for older sediment. It is clear that if account is not taken of the loss by subsequent erosion of a certain proportion of older sediment, a false impression will be gained of the history of deep-sea accumulation rates. If, as is suggested by Fig. 2, apparent accumulation rate shows a similar pattern through the Cenozoic to that shown by sediment survival, then it is possible that in fact integrated sediment accumulation in the ocean basins may not have fluctuated greatly during the Cenozoic, and that the age distribution of the sediments present today is affected more by survival than by changing deposition rate.

In a more recent compilation Davies and Worsley (1981) did in fact adjust their data to take account of the survival curve of Moore and Heath (1977). However, at the same time they attempted to take account of the uneven weighting of their data in terms of ocean depths and area. In addition Davies and Worsley (1981) refined their compilation by breaking it into 3 m.y. increments. This renders its relationship to the timescale on which it is based less clear, so that their latest compilation, although superior to the earlier one, has not been used as a basis for the present recalculation.

Fig. 2 is interpreted here to imply that when averaged over the whole of the ocean basins, sediment may have accumulated at a fairly constant rate through time. The global variations of almost a factor of ten that were implied by the important first paper of Davies *et al.* (1977) could easily be detected, but were probably an artefact of the timescale used. Although it is likely that there were changes of smaller magnitude in global accumulation rates, it seems unlikely that they could be detected without more refined biostratigraphic data than is obtainable given the inter-

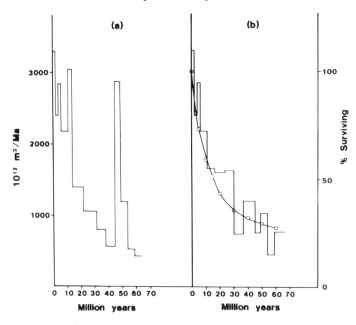

FIG. 2. Left, accumulation rate of calcite in the world oceans using the data in Whitman and Davies (1979); Right, the same data, recalculated using versions of the timescale of Berggren, Kent and Flynn (1985) and Berggren, Kent and van Couvering (1985). The scale to the right shows the percent of sediment surviving (circles) for the same stratigraphic intervals, as estimated by Moore and Heath (1981).

mittent coring, poor recovery and prevalent drilling disturbance that characterized most of the sites drilled in the early phases of the Deep Sea Drilling Project.

If there have not in fact been such large variations in Cenozoic global carbonate accumulation rates as appeared from the work of Davies *et al.* (1977), it may be reasonable to model changes in the global organic carbon budget on the assumption that the total carbon input to the ocean (and its isotopic composition) is constant. If this flux of carbon is partitioned between two sinks, one the limestone and the other organic matter with a ^{13}C composition that is about 25 per mil lighter, then a knowledge of the ^{13}C content of the limestone permits the fraction entering the organic pool to be estimated; (see Fig. 3 for estimate). The construction of Fig. 3 assumes a long-term global input rate of 150×10^{18}g carbon per million years, and assumes that at long-term steady state 120×10^{18}g per Ma of this is stored up as carbonate with a δ^{13}C content of $+2.25$ per mil and the remaining 30×10^{18}g per m.y. in organic matter with a ^{13}C content of -22.75 per mil. To facilitate comparison, these accumulation figures are identical with those of Garrels and Perry (1974) and Garrels and Lerman (1981). The carbonate ^{13}C value chosen is the mean of all the pre-15 m.y. data in Fig. 1.

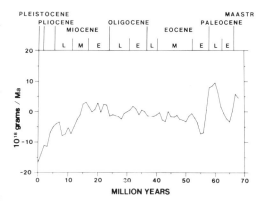

FIG. 3. Estimated deviations from a global net steady-state in the accumulation rate of organic carbon implied by Fig. 1, if (1) the carbon input is assumed to have remained constant at 1.5×10^{20}g per million years, 20% of which derives from the erosion of organic carbon, and (2) in the long-term mean 20% of the accumulating carbon is stored as organic carbon.

Before discussing the implications of Fig. 3, it is appropriate to consider the extent to which these implications will be modified as the assumptions on which it is based are refined.

(1) One might suppose that the initial assumption that the photosynthetic fractionation factor

has been unchanged is false. If this were the case, the ^{13}C event during the Paleocene (with an amplitude of 2 per mil would require that the average photosynthetic fractionation factor for all that 25% of carbon that was buried as organic matter during the Paleocene was 8 per mil greater than normal. This is extremely unlikely.

(2) Our assumption that the ^{13}C content of carbon entering the ocean system is constant is clearly a simplification; in reality the model cannot distinguish between an unusually high rate of erosion of ancient organic deposits (for example, coals) and an unusually low rate of accumulation of fresh organic deposits. The implications for the global organic carbon reservoir are identical in either case; if the present model does not find support in the shape of independent palaeo-oceanographic evidence for changes in the conditions favouring organic carbon accumulation in the ocean, it may be appropriate to reconsider the model.

(3) Most important, one should consider the effect that a different model for the history of global sedimentation rates would have on the inferred history of organic carbon burial. If it is accepted that the ocean ^{13}C record correctly estimates the partitioning of carbon between the two sinks represented as limestone and organic matter, then it may be seen that the chief merit of using a simple model for global sedimentation rates is that it enables one to express the dramatic variations in carbon partitioning demonstrated by Fig. 1 in mass terms rather than percentage terms. In principle, an alternative model could be taken in which the global organic carbon reservoir is taken as fixed, and the data in Fig. 1 used to calculate implied changes in the global carbonate budget. Such a model does not seem to have the merit of plausibility, whereas the simple model that has been chosen here does have some interesting implications which deserve to be followed up.

Another alternative model might be constructed on the assumption that the data shown in Fig. 26 reveals a real increase in oceanic accumulation rates during the Neogene, fed by an increased river flux. However, this model would actually exacerbate the problem posed by the carbon isotope data, since it would increase the quantity of carbonate that has been stored with a ^{13}C content significantly different from the long-term mean.

In Fig. 3 a dramatic event in the Paleocene is apparent; ^{13}C values in bulk carbonate become isotopically heavier by over 2 per mil, only to return to lighter values in the early Eocene. This event may be partly analogous to the isotopically positive peaks in carbonate ^{13}C content associ-

ated with times of black shale deposition during the Cretaceous (Scholle & Arthur 1980). This Paleocene event is tracked in the ^{13}C content of both planktonic and benthonic foraminiferal tests (Shackleton *et al.* 1984). Measurements of the ^{13}C difference between planktonics and benthonics at least as great as is observed today have been made (see below); this implies that low values of dissolved oxygen content were commonplace in the ocean deepwaters. An increase in this ^{13}C gradient from the low values in the basal Paleocene was documented by Boersma *et al.* (1979). It seems likely that there is a relationship between the increasing oxygen depletion in deep waters that this implies and the high rate of burial of organic carbon during the late Paleocene (Fig. 3), and that further investigation of this relationship will shed light on the Cretaceous black shale episodes. These Cretaceous events cannot themselves be studied in equivalent detail because it is difficult or impossible to obtain unaltered benthonic foraminifera for isotopic analysis.

The cumulative effect of variations in the organic carbon accumulation rate on the total buried organic carbon reservoir is presented in Fig. 4. In order to construct Fig. 4, a steady-state is defined as one in which the global buried organic carbon reservoir is constant (i.e. the loss of organic matter contained in sediments that are eroded from the continents is balanced by the formation and accumulation of new organic reservoirs in marine sediments). Fig. 4 records integrated departures from this steady-state, and shows that in fact the total effect of the Paleocene event was small compared with the very large loss from the organic carbon pool that has occurred during the past 15 million years, when about 10^{20} grams organic carbon have dis-

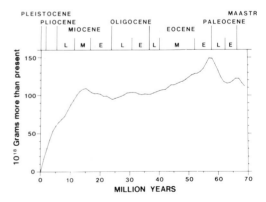

FIG. 4. History of the global organic carbon reservoir over the past 68Ma implied by Fig. 3, expressed as deviations from today's reservoir.

appeared from the globe. The derivation of the data in Fig. 4 is of course dependent on what ^{13}C value is assumed to represent steady-state. A figure has been selected which is an average of data from the Palaeogene to the early Miocene, because it appears that a remarkable change began in the middle Miocene. The choice of a different value would require that there was a long-term trend through the Cenozoic in the mass of organic carbon buried in addition to the post-middle Miocene event. This may or may not be a real additional feature. It will be recalled that the value obtained above for the decrease in the global organic carbon reservoir since the middle Miocene was derived on the basis of a simple model whereby the integrated oceanic accumulation rate has remained approximately constant. It should also be noted that if, as some workers believe, there has been a significant increase in the river-borne input to the ocean since that time, then the computed change in the organic carbon reservoir would be even greater. Thus although the assumption of a constant input is an obvious over-simplification, it also proves to be a rather conservative assumption; the truth may be even more surprising.

Ocean dissolved oxygen content

It is well documented that the ^{13}C content of dissolved CO_2 in the deep sea becomes isotopically lighter as carbon dioxide derived from oxidized organic matter is added to the deep ocean (Duplessy 1972; Kroopnick 1980; Broecker & Peng 1982). Thus there is a relationship between ^{13}C and oxygen content in the deep sea. This means that to a first approximation the oxygen content of oceanic deep water may be estimated by the carbon isotopic difference between surface and deep waters. In detail, two other important factors intervene.

(1) Deep waters acquire carbon from dissolving carbonate as well as from oxidized organic matter, so that organic carbon is not the only source that can change the ^{13}C content of the carbon in the deep water. However, since the dissolving carbonate is isotopically similar to the dissolved CO_2, this is a minor factor when one is comparing ^{13}C and dissolved oxygen content, and only becomes a significant factor if one is comparing ^{13}C with total dissolved CO_2.

(2) The more complex factor is that the ^{13}C content more accurately estimates 'apparent oxygen utilization' (AOU) than oxygen content; the actual dissolved oxygen content depends on the dissolved oxygen content at the time the water mass left the ocean surface, as well as on the

amount that has subsequently been lost in oxidizing organic matter since that time. The initial dissolved oxygen content of a deep water mass may be estimated from its temperature, by assuming that it started in equilibrium with the atmosphere at the surface at this same temperature. This temperature may be obtained in the geological record from the ^{18}O content of benthic Foraminifera. The initial ^{13}C content of dissolved CO_2 in this water may be estimated from ^{13}C measurements in planktonic Foraminifera.

The gross pattern of ocean deep water circulation today consists in the sinking of cold, oxygen-rich water in the North Atlantic (primarily the Norwegian Sea) and its upwelling in the rest of the ocean. Some bottom water from Antarctica is added while dense water from the Mediterranean outflow forms another important component. Within the deep water masses, oxygen is gradually depleted as organic matter that falls from the photic zone is oxidized at depth. Figure 5 shows the approximate range of deep water ^{13}C content and dissolved oxygen content from GEOSECS data (Kroopnick 1980). The values for the deep Norwegian Sea are emphasized. Also plotted is a value for the Mediterranean Sea (Duplessy 1972). This water is formed with about the same ^{13}C content as the Norwegian Sea, since both seas are in free CO_2 exchange with the atmosphere, but the dissolved oxygen content is much lower in the Mediterranean because the solubility is so much less in such warm (13°C) water. Inspection of Fig. 5 shows that if all other factors (especially chemical properties) remained the same, and deep water were produced in the Norwegian Sea but with the characteristics of Mediterranean deep water, then one would perceive about the same distribution of ^{13}C values as are found today, but that dissolved oxygen content would be globally reduced by about 100 micromoles/kg. Since much of the water in the North Pacific has a present-day oxygen content below 100 micromoles/kg, it would become anoxic under this scenario. Thus, although in principle ^{13}C data enable the past dissolved oxygen content of ocean water to be reconstructed, this can only be attempted with a knowledge of ^{13}C values for planktonic foraminifera, which constrain the ^{13}C content of newly formed deep water, and with a knowledge of deep water temperature (which may be estimated from ^{18}O measurements made in benthonic foraminifera) which constrains the dissolved oxygen content of the newly formed deep water.

Fig. 6 shows some ^{18}O data for the Cenozoic which provide the base for deriving a history of the dissolved oxygen content of the ocean deep water masses. The chief limitation on actually

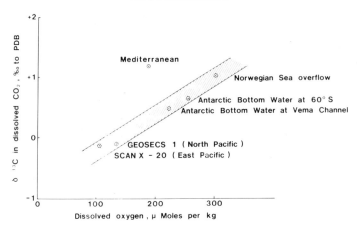

FIG. 5. ^{13}C content of dissolved CO_2 in selected water masses. Data (Table 2) from Kroopnick (1974b and 1980) and Duplessy (1972). A great deal more data are available; the hatched area represents the approximate field within which deep water values lie (today, NADW and AABW fall in the same field, but the Mediterranean Sea deep water is well outside it).

TABLE 2. *Data for Figure 5, showing relationship between* ^{13}*C and dissolved oxygen content in deep water masses*

Latitude	Longitude	Depth m	δ^{13}C	diss. oxygen μmole/kg	Ref.
64.17°N	5.59°W	below 756	1.03	303	(1)
59.95°S	0.07°W	4501–4920	0.66	256	(1)
17.97°S	31.03°W	4340–4680	0.48	228	(1)
28.48°N	121.63°W	2985	−0.10	136	(2), (3)
0.64°N	86.11°W	2609–2722	−0.13	107	(4)
43.1°N	8.1°E	1000–2500	1.2	200	(5)

References: (1) Kroopnick (1980); (2) Kroopnick (1974a); (3) Broecker *et al.* (1982); (4) Kroopnick (1974b); (5) Duplessy (1972).

achieving this is the difficulty in ascertaining a valid estimate for ^{13}C in surface waters from the isotopic analysis of extinct planktonic foraminiferal species. A knowledge of the atmospheric oxygen content is also essential; (see below), the changing global organic carbon budget may imply changes in the oxygen concentration of the atmosphere. Fig. 6 shows the estimated temperature history of ocean deep waters, and also shows the scale for dissolved oxygen content that would apply while the atmospheric oxygen concentration was as today.

Discussion

In the paper which first discussed the global implications of the oceanic ^{13}C record, Scholle and Arthur (1980) showed a relationship between isotopically positive peaks in the ^{13}C content of Mesozoic limestones, and episodes of black shale deposition; for example at the Aptian–Albian boundary, ^{13}C values rise to about +4 per mil. Scholle and Arthur (1980) were not able to make an accurate estimate of the quantities of carbon involved because this would have required a timescale of greater precision than is available for the Mesozoic.

The isotopically positive peaks in the late Paleocene (at about 60 m.y.) and in the middle Miocene (about 15 m.y.) that are evident in Fig. 1 (and have been suspected since they were encountered in isotopic analyses of foraminifera by Shackleton and Kennett in 1975) are similar in scale to those discussed by Scholle and Arthur for the Mesozoic. They also correspond in an approximate way with the last two 'polytaxic' episodes according to the discussion of Fischer and Arthur (1977). Although black shales did not accumulate either during the Paleocene or the Miocene, it seems likely that the deep ocean was less oxygenated during these than other times. It

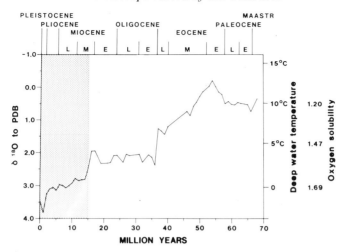

FIG. 6. Deep water temperature estimated from [18]O data. This figure is based on data in Shackleton, Hall and Boersma (1984); it is probable that after 15Ma (the dotted area) changes in ice volume complicate the estimation of temperature according to the model of Shackleton and Kennett (1975) whereby the Antarctic ice sheet is assumed to have formed about 13Ma ago. The scale to the right shows the saturation dissolved oxygen content (in micromoles per kg), that would be observed in deep water if the atmospheric oxygen concentration had been the same as today.

is also clear that anomalous amounts of organic carbon accumulated somewhere on the globe during these episodes. Future work should investigate the possibility of quantifying changes in deep water dissolved oxygen content by a careful evaluation of the factors which limit our ability to estimate surface-water ^{13}C content from the isotopic analysis of planktonic microfossils.

On a long timescale, it is generally believed that there is an association between high sea levels, high global temperature and a high rate of organic carbon accumulation. However, neither the dramatic collapse in ^{13}C values very close to the Paleocene–Eocene boundary, at 57.6Ma on the timescale in use here (see Fig. 1), nor the important cooling in ocean deep waters about 50Ma on this timescale (see Fig. 6), can be associated with major sea level events according to the data summarized by Vail and Hardenbol (1979). Despite this the ^{13}C events that have been discussed are of sufficient importance in terms of changes in the burial of organic carbon to warrant further study, and their possible association with changes in sea level cannot be adequately tested until the sea level record is better known and understood.

The data shown in Fig. 4 show another interesting aspect of the ^{13}C record. It is generally accepted that the atmospheric oxygen concentration is kept in balance through a subtle interaction between the accumulation of organic carbon and

its oxidation, with contributions from the oxidation or reduction of sulphur and iron compounds (Veizer *et al.* 1980; Garrels & Lerman 1981). This balance in atmospheric oxygen is presumably maintained through the oxygen levels in the ocean, acting on the carbon, sulphur and iron in the sediments of the shelves and in the deep sea.

Walker (1977) pointed out that the cooling of ocean deep waters during the Cenozoic would have increased the dissolved oxygen content of ocean deep water. If the hypothetical mechanism by which oxidation/reduction maintains the atmospheric oxygen level does operate in the ocean, such a rise in the oxygen dissolved in ocean deep water might have been followed by an enhanced rate of oxygen removal, accomplished by the oxidation of organic carbon. This would have continued until such time as the dissolved oxygen content of the ocean returned to its steady-state value, which would require that a significant amount of oxygen was removed from the atmosphere. Figure 4 suggests that an excess of over 10^{20}g (almost 10^{19} moles) of carbon have been oxidized since the middle Miocene, withdrawing almost 10^{19} moles oxygen from the atmosphere. Since the total oxygen content of the atmosphere is only 3.8×10^{19} moles, this implies that the atmospheric oxygen content was almost 20% higher prior to the Middle Miocene than it is today. This figure is consistent with the model suggested by Walker (1977); the 20% rise in oxygen solubility that would result from a 10°C ocean cooling, was compensated by a 20% reduction in the atmospheric oxygen concentration. This order-of-magnitude agreement suggests that the present new interpretation of the global ^{13}C record deserves serious consideration.

The post-Miocene change in the global organic carbon reservoir, which is here attributed to the effect of ocean temperature on the solubility of oxygen in the ocean, could alternatively be plausibly explained as resulting from a sea-level lowering associated with the accumulation of ice on Antarctica. If the major cooling of the ocean deep water occurred near the Eocene–Oligocene boundary (Shackleton & Kennett 1975), it would have been at this time rather than during the Miocene that the dissolved oxygen content of ocean deep waters increased. Possibly a rapid response through the oxidation of organic-rich sediments could not occur until the disruption of shelf sediments caused by the glacio-eustatic sea level variations associated with the Miocene glaciation of Antarctica. Alternatively, there is increasing evidence for Antarctic glaciation having begun earlier than the middle Miocene (Matthews & Poore 1980; Miller & Fairbanks 1983), in which case the major refrigeration of the deep sea may have occurred in the middle Miocene, well after the onset of Antarctic glaciation, rather than preceding this event as Shackleton and Kennett (1975) supposed. This scenario would be consistent with the data reported in this paper.

Conclusions

Carbon and oxygen isotope palaeo-oceanography is capable of yielding information on changing global budget of organic carbon accumulation, and on the climatic and oceanographic events that are associated with these changes. Changes in the atmospheric oxygen concentration are also implied.

A major post-Miocene decrease in organic carbon storage was probably climatically controlled. It was associated with a 20% decrease in the oxygen concentration of the atmosphere. It is likely that palaeoclimatic and palaeo-oceanographic studies will elucidate the causes of this and earlier changes in the global carbon budget. The fundamental question that is posed is whether changes in the global organic carbon reservoir are controlled mechanically, by the effect of global sea level change on the accumulation and erosion of organic-rich sediment, or geochemically, through atmospheric and oceanic oxygen levels.

ACKNOWLEDGEMENTS: I am grateful to Andy Fleet and Jim Brooks for the encouragement to write this paper, and to Mike Arthur, Max Coleman, Ted Moore, Tom Pedersen and Phil Park for helpful comments on various versions of the manuscript. Since writing the first draft I have had the benefit of fruitful and enjoyable discussions with Bob Garrels, Jan Veizer and many other of those who attended the AGU Chapman Conference on the global carbon cycle in January 1984. This work was supported by NERC grant GR3/3606.

References

ANDERSEN, N. R. & MALAHOFF, A. (eds) 1977. *The Fate of Fossil Fuel CO$_2$ in the Oceans*. Plenum Press, New York.

ARTHUR, M. A. 1983. The carbon cycle-controls on atmospheric CO$_2$ and climate in the geologic past. *In: Climate in Earth History*. Washington: National Academy Press. pp. 55–67.

BENDER, M. M. 1968. Mass spectrometric studies of carbon-13 variations in corn and other grasses. *Radiocarbon*, **10**, 468–472.

BERGER, W. H., KILLINGLEY, J. S. & VINCENT, E. 1978. Stable isotopes in deep-sea carbonates: Box Core ERDC-92, West equatorial Pacific. *Oceanologica Acta*, **1**, 203–216.

BERGGREN, W. A., KENT, D. V. & FLYNN, J. J. 1985a. Paleogene geochronology and chronostratigraphy. *In*: N. J. SNELLING (ed.) *Geochronology and the Geological Record*. Geol. Soc. London Special Paper.

——, —— & VAN COUVERING, J. A. 1985b. Neogene geochronology and chronostratigraphy. *In*: N. J. SNELLING (ed.) *Geochronology and the Geological Record*. Geol. Soc. London Memoir **10**, 211–260.

BOERSMA, A. & SHACKLETON, N. J. (1977a). Tertiary oxygen and carbon isotope stratigraphy, Site 357 (mid-latitude South Atlantic). *In*: SUPKO, P. R. *et al.* (eds) *Initial Reports of the Deep Sea Drilling Project*, Vol. 39, pp. 911–924. Washington: U.S. Govt. Printing Office.

—— & —— (1977b). Oxygen and carbon isotope through the Oligocene, DSDP Site 366, Equatorial Atlantic. *In*: LANCELOT, Y. *et al.* (eds) *Initial Reports of the Deep Sea Drilling Project*, Vol. 39, pp. 957–962. Washington: U.S. Govt. Printing Office.

——, ——, HALL, M. A. & GIVEN, Q. C. (1979). Carbon and oxygen isotope records at DSDP Site 384 (North Atlantic) and some Paleocene paleotemperatures and carbon isotope variations in the Atlantic Ocean. *In*: TUCHOLKE, B. E. *et al.* (eds) *Initial Reports of the Deep Sea Drilling Project*, Vol. 62, pp. 695–717. Washington: U.S. Govt. Printing Office.

BROECKER, W. S. 1974. *Chemical Oceanography*. Harcourt Brace Jovanovich, New York.

—— 1982. Glacial to interglacial changes in ocean chemistry. *Progr. Oceanogr.*, **11**, 151–197.

—— & PENG, T-H. 1982. *Tracers in the Sea*. Eldigio Press, Palisades, New York. 690pp.

——, SPENCER, D. W. & CRAIG, H. 1982. GEOSECS Pacific Expedition Vol. 3: *Hydrographic Data 1973–1974*. Washington: U.S. Govt. Printing Office.

CRAIG, H. 1953. The geochemistry of the stable isotopes of carbon. *Geochim. et Cosmochim. Acta*, **3**, 53–72.

DAVIES, T. A., HAY, W. W., SOUTHAM, J. R. & WORSLEY, T. R. (1977). Estimates of Cenozoic oceanic sedimentation rates. *Science*, **197**, 53–55.

—— & WORSLEY, T. R. 1981. Paleoenvironmental implications of oceanic carbonate sedimentation rates. *In*: WARME, J. E., DOUGLAS, R. G. & WINTERER, E. L. (eds) *The Deep Sea Drilling Projects: a Decade of Progress*. Tulsa: Society of Economic Paleontologists and Mineralogists Special Publication No. 32.

DENIRO, M. J. & EPSTEIN, S. 1978. Influence of diet on the distribution of carbon isotopes in animals. *Geochim. et Cosmochim. Acta*, **42**, 495–506.

DOUGLAS, R. G. & SAVIN, S. M. 1971. Isotopic analyses of planktonic foraminifera from the Cenozoic of the Northwest Pacific, Leg 6. *In*: FISCHER, B. C. *et al.* (eds) *Initial Reports of the Deep Sea Drilling Project*, Vol. 6, pp. 1123–1127. Washington: U.S. Govt. Printing Office.

—— & —— 1973. Oxygen and carbon isotope analyses of Cretaceous and Tertiary foraminifera from the central North Pacific. *In*: WINTERER, E. L. *et al.* (eds) *Initial Reports of the Deep Sea Drilling Project*, Vol 17, pp. 591–605. Washington: U.S. Govt. Printing Office.

—— & —— 1976. Oxygen and carbon isotope analyses of Tertiary and Cretaceous microfossils from Shatsky Rise and other sites in the North Pacific Ocean. *In*: LARSON, R. L. *et al.* (eds) *Initial Reports of the Deep Sea Drilling Project*, Vol 32, pp. 509–520. Washington: U.S. Govt. Printing Office.

DUPLESSY, J. C. 1972. *La géochimie des isotopes stables du carbone dans la mer*. Commisariat à l'Energie Atomique. Paris.

——, SHACKLETON, N. J., MATTHEWS, R. K., PRELL, W., RUDDIMAN, W. F., CARALP, M. & HENDY, C. H. 1984. ^{13}C record of benthic Foraminifera in the Last Interglacial ocean: implications for the carbon cycle and the global deep water circulation. *Quaternary Research*, **21**, 225–243.

FISCHER, A. G. & ARTHUR, M. A. 1977. Secular variations in the pelagic realm. *In*: COOK, H. E. & ENOS, P. (eds) *Deep Water Carbonate Environments*. Society of Economic Paleontologists and Mineralogists, Tulsa. Special Publication No. 25, pp. 19–50.

FONTUGNE, M. R. & DUPLESSY, J.-C. 1981. Organic carbon fractionation by marine plankton in the temperature range −1 to 31°C. *Oceanologica Acta*, **4**, 85–90.

GARRELS, R. M. & PERRY, E. A. 1974. Cycling of carbon, sulfur, and oxygen through geologic time. *In*: GOLDBERG, E. (ed) *The Sea*. Wiley-Interscience, New York, Vol 5, pp. 303–336.

—— & LERMAN, A. 1981. Phanerozoic cycles of sedimentary carbon and sulfur. *Proc. Natl. Acad. Sci. USA*, **78**, 4652–4656.

GRAHAM, D. W., CORLISS, B. H., BENDER, M. L. & KEIGWIN, L.D. 1981. Carbon and oxygen isotopic disequilibria of recent deep-sea benthic foraminifera. *Marine Micropalaeontology*, **6**, 483–497.

HARRISON, C. G. A., McDOUGAL, I. & WATKINS, N. D. 1979. A geomagnetic field reversal time scale back to 13.0 million years before present. *Earth and Planetary Science Letters*, **42**, 143–152.

HEIRTZLER, J. R., DICKSON, G. O., HERRON, E. M., PITMAN, W. C. & LE PICHON, X. 1968. Marine magnetic anomalies, geomagnetic field reversals, and motions of the ocean floor and continents. *J. Geophys, Res.*, **73**, 2119–2136.

KEELING, C. D., BACASTOW, R. B., BAINBRIDGE, A. E., EKDAHL, C. A., GUENTHER, P. G., WATERMAN, L. S. & CHIN, J. F. S. 1976. Atmospheric carbon dioxide variations at Mauna Loa Observatory, Hawaii. *Tellus*, **28**, 538–551.

KEMPE, S. 1977. Carbon in the rock cycle. *In*: BOLIN, B., DEGENS, E. T., KEMPE, S. & KETNER, P. (eds) *The Global Carbon Cycle*, Wiley, New York.

KROOPNICK, P. 1974a. Correlations between ^{13}C and CO_2 in surface waters and atmospheric CO_2. *Earth and Planetary Science Letters*, **22**, 397–403.

—— 1974b. The dissolved $O_2 - CO_2 - {}^{13}C$ system in the eastern equatorial Pacific. *Deep-Sea Research*, **21**, 211–227.

—— 1980. The distribution of ^{13}C in the Atlantic Ocean. *Earth and Planetary Science Letters*, **49**, 469–484.

LETOLLE, R. & RENARD, M. 1980. Sedimentologie—Evolution des teneurs en ^{13}C des carbonates pelagiques aux limites Cretace-Tertiaire et Paleocene-Eocene. *C. R. Acad. Sci. Paris*, **290**, 827–830.

MATTHEWS, R. K. & POORE, R. Z. 1980. Tertiary δO^{18} record and glacio-eustatic sea-level fluctuations. *Geology*, **8**, 501–504.

MILLER, K. G. & FAIRBANKS, R. G. 1983. Evidence for Oligocene-Middle Miocene abyssal circulation changes in the western North Atlantic. *Nature*, **306**, 250–253.

MOOK, W. G., KEELING, C. D. & HERRON, A. 1981. Seasonal and secular variations in the abundance and $^{13}C/{}^{12}C$ ratio of atmospheric CO_2. *Proc. WMO/ICSU/UNEP Scientific Conference on Analysis and Interpretation of Atmospheric CO_2 data, Berne*, pp. 14–18 Sept. 1981.

MOORE, T. C. & HEATH, G. R. 1977. Survival of deep-sea sedimentary sections. *Earth and Planetary Science Letters*, **37**, 71–80.

SACKETT, W. M., ECKELMANN, W. R., BENDER, M. L. & BE, A. W. H. 1965. Temperature dependence of carbon isotope composition in marine plankton and sediments. *Science*, **148**, 235–237.

SCHOLLE, P. A. & ARTHUR, M. A. 1980. Carbon isotope fluctuations in Cretaceous pelagic limestones: potential stratigraphic and petroleum exploration tool. *America Association of Petroleum Geologists Bulletin*, **64**, 67–87.

SHACKLETON, N. J. 1977. Carbon-13 in UVIGERINA: tropical rainforest history and the Equatorial Pacific carbonate dissolution cycles. *In*: ANDERSEN, N. R. & MALAHOFF, A. (eds) *The Fate of Fossil Fuel CO_2*

in the Oceans. Plenum Press, New York, pp. 401–427.

—— & KENNETT, J. P. 1975. Paleotemperature history of the Cenozoic and the initiation of Antarctic glaciation: oxygen and carbon isotope analyses in DSDP sites 277, 279 and 281. *In:* KENNETT, J. P. *et al.* (eds) *Initial Reports of the Deep Sea Drilling Project,* Vol 29. U.S. Govt Printing Office, Washington.

—— & HALL, M. A. 1984. Carbon isotope data from Leg 74 sediments. *In:* MOORE, T. C. *et al.* (eds) *Initial Reports of the Deep Sea Drilling Project,* Vol. 74. pp. 613–619. U.S. Govt. Printing Office, Washington.

——, —— & BOERSMA, A. 1984. Oxygen and carbon isotope data from Leg 74 Foraminifera. *In:* MOORE, T. C. *et al.* (eds) *Initial Reports of the Deep Sea Drilling Project,* Vol. 74, pp. 599–612. U.S. Govt. Printing Office, Washington.

—— & MEMBERS OF THE SHIPBOARD PARTY 1984. Accumulation rates in Leg 74 sediments. *In:* MOORE, T. C. *et al.* (eds) *Initial Reports of the Deep Sea Drilling Project,* Vol. 74. pp. 621–644. U.S. Govt. Printing Office, Washington.

——, HALL, M. A. & BLEIL, U. 1985. Carbon Isotope Stratigraphy, Site 577. *In:* HEATH, G. R. *et al.* (eds) *Initial Reports of the Deep Sea Drilling Project,* Vol. 86. U.S. Govt. Printing Office, Washington. pp. 503–511.

VAIL, P. R. & HARDENBOL, J. 1979. Sea-level changes during the Tertiary, *Oceanus,* **22,** 71–79.

VEIZER, J., HOLSER, W. T. & WILGUS, C. K. 1980. Correlation of $^{13}/^{12}C$ and $^{34}/^{32}S$ secular variations. *Geochimica et Cosmochimica Acta,* **44,** 579–587.

WALKER, J. C. G. 1977. *Evolution of the Atmosphere.* Macmillan Publishing Co., New York, p. 268.

WHITMAN, J. M. & DAVIES, T. A. 1979. Cenozoic oceanic sedimentation rates: how good are the data? *Marine Geology,* **30,** 269–284.

WORSLEY, T. R. & DAVIES, T. A. 1979. Sea-level fluctuations and deep-sea sedimentation rates. *Science,* **203,** 455–456.

N. J. SHACKLETON, The Godwin Laboratory for Quaternary Research, Free School Lane, Cambridge, CB2 3RS, U.K.

INDEX

435